D1188236

Plant Pathology

VOLUME III

Plant Pathology

An Advanced Treatise

Edited by

J. G. HORSFALL AND A. E. DIMOND

The Connecticut Agricultural Experiment Station
New Haven, Connecticut

VOLUME III

The Diseased Population
Epidemics and Control

1960

ACADEMIC PRESS, New York and London

CONTRIBUTORS

L. Broadbent, *Rothamsted Experimental Station, Harpenden, Hertfordshire, England* *

H. P. Burchfield, *Boyce Thompson Institute for Plant Research, Inc., Yonkers, New York*

J. J. Christensen, *University of Minnesota, St. Paul, Minnesota*

H. Darpoux, *Station Centrale de Pathologie Vegetale, Centre National de Recherches Agronomiques, Versailles, France*

A. E. Dimond, *The Connecticut Agricultural Experiment Station, New Haven, Connecticut*

S. D. Garrett, *Sub-Department of Mycology, Botany School, University of Cambridge, Cambridge, England*

Ernst Gram, *Statens Plantepatologische Forsog, Lyngby, Denmark*

J. G. Horsfall, *The Connecticut Agricultural Experiment Station, New Haven, Connecticut*

C. T. Ingold, *Department of Botany, Birkbeck College, University of London, England*

W. A. Kreutzer, *Agricultural Research Division, Shell Development Company, Modesto, California*

A. E. Muskett, *The Queen's University, Belfast, Northern Ireland*

Harald Schrödter, *Agrarian Meteorological Research Station, Aschersleben, Germany*

E. C. Stakman, *University of Minnesota, St. Paul, Minnesota*

Russell B. Stevens, *Department of Botany, The George Washington University, Washington, D. C.*

J. E. van der Plank, *Division of Plant Pathology, Department of Agriculture, Pretoria, Union of South Africa*

Paul E. Waggoner, *Department of Soils and Climatology, The Connecticut Agricultural Experiment Station, New Haven, Connecticut*

* Present address: Glasshouse Crops Research Institute, Rustington, Sussex, England.

v

CONTENTS

6. Dispersal by Air and Water—The Flight and Landing
By Harald Schrödter

7. Analysis of Epidemics
By J. E. van der Plank

8. Forecasting Epidemics
By Paul E. Waggoner

9. Quarantines
By Ernst Gram

14. The Problem of Breeding Resistant Varieties

By E. C. Stakman and J. J. Christensen

PLANT PATHOLOGY, VOLUME I

The Diseased Plant

PLANT PATHOLOGY, VOLUME II

The Pathogen

CHAPTER 1

Prologue

Inoculum and the Diseased Population

A. E. DIMOND AND J. G. HORSFALL

The Connecticut Agricultural Experiment Station, New Haven, Connecticut

I. INTRODUCTION

When plant pathology first emerged as a discipline, there was much interest in the causation of disease, and interest centered on the diseased plant as an individual. There is still much to be learned about the processes that lead to disease in the individual plant and the mechanisms by which the plant wards off infection. These considerations have been dealt with in Volume I.

There is also much to be learned about the methods of infection by pathogens and the biochemical processes within the pathogen that lead to infection and disease. Even in the development of control measures,

1

interest still centers about the individual pathogen. Too little is known of the biochemical pathways that are unique to microorganisms for us to generalize when we are attempting to develop a pesticide.. Perhaps this will always be so. These are the domain of Volume II.

The realm of Volume III is the youngest phase of plant pathology and deals with populations of plants in relation to infection and to control. We must deal with populations of inoculum and also with the consequences of cultivation, which results in populations of uniform plants. Just as populations of people present unique problems in public health medicine, so in plant pathology populations of inoculum or of plants exhibit characteristics that are not apparent when attention is focused on the individual plant only.

II. INOCULUM POTENTIAL

Injuries and inanimate pathogens aside, there is no disease without inoculum, a principle that arose with Pasteur. The production of inoculum is, therefore, our first order of business in Volume III and is considered by Garrett in Chapter 2. Inoculum may be considered to be any material capable of producing infection. It may consist of such propagules as conidia, sclerotia, or mycelium. It may consist of virus particles.

A plant pathologist, interested in disease in populations of plants, needs to know how severe a disease is likely to be. When inoculum lands on the host under conditions favoring disease development, we know that the frequency of infection is somehow related to the number of inoculum units that encounter the host. To describe this situation, Horsfall (1932) first used the term inoculum potential, and, as initially defined, it is the number of infective particles present in the environment of the uninfected host. According to Horsfall (1932) "such a concept carries with it the idea of mass action—the greater the mass of organisms present, the more severe will be the disease. This idea also carries with it the idea of virulence—the more virulent the organism the more severe will be the disease. This view of inoculum potential is concerned only with the amount or virulence of inoculum rather than with the influence of environment on the severity of infection." Later, Zentmyer and associates (1944) modified the original definition and considered inoculum potential as the disease-producing power of the host environment, assuming that pathogens constitute a part of that environment. Wilhelm (1950) adopted the term inoculum potential in its original sense, i.e., the amount of inoculum in a unit volume of soil. His measure of inoculum potential was the infection index, which is the percentage of tomato plants becoming infected with *Verticillium* when planted in a unit volume of soil in a stated manner. In this use, therefore, it reflects the infective power of the pathogen in the soil (Wilhelm, 1951). Garrett (1956, and in Chapter 2 of this volume) defines inoculum potential in another sense: the energy of growth of the pathogen available for infection of the host at the surface of the host to be infected.

Although those studying root diseases and soil-borne pathogens first sensed the need for this term, the concept of inoculum potential is equally applicable to pathogens that are borne in any manner: by air, water, insects, on crop residues, or on seeds. Probably the term arose initially because those working with soil-borne pathogens found it very difficult to measure the quantity of infective units in a given volume of soil, whereas with air-borne and seed-borne infections, the measurement of this quantity was a simple matter, and different terms were applied to the problem. Thus Heald (1921) used the term spore load to describe the number of bunt spores per wheat kernel.

In the following discussion the term "inoculum potential" is the number of independent infections that are likely to occur in a given situation in a population of susceptible healthy tissues. The amount of tissue that can be invaded from a single infection is the unit taken, whether it be a part of a leaf in a localized disease or an entire plant in a systemic infection. In this sense inoculum potential is the resultant of the action of the environment, the vigor of the pathogen to establish an infection, the susceptibility of the host and the amount of inoculum present. This is precisely the index needed in describing the rise and decline of epidemics (Chapter 7) and in forecasting epidemics (Chapter 8).

We may find it convenient to think of inoculum potential as a form of potential energy. In physics we learn that all forms of energy contain an intensity factor and a capacity factor. The magnitude of the energy is the product of these two. Thus heat energy can be measured as the product of the temperature (the intensity factor) and heat capacity (the capacity factor). Light energy is the product of the intensity of the light and the proportion of the light that is absorbed by a system to do photochemical work. Electrical energy is the product of the potential difference across the terminals of a circuit and the current flowing through it. By this analogy inoculum potential is the product of the quantity of inoculum present (the intensity factor) and the capacity of the environment, used in a broad sense, to produce disease in a host of given susceptibility with a pathogen of stated characteristics.

In this sense inoculum potential is a useful concept. Energy is the ability to work. Work is done when inoculum is moved from a source to an infection court and successful infection occurs. The operation may proceed efficiently under favorable conditions or very inefficiently under unfavorable conditions. We may consider all factors that tend to reduce the number of successful infections as analogous to frictional losses when work is done in a real system. Thus, when the environment is unfavorable to the establishment of infection or when a large percentage of the inoculum arrives at the infection court in nonviable condition, the net work is small and the efficiency is low.

Plant pathologists have tended to confine their measurements of inoculum potential to the resultant of the action of both the intensity and the capacity factors and have devoted but little effort to attempts to measure the numerical influence of the capacity factors. Thus, the studies of Horsfall (1932), of Wilhelm (1950, 1951), and of Nusbaum and associates (1952) are all cases in which the value of the inoculum potential as a whole was measured. The measurement of the magnitude of disease must be perfected if estimates of the inoculum potential are to be precise. Horsfall and Barratt (1945) devised one method of doing so, while Chester (1950, and Volume I, Chapter 4) has given us an excellent appraisal of the factors underlying estimates of disease and of the methods that can be employed in making these measurements.

A. *The Intensity Factor of Inoculum Potential*

The amount of inoculum present is the intensity factor of inoculum potential. How the amount of inoculum varies with distance and how much inoculum is deposited upon plant surfaces in varying circumstances are interesting problems that require quantitative solution to make use of the measurements of the inoculum potential.

To construct a simplified model of the way in which the amount of inoculum varies, it will be useful to consider the subject from three points of view: variation of the amount of inoculum with distance, factors affecting the viability of inoculum during dispersal, and the trapping of inoculum by plant surfaces.

1. *Variation of Inoculum with Distance from the Source*

In considering how the amount of inoculum varies with distance, we must account for a number of situations observed in the field. The most commonly observed situation is that where the amount of disease diminishes with distance from a point source and finally disappears, that is, where there is no transmission beyond a certain distance. The second case is that where the amount of disease diminishes with distance from a point source, but where there is no limit to the distance to which the disease will spread from this source, if sufficiently strong. Finally there are those cases where the disease outbreak appears "out of the blue" and the source from which the outbreak arose is not readily apparent.

We may look at these situations in another way. Inoculum may be carried from the source to the infection court in one, two, or three dimensions. The gradient of disease is useful for inferring what the nature of transmission has been. Here the gradient of disease is defined as the slope of the line when the logarithm of the amount of disease is plotted against the logarithm of distance from the source of inoculum.

Let us imagine that a bird carries spores from their source to the infection court and flies at least 50 miles before landing. It may fly any distance greater than this before landing but never less. If the bird loses no inoculum in flight, the quantity of inoculum will be the same in the infection court when the bird lands as it was at the source of inoculum. It may fly 50, 60, or 100 miles before landing and the same will be true. Here, the strength of the inoculum does not vary with distance from the source, so the gradient of disease will be zero because the line relating log disease to log distance will be horizontal and have a slope of zero. In such a case it is easy to see why the outbreak of disease in a new locality would appear "out of the blue."

The second case is that in which a disease spreads in two dimensions only, as in the case of rhizomorphs of *Armillaria mellea,* fanning out from an infected host but maintaining reasonably constant depth in the soil. Here, the strength of the inoculum varies inversely as the distance itself.

One can derive this relationship quite simply. Imagine a group of nematodes concentrated at a point, the number of nematodes being Q. Imagine a circle of radius x_1 about the center Q and a second circle with twice this radius, x_2, also about Q as a center. Assume that the nematodes can move outward equally in all directions from the center of a plane, as in a film of water on a flat surface. When they arrive at the first circle, they are dispersed over a length equal to the circumference of the circle, a length of $2\pi x_1$ cm., and the intensity of inoculum, I, along this line is

$$I_1 = \frac{Q}{2\pi x_1} \text{ nematodes per centimeter.} \tag{1}$$

Similarly, if the nematodes all swim on to the second circle, the intensity of inoculum per unit length at the second circle is $I_2 = Q/2\pi x_2$. Then

$$\frac{I_1}{I_2} = \frac{Q/2\pi x_1}{Q/2\pi x_2} \tag{2}$$

Canceling out common terms, we have

$$\frac{I_1}{I_2} = \frac{x_2}{x_1} \tag{3}$$

Hence, in this case, intensity of inoculum varies inversely with distance from the source.

Equation (1) can be stated in other terms. When Q, the source strength, is constant, then $Q/2\pi$ is also constant, and the equation becomes

$$I = \frac{k}{x} \tag{4}$$

where k, a constant, equals $Q/2\pi$. In logarithmic terms, this equation becomes

$$\log I = \log k - \log x \tag{5}$$

which is the equation of a straight line, having a slope of -1 when $\log I$ is plotted against $\log x$. In this curve the slope of the line is the gradient of disease and the value of $\log k$ defines the scale of distance, as discussed by Van der Plank (Chapter 7). In this case, also, the source of inoculum may be difficult to locate when only the points of new outbreak of disease are known.

In the third case, the dispersion of inoculum is three-dimensional. A derivation analogous to the case for two-dimensional dispersal indicates that the strength of inoculum varies inversely with the square of the distance from the source. When an inverse square law is followed, from a sufficiently powerful source of inoculum there should be an infinite horizon in the spread of disease, i.e., the abundance of new infections arising from a point source should vary inversely as the square of the distance. Some infections will occur, though rarely, at an infinite distance from a sufficiently strong source of inoculum. In this case the disease gradient has a value of -2.

In many diseases the gradient obtained by actual counts of disease incidence indicates that the strength of inoculum varies as a higher power than the square of the distance from the source. In these cases there is a definite horizon for the spread of disease from a point source, that is, the distance to which a disease is spread is limited no matter how strong the source is, and beyond this limit no spread will occur. Van der Plank discusses this case in Chapter 7.

As Wood has discussed in Chapter 7 of Volume II, a host may require more than one and perhaps many spores in an infection court if infection is to become established. Thus the experimental placement of a single spore upon a host surface seldom results in infection, whereas the presence of many spores in an infection court invariably results in infection.

This phenomenon is partly ascribable to variation in vigor of individual spores. Partly it is the necessity of the "sacrifice hit" in baseball —the necessity of a number of spores to modify the host barrier if one spore is to breach it. Herein lies an advantage of organization of cells, such as the multicellular spores of *Helminthosporium*, the multicellular sclerotium, or the nematode. These frequently invade the host in the absence of others of their kind. Thus each infection may require several propagules and

$$D = nI \qquad (6)$$

where D is a successful infection resulting in disease, and nI is the number of propagules necessary. Herein also lies the reason for the greater success of the *Fusarium* associated with a nematode, which can invade an otherwise *Fusarium*-resistant host. In this case the nematode provides a penetrating mechanism that many *Fusarium* cells fail to accomplish in the absence of the nematode because the host barrier is invulnerable to them when the host is resistant.

2. Infectiousness of Inoculum

Inoculum liberated from the source may not be capable of producing an infection in a susceptible host on arrival in the infection court. This may be because the inoculum is liberated from the source in nonviable or weakened condition or because the inoculum loses infectiousness in transit to the infection court.

The application of a fungicide to the source of inoculum is an illustration of loss in viability at the source. The dispersal of spores through hot, dry air may result in death in transit. In either case only a proportion of the inoculum arrives in the infection court in a condition capable of infection. The value of this proportion, i, can be determined experimentally under different environmental conditions, or it can be expressed as an equation when the law governing how inoculum dies is known, and be used to predict the value of i for a given transit from source to the infection court.

The resistant plant has the effect of reducing the proportion of spores capable of infection. Looked at from this view, therefore, resistance or immunity of the host reduces the infectiousness of the inoculum.

3. Trapping of Inoculum

The trapping of inoculum by bodies having different shapes has been studied by Gregory (1950, 1951) and by Gregory and Stedman (1953). In simplest terms, the shape of the host surface and of the spore undergoing dispersal both determine the number of spores deposited. One can visualize this process by considering the passage of light through a colored solution. The light corresponds to spores undergoing dispersal, and the colored solution corresponds to the plant surface which traps the spores. Light of a given wave length, absorbed by the solution, is absorbed in accordance with the Beer-Lambert law: the same proportion of the light is absorbed per unit length of solution traversed by the light at unit concentration of the solution. This can be stated as an equation:

$$I = I_0 e^{-klc} \tag{7}$$

where c is the molar concentration of the solution, l is the length of the light path through the solution, I_0 is the initial intensity of the light, I is the intensity of the light after traversing a path of length l through the solution, and k is a constant characteristic of the solute.

We may think of the deposition of spores across a surface as following a similar law. In this case the terms in the equation above must be redefined, c being the density of the crown of foliage through which the spores travel, l the length of the path of the spores through the foliage, I_0 the intensity of the inoculum at the beginning, and I the intensity of inoculum after any distance l is traversed. The constant k then becomes a characteristic of the trapping surface for a spore of given shape.

In the production of disease our concern is not with the intensity of the inoculum which successfully traverses this crown of foliage but rather with the amount of inoculum deposited per unit length of path traversed, and this is obviously the quantity $I_0 - I$.

Although a convenient way of thinking about the trapping of inoculum, the above equation describes the situation incompletely. First, the crown of foliage is discontinuous, that is, plants and fields are spaced apart from one another and only in a tomato or a potato field does the foliage approximate a continuous system at maturity. Second, the movement of spores is through turbulent air, and when long distances are involved, dispersal between plants involves no crown of foliage at all. The above equation, therefore, approximates reality only when a cloud of spores traverses continuous foliage.

In Chapter 6 Schrödter has discussed the biophysical aspects of the landing of spores and the processes by which deposition is accomplished. Unfortunately, our ability to forecast the deposition of spores in actual field problems is primitive, and the mathematical treatment of the subject necessarily applies only under idealized conditions.

The effect of precipitation in washing air-borne spores out of the atmosphere and bringing them to the ground is also discussed in Chapter 6. This process reduces the intensity of inoculum because it reduces the spore content of the air, but results in the arrival of very little inoculum in the infection court.

4. Intensity of Inoculum in the Infection Court

The above discussion can now be tied together to give an approximation to the total picture. The amount of inoculum arriving in the infection court will be the resultant of the factors influencing the inoculum during transit. We have seen how the intensity of inoculum may vary in intensity with distance from the source. This may be expressed by the equation

$$I = \frac{mQ}{x^b} \qquad (8)$$

where I is intensity of inoculum, m, is a constant, Q is the strength of inoculum at the source, x is the distance from the source, and b is a constant, varying in value from 0 in the case of one dimensional dispersal to values as high as 4 or 5 in cases discussed by Van der Plank (Chapter 7).

We have seen further that the proportion of spores capable of infecting a host can be expressed by the term i. Finally we have seen how the deposition of spores may follow a law analogous to the Beer-Lambert law or $I = I_0\, e^{-klc}$. The resultant of the action of these factors is

$$I = \frac{miQ}{x^b}\, e^{-klc} \qquad (9)$$

If the crown of foliage is continuous from source to infection court, then Q is the same as I_0, the initial strength of the inoculum. In this equation I is the intensity of inoculum remaining after deposition along a stated path and capable of producing an epidemic elsewhere.

The resemblance of this equation to that given by Waggoner (Chapter 8) is obvious although different symbols have been used in the two cases because different significance has been attached to them. Other approaches to this problem have been presented by Gregory (1945) and by Waggoner (1951, 1952, Chapter 8).

From this equation we can visualize how disease gradients arise as a linear relation in the field. The equation given just above can be rewritten in logarithmic form as follows:

$$\log I = -b \log x + (\log m + \log i + \log Q - klc) \qquad (10)$$

where terms are expressed in natural logarithms to the base e. In a given disease situation all factors are constants other than I and x, and under these circumstances the equation defines a line on log-log co-ordinates such as that the slope of the line, $-b$, is the disease gradient and the sum of the factors in parentheses is the scale of distance, discussed by Van der Plank (Chapter 7).

B. *The Capacity Factor of Inoculum Potential*

Plant pathologists have discovered no simple way of treating the capacity factor of inoculum potential quantitatively. The influence of environmental temperature, relative humidity, and the susceptibility of the host all contribute to the capacity of the environment to produce disease.

We know that infection generally increases with temperature and is roughly proportional to it up to the optimum for the disease under consideration. Beyond this point infection becomes inversely proportional to temperature. Equations that describe this situation are known and could be applied to most diseases. In a general way we also know the influence of atmospheric humidity on the infection process. Being moisture sensitive, fungus pathogens fail to germinate unless relative humidity is high. As one approaches the saturation point, the capability of a pathogen to germinate and to infect the host increases very sharply. At the saturation point condensation occurs, and infection becomes a maximum. Equations are also known that describe this situation. The effect of host susceptibility on the infection process can be handled simply as an efficiency factor in which, for a given intensity of inoculum and for a given environment, the number of infections becoming established is stated as a number relative to the most susceptible condition that can be imagined. Each of these terms separately can be described mathematically and independently of the others when the others are held constant. Thus, the influence of temperature at a given humidity and for a host of stated susceptibility can be stated. We may deal similarly with the influence of humidity and of host susceptibility. By using the techniques already employed for kinetic studies in chemistry and physics, the plant pathologist can use differential equations to increase his power to analyze and therefore to predict the real value of the inoculum potential. When this has been done and is put to use, the plant pathologist will have a powerful tool at his disposal.

C. Inoculum Potential as a Tool

In the preceding discussion inoculum potential has been treated as a function of distance, infectiousness, trapping efficiency, and of the environmental factors that enter into the amount of disease that is likely to develop. These are the factors that enter into an energy concept of inoculum potential.

The rate at which disease development occurs is dealt with in Chapter 7 by Van der Plank. By the analogy that inoculum potential has the dimensions of energy or work, the rate of increase of inoculum potential is analogous to power in physics; power is the rate of doing work. Van der Plank has presented in his chapter expressions for the rate of disease development which, in our analogy, is the power of the system to produce disease in a population of plants.

Frequently over a period of time the course of development of disease in a population of plants describes a sigmoid curve when a true epidemic is involved. In the early phases of disease development, there is logarithmic growth in the amount of disease over a period of time and only after the number of susceptible healthy individuals becomes limited or some other factor limits disease development is there departure from a logarithmic growth curve.

The sigmoid character of the curve relating amount of disease to time, in fact, is the same whether an epidemic is involved or not. If disease levels remain low, we are concerned only with the first part of the curve. When disease levels are high, then the sigmoid character of the total relation appears. Whether disease develops in an unrestricted manner, a manner restricted naturally, or by control measures devised by man, the mathematics of the disease development curve are similar. The application of a control measure merely reduces the magnitude of the factors already in the equation. Chapter 7 is concerned with this concept to some extent although only with the logarithmic portion of the curve.

The usefulness of inoculum potential as a tool rests upon an appreciation of this fact. Estimates of how large the inoculum potential is at a given time and particularly of the change in inoculum potential over a period of time permit forecasts of disease incidence. An understanding of the mathematical equation that describes this change, and particularly that the same equation is valid for an epidemic or an abortive disease occurrence held in check by a control measure, is a step forward in our ability to forecast the development of disease in a population of plants.

III. The Dispersal of Pathogens

We have seen that the amount of inoculum in the infection court is directly proportional to that produced at the source. The method by which inoculum is dispersed from the source to the infection court does not alter this fact. It merely changes the effect of distance, the proportion of viable propagules arriving, the trapping characteristics on arrival at the host, and the likelihood of finding a host. If a dispersal mechanism is highly efficient, the effect of these factors is small; if the mechanism is inefficient, their effect is great. In a general way the more efficient a dispersal mechanism is, the fewer are the propagules needed to produce a given level of disease. For survival of a pathogen in an evolutionary sense, when dispersal is inefficient, a large amount of inoculum must be produced at the source. This relationship can be seen in the abundance of inoculum produced by air-borne pathogens, relative to ones that are seed-borne.

A. *Autonomous Dispersal*

In the soil the climate is not subject to wide variation as it is in the air. In an evolutionary sense the structure of roots is conservative, that is, primitive. Thus the vascular anatomy of fossil plant stems resembles that of roots. Stems gradually became varied in structure in response to a varied environment in the atmosphere. Likewise, in an evolutionary sense, as has been stressed by McNew in Chapter 2 of Volume II, the most primitive types of pathogens are those that live in the soil and cause root diseases.

The dispersal of pathogens in the soil is likewise primitive. We should remember that plant pathogens frequently have more than one method of dispersal available to them. In the discussion that follows we are concerned with individual dispersal mechanisms, rather than with the habit of individual pathogens. Soil-dwelling fungi, such as *Rhizoctonia* and the root-rotting *Fusaria*, are facultative parasites living on organic matter in the soil, and are not dependent upon their ability to find a host in order to survive. Their attack of plants involves the chance encounter by mycelium or spores of plant roots that are susceptible. When a propagule lies in wait for a susceptible host, the source of inoculum and the infection court are the same, and the distance between them is either zero or very small. The inoculum potential changes little, if any, between the source and the infection court.

When mycelial growth occurs from a substrate, it fans outward and eventually encounters more organic matter or a new host. Rhizomorphs behave in a similar fashion. Dispersal occurs slowly because the growth of mycelium in the soil is a relatively slow process, and from a point source the inoculum potential drops rapidly with distance to zero. However, because the environment in the soil is not ordinarily subject to wide fluctuations, these pathogens can survive in the soil for a long time as compared with pathogens that are characteristically dispersed in the air. Cysts of nematodes, sclerotia, mycelia, and rhizomorphs all fall into this group. Ability to survive adversity, a facultatively parasitic habit, and adaptation to an environment in which fluctuations are not great are all factors that favor ubiquitous distribution, a characteristic of *Rhizoctonia* and the root-rotting *Fusaria*. These matters have been discussed by Garrett in Chapter 2.

The soil dwelling nematodes behave in a manner comparable with the pathogens that are dispersed in the soil through the growth of their own mycelium. The nematodes, on hatching from eggs, swim short distances in the moisture available in the soil until they find food. Because they do not swim rapidly, their dispersal is slow. All of these are examples of autonomous dispersal, a subject discussed by Muskett in Chapter 3 of this volume.

The chemotropic responses exhibited by propagules of pathogens favor the finding of a suitable host. Although a chemotropic response does not enable a pathogen to distribute itself more widely in the soil in terms of space, it increases the probability that a favorable host will be found. In this sense chemotropism has survival value for soil-dwelling organisms even though it operates only over short distances. Thus the cyst-forming nematodes, when encysted, are well adapted to resist desiccation and the absence of a host for a period of years. However, when a host occurs nearby, the liberation of a hatching factor by its roots stimulates the germination of eggs in cysts of nematodes belonging to the genus *Heterodora*, and the resulting nematodes then migrate to the roots of the host and complete their life cycle.

B. *Dispersal by Water*

The dispersal of inoculum in water can occur in one of two ways. In the case of free-swimming nematodes or zoospores or motile bacteria, inoculum is dispersed autonomously. When the water itself provides the motion that causes dispersal, then inoculum is carried along with the water, and self-motility of the inoculum can for all intents and purposes be ignored. When water provides a continuous medium and the pathogen is motile, as with nematodes in the soil, the variation in intensity of inoculum with distance from the source will approach the inverse square law because dispersal is three-dimensional. When moisture exists in a thin film over a surface and inoculum swims out from a point source, then inoculum intensity varies inversely with the distance itself.

Water-borne pathogens are not necessarily efficient in finding a new host. When secondary spores of the apple scab fungus are released and are carried by rain over leaves, they are in an advantageous position because of the proximity of susceptible host tissue in the path of water flow. In this case the dispersal mechanism favors finding uninfected host tissue on the same plant, but is not well-adapted to finding new plants and, accordingly, is better suited to local lesion than to systemic diseases.

However, inoculum may be adapted to being dislodged by water. By the splashing of the water-borne inoculum, tiny droplets are created. These droplets may then become air-borne, and the probability that inoculum will find a new host plant is increased. Gregory (1952) has discussed the manner in which this phenomenon occurs.

C. *Dispersal on Crop Residues*

Pathogens that are dispersed mechanically by being present in crop residues can be transported over limited distances. In perennial plants these pathogens may survive on the overwintering part of the host and maintain themselves for long periods. Among the nematodes, both the root knot and the foliar nematodes can overwinter in the plant. The habit of *Verticillium* and *Fusarium* of invading the host generally after its death and fruiting on the surface of the host makes these pathogens well-suited to dispersal on crop residues.

As with crop residues, so it is with refuse piles containing pathogens. Under cultivation there is a reasonable likelihood that a susceptible crop will be planted in an ensuing year close to the refuse pile. The proximity of the refuse pile to the field and man's habit of successive cropping, season after season, makes necessary only a short dispersal for the pathogen to make successful contact with its host.

D. *Dispersal by Insects*

Insect-borne pathogens are specialized. These pathogens, to speak teliologically, have hedged their bet between the widespread dispersal possible when spores are three-dimensionally air-borne and the reasonable assurance of finding a host because of the preference of an insect for a particular plant. When the pathogen rides along with an insect, that already has a preference as to the host in which it lands, the finding of a host is less a matter of chance than when dispersal of the pathogen is strictly random, but because the flight of an insect may be in any direction from the source, the variation in intensity of inoculum with distance from the source tends to vary inversely as a power of the distance from source to infection court.

For the viruses that persist with their insect vectors, the relation is unique. Here, the insect itself is a host and is capable of transmitting the virus to plants for a long time because the virus multiplies in the insect. This aspect of the subject has been treated by Broadbent in Chapter 4.

E. *Dispersal in the Air*

Air-borne spores must be liberated forcibly to push them through the layer of quiet air surrounding the plant into the layer of turbulent air above. How pathogens shoot their spores into the layer of moving air above the leaf has been discussed by Ingold in Chapter 5 of this volume.

Air-borne spores are well-suited to travel over long distances but are not efficient in finding a new host, and usually multitudes of spores must be produced in order that the pathogen can flourish. Witness the profusion of spores produced by *Endothia parasitica*, the chestnut blight pathogen, which is air-borne. When air-borne spores are produced on refuse piles, the distance over which dispersal must occur is short, and, inasmuch as air-borne dispersal is usually a dispersal in three dimensions, the number of spores varies inversely as the square or higher power of the distance from the source. It is for this reason that the inoculum potential drops rapidly with distance from the source of inoculum. Stated conversely, the greater the distance of a susceptible crop from the source of inoculum, logarithmically the more spores must be produced in order that infection remains equally likely.

Generally speaking, in air-borne dispersal the landing of inoculum is distributed at random, and the inoculum lands more frequently on nonsusceptible hosts than on susceptible ones unless the inoculum is dispersed over short distances in cultivated fields, planted to a single species.

The aerodynamic aspects of spore dispersal are discussed by Schrödter in Chapter 6. This chapter stresses the theory underlying the broad aspects of the subject. Frequently illustrations are given to show how observations made in the field have confirmed the soundness of the theory.

The need for devising new ways of making measurements in this area is often apparent. An excellent illustration of how adequate instrumentation has changed conceptions in this part of plant pathology is the spore trap devised by Hirst (1952) and a modification of it for special use made by Gregory (1954). An instrument of cascade impactor design, the Hirst spore trap permits a study of the changes in spore content of the air diurnally, seasonally, and from point to point (Gregory and Hirst, 1957). As a result of the astute use of a well designed spore trap, Hirst (1953) has shown the effects of weather on the types and abundance of spores in the air. We are beginning to learn much about the factors governing how and when spore discharge occurs (Hirst *et al.*, 1955; Hirst, 1959). As a consequence, our ability to forecast disease outbreaks and epidemics has been greatly improved. To paraphrase an Americanism, the world has beat its way to the door of the man who built a better spore trap!

F. *Dispersal on Seeds*

By contrast, seed-borne pathogens, although not mobile themselves, move with the seed and are practically guaranteed the presence of a host if the seed survives or one nearby if the seed is planted with others of its kind. This is a highly efficient means of dispersal of inoculum, and no great number of spores is necessary for survival of seed-borne pathogens.

The smuts, however, are often diseases of reproductive organs, and in the case of the stinking smut, *Ustilago tritici,* the entire seed may become nongerminable in terms of the host, but a mass of spores in terms of the pathogen. Because of the manner in which wheat is grown, harvested, and planted, this method of dispersal is highly efficient, and inoculum potential does not vary with distance between the infection court and the source of the inoculum. Muskett has discussed dispersal of pathogens on seeds in Chapter 3.

G. *Dispersal by Man*

Of all the methods of dispersal only those where the pathogen is dispersed on plant parts can be altered in a significant way by plant quarantines. We have seen in the case of the seed-borne pathogens that their dispersal is highly efficient. The same is true of pathogens that live on material in transit. Insofar as quarantines are designed to intercept such material, they are well conceived so long as the pathogen can be recognized when it is present. Unfortunately, some quarantines are not of this type. We already know how hard it is to legislate a pathogen out of existence; the pathogens do not read the statutes. Gram has discussed quarantines in Chapter 9. In addition, a principle that is useful in deciding whether a quarantine will be worthwhile is inherent in the discussion below and in Chapter 7.

IV. Control Measures and Inoculum Potential

Van der Plank's equation 12 (Chapter 7) states that

$$dt = \frac{230}{r} \log \frac{I_0}{I'_0}$$

where dt is the delay in onset of disease, r is the rate of increase of disease (and of inoculum) in per cent per unit of time, I_0 is the amount of inoculum in the absence of a control measure, and I'_0 is the amount of inoculum remaining after a control measure has been applied. In Chapter 7 there is a discussion of the extent to which the onset of an epidemic is delayed by reducing the inoculum by a stated amount. How much the onset of the epidemic is delayed depends upon how rapidly the inoculum is reproducing itself.

We may look upon all control measures in terms of this equation. Some control measures have their primary influence on reducing the available inoculum. Other control measures have their effect primarily on the rate at which inoculum builds up. These two effects are qualitatively different from each another.

In fact we may look upon factors that affect the amount of inoculum available for producing disease directly as factors affecting the intensity factor of inoculum potential. Protective fungicides, seed treatments, the planting of trap crops, and soil treatments are cases in point. These are discussed in Chapters 10, 11, and 12 of the present volume. By contrast, control measures that primarily affect the value of r, affect the capacity factor of inoculum potential. The planting of disease-resistant hosts and many cultural methods of controlling disease are examples. These are discussed in Chapters 10 and 14.

The fundamental clue as to which control measures will work best in a given case rests upon the numerical value of r. When the amount of disease is plotted against time in the development of an epidemic, the curve is usually sigmoid in shape, and the slope of the curve at any time is the value of r. Thus what the most efficient control measure to employ is depends upon what value of r has been attained in the epidemic curve. When r values are very low, a small reduction in inoculum can be effective. When values of r are high either because of the nature of the disease itself or because of the position attained along the epidemic curve when a perennial and systemic disease is involved, then control measures that affect the value of r primarily are the ones that will affect the development of disease most satisfactorily. Thus inspection of the equation shows that halving the value of r produces a delay in onset equivalent to reducing the amount of inoculum one-hundredfold. The choice of proper fertilizers to produce a crop that resists infection and the use of crop varieties resistant to disease both reduce the value of r. A striking illustration of reducing the value of r is the use of p-dichlorobenzene or benzene in seedbeds to control downy mildew of tobacco. This compound prevents the production of spores on lesions by acting as an antisporulant (Horsfall, 1945). Rapidly spreading downy mildew infections in tobacco seedbeds can be wiped out through use of p-dichlorobenzene or benzene, because they primarily affect the value of r. With the development of the dithiocarbamate fungicides and the application of ferbam to tobacco seedlings, inoculum intensity can be so drastically reduced that the development of an epidemic is held below its onset by reduction of inoculum levels alone.

From the epidemiological view, plant chemotherapy is a technique of reducing the value of r when the treatment increases the resistance of the plant to infection (Dimond and Horsfall, 1959). There are instances, of course, in which natural factors tend to hold the value of r at a low level. Some of these are discussed by Darpoux in Chapter 13. Another instance, that of disease resistance of a genetic nature, is discussed by Stakman in Chapter 14. Of the cultural practices that control disease, some of those discussed by Stevens in Chapter 10 are designed primarily to reduce inoculum as such, as for example, the spraying of orchard floors to reduce the number of apple scab spores prior to the infection period or the roguing out of diseased plants. Others, such as variations in timing or spacing of planting, or the destruction of weeds that serve as hosts and therefore as sources of inoculum have their value primarily in reduction of the value of r.

Both chemical soil treatment, discussed by Kreutzer in Chapter 11, and foliar and seed protection with chemicals, discussed by Burchfield in Chapter 12, are examples of control measures whose primary purpose is to destroy inoculum.

This way of looking at things is useful in considering when plant quarantines will be effective, a topic discussed by Gram in Chapter 9. As Van der Plank discussed in Chapter 7, epidemics can arise because the birth rate of inoculum (and diseased plants) is high or because the death rate is low. Those diseases in which the death rate is low characteristically have low reproductive rates. This characteristic makes such diseases amenable to control by sanitation (Chapter 7). Quarantines are well-suited to control of such diseases if diseased material can be surely and readily detected.

Under special situations quarantines can also be reasonably applied when inoculum (and diseased plants) characteristically have a high birth rate. First, the value of r must be low. We know that the rate of reproduction of a pathogen is low when it first enters a new area and that the value of r increases thereafter. But the value of r is partly a characteristic of the pathogen itself and partly of the environment, neither being influenced by a quarantine. A quarantine can affect only the value of the intensity of inoculum, and this under special conditions: when the dispersal of inoculum into a locality where the disease is absent is exclusively imported by shipment on plant material. Then the efficiency of the quarantine is measured by the ratio $(I_0 - I'_0)/I_0$ where I'_0 is the intensity of inoculum entering under a quarantine and I_0 is the amount entering in the absence of the quarantine. How long an epidemic is delayed by reducing the amount of inoculum entering an area by given percentage when the value of r is low is a convenient way of estimating the value of a quarantine.

Unfortunately this approach has often been ignored. Quarantines have sometimes been continued after the value of r has become high and the amount of inoculum intercepted is but a small proportion of the total present in the area.

Some useful criteria can be devised to guide decisions on the merits of a proposed quarantine or of abandoning other quarantines. The inoculum arriving must be restricted to plant material in shipment. Diseases can be considered in terms of whether they have a low death rate or a high birth rate. If they are of the latter type, an appreciation of the importance of r and measurements of its value in specific circumstances, together with estimates of the extent to which inoculum will be reduced by the quarantine, will be helpful guideposts.

Inoculum can be combated at the source or in the infection court. Some control practices are designed to reduce inoculum at the source whereas others combat it in the infection court itself. When dispersal of inoculum is three dimensional, it would seem that the control of inoculum in the infection court would be more efficient because much of what is present at the source never finds a host and its destruction is relatively unimportant.

This is why the efficiency of eradication programs is often low. What is important here is not the amount of inoculum destroyed, but rather the amount that is missed and is still free to produce an infection. The destruction of 99% of an infinite amount of inoculum leaves an infinite amount of inoculum still. Man has wasted his effort in this case by laboring to destroy a proportion of the inoculum that will be ineffective in producing disease in any case. What remains may suffice to produce an inappreciably lower level of disease in the next crop.

Destruction of diseased plants and its ultimate goal, eradication, are wisely used when the amount of inoculum is low at the source and its reproduction rate is low. When there are overwhelming strategic advantages other than the destruction of inoculum as such, then eradication may achieve a desired end. The destruction of barberry, the host of wheat rust responsible for development of new rust races, is a case in point.

The choice of whether to combat inoculum at the source or in the infection court is critical, and both entomologists and plant pathologists have had to learn the hard way how critical this choice can be. The control of inoculum involves pesticides—whether fungicides or bactericides —to control the inoculum directly, or insecticides to combat a vector in dispersal and inoculation. All pesticides kill only a proportion of the inoculum or the vector population, and while this proportion can be increased by increasing the dosage of pesticide, the increase in mortality becomes slight when concentration of pesticide is increased logarithmically at high levels of mortality. There are, therefore, limits beyond which we cannot economically go in the killing of inoculum or vectors. When the population of inoculum and vectors is already very high, the proportion of inoculum or vectors that survive treatment with a pesticide may also be adequate to produce disease. This is one of the reasons why, in an average year, almost any fungicide is effective whereas in an epidemic year, almost no fungicide is.

The choice between the source of inoculum and the infection court as locations to which a pesticide is to be applied can sometimes be simply answered. When inoculum is produced in prodigious quantities at the source and is dispersed by air and when no other considerations are involved, the decision to apply the pesticide at the source of inoculum is poor, and the decision to apply the pesticide in the infection court results in more effective disease control. Thus attempts to control apple scab by eradicating the inoculum on the orchard floor were not successful because the population of inoculum surviving treatment was sufficiently high to produce approximately the same amount of disease as would have occurred had no control measure been applied at all. On the contrary, the application of fungicide to the infection court has been and continues to be an effective method of controlling apple scab. The chestnut blight fungus produces prodigious amounts of inoculum, but few of these spores find the infection courts. Whether it is better from a disease-control standpoint, and, economics aside, to concentrate on the trees that are diseased and are producing inoculum or on the trees that remain healthy is simple to decide. When the disease is first present in an area, the number of inoculum sources is small. But to find them all and with certainty is well nigh impossible. To miss a few is to leave sufficient inoculum to permit the disease to spread at an almost uncontrolled rate. To control the inoculum in the infection court, if it were economically worthwhile, would seem the more efficient way to proceed because no effort need be spent in searching out the material to be protected. The total effort would be spent on reducing inoculum in the infection court where the absolute numbers of the amount of the inoculum would be a minimum. In a similar fashion, it would seem a more efficient procedure to develop compounds that render the plant toxic to nematodes than to attempt to reduce the level of nematodes in the soil by the use of nematocides, and although the problems of plant chemotherapy are remarkably difficult from the biochemical point of view, the over-all strategy is sound.

The choice between application of a pesticide at the source of inoculum or in the infection court may likewise be related to how rapidly the pesticide kills or how long the inoculum or the vector is in a vulnerable condition. Thus Broadbent (1957) has discussed the frequent failure on the part of insecticides to restrict the spread of aphid-borne viruses when the insecticide is applied to the infection court. Before the insecticide can act, the plant is already inoculated and even though insect control is reasonably good, the control of spread of virus disease is not. When insecticides are applied to the source of inoculum, however, the extent to which virus spread is reduced depends upon whether the virus is a persistent or a nonpersistent one. Vectors of a persistent virus, once they are able to infect healthy plants, maintain this ability for a long time, whereas vectors of nonpersistent viruses can transmit the virus for a short time only. Because, with the persistent viruses, there is an incubation period between the time when an insect feeds and the time when it is capable of transmitting the virus to a healthy plant, there is opportunity for an insecticide to act upon the insect, and insecticides that kill quickly are more effective than those that kill slowly.

When a disease is being spread from plant to plant within a cultivated field, the application of pesticide is to the source of inoculum and to the infection court as well, but when the strategy is to prevent the introduction of disease into a field that is healthy, one often has a difficult and sometimes an impossible choice of whether to apply the pesticide to crops nearby or to crops that are to be protected.

In the case of some diseases there is sometimes a sufficient time period for a pesticide to act either at the infection court or at the source, and with rapidly acting insecticides, it may make little difference to which locus the pesticide is applied. Dutch elm disease is apparently a case in point. This disease, being carried by the elm bark beetle, can be combated by the application of insecticide either to infected trees in which bark beetles are breeding or to healthy trees to which infested bark beetles may fly. In either case the beetle remains on the host a sufficient time to be inactivated by a rapidly acting insecticide such as DDT. Although great promise was given the systemic insecticides, we now know that their use in preventing the spread of disease by insects is somewhat limited. Thus, a systemic insecticide may be useful in killing bark beetles at the source of inoculum but probably would not be useful in the infection court. There the vector wounds the tree sufficiently to inoculate it with the Dutch elm disease pathogen while it gets a toxic dosage of insecticide.

REFERENCES

Broadbent, L. 1957. Insecticidal control of the spread of plant viruses. *Ann. Rev. Entomol.* 2: 339–354.

Chester, K. S. 1950. Plant disease losses: an appraisal and interpretation. *Plant Disease Reptr. Suppl.* **193.**

Dimond, A. E., and J. G. Horsfall. 1959. Plant chemotherapy. *Ann. Rev. Plant Physiol.* **10:** 257–276.

Garrett, S. D. 1956. "Biology of Root Infecting Fungi." *Cambridge Univ. Press,* London and New York. 294 pp.

Gregory, P. H. 1945. The dispersion of air-borne spores. *Trans. Brit. Mycol. Soc.* **28:** 26–72.

Gregory, P. H. 1950. Deposition of air-borne particles on trap surfaces. *Nature* **166:** 487–488.

Gregory, P. H. 1951. Deposition of air-borne *Lycopodium* spores on cylinders. *Ann. Appl. Biol.* **38**: 357–376.

Gregory, P. H. 1952. Fungus spores. *Trans. Brit. Mycol. Soc.* **35**: 1–18.

Gregory, P. H. 1954. The construction and use of a portable volumetric spore trap. *Trans. Brit. Mycol. Soc.* **37**: 390–404.

Gregory, P. H., and J. M. Hirst. 1957. The summer air-spora at Rothamsted in 1952. *J. Gen. Microbiol.* **17**: 135–152.

Gregory, P. H., and O. J. Stedman. 1953. Deposition of air-borne *Lycopodium* spores on plane surfaces. *Ann. Appl. Biol.* **40**: 651–674.

Heald, F. D. 1921. The relation of spore load to the percent of smut appearing in the crop. *Phytopathology* **11**: 269–287.

Hirst, J. M. 1952. An automatic volumetric spore trap. *Ann. Appl. Biol.* **39**: 257–265.

Hirst, J. M. 1953. Changes in atmospheric spore content: diurnal periodicity and the effects of weather. *Trans. Brit. Mycol. Soc.* **36**: 375–393.

Hirst, J. M. 1959. Spore liberation and dispersal. "Plant Pathology, Problems and Progress, 1908–1958." Univ. Wisconsin Press, Madison, Wisconsin, *in press*.

Hirst, J. M., I. F. Storey, W. C. Ward, and H. J. Wilcox. 1955. The origin of apple scab epidemics in the Wisbech area in 1953 and 1954. *Plant Pathol.* **4**: 91–96.

Horsfall, J. G. 1932. Dusting tomato seed with copper sulfate monohydrate for combating damping-off. *N. Y. State Agr. Expt. Sta. Tech. Bull.* **198**: 34 pp.

Horsfall, J. G. 1945. "Fungicides and Their Action." Chronica Botanica, Waltham, Massachusetts. 240 pp.

Horsfall, J. G., and R. W. Barratt. 1945. An improved grading system for measuring plant disease. *Phytopathology* (Abstr.) **35**: 655.

Nusbaum, C. J., G. B. Lucas, and J. F. Chaplin. 1952. Estimating the inoculum potential of *Phytophthora parasitica* var. *nicotianae* in the soil, *Phytopathology* (Abstr.) **42**: 286.

Waggoner, P. E. 1951. Influence of host temperature and pathogen variability upon spread of *Phytophthora infestans*. Thesis. Iowa State College, Ames, Iowa. 202 pp.

Waggoner, P. E. 1952. Distribution of potato late blight around inoculum sources. *Phytopathology* **42**: 323–328.

Wilhelm, S. 1950. Vertical distribution of *Verticillium albo-atrum* in soils. *Phytopathology* **40**: 368–375.

Wilhelm, S. 1951. Effect of various soil amendments on the inoculum potential of the *Verticillium* wilt fungus. *Phytopathology* **41**: 684–690.

Zentmyer, G. A., P. P. Wallace, and J. G. Horsfall. 1944. Distance as a dosage factor in the spread of Dutch elm disease. *Phytopathology* **34**: 1025–1033.

CHAPTER 2

Inoculum Potential

S. D. GARRETT

Sub-Department of Mycology, Botany School, University of Cambridge,
Cambridge, England

I. INTRODUCTION

"Hordes of soldiers will overrun almost any defense."

J. G. Horsfall

Within the context of plant pathology the word "inoculum" signifies an indefinite quantity of a parasitic microorganism or virus that meets, or may be placed upon or near, the surface of a potential host plant. The inoculum may consist of one or many cells of the microorganism, and conceivably of one or many infective particles of a virus; the cells of the microorganism may be separate and free from one another, or they may be organized into filaments, or into a tissue; they may be separated or

23

not from the substrate upon which they were originally produced. According to general usage, the term "inoculum" is employed to describe something that has merely the potentiality of causing infection; thus, it is possible to speak of "effective inoculum" and, conversely, of "ineffective inoculum." The plant pathologist is chiefly interested in effective inoculum; his interest in ineffective inoculum is conditioned by the indications it may give of what makes an inoculum effective. It thus becomes necessary to define, in turn, what we mean by an "effective inoculum"; an effective inoculum may be described as one that is adequate to produce, under the particular conditions of the situation or trial, a successful, progressive infection. The next query, as to what constitutes a "progressive infection," can be referred back to nature, the ultimate court of appeal, where host and parasite live side by side. Some infections, once successfully initiated, may progress indefinitely until all the contiguous host tissue has been infected, whereas in others, e.g., many leaf spot diseases, the lesion is normally arrested by host resistance when it reaches a certain—and usually fairly typical—size. Such arrest of the expanding lesion generally occurs when the volume of microbial protoplasm in the original inoculum has been multiplied many times, so that the size of the lesion is not usually determined by the volume of the original inoculum; an inoculum that produces a lesion approximating the size normally found in nature can therefore be considered an effective inoculum.

A. Varieties of Inoculum

Effective inocula may be of very diverse kinds. With plant-infecting bacteria it is possible and even probable that a single bacterial cell can cause infection if it arrives in the right condition at a suitable infection court. This may seem a somewhat academic question, because in nature, bacteria are usually dispersed as aqueous suspensions in rain droplets or carried in masses by insects; they may be surrounded by capsular material or suspended in a viscous slime. In stem and leaf diseases caused by fungi, air-borne spores are the chief type of effective inoculum. Such spores are usually large enough to be observed under the lower powers of the microscope and to be handled individually without great technical difficulty. In the great majority of air-borne diseases that have been sufficiently studied, there seems to be little doubt that a single spore can establish a successful, progressive infection, and that it can be considered as an effective inoculum. For seed-borne diseases caused by fungi, effective inoculum may consist of spores adhering to the outer coat of the seed or to the outer covering of the fruit or trapped within the surrounding bracts, as in grain of cereals and grasses. Mycelia established by the germination of such spores and becoming dormant as the seed ripens and dries out, may be considered a stage in infection from the original inoculum; so may dormant mycelia within the actual embryo, as occurs in seed infected by the loose smut diseases of wheat and barley, caused by *Ustilago tritici* and *U. nuda.*

Effective inoculum exists in a greater variety of forms for soil-borne diseases caused by root-infecting fungi. For young rootlets and even for older but not too well-protected parts of the root system in mono-cotyledons and herbacious dicotyledons, thin-walled dispersal spores may constitute an effective inoculum. Thick-walled resting spores well-furnished with food reserves, such as are typically formed by oomycetous fungi, can certainly serve individually as effective inocula. Mycelia of some root-infecting fungi that are also soil saprophytes (i.e., soil-in-habiting fungi, *sensu* Garrett, 1950) can grow through the soil from one saprophytic substrate to another, and this growing mycelium can act as effective inoculum for parasitic invasion of living roots. Mycelia of more specialized pathogens (i.e., root-inhabiting fungi, *sensu* Garrett, 1950) can sometimes grow out from an infected root through the soil, although root infection occurs more commonly through actual contact with another infected root or with a dead infected root containing still viable mycelia of the parasite. Lastly, mycelia of root-infecting fungi may be organized into multicellular resting bodies (sclerotia) or into organs of migration and infection (mycelial strands and rhizomorphs). All these can act as effective inocula, and an attempt will be made later on to explain the significance of this diversity.

Finally, a single "infective virus particle" may, at least for certain possible sites of infection, be able to act as an effective inoculum. Until the advent and development of the electron microscope some 20 years ago, the properties of infective virus particles had to be inferred from various kinds of observations and experiments; the surprising accuracy of many or even most of these inferences has since been proved by "the evidence of things seen" under the electron microscope.

B. *Effective and Ineffective Inoculum*

Despite the efforts of a few outstanding investigators, who were the sole pioneers in earlier centuries, the origins of plant pathology as an organized science can be traced back to just over a century ago. Not until recently has this science found an historian truly worthy of it—in E. C. Large (1940), whose work has been as important for plant pathologists as any of the events he has described with so much insight. Comparatively recent in this history has been the concept of "effective inoculum." The earliest diseases to be investigated, which indeed have continued to claim much attention ever since, were the rusts, mildews, and blights of the foliage and shoot system. These diseases were not only the most obvious even to the inexpert eye, but also—and more important —sporulating fungal mycelia could be seen on the infected foliage. To associate a possible cause (the visible fungus) with an observed effect (the disease), still required from the pioneer plant pathologists a difficult conquest of traditional opinion, first in themselves and later in others, and the required proof was then not easy to obtain. But once this proof had been obtained for a few diseases, it was not difficult to show that for many more, air-borne fungal spores constitute the inoculum. For the great majority of such air-borne fungal diseases of the foliage, therefore, the only known inoculum was effective inoculum, and the question of effectiveness never presented any problem.

For root-disease investigators, on the other hand, the problem of what constitutes an effective inoculum arose as a very practical and immediate difficulty in the way of further research. In order to determine the cause of an unknown disease suspected of being caused by a pathogen, it was necessary to satisfy Koch's postulates, the third of which requires experimental reproduction of the disease by inoculation with a pure culture of the suspected pathogen. Unfortunately for many pioneer root-disease investigators artificial reproduction of diseases by inoculation proved unexpectedly difficult. Thus, through its constant association (Koch's first postulate) with cotton plants suffering from Texas root rot, a species of *Ozonium* (now known as *Phymatotrichum omnivorum*) was correctly described as the cause of this disease by Pammel in 1890. Yet the first successful experimental inoculations were not reported until 33 years later by King (1923), and by Taubenhaus and Killough (1923). One of the most important, and since then, most studied root diseases in the world had thus to wait a third of a century before formal proof of its causation was obtained and before experimental work with artificial inocula could begin. It is interesting to note that these first successful experimental inoculations were made either with natural inocula or with artificial inocula closely simulating the natural product. Thus, King employed both naturally infected cotton roots and sterilized cotton root lengths inoculated with *P. omnivorum* whereas Taubenhaus and Killough used pure cultures of the fungus on sterilized lengths of cotton root and mulberry stem. Indeed, the history of root disease investigation abounds with illustrations of the precept that, in experimental work, it is advisable to begin by creating artificial situations as similar to the natural situation as the requirements of experimentation will permit. This, and many of the other difficulties and puzzles encountered by early root-disease investigators, can now be ascribed to the very artificiality of the experimental situations that they themselves created.

In particular, it was the root diseases of tree crops that presented the greatest difficulty in successful inoculation. Final solution of the problem would certainly have been delayed had it not been for the acute field observations of Petch (1921) who, working in Ceylon, seems to have been the first to emphasize the importance of a "food base" for any fungus invading tree roots. The final solution of the problem was really achieved by De Jong (1933), who compared natural inocula of *Fomes lignosus* with a variety of artificial inocula on the roots of rubber trees. Successful, progressive infections were obtained only by the use of naturally or artificially infected wood, and with these only if the actual volume of the inoculum was sufficient. De Jong's paper was followed by a very timely article by Gadd (1936) on the importance of the food base for infection of tree roots by fungi.

Our present ideas as to what constitutes an effective inoculum for the establishment of any particular host-pathogen relationship, although derived in the first instance from observations and experiments on fungi infecting tree roots, probably have a fairly general application and may be summarized as follows. For successful invasion and progressive infection of the host, the pathogen requires a certain minimum invasive force, which must be supplied by the inoculum until a progressive and self-supporting infection is established. This invasive force is required first of all for the penetration of passive host defenses, i.e., the cuticle or cork barrier, and then for early growth in host tissues that may be far from an ideal culture medium for the parasite. It is unnecessary here to discuss the nature of "active host resistance" (see Chapter 12 of Volume I), but the effect of it is to make the host tissues unfavorable for growth and eventually even for the survival of the invading pathogen. But it is helpful to recall here Brown's (1922b) generalization from his investigation into the germination and growth of various mold fungi in different concentrations of carbon dioxide. He concluded that the inhibiting effect of carbon dioxide was greatest when the energy of growth of the fungus was least. It seems likely, therefore, that for invasion of host tissues offering an unfavorable growth medium for a particular pathogen, a higher invasive force will need to be generated by the inoculum than for invasion of more congenial host tissues. We can push speculation yet one step further by suggesting that the invasive force which the inoculum must supply is likely to reach its minimum values in symbiotic host-parasite relationships, such as those in ectotrophic mycorrhizas and in the legume nodule association with species of *Rhizo-*

bium, because in symbiosis the microorganism does not encounter, or does not provoke, so active a host resistance as occurs in less well-adjusted host-parasite relationships.

II. INOCULUM POTENTIAL

Like most other useful descriptive phrases the term "inoculum potential" has been used by different authors at different times with various shades of meaning. In its widest meaning, for instance, it is possible to speak of the inoculum potential of *Phytophthora infestans* increasing during the development of an epidemic of potato blight. Used thus, it is self-explanatory and scarcely needs a precise definition. This general concept of inoculum potential has an important application in the sphere of fungicidal action, as was emphasized by Horsfall (1945, p. 13). In one usage of this phrase, Horsfall equates "inoculum potential" with "spore load," by reference to Heald's (1921) demonstration of the relationship between spore load and the development of bunt, caused by *Tilletia caries* and *T. foetida,* in wheat; the relevance of this to fungicidal treatment, as Horsfall has explained, is that the higher the load of bunt spores, the heavier must be the seed dressing of fungicide to ensure complete protection. On the same page, Horsfall also conveniently illustrates a wider usage of "inoculum potential," similar to that illustrated above by the reference to *Phytophthora infestans;* he cites the definition given by Zentmyer and associates (1944), of "inoculum potential" as the equilibrium between number of hosts, number of spores, randomness of host distribution, and weather factors. Horsfall expands this as follows: "If the hosts are few and scattered, the pathogen spreads slowly, the potential amount of disease is small and amount of fungicide required is small. When the hosts are congregated as in orchards, groves or fields, they are sitting ducks to the pathogens, the potential amount of disease is large, and the amount of fungicide required is large."

Despite these various already current usages of the term "inoculum potential," it was deemed by Garrett (1956a,b) to be so apt an expression for the one essential characteristic of inoculum, i.e., the degree of its infectivity, that he redefined it for use in a restricted sense thus: inoculum potential may be defined as the energy of growth of a pathogen available for infection of a host at the surface of the host organ to be infected. For the remainder of this chapter, therefore, the term "inoculum potential" will be used with the implied addition "*sensu* Garrett, 1956"; like the addition of an author's name to that of a species, this arrangement is designed primarily to avoid confusion.

The inoculum potential of a pathogen may be increased in either or both of two ways. (a) Increase in the number of infecting units or propagules of the pathogen per unit area of host surface. Such propagules may be, for instance, cells of bacteria, germ tubes of fungal spores, individual fungal hyphae of unorganized mycelia, or hyphae organized into mycelial strands or rhizomorphs. (b) Increase in the nutritional status of such units. Evidence for the view that there is a critical level of inoculum potential for the establishment of any particular host-pathogen relationship under any given set of environmental conditions is as follows: First, inoculation experiments with some diseases have shown that the percentage of visibly diseased hosts declines with decreasing concentration of free infective propagules in the inoculum; when the concentration of propagules falls below a certain critical level, no hosts may develop disease symptoms. Second, in some diseases caused by fungi, the occurrence or not of successful infection from a mycelial inoculum is determined by the volume and nutritional status of the inoculum. Third, in certain diseases caused by root-infecting fungi, infection seems to be successfully accomplished only by means of mycelial aggregates (mycelial strands and rhizomorphs).

III. MECHANISM OF INOCULUM POTENTIAL

A. *Mechanism of the Inoculum Potential Effect with Varying Concentration of Free Infective Propagules*

This effect can be demonstrated by a procedure known as an infectivity titration as follows: Let a strong concentration of infective propagules be prepared in water or in some suitable aqueous medium; this initial suspension is then serially diluted until a very low concentration of propagules is obtained in the medium. Uniform sets of host individuals are then inoculated with the original suspension of infective propagules and with each of the dilutions made from it. The percentage of host individuals manifesting disease symptoms in the sets thus inoculated will decline with progressive dilution of the original suspension of infective propagules until a dilution is reached below which no host individuals manifest disease symptoms as a result of inoculation. This dilution is termed the "dilution end point." Such infectivity titrations are suitable for those host-pathogen combinations in which infection is manifested by means of a quantal (all or none) host response, e.g., production of a lesion or any other clear-cut symptom of disease, or death of the whole host individual.

The results of such infectivity titrations have been interpreted in two ways: (a) that out of a number of infective propagules inoculated only one will be both capable of causing infection and of having the opportunity of doing so; (b) that no single propagule by itself is capable of initiating a successful and progressive infection, which can only be produced by synergistic action of a minimal number of propagules infecting the host together. The two hypotheses have been termed the hypothesis of independent action and the hypothesis of synergistic action, respectively (Meynell and Stocker, 1957).

If we assume that infection occurs through independent action by one propagule alone, then we can imagine the extreme case in which infection from every propagule is certain to occur, and we can say that the probability of infection, p, equals unity $(p = 1)$. In this case, if we inoculate 100 host individuals with one propagule each, then 100 individuals will be infected. Almost always, however, p is < 1, but this situation is still compatible with the hypothesis of independent action and can be explained as follows: (1) in any population of propagules, only a proportion may be even potentially infective, i.e., having an adequate infectivity for independent establishment of a successful infection; (2) of these potentially infective propagules, only a proportion, once again, may successfully germinate on the surface of the host; germinability is controlled both by internal factors (degree of ripeness) and by external factors (environmental); (3) of those propagules that successfully germinate, only a portion, once more, will succeed in infecting the host depending on position effects which will determine the degree of stimulus by the host, opportunity for penetration (e.g., through stomata or perhaps through weak places in the cuticle), and the degree of host resistance to be encountered during penetration and the early stages of invasion by the parasite.

The hypothesis of synergistic action, on the other hand, implies that the infectivity of a single propagule is inadequate for the production of a quantal host response; no matter how many times we care to make the attempt, no host response will follow inoculation with one propagule, nor with any number of propagules less than the minimal effective dose. This hypothesis of synergistic action thus implies that there must be an additive effect to build up the collective inoculum potential of the propagules to a certain level, the minimal effective dose, before a quantal host response is elicited by inoculation. Such a mechanism of infectivity is thus strictly analogous to the mechanism by which a quantal response to the administration of drugs or poisons is thought to be produced; the least number of molecules producing such a response is termed the minimal effective dose (Finney, 1952).

The distinction between the alternative hypotheses of independent and synergistic action of propagules in infection has been neatly represented by Meynell and Stocker (1957) with the following analogy: "The situation when the LD_{50} dose contains many organisms is analogous to that of a poor marksman firing at a bottle. Since his aim is poor, the bottle is unlikely to have been broken after a small number of shots has been fired but if he persists he will probably hit the bottle eventually. A local observer might be aware that the bottle was broken by the action of one bullet. On the other hand, a distant observer, informed only of the total number of shots fired before the bottle broke, would not be able to exclude the hypothesis that the breakage was due to the accumulated stresses produced by all the bullets fired." At present the technical difficulty of observing the infection behavior of individual bacteria (and *a fortiori* of virus particles) is so extremely great as to make a solution of this problem by direct observation experimentally impracticable. For the present, therefore, bacteriologists and virologists must remain in the position of Meynell and Stocker's distant observer.

The first paper to attract the attention of plant pathologists to this problem seems to have been that by Heald (1921) on the relation of spore load to the development of bunt in wheat. This paper has been

TABLE I

RELATION BETWEEN SPORE LOAD OF ARTIFICIALLY SMUTTED WHEAT GRAIN AND PERCENTAGE SMUT IN THE CROP GROWN FROM IT [a]

With spring wheat, variety Marquis

Wt. smut (gm.) per 100 gm. grain	No. spores per grain	% Smutted plants [b]	% Smutted ears [b]
0	104	0	0
0.005	333	0	0
0.01	542	0	0
0.1	5043	7	2
0.25	19687	15	3
0.5	34937	1	0.3
1.0	59229	25	8
2.0	96958	56	16
3.0	183375	15	9

[a] From Heald, 1921.

[b] Percentage figures are given here to the nearest whole number.

widely quoted, and its practical implications have been fully appreciated (Horsfall, 1945), but the more fundamental problem to which Heald drew attention has been subsequently ignored by mycologists. Table I is reproduced from Heald's paper.

The following passage from Heald's paper seems to be the first formulation by a plant pathologist of the hypothesis of synergistic action: "It seems to have been the general opinion of plant pathologists that infection of a wheat plant with bunt might be accomplished from a single spore, but our results seem opposed to such an idea. Food for thought should be found in the fact that a considerable number of spores per grain may not be sufficient to cause any infection. At present, two possible explanations may be suggested. Either what we may term a multiple infection occurs, that is an infection in which a number of spores participate, or there is a chemical mass effect due to numbers of spores, and infection may then be from a single infection thread."

B. *Interpretation of Infectivity Titrations and Other Infection Data Obtained with Bacteria and Viruses*

By plotting graphically the results of an infectivity titration, it may be possible to decide from the form of the dose-response curve which hypothesis—that of individual action or that of synergistic action—is in better accord with the experimental results. Units of dose (i.e., number of infective propagules) are plotted along the x-axis, and the proportion of hosts giving a quantal response to inoculation is plotted along the y-axis. Interpretation of the results is facilitated by plotting the logarithms of doses against the proportions of hosts giving a quantal response expressed in units termed "probits" (Bliss, 1935). The resulting curve is called the log-dose: probit-response curve. Plant pathologists can find a clear and simple exposition of the principles underlying these various forms of the dose-response curve in Horsfall's (1956) "Principles of Fungicidal Action." Those who wish to go more deeply into the statistical theory of these tests should consult "Probit Analysis" by Finney (1952). It will suffice to say for our present purpose that if the slope of the dose-response curve significantly exceeds a value of 2, the experimental results are incompatible with the hypothesis of independent action by infective propagules, and synergistic action must be involved (Peto, 1953). If the slope is less than 2, however, this does not exclude the possibility of synergistic action because a curve of shallow slope can be produced by synergistic action if the variation in resistance of the host population is sufficiently wide. This difficulty is not necessarily insuperable, however, since it is often possible to select host populations for uniformity of response and in other ways to decrease variability. Nevertheless, evidence for one hypothesis or the other, based solely upon the results of such infectivity titrations, is not considered absolutely conclusive since the theory of the statistical method is based upon various biological and mathematical assumptions that can be questioned. For this reason investigators have sought other kinds of evidence that will help in discriminating between the hypotheses of independent and synergistic action in infection, as we shall see from the examples to follow.

Examples to illustrate the use of these experimental techniques will be taken from a series of papers by Meynell and his collaborators, which can be particularly recommended for the clarity of their exposition in modes of thinking that are difficult for many biologists (Meynell, 1957a,b; Meynell and Meynell, 1958; Meynell and Stocker, 1957). In the first of these papers Meynell and Stocker (1957) reported two quite distinct lines of experimentation in which mice were inoculated with *Salmonella paratyphi B* and *S. typhimurium,* respectively, for the purpose of discriminating between these two hypotheses.

The slope of the dose-response curve was determined by the first method. From the hypothesis of independent action it was expected that the slope of the log-dose : probit-mortality curve would be 2 if the population of host organisms were homogeneous for resistance or less than 2 if the host population varied in resistance. A slope of more than 2, on the other hand, would indicate synergistic action. The slopes of the actual log-dose : probit-mortality curves calculated from the data obtained by Meynell and Stocker were 1.81 for *Salmonella paratyphi B* and 0.66 for *S. typhimurium;* these slopes are thus compatible with the hypothesis of independent action and show further that the test populations of mice differed in the degree of their resistance to *S. typhimurium* and possibly also in that to *S. paratyphi B.*

The second method employed by Meynell and Stocker was one originally devised by Kunkel (1934) working with tobacco mosaic virus and its aucuba mosaic variant. For this method, two variants of the selected pathogen, which differed only in some stable "marker" characteristic, unrelated to virulence, had to be isolated. These two variants were then mixed in equal proportions to give an inoculum, which was next progressively diluted so that a suitably wide range of host response was obtained after inoculation with the different dilutions; at the conclusion of the experiment, all hosts that died were sampled for their terminal microbial populations. The prediction of the hypothesis of individual action for this experimental set-up is that with doses of less than one LD_{50} most of the fatally infected hosts will die as a result of the multiplication of a single bacterium, and each should yield a sample at analysis containing only bacteria with the same marker characteristic. Hosts dying after inoculation with doses of many LD_{50}, however, will have been killed by the multiplication of many bacteria present in the original inoculum, and so samples from such hosts should yield the two bacterial variants in about equal proportions as in the original inoculum. These predictions were largely fulfilled by the actual data obtained by Meynell and Stocker, although many dying mice inoculated with a dose of less than one LD_{50} contained not one variant alone, as predicted by the hypothesis of independent action, but instead an excess of one variant with a small proportion (approximately 0.2 or less) of the other. The appearance of this minority of the second variant was attributed by Meynell and Stocker to a terminal breakdown in host resistance, which might be expected to permit multiplication of some bacteria from the original inoculum that had survived in the host without being able to infect the tissues and multiply at an earlier stage of higher host resistance. A supplementary experiment with a lethal dose of *Salmonella typhimurium* mixed with a nonlethal dose of *S. paratyphi B* demonstrated this possibility; the dose of *S. paratyphi B* was so small that it was unlikely to have caused either death or bacteremia if inoculated by itself, yet *S. paratyphi B* appeared in the final blood samples.

Meynell and Stocker have, therefore, concluded that their results are best explained by the hypothesis of independent action of infective propagules. A further application of the second method (i.e., the one originated by Kunkel) was also used by Meynell (1957a), who selected as his two variants of *Salmonella typhimurium* a streptomycin-sensitive (Str.⁻) and a streptomycin-resistant (Str.⁺) strain, which could be distinguished at the final analysis by plating blood samples on nutrient agar and on streptomycin agar, respectively. The essential modification of Kunkel's original method for this experiment lay in the fact that one variant (the Str.⁺) was deliberately chosen for the sake of its slow growth in the host, as compared with the relatively rapid growth *in vivo* of the other variant (the Str.⁻). As had been anticipated, post-mortem blood samples of the mice inoculated with many LD_{50} doses of the two variants in equal proportions contained an excess, and sometimes even a pure culture, of the Str.⁻ variant—with the faster growth rate *in vivo*. But with doses of less than one LD_{50} Meynell actually obtained only the slow-growing Str.⁺ variant from many of the mice. He therefore concluded: "Hence, the bacteria which initiated the fatal infection in these mice must all have been Str.⁺ and their number must have been quite small (say, less than 10), or else at least one Str.⁻ bacterium would have been included and its progeny would have been present in the heart blood post mortem. It seems implausible to suggest that a fatal infection can only be initiated by the cooperation of such a small number of bacteria; so that it seems justifiable to conclude that it could have been initiated by only one bacterium. This implies that the bacteria were acting independently as postulated by the hypothesis of independent action, which therefore applies to this system."

Further evidence in support of the hypothesis of independent action of infective propagules has been presented by Meynell (1957b) in a theoretical paper reviewing the results of other workers and also describing two other tests designed to provide independent evidence for or against the hypothesis. Results of infectivity titrations with eleven animal viruses, with several plant viruses, and with nine bacteria pathogenic to animals have been analyzed and tabulated by Meynell, who has concluded that nearly all the dose-response curves here examined are compatible with the prediction of the hypothesis of independent action.

The first of the other two criteria that have been devised to test this hypothesis depends upon the observation that in most infection systems an increase in dosage of the infective propagules constituting the inoculum shortens the latent period between inoculation and host response. Meynell has pointed out that if most responses to doses not exceeding the LD_{50} are due to the multiplication of a single infective propagule, then the latent period should tend to become constant for doses below the LD_{50}. Such data as are available on variation of latent period with dose agree with Meynell's prediction from the hypothesis of independent action.

The second recent test involves comparison of the quantal response to a given number of infective propagules presented in one dose with response to the same number of infective propagules divided among smaller doses which are inoculated either simultaneously at different sites or at different times by the same route. The hypothesis of independent action predicts that the proportion of hosts responding to a given dose of infective propagules will be the same whether or not the dose has been divided. Meynell records the occurrence of this predicted result from each of the two tests that have been made.

The balance of evidence thus seems to be adverse to the alternative hypothesis of synergistic action by infective propagules. This hypothesis has no doubt proved attractive to animal pathologists familiar with the analogous type of pharmacological titration with drugs and poisons. Drug and poison molecules are not self-reproducing, and there can be little doubt that synergism between molecules must be responsible for production of a quantal host response at doses equaling or exceeding the minimal effective dose. The essential distinction between infective propagules and drug molecules is that infective propagules are self-reproducing within the host, whereas drug molecules are not. In the eventual production of a quantal host response, however, there is more of similarity than of difference between the action of infective propagules and that of drug molecules. In each case a quantal host response requires for its elicitation a minimal number of drug molecules, on the one hand, and a minimal volume of active microbial protoplasm, on the other. Instances are certainly known in which a quantal host response can be produced by a volume of active microbial protoplasm, scarcely or not at all exceeding that in the original infective propagule. The example most familiar to plant pathologists will be the "infection flecks" just visible to the naked eye, produced by the hypersensitive reaction of a highly resistant leaf to attempted invasion by the germ tube of a rust spore. Much more commonly, however, the volume of active microbial protoplasm required for production of a quantal host response is a high multiple of that contained in the original infective propagule. This comparison between units of active microbial protoplasm and drug or poison molecules becomes closer when we consider those infections in which production of disease symptoms can be confidently ascribed to the liberation of a toxin by the pathogen *in vivo* (Dimond and Waggoner, 1953); this seems now a reasonable assumption for the vascular wilt diseases of plants if the term "toxin" is used in an inclusive sense to embrace all possible agents, including enzymes. As Miles (1955) has pointed out, evidence for mediation of the disease syndrome by a toxin, and by that alone, is most complete among animal diseases in the case of tetanus, caused by *Clostridium tetani*.

We can therefore conclude that synergism is involved in production of a quantal host response to infections as well as to intake of drugs and poisons. The essential distinction between these two phenomena depends upon the fact that infective propagules are self-reproducing within the host tissue, so that synergistic effects in infection usually follow, but do not necessarily precede, initiation of an infection. This is merely to state a familiar truth in other words: infection is a continuous process in which host resistance has continually to be overcome by the momentum of the pathogen; otherwise arrestment follows. A certain inoculum potential of the pathogen, which may be provided by a single infective propagule, is necessary for successful initial invasion of the host tissues; in subsequent phases of the infection the momentum of the pathogen must be maintained at a sufficient level if infection is to continue. For the successful continuation of an infection, therefore, momentum of the pathogen plays just as critical a role as does inoculum potential in the original initiation of that infection. The successive obstacles to be surmounted by the pathogen during successive phases of an infection are well illustrated in a recent study of the infection by *Verticillium albo-atrum* of susceptible and resistant varieties of hop (Talboys, 1958a,b). This idea of infection as a continuous process, in which the pathogen may have to survive hazards other than those imperiling initial accomplishment of infection, has been expressed by Miles (1955) as follows: "During the course of an infection from primary lodgement of the parasite to death of the host, the moment when the number of infecting organisms is critical, in the sense of determining death, may in some diseases occur *at* the primary lodgement, when we put in the counted dose; but in others it may take place much later, when some virulence factor, up to this point useless in promoting infection, becomes effective."

C. *Infectivity of Individual Fungus Spores*

Indisputable proof of the infectivity of individual spores in some fungal pathogens has been incidentally provided by the many investigators who have followed in the wake of E. C. Stakman and his collaborators in their study of the biotypes of rust fungi. It is obviously necessary that each culture of a rust fungus should be initiated from a single spore; since the rust fungi are obligate parasites and have to be cultured on the living host plant, each culture must be established by carefully controlled single spore inoculation. The percentage success obtained in such single spore inoculations is clearly relevant to this general discussion of the infectivity of individual propagules, and two examples from the recent literature will suffice for illustration. Manners (1950), working with yellow rust of cereals and grasses, (caused by *Puccinia glumarum*) states: "Under optimum conditions, 5.5% of the spores inoculated caused infections." Griffiths (1958), working with *Puccinia coronata avenae* causing crown rust of oats, reports: "It was necessary to make a number of single spore inoculations from each collection, since even under optimum conditions less than 20% caused infection." Mr. D. J. Griffiths has kindly supplemented this general statement by providing unpublished figures for twelve series of single spore inoculations, which are given in Table II.

Such single spore inoculations, albeit made for quite a different purpose, thus represent the most substantial and direct contribution by mycology toward the solution of the problem under review, i.e., independent or synergistic infection by individual propagules. Nevertheless, the indirect approach that has been forced upon virologists and bacteriologists has recently attracted some mycologists. Thus, a technique for infectivity titrations with spores of leaf-infecting fungi has been developed by Last and Hamley (1956), using conidia of *Botrytis fabae* on leaflets of broad bean *(Vicia faba)*. The technique was closely modeled on the local lesion method originally devised by Holmes (1929) for infectivity titrations with plant viruses, and incorporates the experimental and statistical refinements designed both to increase precision and to permit analysis of residual variability (Bawden, 1950). The dose-response curves obtained by Last and Hamley for the plot of local lesions per half-leaflet against concentration of *B. fabae* conidia in the inoculum are compatible with the hypothesis of independent action of the conidia in their initiation of the primary infections. These primary infections resulted in development, within 24 hours, of the full number of local lesions obtainable with any particular concentration of the inoculum.

For any population of spores that arrives at, or is placed upon, the surface of a host leaf, only a portion will germinate. Of these germinating spores only a portion, once more, will be so situated that infection is possible. And of these, only a portion, again, will possess the necessary degree of infectivity to initiate a successful, progressive infection. The degree of infectivity that is necessary for achievement of infection is determined by the level of host resistance, and is therefore not an abso-

TABLE II

PERCENTAGE SUCCESS IN ESTABLISHING CULTURES OF *Puccinia coronata avenae* FROM SINGLE SPORE INOCULATIONS ON OATS [a]

Year of collection	No. single spore inoculations made	No. single spore cultures established	Per cent success
1948	34	3	9
1949	40	18	45
1949	30	12	40
1949	32	5	16
1949	28	4	14
1949	30	6	20
1949	34	5	14
1950	31	6	19
1950	36	4	11
1950	30	3	10
1950	37	6	16
1950	36	5	14

[a] From unpublished data made available by D. J. Griffiths.

lute quantity for any given host-pathogen combination, because host resistance varies from one individual host plant to another of the same species, from one leaf to another on the same plant, and even from one part of a leaf to another. This variability is recognized in inoculation with plant viruses for the production of local lesions, and is minimized by the use of the half-leaf method with its ancillary refinements.

The use of the terms "infective" or "noninfective" to describe either the potentiality or the actual behavior of a fungus spore is merely a brief way of saying that the individual inoculum potential of that spore is or is not adequate to overcome host resistance and so to initiate a successful infection. The degree of infectivity among any population of fungus spores can vary over a wide range in the same way as can size or any other characteristic. Other things being equal, large spores will contain greater reserves of nutrients, and are hence likely to have a higher degree of infectivity than have smaller spores of the same kind.

But any particular spore may be infective in one situation and non-infective in another, depending upon the level of host resistance that it chances to encounter. Moreover, at any particular site of infection host resistance does not remain constant, but may either fluctuate or trend progressively in one direction. In senescence, for instance, host resistance declines progressively with the gradual approach of death in the tissues. A fungus spore may thus be characterized by a degree of infectivity that is inadequate for infection of host tissues in their prime but may yet be quite sufficient for infection of senescent tissues.

An important ecological niche is indeed occupied by the fungal parasites of senescent plant tissues. Many of these fungi have a wide host range, if their invasion of damaged or debilitated tissues can be dignified by such an expression; many of them are remarkably widespread and common fungi, despite the fact that their activity may be delimited on one side by the virtual immunity to infection of host tissues in their prime, and on the other by the greater competitive saprophytic ability of many obligate saprophytes in the competition for colonization of dead plant tissues.

The best-known and most widely studied of these fungal invaders of senescent tissues is *Botrytis cinerea,* causing the gray mold disease. Its spores can infect wounded, damaged, or senescent tissues, and also poorly cuticularized plant parts such as the petals of flowers. Some of the earliest observations and experiments relating to what we can now term the inoculum potential of spore populations were made with this fungus. Thus Brooks (1908) found that spores of *B. cinerea* sown in water on healthy green leaves of lettuce were unable to infect; nevertheless, if the spores were left *in situ* until the leaves started to turn yellow in senescence, then infection eventually occurred. Brooks further showed that if spores were sown on healthy green lettuce leaves in a nutrient solution (e.g., grape juice) instead of in water, then infection quickly followed. This observation was later confirmed by Brown (1922a), working with the same fungus on the leaves of broad bean *(Vicia faba).* It seems reasonable to ascribe the increased inoculum potential of a spore population sown on the leaf in nutrient solution to a direct effect of the nutrient on the infectivity of individual spores. There can be little doubt that such a direct effect must occur, but Brown further observed that another effect of the nutrient solution was to increase substantially the number of spores actually germinating on the leaf surface; an external supply of nutrients thus also increased (in military parlance) the "number of effectives." Although Brown, under the conditions of his experiments, failed to get appreciable infection of *Vicia faba* by spores sown in water on the leaves, Wilson (1937) successfully achieved this; his success can probably be attributed to the use of spore suspensions more concentrated than those employed by Brown.

Infection of healthy and vigorous green tissues by *Botrytis cinerea* will occur if, and only if, the inoculum potential of the fungus is raised to a sufficient level, such as can be provided by a substantial food base in the form of a corpus of infected tissue. In the field this can occur through the falling of infected flowers onto green leaves, or by contact of green leaves with infected senescent leaves; infection of the green leaves follows such chance contacts. In the glasshouse the requisite inoculum potential for infection can be secured either by sowing a suspension of spores on the leaf in a suitable nutrient solution, as was done by Brooks and later by Brown, or by using a sufficiently concentrated suspension of spores in water, as was employed by Wilson. Such relatively dense populations of spores are unlikely to be deposited on leaves in the field as a result of wind dispersal, however, and this consideration reveals a weakness in Wilson's claim from his glasshouse inoculations that *Botrytis cinerea* is the chief cause of the chocolate spot disease of beans in the field. Wilson's claim was indeed later refuted by the extensive field work of Leach (1955), who found that a more specialized pathogen, *Botrytis fabae,* was much the more widespread and important cause of the disease in Britain. Chocolate spot due to *B. cinerea,* which can fittingly be termed "Wilson's disease of broad beans," can easily be produced in the glasshouse, but seems to be relatively uncommon in the field.

Sufficient studies have already been made of the infection of senescent plant tissues by such pathogens as *Botrytis cinerea* to suggest that every species of green plant has its characteristic fungal invaders of shoot and root systems as resistance to infection falls during senescence. One particular example of this failure to establish a progressive infection before onset of senescence, which was first described more than 30 years ago, is the occurrence of "latent infection" in unripe fruits. This has attracted much attention on account of its economic importance, but references to two recent papers will suffice for illustration and as a guide to the earlier literature. One such type of latent infection is that of green banana fruits by *Gloeosporium musarum.* Chakravarty (1957) showed that if hard green banana fruits were inoculated with conidia of *G. musarum,* the conidia produced germ tubes and appressoria, and the cuticle of the fruit was penetrated by infection hyphae, which developed briefly between the cuticle and the outer cellulose wall of the epidermis and then became quiescent. This confirmed the earlier observations of Simmonds (1940) for latent infections of banana, papaw, and mango. As ripening of the fruit reached a certain stage, the quiescent infection hyphae of *G. musarum* resumed activity; infection developed at first intercellularly and then intracellularly to give the characteristic superficial lesion of anthracnose. Chakravarty compared germination of *G. musarum* conidia in the juice expressed from skins of green and yellow bananas respectively; she found that the juice of green skins exercised an inhibiting effect which, by reference to the earlier work of Barnell and Barnell (1945) she ascribed to tannin.

Such latent infections have an important bearing on the practical problem of disease control, as demonstrated by Wade (1956) for brown rot of apricots caused by *Sclerotinia fructicola*. Microscopical examination of unripe fruits revealed conidia of *S. fructicola* lying within the stomatal cavities; some of these conidia had germinated and then infected the cells surrounding the cavity, but no further penetration of the fungal hyphae had occurred in the unripe fruit. Wade was able to demonstrate the outward diffusion of an inhibiting substance from the skin of green apricot fruits placed upon agar and the absence of this inhibitor from the skin of ripe fruits. He further demonstrated that spraying of apricot trees with a protective fungicide must begin at the petal fall stage if development of brown rot—at first on the tree but later and more extensively in storage—is to be avoided.

The foregoing review of evidence on the infection behavior of *Botrytis cinerea* and of some similar pathogens thus suggests that the infectivity of the average spore is adequate for infection of senescent, debilitated, or damaged tissues, although not for infection of green tissues in full vigor. Neither this nor other evidence for air-borne fungi conflicts with our logical expectation that the infectivity of the average spore should be adequate for infection of its "natural" host plants, provided the spores are dispersed individually. Dispersion of individual spores by air or water must make opportunities for synergistic infection a rare occurrence in nature, except in the immediate vicinity of the infected host plant serving as a source of spores. The rapid dilution of a spore cloud with increasing distance from its source has been calculated and discussed by Gregory (1945). The conclusion that the infectivity of the average air- or water-borne fungal spore is adequate for infection of its natural host plants therefore seems inescapable; the alternative conclusion that inoculum is produced and then dispersed to a limit beyond its infectivity seems impossible to accept. The general conclusion thus attained is not affected by the observation that by artificial concentration of a sporal inoculum it is possible to cause a parasite to infect a host that is usually resistant to natural inocula, e.g., by inoculation of healthy green leaves of *Vicia faba* with a concentrated spore suspension of *Botrytis cinerea*.

While admitting that during the evolution of dispersal spores in fungal pathogens a lower limit to spore size must have been imposed by the requirements of infectivity, it is also relevant to note that the dimensions of such dispersal spores may have been determined by various aerodynamic requirements in addition to the most obvious one, namely, that they have to become truly air-borne. In a discussion of unusual interest Gregory (1952) has suggested that the evolution of spore size in some air-borne fungi has led to a compromise between the conflicting requirements for efficient landing on the chosen aerodrome (i.e., for pathogens, the stems, leaves, or stigmas of the host) and for successful initial penetration of the herbage among which spores are produced and through which they have to be dispersed. The larger the aerodrome, the larger must be the spore for deposition by impaction with any given degree of efficiency; spores that need to alight on tree trunks have to be considerably larger for efficient landing than those that have to impact on floral stigmas. But if spores typically produced in grassy herbage, on which efficiency of impaction is fairly high, impact too efficiently, they will not get far from their source. Gregory has therefore suggested that evolution of spore size in some air-borne fungi must have been influenced by the need for a compromise between these conflicting requirements.

The argument from design, as applied to the infectivity of single propagules, is relevant only to those propagules that are freely dispersed as separate individuals by the natural agencies of wind and water. This argument is not applicable, for instance, to those pathogenic bacteria that are naturally distributed in clumped masses, held together by capsular material or by a viscous exudate (slime). Thus both bacteria and fungi that are chiefly transmitted from one host to another by insects may normally be carried as masses rather than individually as single propagules. The same is true of insect-transmitted viruses in which the average dose transmitted by the insect carrier may greatly exceed that required to establish infection. In such cases the question of the infectivity of single propagules acting individually may not arise as a problem of epidemiology. Such aggregations of propagules, although secured in various ways, are thus comparable, in their pooling of individual inoculum potential, to the mycelial strands and rhizomorphs of root-infecting fungi, which are considered next.

D. *Inoculum Potential of Mycelial Strands and Rhizomorphs in Root-Infecting Fungi*

Mycelial strands and rhizomorphs are produced by a wide variety of fungi that live in soil and in the surface accumulation of forest humus

known as "litter." They are unknown among members of the Phycomycetes, are produced by many species in the Ascomycetes, and reach
their most abundant development in the Basidiomycetes. Mycelial
strands and rhizomorphs are produced by many fungi that are obligate
saprophytes, so they cannot be considered to have evolved as an adaptation toward the habit of root infection. Nevertheless, most fungi infecting tree roots are characterized by this organization of individual
hyphae into composite mycelial strands or rhizomorphs. In general,
mycelial strands and rhizomorphs may be considered as organs of
migration whereby nutrients are translocated from an old substrate—the
food base—to a potential new one lying some distance away through the
soil. By means of these organs of mycelial migration, an inoculum
potential adequate for competitive saprophytic colonization of a new
substrate is secured. The possible reasons for requirement of a definite
inoculum potential for competitive colonization of a substrate like lignin
have been discussed by Garrett (1951, 1954, 1956a) in relation to the
evolution of mycelial strands and rhizomorphs. He has rejected the
earlier explanation of the significance of such mycelial aggregation as
being primarily a protection against desiccation, on the following
grounds: (1) Desiccation is not so important a natural hazard for soil
fungi as might be supposed; the relative humidity of the soil atmosphere
remains at or near 100% until the soil moisture content has fallen below
the wilting point. (2) Mycelial strands and rhizomorphs, so far as they
have been investigated, are not tolerant of severe desiccation. The
mycelial strands of the Texas cotton root rot fungus (*Phymatotrichum
omnivorum*), for instance, are quickly killed by drying (King *et al.*, 1931).

To these arguments can be added the more general one that saprophytic fungi colonizing substrates other than lignin and parasites infecting roots other than those of arboreal plants seem to be able to grow
and survive well enough in the soil without this putative protection
against desiccation. If the organization of mycelium into strands or
rhizomorphs secured a significant protection against desiccation, we
should expect to find such organs particularly characteristic of fungi
living in arid soils, but this is not so. On the contrary, mycelial strands
and rhizomorphs are most abundant in a habitat that has a higher
moisture-holding capacity than have any of the other soil horizons, i.e.,
the surface litter accumulating on the forest or woodland floor. Garrett
has therefore argued that the significance of mycelial aggregation into
strands and rhizomorphs lies in aggregation per se, and not in possible
ancillary advantages, such as some protection against desiccation. By
such aggregation the maximum possible concentration of hyphae is

secured, giving the maximum inoculum potential available for a given number of hyphae, whether for competitive colonization of substrates by saprophytes or for invasion of host roots by parasites.

1. *Morphogenesis of Mycelial Strands and Rhizomorphs*

So far, reference has been made collectively to mycelial strands and rhizomorphs. In the past authors have often used these two terms indiscriminately and sometimes even interchangeably for the same fungus. This is not surprising, since superficially some mycelial strands are difficult or impossible to tell from rhizomorphs. The difficulty may remain even after a casual examination of longitudinal sections under the microscope because both strands and rhizomorphs appear as a fascicle of more or less longitudinally running hyphae. Nevertheless, the morphogenesis of a strand is entirely different from that of a rhizomorph. As a typical example of a true rhizomorph, we may select that of *Armillaria mellea,* which is the best known (Fig. 1). In the apex of the rhizomorph as it arises from a colony of unorganized mycelium (Garrett, 1953) or as a branch from a parent rhizomorph, there is an apical meristem (Brefeld, 1877). The apex of a rhizomorph is thus strictly comparable to the meristem of a root apex. This type of morphogenesis produces an organ that is of similar diameter all along its length from apex to base although the actual apex itself may be somewhat swollen, just as a root apex may be. The form as well as the morphogenesis of a rhizomorph is thus very similar to that of a monocotyledonous root having no secondary thickening.

In mycelial strands, on the other hand, there is no apical meristem. Mycelial strands do not grow as such from the apex although they have leading hyphae; they become gradually built up, as growth of the main hypha or hyphae proceeds. Two principal types of mycelial strand have so far been described although other types may well exist undiscovered. Both types occur in root-infecting fungi as well as in obligate saprophytes.

Development of the first type of strand is well exemplified in the violet root rot fungus *Helicobasidium purpureum* (imperfect stage = *Rhizoctonia crocorum*) and has been described in detail by Valder (1958). Such strands consist essentially of a fairly loose federation of individual hyphae growing together; coherence is secured by an interweaving growth of the main hyphae, by the binding action of short side branches of limited growth, and by anastomoses (Fig. 2). Valder studied the sequences of strand formation as mycelium of *H. purpureum* grew out from a food base through unsterilized soil over the surface of a glass slide. A sparse growth of robust hyphae initially spread out from the food base; further hyphae growing out from the food base sooner or later encountered one of these leading hyphae, and then followed it. By continued accretion of further "following" hyphae and also of smaller strands from the food base, each of the original leading hyphae developed into a main strand, the base of which might thus come to resemble a river delta. Because of this method of formation, cross-sections of strands tended to be widest near the base and to taper off towards the apex, thus contrasting with the uniform cross-section of a rhizomorph

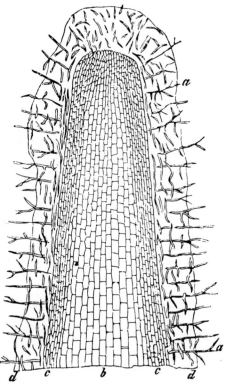

Fig. 1.   Apex of rhizomorph of *Armillaria mellea* in longitudinal section: (a) Mantle of filamentous hyphae. (b) Central conducting cells. (c) Cells of the rind. (d) Boundary of enveloping mucilaginous layer. (After R. Hartig.)

from base to apex, as described for *Armillaria mellea* above. Some anastomoses occurred between strands as well as between individual hyphae within a single strand thereby giving a network of strands in some places, and this was more common near the food base. Branching of a strand was usually caused by the branching of the original leading hypha, with the branch attracting some of the "following" hyphae away from the parent hypha. Nevertheless, a characteristic feature of strand morphogenesis was the usual restriction of growth in the side branches of the main strand hyphae, and these short side branches tended to curl around the main hyphae and bind them together, in which action frequent anastomoses assisted. Some observations made by Garrett (1954), incidental to an experimental study of compost colonization by the cultivated mushroom *Psalliota hortensis*, suggest that strand formation by this saprophyte occurs in a manner somewhat similar to that elucidated by Valder for *H. purpureum*.

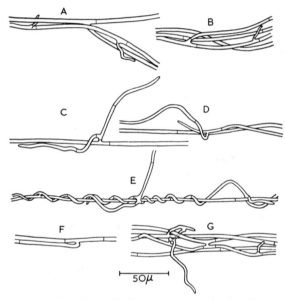

FIG. 2. A–G, details of strand formation in *Helicobasidium purpureum*: the general direction of growth is from left to right. Note hyphal branches of limited growth in (A) and (B), and hyphal anastomoses in (G). (After Valder, 1958.)

The second type of mycelial strand consists, in its simplest form, of a single branch system in which the branches do not spread out, as in growth over or through a nutritive medium, but instead wrap themselves around the main parent hypha. This type of strand (Fig. 3) is to be found in *Phymatotrichum omnivorum*, the fungus causing Texas root rot of cotton and other crops; its development has been elucidated by Rogers and Watkins (1938). Single hyphae of large diameter become ensheathed by their own branch hyphae, which are of much smaller diameter. By subsequent adjustment of position and septation in the ensheathing branch hyphae a compact cortex of several layers in thickness is eventually formed around the single large hypha at the center of each strand. This type of strand is also produced by a well-known saprophyte, *Merulius lacrymans*, which causes dry rot of timber (Fig. 4).

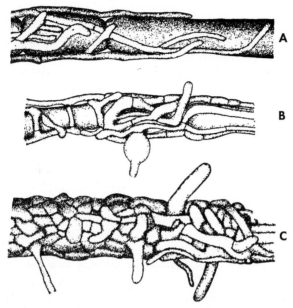

FIG. 3. Stages of strand formation in *Phymatotrichum omnivorum:* (A) Branch hyphae beginning to grow over the surface of a large central hypha. (B) Central hypha surrounded by a loose network of branch hyphae. (C) Deposition of the second hyphal layer. (After Rogers and Watkins, 1938.)

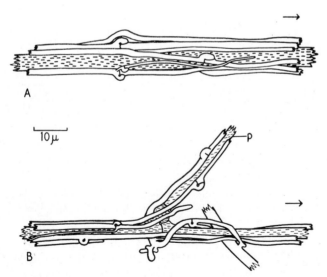

FIG. 4. Surface view of young developing strands of *Merulius lacrymans* (main hyphae are stippled): (A) wide main hypha with a covering of narrower tendril hyphae; (B) tendril hyphae growing along a wide main hypha and its free primary branch, *p.* (After Butler, 1957).

Strand morphogenesis in *M. lacrymans* was first described and interpreted by Falck (1912) in a classic paper displaying a wealth of acute
observations. Falck's interpretation of morphogenesis in these strands
has been largely confirmed and much amplified by Butler (1957).

Strand formation, both by saprophytes and by parasites, typically
occurs when a mycelium is growing over a surface or through a medium
having a negligible content of free nutrients. As might be expected,
therefore, strands may also be developed in an aerial mycelium out of
actual contact with the nutritive substrate, as has been described for
Merulius lacrymans on agar plates by Butler (1957). Strands are not
usually produced among mycelia growing on the actual surface of, or
within, a nutrient medium. Similarly, strands produced by root-infecting
fungi are responsible for initiating root infection and for extending it
along the root by ectotrophic growth; inside the host tissues, however,
the mycelium ramifies as independent hyphae. The behavior of rhizomorphs, on the other hand, may be somewhat different in these respects
from that of mycelial strands if rhizomorph behavior in *Armillaria mellea*
is at all typical. Thus rhizomorphs of *A. mellea* are actually initiated
from an inoculum of unorganized mycelium placed on a nutrient agar
plate, and the number of rhizomorph initials thus produced increases
with increase in nutrient concentration of the medium. Nevertheless,
the flexibility of the fungal organization is demonstrated by the fact that
those parts of the grown rhizomorph in actual contact with the nutrient
medium invariably produce a mantle of fringing mycelium, whose like-
ness to root hairs illustrates the aptness of the term "rhizomorph"
(Garrett, 1953).

Fungi forming such strands have all the advantages of a flexible
growth habit by which the mycelium is concentrated when traveling
from a food base through soil or over an inhospitable surface toward the
next substrate or host root that it may chance to encounter. This concentration of the mycelium secures the necessary inoculum potential for
colonization of the substrate or for infection of the host root, as the case
may be, but once inside the substrate or the living root, the mycelium is
deployed as individual hyphae. While it now seems possible to understand the function of mycelial strands, the actual mechanism of their
formation is still obscure. There seems to be a tendency for hyphae of
the same fungus individual or of the same species to grow together, as
shown by recent studies of Valder (1958) and Butler (1957), referred
to above, and this suggests that there is some stimulus bringing and
holding hyphae together in their growth. If this is so, it must be postulated that under conditions in which strands fail to form and preformed
strands disintegrate into their constituent hyphae during growth over or

through a nutritive substrate, this tendency of hyphae toward associated growth is overcome by a stronger tendency to grow up a diffusion gradient of nutrients (or perhaps down a diffusion gradient of staling products) and thus away from neighboring hyphae.

2. Mycelial Strands and Rhizomorphs as a Vehicle for Transmission of Inoculum Potential

As outlined in the historical introduction to this chapter, it is not surprising that the concept of inoculum potential in its restricted sense, as defined by Garrett (1956a), has arisen in the first instance from pioneer work on root diseases. The older, cork-covered parts of a tree root system offer higher resistance to infection than any other part of a green plant commonly invaded by fungi; because of the lower humidity of the atmosphere above ground, the uninjured trunks of trees are fairly safe from fungal attack. The high resistance of older parts of a tree root system to infection demand a correspondingly high inoculum potential of the fungus if infection is to be successful. There is now ample experimental as well as observational evidence for this general conclusion (Garrett, 1956a, Chapter 4). By way of illustration Table III shows data obtained by Altson (1953) on the relation between volume of woody inoculum and percentage of successful root inoculations in rubber seedlings with *Fomes lignosus*.

TABLE III

EFFECT OF INOCULUM VOLUME ON SUCCESS OF ROOT INOCULATION OF YOUNG RUBBER TREES WITH *Fomes lignosus* IN INFECTED WOOD SEGMENTS [a]

No. trees inoculated	15	13	9	8	18
Vol. inoculum (cu. in.)	5.0+	5.0–1.0	1.0–0.5	0.5–0.25	<0.25
Percent infections	100	69	22	12	0

[a] From Altson, 1953.

Table IV is taken from a laboratory study of infection of potato tubers by *Armillaria mellea* (Garrett, 1956b).

For both *Fomes lignosus* on roots of rubber and *Armillaria mellea* on potato tubers there is a limiting size of inoculum, below which infection fails to occur. In other experiments described in this paper Garrett sought to correlate the inoculum potential of rhizomorphs, expressed as extent of potato tuber infection, with some growth characteristic that would estimate the energy of growth of the rhizomorph apexes. This was measured by burying a woody inoculum segment at the mid-point of a glass tube filled with moist, unsterilized soil, and calculating successive weekly growth increments for the leading rhizomorphs growing out of each end of the woody inoculum. These growth measurements showed first, that rhizomorph growth rate increased with the volume of the inoculum segment over the range 0.5–4.0 gm. fresh weight. Second, rhizomorph growth rate progressively declined with increasing distance from the food base; this decline was attributed to: (a) gradual consumption of nutrient reserves in the inoculum through fungal respiration

TABLE IV

EFFECT OF INOCULUM SIZE ON VIGOR OF *Armillaria mellea* IN INFECTION OF POTATO TUBERS FROM SMALL WOODY INOCULA [a]

Inoculum weight (gm.)	Fresh wt. infected potato tissue (gm.)	Radial extent of infection (mm.)
2	10	16
1	4	11
0.5	0.2	3
0.25	0	0
Standard errors	1.72	2.53

[a] From Garrett, 1956b.

and growth, and (b) increasing competition for nutrients between the main growing apex of the rhizomorph and its subordinate branch apexes, and also between the leading rhizomorph and others produced later. These growth rate data for rhizomorph apexes could be correlated fairly closely with infection behavior; thus speed of infection increased with size and decreased with distance away of the inoculum.

IV. IMPORTANCE OF THE LIVING HOST PLANT AS AN INOCULATING AGENT AND AS A SOURCE OF INOCULUM

More often than not the most difficult task a plant pathologist ever has to undertake is the reproduction of an unknown or insufficiently studied disease by inoculation. This problem involves more than the choice of a suitable inoculum; an adequate knowledge of how the disease is transmitted in the field and what environmental conditions are optimum for infection and for further development of the disease may be equally essential for success. It can often happen, therefore, that when a research worker has succeeded in reproducing the symptoms of an unknown disease of parasitic origin by means of inoculation, he has gone more than half way toward a fairly complete understanding of its epidemiology. An essential preliminary to any such investigation is a wide and thorough survey of the unknown disease as it occurs in the field, before any inoculation experiments are undertaken; the safest guide to the success of such experiments is as close an approximation as possible to the natural conditions under which the disease occurs. To stress this may seem to belabor the obvious, but the history of experimental inoculations has shown repeatedly that a great number of failures have been due to neglect of this prime precaution.

The greater part of this chapter has been concerned with a single characteristic of inoculum, i.e., the degree of its infectivity, as expressed by the concept of inoculum potential (*sensu* Garrett, 1956a, b). Although this property of being potentially able to cause infection is the one essential characteristic of inoculum, yet in studying a disease in the field, or in attempting to reproduce it artificially for experimental purposes, the plant pathologist must be equally concerned with the dispersal of inoculum, with the way in which it achieves actual infection of the host, and with the influence of environmental conditions upon the success or failure of inoculation. These problems, however, are discussed in other chapters, and need not detain us further here.

Varieties of inoculum for different types of infections have been considered in an earlier section of this chapter, but the importance of the living host plant needs further emphasis. There is a saying still current among English farmers that "a sheep's worst enemy is another sheep"; epidemiologists are always saying the same thing but usually in many more words. For the majority of diseases caused by root-infecting fungi, infection is spread by direct root contact between adjacent plants, and in some virus diseases the only known method of spread is by contact, either between roots or between foliage of plants in juxtaposition. In other diseases the infected host plant serves as a source of inoculum for dispersal, rather than as an inoculating agent in itself. The majority of plant viruses do not survive in dead host tissue for any appreciable period, and so the living host plant becomes of paramount importance as a reservoir of virus for insect transmission.

A. Weeds as Carriers of Disease

Control of diseases and pests by crop rotation means effective control of weeds as well; otherwise the best planned crop rotation exists merely on paper. Weeds exert their most directly harmful effect, perhaps, in the case of soil-borne diseases, because the roots of weeds infected by a particular parasite act as direct inoculum for the roots of any following crop susceptible to infection by that parasite. Thus, *Ophiobolus graminis,* causing the take-all disease of cereals, also infects the underground parts of a number of perennial rhizomatous weed grasses. A noncereal crop heavily infested with one of these perennial grass weeds may be more dangerous to a following wheat crop than a preceding wheat crop may be, even if this preceding wheat crop has shown a sprinkling of "whiteheads" due to the disease. The reason for this is a simple one: after a wheat crop is harvested, loss of viability by *O. graminis* in the dead infected roots begins, even though slowly at first, whereas when living grass hosts are present on the ground, *O. graminis* not only survives but actually continues to spread vigorously along the grass rhizomes and roots, from where it passes to the young roots of the next wheat crop.

This last example illustrates not only the paramount importance of the living host plant as the most dangerous inoculum or source of inoculum, but also the fact that the survival of inoculum, as well as production of inoculum, provides problems worthy of intensive study. Problems of inoculum survival in the form of fungal mycelium in dead infected host tissues, of resting spores, or of sclerotia (and how this is differentially affected by soil conditions) have already received much attention from root disease investigators (Garrett, 1956a, Chapters 8 and 9). A similar problem is presented by such air-borne diseases as clover rot, caused by *Sclerotinia trifoliorum*. This fungus produces sclerotia in and upon the stems and rootstocks of diseased plants, and these sclerotia find their way into the soil. A proportion of such sclerotia germinates in the first autumn after formation to produce apothecia, from which ascospores are ejected, and it is these ascospores that produce the minute primary lesions on clover leaves. Not all the sclerotia lying in the soil germinate in their first autumn. Some germinate in their second year and others in subsequent years, and it is these delayed-action sclerotia that make control of clover rot through crop rotation either difficult or impossible.

Lastly, the definition of a weed as a plant out of place is singularly apt for plant pathologists because volunteer cultivated plants, whether persisting or self-sown, are frequent carriers of disease. Anyone who is accustomed to walk observantly through growing crops will know that such "ground keepers" are far more common within a crop than casual inspection from the outside would suggest.

B. *Symptomless Carriers of Disease*

Both kinds of weeds—wild plants and volunteer cultivated plants—may show either inconspicuous symptoms of disease or none at all, and this aggravates the difficulty of getting farmers to pursue weed control with sufficient zeal. The term "symptomless carrier" is a perfectly correct description of many host plant: virus combinations, but fungal root infections may be equally difficult to detect by above-ground inspection in the field, and many leaf spot diseases are inconspicuous and easily escape notice. Volunteer cultivated plants are less likely to be symptomless, or near-symptomless, carriers than are truly wild plants because so many cultivars have been selected without much thought for disease resistance. Races of wild plants, on the other hand, have tended to evolve through the natural selection of both host and parasite toward a tolerance of their various parasites.

Often enough, however, it is the crop itself that functions as a population of symptomless carriers of one or more diseases. If such a crop is used for vegetative propagation, clones derived from it may eventually suffer severely in the fullness of time or under particular environmental conditions from the diseases thus carried. Hence the need for governmental inspection and registration of propagating material, which is particularly important for systemic virus diseases and vascular wilts. A crop that is carrying hidden infection may transmit disease in other ways than through living infected tissues, as, for example, through propagating sets and true seeds. Thus a wheat crop, showing no perceptible signs of disease above ground, may leave in the soil a sufficient number of dead roots infected by *Ophiobolus graminis* to cause a disastrous failure through the take-all disease in a second crop of wheat that is subsequently sown too soon. Few farmers make this mistake twice, yet such an occurrence has to be seen to be believed, and no one with first hand experience of this disease can afford to appear wiser than Kirby and Thomas (1920) when they reported, with no little urgency, the first known appearance of take-all in the United States. Nevertheless, the weight of subsequent evidence on the behavior of *O. graminis* and the cosmopolitan distribution of this fungus now make it seem probable that the take-all disease was endemic on native grasses in the United States long before the first crop of wheat was raised in the New World.

Many other diseases besides take-all have from time to time made sudden, spectacular, and disastrous appearances for the first time in living memory. The hypotheses evolved to explain such visitations have been almost as numerous. It may not be so exciting, but it will usually be more rewarding, to search for the inoculum close at hand—in the soil, among the wild plants of surrounding vegetation, or among the weeds growing in the very fields themselves.

ACKNOWLEDGEMENT

The author wishes to express his gratitude to Dr. G. G. Meynell, who read the entire chapter in manuscript and made valuable suggestions.

REFERENCES

Altson, R. A. 1953. Diseases of the root system. *Rubb. Research Inst. Malaya Rept. 1951* p. 34.

Barnell, H. R., and E. Barnell. 1945. Studies in tropical fruits. XVI. The distribution of tannins within the banana and the changes in their condition and amount during ripening. *Ann. Botany (London)* **9:** 77–99.

Bawden, F. C. 1950. "Plant Viruses and Virus Diseases," 3rd ed. Chronica Botanica, Waltham, Massachusetts.

Bliss, C. I. 1935. The calculation of the dosage-mortality curve. *Ann Appl. Biol.* **22**: 134–167.

Brefeld, O. 1877. "Botanische Untersuchungen über Schimmelpilze. III. Basidiomyceten," pp. 136–173. Felix, Leipzig.

Brooks, F. T. 1908. Observations on the biology of *Botrytis cinerea. Ann. Botany (London)* **22**: 479–487.

Brown, W. 1922a. Studies in the physiology of parasitism. VIII. On the exosmosis of nutrient substances from the host tissue into the infection drop. *Ann. Botany (London)* **36**: 101–119.

Brown, W. 1922b. On the germination and growth of fungi at various temperatures and in various concentrations of oxygen and of carbon dioxide. *Ann. Botany (London)* **36**: 257–283.

Butler, G. M. 1957. The development and behaviour of mycelial strands in *Merulius lacrymans* (Wulf.) Fr. I. Strand development during growth from a food-base through a non-nutrient medium. *Ann. Botany (London)* **21**: 523–537. (See also following papers in this series in same journal.)

Chakravarty, T. 1957. Anthracnose of banana (*Gloeosporium musarum* Cke. and Massee) with special reference to latent infection in storage. *Trans. Brit. Mycol. Soc.* **40**: 337–345.

De Jong, W. H. 1933. Het parasitisme van *Rigidoporus microporus* = *Fomes lignosus,* bij *Hevea brasiliensis* (with English summary). *Arch. Rubbercult. Ned.-Indië* **17**: 83–104.

Dimond, A. E., and P. E. Waggoner. 1953. On the nature and role of vivotoxins in plant disease. *Phytopathology* **43**: 229–235.

Falck, R. 1912. Die Merulius des Bauholzes. *Hausschwammforsch.* **6**: 1–405.

Finney, D. J. 1952. "Probit Analysis," 2nd ed. Cambridge Univ. Press, London and New York.

Gadd, C. H. 1936. Diseases of the tea bush. II. Root diseases. *Tea Quart.* **9**: 5–12.

Garrett, S. D. 1950. Ecology of the root-inhabiting fungi. *Biol. Revs. Cambridge Phil. Soc.* **25**: 220–254.

Garrett, S. D. 1951. Ecological groups of soil fungi: a survey of substrate relationships. *New Phytologist* **50**: 149–166.

Garrett, S. D. 1953. Rhizomorph behaviour in *Armillaria mellea* (Vahl) Quél. I. Factors controlling rhizomorph initiation by *A. mellea* in pure culture. *Ann. Botany (London)* **17**: 63–79.

Garrett, S. D. 1954. Function of the mycelial strands in substrate colonization by the cultivated mushroom, *Psalliota hortensis. Trans. Brit. Mycol. Soc.* **37**: 51–57.

Garrett, S. D. 1956a. "Biology of Root-infecting Fungi." Cambridge Univ. Press, London and New York.

Garrett, S. D. 1956b. Rhizomorph behaviour in *Armillaria mellea* (Vahl) Quél. II. Logistics of infection. *Ann. Botany (London)* **20**: 193–209.

Gregory, P. H. 1945. The dispersion of air-borne spores. *Trans. Brit. Mycol. Soc.* **28**: 26–72.

Gregory, P. H. 1952. Fungus spores. *Trans. Brit. Mycol. Soc.* **35**: 1–18.

Griffiths, D. J. 1958. Physiological specialization of oat crown rust (*Puccinia coronata* Corda F. sp. *avenae* (Erikss. & Henn.) Erikss.). *Trans. Brit. Mycol. Soc.* **41**: 373–384.

Heald, F. D. 1921. The relation of the spore-load to the percentage of smut appearing in the crop. *Phytopathology* **11**: 269–278.

Holmes, F. O. 1929. Local lesions in tobacco mosaic. *Botan. Gaz.* **87**: 39–55.

Horsfall, J. G. 1945. "Fungicides and their Action." Chronica Botanica, Waltham, Massachusetts.

Horsfall, J. G. 1956. "Principles of Fungicidal Action." Chronica Botanica, Waltham, Massachusetts.

King, C. J. 1923. Cotton root rot in Arizona. *J. Agr. Research* **23**: 525–527.

King, C. J., H. F. Loomis, and C. Hope. 1931. Studies on sclerotia and mycelial strands of the cotton root rot fungus. *J. Agr. Research* **42**: 827–840.

Kirby, R. S., and H. E. Thomas. 1920. The take-all disease of wheat in New York State. *Science* **52**: 368–369.

Kunkel, L. O. 1934. Tobacco and aucuba mosaic infections by single units of virus. *Phytopathology* **24**: 13 (abstr.).

Large, E. C. 1940. "The Advance of the Fungi." Jonathan Cape, London.

Last, F. T., and R. E. Hamley. 1956. A local-lesion technique for measuring the infectivity of conidia of *Botrytis fabae* Sardiña. *Ann. Appl. Biol.* **44**: 410–418.

Leach, R. 1955. Recent observations on the *Botrytis* infection of beans. *Trans. Brit. Mycol. Soc.* **38**: 171 (abstr.).

Manners, J. G. 1950. Studies on the physiologic specialization of yellow rust (*Puccinia glumarum* (Schm.) Erikss. & Henn.) in Great Britain. *Ann. Appl. Biol.* **37**: 187–214.

Meynell, G. G. 1957a. The applicability of the hypothesis of independent action to fatal infections in mice given *Salmonella typhimurium* by mouth. *J. Gen. Microbiol.* **16**: 396–404.

Meynell, G. G. 1957b. Inherently low precision of infectivity titrations using a quantal response. *Biometrics* **13**: 149–163.

Meynell, G. G., and E. W. Meynell. 1958. The growth of micro-organisms *in vivo,* with especial reference to the relation between dose and latent period. *J. Hyg.* **56**: 323–346.

Meynell, G. G., and Stocker, B. A. D. 1957. Some hypotheses on the aetiology of fatal infections in partially resistant hosts and their application to mice challenged with *Salmonella paratyphi-B* or *Salmonella typhimurium* by intraperitoneal injection. *J. Gen. Microbiol.* **16**: 38–58.

Miles, A. A. 1955. The meaning of pathogenicity. *Symposium Soc. Gen. Microbiol. 5th* pp. 1–16.

Pammel, L. H. 1890. Cotton root rot. *Texas Agr. Expt. Sta. Rept. for 1889* pp. 61–91.

Petch, T. 1921. "The Diseases and Pests of the Rubber Tree." Macmillan, London.

Peto, S. 1953. A dose-response equation for the invasion of micro-organisms. *Biometrics* **9**: 320–335.

Rogers, C. H., and G. M. Watkins. 1938. Strand formation in *Phymatotrichum omnivorum. Am. J. Botany* **25**: 244–246.

Simmonds, J. H. 1940. Latent infection in tropical fruits discussed in relation to the part played by species of *Gloeosporium* and *Colletotrichum. Proc. Roy. Soc. Queensland* **52**: 92–120.

Talboys, P. W. 1958a. Some mechanisms contributing to Verticillium resistance in the hop root. *Trans. Brit. Mycol. Soc.* **41**: 227–241.

Talboys, P. W. 1958b. The association of tylosis and hyperplasia of the xylem with vascular invasion of the hop by *Verticillium albo-atrum. Trans. Brit. Mycol. Soc.* **41**: 249–260.

Taubenhaus, J. J., and D. T. Killough. 1923. Texas root rot of cotton and methods of its control. *Texas Agr. Expt. Sta. Bull.* **307.**

Valder, P. G. 1958. The biology of *Helicobasidium purpureum* Pat. *Trans. Brit. Mycol. Soc.* **41:** 283–308.

Wade, G. C. 1956. Investigations on brown rot of apricots caused by *Sclerotinia fructicola* (Wint.) Rehm. I. The occurrence of latent infection in fruit. *Australian J. Agr. Research* **7:** 504–515.

Wilson, A. R. 1937. The chocolate spot of beans caused by *Botrytis cinerea. Ann. Appl. Biol.* **24:** 258–288.

Zentmyer, G. A., P. P. Wallace, and J. G. Horsfall. 1944. Distance as a dosage factor in spread of Dutch elm disease. *Phytopathology* **34:** 1025–1033.

CHAPTER 3

Autonomous Dispersal

A. E. Muskett

The Queen's University, Belfast, Northern Ireland

I. Introduction

For the purpose of this treatise autonomous dispersal is interpreted as the spread of vegetable, fungal, bacterial, virus, or nematodal plant pathogens through the agency of soil, seeds, or plant parts in the normal practice of crop husbandry and in the distribution of plants and plant products, and not through the intervention of any extraneous agency such as insect, wind, or water. Such dispersal involves the consideration of both space and time; adaptation for dispersal and the consequences of adaptation are also discussed. The subject is dealt with under the three main headings of soil, seeds, and plant parts.

II. Soil

A. *General*

Soil is the medium in which all the world's major crops are grown, and to the agronomist it means the substratum in which the crop plant is anchored by its root system and from which water, nitrogen, and mineral nutrients are derived. The basic structure of soil is a rock complex, be it coarse sand or fine clay; this part of soil is inanimate and inert; its function is almost completely physical, and it provides the anchorage for the plant's root system. Whether originally formed by the breakdown and crumbling of igneous rocks or by sedimentation, this inert medium, bathed with water and dilute salt solutions, forms the basis for the colonization of the earth by plant life. Long before the intervention of man, the algae, liverworts, mosses, ferns, and flowering plants gradually occupied and spread over this rock matrix to build up the wild flora of today. But with the death and decay of succeeding generations of plants and the attendant wild fauna dependent upon the flora for its existence, the dead, unyielding rock, sand, and clay began to develop a new look: and there became introduced into it a new, near-living component, which may be loosely described as its humus.

It is this humus content of the soil which is of such great importance in agriculture and horticulture; not only does it improve the condition of the soil by ameliorating its physical structure, but it provides much of the food for ensuing generations. The dead bodies of plants and animals do not break down and decay to form humus as the result of slow inanimate oxidation or combustion. The death of one organism quickens the life of another, and so it is that the process of degeneration and decay is assisted and hastened by the advent of countless saprophytic, chlorophyll-less organisms, mainly microscopic, which depend for their very existence upon organic food made available through the death of previous generations. It is through the action of this multitude of microsaprophytes that ash again becomes ash and dust becomes dust. The introduction of humus to the soil converts it from an inanimate and inert matrix to a medium seething with life ecologically varied according to the origin from which it was derived. It is this living nature of the soil of farm and garden which is now attracting greater attention, and the microbiologist, finding here a field of work not only of intense academic interest but also one of great importance in crop husbandry, comes to the aid of physicist and chemist in the study of soil science. It is true that in hydroponics, where the plant is grown in a bath of sterile nutrient solution in pure liquid form with or without a gravel base, the problem of humus does not arise, but until such practice becomes much more widespread, the soil as such must remain the husbandman's main medium for crop growth. That the bulk of the microorganisms which go to make up the flora and fauna of the soil are, on the whole, beneficial and play an essential part in building up soil fertility is abundantly clear—e.g., the action of the nitrifying bacteria—but the soil humus offers equal opportunity for the persistence or growth of pathogenic organisms capable of causing crop disease. It is this aspect of soil microbiology which is of such importance to the plant pathologist, who is mainly concerned with the soil as a reservoir and source of plant pathogens. The presence or absence of such pathogens frequently bears little or no relationship to the rock structure of the soil; it is the character of the decaying vegetation present and the system of cropping followed which mainly determine their presence or absence.

B. *Autonomous Dispersal in Soil*

1. *The Contamination of Soil*

The original contamination of the soil with pathogens may occur in a variety of ways. It may take place by the gradual spread of the pathgen from a contaminated area to a noncontaminated area, or it may occur by the accidental introduction of contaminated material, such as crop debris or soil itself, into a clean area from one which is contaminated. The pathogen may also be introduced by the use of contaminated or infected seeds, or planting stock.

2. *Spread and Build-Up of the Pathogen*

When once the soil has become contaminated, the spread and build-up of the pathogen will be determined by a number of interacting factors. The most obvious is the frequency with which a susceptible crop is grown. The nature of modern farming and cropping has frequently been such as to encourage systems of intensive cropping which tend to the production of a soil rich in plant pathogens capable of causing disease in epidemic form. Commonplace examples of such practice are world-wide. Spread by the mechanical transfer of soil is also of importance, but the spread and build-up of the pathogen will also depend upon its adaptation to the soil, and for this purpose soil-borne pathogens may be conveniently grouped into the three categories of nonspecialized facultative parasites, specialized facultative parasites, and obligate parasites.

a. *Nonspecialized Facultative Parasites.* These pathogens are capable of a complete saprophytic existence, but they possess the faculty of attacking live tissues and behaving pathogenically. They are considered as nonspecialist in that they can spread and build up in soil interpreted in the widest sense. Typical examples are *Pythium ultimum,* a common cause of the damping-off of seedlings as well as of other crop diseases; *Rhizoctonia solani,* which causes stem canker and black scurf of the potato and diseases of a great variety of host plants, and *Pectobacterium carotovorum,* the cause of soft rot of a variety of root vegetables. Both *Pythium ultimum* and *R. Solani* will grow readily in a typical cultivated soil, and when once the soil has become contaminated, the pattern of mycelial spread resembles that of an ever-widening circle such as is made by throwing a stone into a pond or by a fairy ring in a lawn. The growth in soil of *P. ultimum* has been studied by Smith (1954) and that of *R. solani* by Blair (1943). The rate of spread and build-up of the organism may depend to some extent upon the original food base supplied, but it also depends upon the general nutritive value of the soil. Blair found that in the case of pure sand the growth of *R. solani* is greatly diminished after the removal of the food base, although in the case of the three samples of soil which he used, the diminution of growth was negligible in two of them but noticeable in the third after the food base had been removed. Factors such as soil temperature, aeration, and microbial antagonism also influence the rate of build-up and spread. Not much information is available regarding the spread and build-up of *Pectobacterium carotovorum* in soil although, according to Dowson (1957), the pathogen appears to live indefinitely in patches of inadequately drained soil. It was demonstrated by Kerr (1953) to be present in twenty separate Scottish soils.

b. *Specialized Facultative Parasites.* Specialized facultative parasites are those which, although capable of a complete saprophytic existence, depend in large measure upon the crop detritus of the host upon which they are pathogenic. They will not grow and build up in soil itself irrespective of its humus content. Some typical examples are *Armillaria mellea,* the cause of tree root diseases; *Ophiobolus graminis,* the cause of the take-all disease of wheat; and *Phymatotrichum omnivorum,* the cause of root rot of cotton. These pathogens will not grow and ramify through the soil as do the nonspecialized types but require a food base such as the roots or crop debris of the host plants which they attack. Their spread and build-up in the soil is, therefore, closely linked with the frequency of growing susceptible crops. Taubenhaus and Ezekiel (1930a) found that no spread of the mycelium of *Phymatotrichum omnivorum* occurred away from the roots of cotton, and they could produce no evidence for the independent growth of the fungus in the soil. At the same time it has been found that the fungus exists on some of the native plants of the uncultivated desert and spreads by the movement of infected roots from higher to lower lands by soil erosion and drainage (King *et al.,* 1934). It has also been shown that *Ophiobolus graminis* only grows through the soil in association with the roots of its cereal and grass hosts (Padwick, 1935). In the case of *Armillaria mellea* the growth of the fungus in space is extended through its ability to produce the typical rhizomorphs which grow out from the food base in infected wood. As examples of this, rhizomorphs were found to extend for 22 yd. from an infected pit prop in a mine-working by Ellis (1929), and Findlay (1951) found two rhizomorph systems of this fungus extending for 10 ft. and 30 ft., respectively, in a water tunnel leading out of a reservoir 200 ft. below ground level; the food base for these was believed to be the timber used in the construction of the tunnel. Apart from adaptations such as this, however, the range of the specialized facultative parasite is strictly limited to the range of the host plant, and the pattern of soil contamination will largely conform with that for host cropping. The power of infectibility may not remain unimpaired in cases of rhizomorph production, such as that of *Armillaria mellea,* for Garrett (1956) states that "the radius of spread of rhizomorph systems from a food base is often much greater than the effective radius for successful infection." This is supported by Wallace (1935), who observed that infected roots of coffee and tea in Tanganyika are found only in close association with dead bushes. In considering automonous dispersal, however, the question of inoculum potential cannot be given full weight since the transfer of a pathogen in a viable state to a new site could bring about the raising of the potential necessary to procure successful infection. Conditions of soil and climate will also affect autonomous dispersal, and in this connection the work of Ezekiel (1940) with *Phymatotrichum omnivorum* is important. Ezekiel defines the cotton belt affected with root rot in the United States to be "from a point in southern Utah southwest into Mexico (where the southern limit is yet to be established) and from

the eastern margin of Texas westward to southern California." Taking
the isotherm delimiting the area where the lowest air temperature observed between 1899 and 1938 was −23° C., he points out that this
follows rather accurately the northern limit of the occurrence of root rot
from Arkansas west to Nevada. He further suggests that "root rot has
persisted where the temperature has not fallen below −23° C., where
the annual mean temperature has been 15.6° C. or higher, and where the
frost-free period has averaged at least 200 days per year." Little alarm
is expressed for the significant advance of the pathogen either by growth
through the soil, which he estimates as 1 mile in 100 years, or by the
more rapid introduction of the roots of diseased plants into the soil.
McNamara (1926), working at Greenville, Texas, recorded an annual
spread of about 10 ft. during the years 1921–1924. To the extreme west
and east of the line denoted above, temperature does not appear to be
the limiting factor. Taubenhaus and Ezekiel (1936) observe that the
pathogen is favored by dark alkaline soils.

c. *Obligate Parasites.* The nature of the obligate fungal parasite is
such that its existence is confined to the host plant which it attacks, and
when the host plant dies, it can only survive in the soil in a resting state
until reactivated by the renewed growth of the host. An obligate parasite, therefore, cannot grow and spread in the soil, its range and pattern
will ideally be confined to the range and pattern of its host, discounting
the mechanical transfer of contaminated soil. The rate and extent of the
build-up of the pathogen will depend very much upon the frequency
with which a susceptible crop is grown. Typical examples of soil-borne
obligate parasites are *Plasmodiophora brassicae,* the cause of clubroot
disease of Brassicae; *Synchytrium endobioticum,* the cause of potato
wart disease; and *Spongospora subterranea,* the cause of powdery scab
of potato. The only period during which obligate parasitic fungi could
effect the spread of the pathogen in soil is when a sporangium or a resting
sporangium germinates to liberate free-swimming zoospores. The range
of such zoospores, however, and the length of their active life are regarded as too limited to bring about any significant spread of the pathogen in the soil. Furthermore, when a zoospore is unable to contact and
infect a susceptible host, it dies and the problem of soil contamination
disappears. With regard to *Heterodera rostochiensis,* the nematode
responsible for potato sickness, the larvae hatching from cysts will,
according to Fuchs (1911), travel a distance of from 3 to 4 meters,
while Baunacke (1922) records a distance of just over 9 meters. Here
the spread of the pathogen in any year will also depend upon the number of generations passed and the soil type. The extent to which the
pathogen is suitable for adaptation to new soil and climatic conditions

to which it may be introduced are also factors of importance in determining the measure of its build-up and spread. Evidence is available indicating that when potato tubers severely affected with *Spongospora subterranea* were introduced for 3 successive years from a country where powdery scab is common and grown in another where the climate is warm and dry and yet where powdery scab is a prohibited disease, the occurrence of powdery scab on the crops grown from diseased tubers was never recorded in the country of introduction for the whole 3-year period.

The number of plant-pathogenic viruses reported as soil-borne is, so far, comparatively small. Some typical well-known examples are those causing tobacco mosaic, tobacco necrosis, wheat mosaic, and big vein of lettuce. There is no doubt, however, that soil transmission of plant viruses is more common than has hitherto been supposed and the number of known examples will be greatly increased as the study of this comparatively new branch of plant virology receives the attention it merits. Recently Cadman (1956) and Harrison (1956, 1958) have reported on soil-borne viruses responsible for disease of the raspberry in Scotland, while Walkinshaw and Larson (1958) have found a soil-borne virus associated with corky ring spot disease of potato in the United States. In so far as the active virus is associated with the cells of the host in which it occurs, the pattern of soil contamination will follow that of the distribution of host roots or detritus in the soil. Growing evidence supports the view that weeds play an important part in determining the incidence, spread, and survival of plant viruses so that the interpretation of "host" must be made in the wide sense to include such weeds as well as the crop affected.

3. *Persistence of the Pathogen*

The persistence of the pathogen in soil may vary from a few hours to many years; its effect on autonomous dispersal will closely depend upon the time elapsing between soil contamination and soil dispersal. Potato tubers may become infected with blight, caused by *Phytophthora infestans,* through the contamination of the soil with sporangia falling from the diseased haulms (stems). But the sporangia are short-lived and are mainly operative only in the top layer of the soil. Murphy and McKay (1925) have shown that from 2 to 3 weeks is the longest period that the fungus may be expected to survive and cause tuber infection and that such infection mainly occurs in the top 5 cm. of the soil. *Phytophthora infestans* will not survive for long periods in normal unsterilized soil away from its host plant.

Given continuously ideal growing conditions, there is no reason to suppose that nonspecialized facultative parasites such as *Phytophthora ultimum* and *Rhizoctonia solani* should not contaminate the soil indefinitely without the stimulus of a susceptible crop. Doubtless, they do persist in the soil for long periods, and this persistence is assisted by the production of oospores, chlamydospores, and resting mycelia, all of which help to tide them over periods unfavorable for growth.

More detailed information is available for some of the better-known specialized facultative parasites, and Bliss (1951) has suggested that *Armillaria mellea* will persist for 6 or more years in infected citrus roots of more than 3 cm. in diameter in some California soils. There can be little doubt that the rhizomorphs of this fungus are persistent although very definite evidence as to the extent of their longevity is lacking. For *Ophiobolus graminis,* Garrett (1938, 1940, 1944) and Fellows (1941) have shown that conditions restricting microbiological activity in soil, such as low temperature, dryness, and poor aeration are more likely to support longevity of the fungus in host tissues than those such as high temperature, adequate moisture, and good aeration, which encourage the activity of the fungus as a pathogen. An ample supply of nitrogen also helps to prolong the survival of the fungus by enabling continued mycelial development to occur in infected tissue (Garrett, 1940). The degree of persistence of *O. graminis* in soil will, therefore, depend upon the interaction of all these factors.

In the case of *Phymatotrichum omnivorum* the formation of sclerotia is an important, if not limiting, factor in determining the longevity of the fungus in soil. Taubenhaus and Ezekiel (1930b) and Neal and Maclean (1931) found that the vegetative strands of *Phymatotrichum omnivorum* survive their host roots by only a few weeks, whereas Ratcliffe (1934), Rogers (1937), and Rea (1939) concluded that a 4-years' crop rotation is necessary to obtain satisfactory control of cotton root rot. Neal (1929) first reported the occurrence of sclerotia of the fungus in the field, and it is by their production that the pathogen is enabled to survive. Rogers (1937, 1942) showed that sclerotial formation occurs after the conclusion of the parasitic phase of the pathogen. He found the greatest number of viable sclerotia after the first year's growth of a nonsusceptible crop following cotton. Taubenhaus and Ezekiel (1936) found the viability of sclerotia to range between 10 and 2% after 5 years in soil of medium moisture content. Ezekiel (1940) further recorded 10% germination after 6 years, 8% after 7 years, but found no viable sclerotia after 9 years.

Since the obligate parasite is wholly dependent for existence upon the living host, its persistence in soil away from its host must depend upon the production of resting spores or some such like-resistant structure. *Plasmodiophora brassicae* survives as resting spores, and 7 years seems to be a commonly accepted time for the survival of such spores. Gibbs (1939) has recorded 5 years for New Zealand, and Fedorintchik (1935) obtained infection in cabbage seedlings in land not sown to a crucifer crop for 7 years in Russia. Germination of a high proportion of the spores is likely to occur without much delay in fallow soil without the stimulus of the root of a susceptible host; this is known as "spontaneous germination" (Macfarlane, 1952). Spontaneous germination is more marked in acid soils of high moisture content than in dry alkaline soils in which the spores appear to survive longest (Bremer, 1924). At the same time the marked reduction in the viable spore load in wet acid soils is offset by the fact that a much lower spore load is necessary to produce clubroot in epidemic form under such conditions than when the soil is dry and alkaline (Colhoun, 1953).

The persistence period for *Synchytrium endobioticum* appears to be even longer. In Germany, Schaffnit (1922) suggests at least 10 years in land fallowed and kept free from weeds. In Northern Ireland a susceptible potato variety contracted wart disease in 1956 when planted in land where the disease had first been recorded in 1926; very few, if any, crops of immune potato varieties only had been grown in this land during the interim period. It would thus seem that the resting sporangia of *Synchytrium endobioticum* might survive for periods of more than 10 years and even for as long as 30 years. Little direct evidence is available for the persistence in the soil of spore balls of *Spongospora subterranea* although they are frequently recorded as retaining their viability for several years. Some 6 to 8 years is the period usually accepted for the cysts of the nematode *Heterodera rostochiensis*. Thorne (1923) claims that after 6 years most of the cysts are empty or contain but very few eggs which, for the most part, are dead.

Of the soil-borne plant pathogenic viruses, tobacco mosaic virus, which is relatively stable, will survive in crop detritus and provide a source of infection for both tobacco and tomato crops over a period of at least 2 years (Johnson, 1937). Wheat mosaic virus has been recorded as persisting in the soil in an active condition, with no wheat crop intervening, for from 6 to 9 years, and it has been suggested that it does so in some other soil-inhabiting organism which acts as a vector (McKinney, 1946). Since the disease may be controlled by an insecticide, F. Johnson (1945) concludes that this acts on the vector rather than on the virus and suggests that the vector may be a nematode. The virus responsible for big vein of lettuce will survive in soil for more than a year, and the incidence of crop disease it will cause has been shown to be only slightly reduced when contaminated soil is diluted 800 times with sterilized soil (Pryor, 1946).

C. *Autonomous Dispersal by Soil*

1. *By Soil Alone*

During the mechanical operations of cropping and farming, the movement of soil by plowing, harrowing, farm wagons and trucks, etc., will achieve the dispersal of a pathogen over the farm land. It will also be spread by soil carried on the boots of farm workers and by any soil erosion which may occur. The pattern of such spread will tend to be erratic and will fit in approximately with the pattern of farm activities. Through inter-farm communication such as the loaning of farm equipment by one farmer to another, and by land erosion on a larger scale, the pathogen may be spread from farm to farm and the pattern of such spread will again be erratic. In this way the spread may gradually increase until a whole village, a township, or a province may be involved. Dispersal will also be achieved by the movement of soil in bulk, but as such a transfer tends to be uncommon in farm practice, this mode of dispersal will be more likely to occur in operations involving building or amateur gardening. The pattern of dispersal here will be even more erratic and much greater distances may be involved.

2. *By Soil Adhering to Plant Parts*

The transfer of contaminated soil from one area to another by its adherence to roots, tubers, and other plant parts is a most effective method of dispersal of a pathogen. It is in this way that pathogens may be spread not only from field to field and from farm to farm but from country to country and continent to continent.

D. *The Prevention of Autonomous Dispersal by Soil*

1. *Testing for Soil Contamination*

If soil is to be dispersed, whether avoidably or unavoidably, the knowledge of its freedom from or contamination with pathogens cannot be other than worthwhile. This emphasizes the need for techniques of soil examination for determining the presence of plant pathogens. The devising of suitable techniques which will give speedy, reliable, and accurate results is, however, not a simple matter, especially in the case of microorganisms and viruses whose minuteness makes difficult their direct visual detection in soil. Some success has attended the devising of such methods in the case of parasitic plant nematodes, and the best example is provided by *Heterodera rostochiensis*, the potato root eelworm, which is carried in the soil in cyst form. In many potato-growing countries soil surveys are in progress and are being made with the objects of defining contaminated and noncontaminated areas. Methods are also available for determining soil contamination with *Plasmodiophora brassicae*. These are the seedling host tests devised by Samuel and Garrett (1945) and Macfarlane (1952), and the pot method devised by Colhoun (1957) whereby, as the result of epidemiological studies, susceptible plants can be grown under conditions which will produce the disease in epidemic form (Colhoun, 1953). These techniques provide facilities for differentiating between clean and contaminated soil and allow for advice to be given, not only concerning the dispersal of soil, but also in regard to growing susceptible crops. The ultimate value of soil health surveys will be determined when it is known how control measures, adopted as the result of the knowledge gained, have been successful in preventing the spread of the pathogen and the preservation of noncontaminated areas clean and free from infection. For soil-borne plant pathogenic viruses, soil tests are at present largely limited to the growing of susceptible indicator plants.

2. *The Clearing of Contaminated Soil*

Another approach to the problem of preventing dispersal is by ridding the soil of the pathogen and thereby clearing contaminated areas. The outstanding example of this method is the partial sterilization of soil by heat, steam, or chemicals whereby all pathogenic organisms are killed. This is discussed in detail by Kreutzer in Chapter 11 of this volume.

Soil treatment can be practicably employed only for relatively small land areas such as those in use for glasshouse crops or nurseries where the value of the crop is such as to warrant the expense of the operation. It has, however, also been used in cases of new outbreaks of infection with potato wart disease in the United States (Hartman, 1951) where the focus of contamination is small and where the stamping out of the pathogen can be justified by the prevention of its spread to a wider area. For this purpose Hartman recommends the use of finely pulverized copper sulphate at 2,500 lb. per acre, and claims that by the end of 1950 the disease had been eradicated from 440 infected gardens. Partial sterilization of the soil, using steam or formaldehyde, has become commonplace in the growing of nursery and glasshouse crops in areas where it is difficult or impossible to bring in fresh supplies of noncontaminated soil, and where the build-up of soil pathogens through intensive cropping is so marked as to render impossible the growing of healthy crops without soil treatment.

An alternative method of clearing contaminated soil is by fallowing the land and controlling susceptible weeds. Where immune varieties are available, the growing of these allows for the starving out of the pathogen without having to forego the cultivation of the crop. This method has proved invaluable in the case of potato wart disease where the use of so-called immune varieties had solved a difficult problem in countries where the potato is a major crop. In these countries the tendency for their increasing use grows steadily, and in the United Kingdom no new variety of potato can be registered unless it is immune from attack. In Northern Ireland the potato acreage planted with immune varieties has increased from 69% in 1923 to 92% in 1957. The occurrence of new physiologic races of *Synchytrium endobioticum*, capable of attacking potato varieties hitherto believed to be immune, is an added complication and a development over which careful watch will need to be kept (Moore, 1957).

The use of decoy crops which stimulate the germination of resting spores but do not contract disease with the resultant production of resting spores, such as occurs in the case of *Matthiola incana* and *Lolium perenne* when grown in soil contaminated with *Plasmodiophora brassicae* is an interesting new line of investigation (Macfarlane, 1952).

Many of the major problems of soil contamination have arisen because of the conscious or unconscious neglect of the principles of good crop husbandry, and much of the harm which has been done could undoubtedly be rectified by more cautious cropping and by reverting to a sounder form of husbandry. This has already been realized in take-all disease of wheat, clubroot of Brassicae, and root rot of cotton, where epidemiological studies have brought valuable knowledge to bear upon the incidence of these diseases and how they may be best controlled.

3. *The Prevention of Soil Dispersal*

Where planting stocks and plant products are transported and where there is a risk of pathogens being dispersed with the soil adhering to them, it would not seem unreasonable to require, if at all practicable, that they should be freed from soil before dispatch. In some cases this principle has been adopted, an example being the transport of plants to the United States, where it is required that the roots shall be washed free from soil. The ease of modern transport by rail, sea, and air with the increasing facilities for handling large bulks at greater speed, coupled with the remarkable increase in the volume of travel, has not eased the problem, and the danger of the autonomous dispersal of soil-borne pathogens in this way to new and uncontaminated areas is ever present. Perhaps no better example can be cited than that of the international trade in seed potatoes. In order to keep the potato crop free from virus infection a very considerable international trade in seed potatoes has developed whereby stocks of virus-free seed are imported regularly by countries with drier and warmer climates (unsuitable for virus-free seed production because of the prevalence of insect vectors) from countries where the climate is wetter and cooler and where stocks of such seed can be comparatively easily grown. The countries of northwestern Europe are developing an increasing trade with those of the Mediterranean basin and the continent of Africa; this trade is likely to continue until the importing countries have found it possible to grow their own healthy stocks. Although such seed may be relatively free from virus contamination, there is always, however, the risk of importing such pathogens as *Synchytrium endobioticum, Streptomyces scabies, Spongospora subterranea, Phytophthora erythroseptica, Pectobacterium carotovorum, Heterodera rostochiensis,* and others through the medium of soil adhering to the tubers. Because of the lack of easily applied techniques for determining accurately the presence or absence of many of these pathogens in soil and the lack of knowledge of the epidemiology of the diseases they cause, phytosanitary regulations devised to prevent their introduction through the medium of soil have often had to be framed from the point of view of fear of the unknown rather than in the light of clear scientific knowledge. A more direct and satisfactory solution of the problem of preventing dispersal through soil would be achieved if the principle of washing plants and plant products free from soil before dispatch could be generally applied. Difficulties inherent in putting this into practice become apparent when the need for washing, in an effective manner, large bulks of such produce as potato tubers or bulbs is considered. It is for this reason that a large scale mechanical plant for washing and disinfecting seed potatoes in Scotland presents an interesting new development. By means of this plant, which is illustrated in Fig. 1 the tubers are subjected to jet-pressure washing within 24 to 48 hours after lifting, and then, when completely freed from soil, to a process of disinfection before being quickly dried and stored. This development has been made possible by recent cumulative advances in mechanical engineering, and it shows how, with the facilities provided by an advance in one field of science, problems in another field, incapable of solution at the time, can be relatively easily solved later. One of the advantages claimed for such washed tubers is that they are free from contamination with the cysts of *H. rostochiensis* (Mabbott, 1956) and if this is substantiated, a distinct advance will have been made which should appeal to all importing countries where the introduction of this pathogen is feared. Apart from this, the freeing of the tubers from soil also eliminates the risk of the introduction of soil-borne pathogens as a whole. The disinfection of the

FIG. 1. Pressure jet washed seed potatoes leaving the washing tanks and entering the disinfectant bath at the plant installed for the washing and disinfecting of seed potatoes by Sir Thomas Wedderspoon, Angus, Scotland. (By courtesy of *The Farming News*, Glasgow.)

tubers after washing is not only an added precaution, but it also effects the control of tuber-borne pathogens, reference to which is made in the section dealing with autonomous dispersal by plants and plant parts.

III. SEEDS

A. *General*

Perhaps one of the major developments in plant pathology during the present century has been the realization of the extent to which the true seed may carry plant pathogens, and there is now no important agricultural or horticultural crop where the seed is not associated with one or more of the pathogens responsible for outbreaks of disease.

Seed-borne pathogens may be grouped into those which are carried with the seed and those which are carried on or in the seed. In the first group is included dodder (*Cuscuta trifolii*) occurring as seeds in a clover seed sample, flax rust, caused by *Melampsora lini*, affecting flax straw detritus in a sample of flax seed, ergot (*Claviceps purpurea*) occurring as sclerotia in samples of seeds of cereals and grasses, and the nematode (*Anguillulina tritici*) which occurs in ear cockles in samples of seed wheat. A typical example of a pathogen normally borne on the seed is bunt or stinking smut of wheat (*Tilletia caries*) which is carried as resting or brand spores adhering to the outside of the caryopsis. Fungal pathogens, which are carried on or in the seed are: *Helminthosporium* spp., the cause of seedling blight, root rot, leaf stripe, and leaf spot of cereals and grasses; *Fusarium* spp., the cause of seedling blight, foot rot, and ear blight of cereals and wilt of flax and other crops; *Phoma* spp., the cause of black leg of beet and foot rot of flax; *Ascochyta pisi*, the cause of leaf, stem, and pod spot of pea, *Colletotrichum linicola,* the cause of seedling blight of flax; *Polyspora lini*, the cause of stem break and browning of flax; and *Gloeotinia temulenta,* the cause of blind seed disease of ryegrass.

Corynebacterium michiganense, the cause of bacterial tomato canker, is a typical example of a seed-borne pathogenic bacterium. The cause of loose smut of wheat, *Ustilago tritici,* exemplifies the type of seed-borne fungal pathogen where the contamination is carried as mycelium entirely within the tissues of the caryopsis. Few plant virus pathogens are known to be seed-borne, but those responsible for bean mosaic and lettuce mosaic are two typical examples.

B. *Autonomous Dispersal by Seeds*

The principles underlying the autonomous dispersal of plant pathogens by seeds have much in common with those enunciated for soil. But since the seed, in its dormant state, seldom provides suitable conditions for active growth such as may occur in soil, the pathogen is normally carried as a spore (resting or otherwise) or as mycelium (usually in a dormant state) within the tissues of the seed coat or in the tissues of the seed itself. It is clear that the dispersal of the pathogen will be closely correlated with the movement of seeds, and the pattern will tend to be more deliberate than for soil since there is not the same degree of accidental movement. For instance, soil erosion, the movement of farm machinery, and any communication between farms are all significant factors in bringing about the movement of contaminated soil whereas (although they cannot be completely ruled out) they are not so significant for seeds. There is a close relationship between the pattern of the seed trade and that of the autonomous dispersal of a seed-borne pathogen.

1. *The Contamination of Seeds*

Cases where the contamination of seeds is a simple mechanical admixture of the seeds of both host and pathogen are exemplified by dodder, where the seeds of *C. trifolii* occur mixed with those of clover.

In ergot of rye the open flowers of the host are infected with the asco-spores of *C. purpurea;* the young ovary is attacked and invaded, and eventually becomes replaced by the typical horn-shaped sclerotium of the fungus. The sclerotia so formed become mechanically admixed with the unaffected seeds and are sown with them when putting in the crop. Ear cockles of wheat resulting from crop attack by the nematode *A. tritici* also become admixed with the grain and may be sown with the seed. The pathogen may be carried on the straw or crop detritus of a diseased crop, pieces of which may occur as an impurity in the seed sample. In flax rust, pieces of straw affected with the resting teleutospore stage of *M. lini* are commonly found mechanically admixed with the seed. The bunt balls of *T. caries* occur mixed with seed wheat, but they commonly become broken during harvesting and threshing, whereby the brand spores of the fungus are released to contaminate the grain; thus, this pathogen is normally carried as spores attached to the grain.

Seed contamination with pathogenic fungi and bacteria frequently takes the form of an invasion of the tissues of the seed coat or of the seed itself where it remains viable in a relatively quiescent state until the seed is sown. If the pathogen is capable of free sporulation, it may also be borne in the form of spores adhering to the seed coat. In these cases seed contamination may be translated to seed infection because, if con-tamination occurs in the early developmental stages of the seed and conditions are suitable, the pathogen attacks the seed, and the seed becomes diseased. In *P. lini,* for instance, which causes stem break and browning of flax, all stages may be found in a contaminated seed sample —from where the seed has been attacked and killed in an early stage of development, through seeds which are quite healthy but which carry the pathogen as mycelium in the outer mucilaginous layers of the seed coat, to those which bear only the conidia of the pathogen adhering to them (Lafferty, 1921; Colhoun, 1946). This condition applies equally well to many other seed-borne pathogens included in this group, such as *Fusarium* spp., *G. temulenta, C. linicola,* and *A. pisi.* Contamination or infection of the seed in these cases is normally of external origin, it being brought about by spores of the pathogen during the flowering, maturing, or harvesting of the crop. Pethybridge and Lafferty (1918) and Lafferty (1921) in the investigation of the flax pathogens *C. linicola* and *P. lini* traced the infection of the seed via the boll. The conidia of *Helmintho-sporium avenae,* the cause of seedling blight and leaf spot of oats, may be found attached to the pales, where they germinate to produce resting mycelia. Whereas the conidia of *Gibberella zeae* attacking wheat may bring about flower infection (Adams, 1921) or may attack through the glumes, the attack by other *Fusarium* spp. is normally confined to the glumes (Bennett, 1931). In *A. pisi* the pea seeds contract contamination through the pod-spotting phase of the disease. *G. temulenta* infects ryegrass at the time of flowering through ascospores released from apothecia produced on infected seeds, while secondary infection is brought about by conidia produced in abundance by primary infection with ascospores (Calvert and Muskett, 1945). In this disease it is also easy to find every phase of contamination, ranging from seeds killed by the disease to those bearing conidia externally.

An interesting feature of a number of these diseases, such as those caused by *H. avenae, C. linicola,* and *P. lini,* is the healthy and vigorous growth of the crop, which usually occurs between the primary phase of the disease in the seedling stage and the secondary phase leading to the contamination or infection of the seed. Although it is generally assumed that the source of the inoculum for the secondary phase is supplied by spores produced by the primary and possibly intermediate phases, it is sometimes difficult to trace this in the field, and this fact suggests the need for further research. The diseases mentioned are largely specific, and the pathogens concerned are limited to one or a few kindred hosts. In the case of a nonspecific pathogen, however, such as *Botrytis cinerea* with a wide host range, seed contamination or infection may be contracted from outside sources irrespective of the state of contamination of the seed sample from which the crop is grown. Further contamination of the seed may spread rapidly, if weather conditions are suitable, in harvested and stooked crops of cereals, ryegrass, and flax in the case of such pathogens as some *Fusarium* spp., *G. temulenta,* and *B. cinerea.*

Ustilago tritici, the cause of loose smut of wheat, presents a typical example of a systemic disease where the pathogen is borne in mycelial form entirely within the seed. Flower infection is affected by brand spores released from affected ears at the time of flowering of the crop, and the resultant grain produced may, according to the wheat variety, contain mycelia in the pericarp only or in all parts of the embryo and even in the root primordia (Ruttle, 1934).

The comparative rarity with which plant pathogenic viruses are transmitted by the true seed presents one of the most interesting problems of plant virology. Of the hundreds of plant virus diseases which have been described, only 45 have been reported as seed-transmitted (Crowley, 1957a). Reddick and Stewart (1919) first showed that bean mosaic virus is transmitted by the seeds of *Phaseolus vulgaris.* Later, Ainsworth and Ogilvie (1939) found that lettuce mosaic virus may be seed-transmitted and that some 5% of the seed used produced infected seedlings. The varying claims made for the seed transmission of tomato mosaic virus may be explained by the work of Ainsworth (1934), who showed that the virus occurs in the seed coats of seed grown from infected parents.

The ability of a virus to enter the seed depends upon the interaction of virus and host, for as Bawden (1950) points out, "In the same host, one virus may be seed-transmitted and another not, and the same virus may be seed-transmitted in one host but not in others." Recent work by Crowley (1957a,b), in which 5 mechanically transmitted viruses were used, indicates that host sterility will not account for the lack of seed transmission in any of the cases investigated. All 5 viruses infected the seeds of the hosts but only bean mosaic virus was found to infect the embryo. Crowley found no evidence for the production of virus inactivators in seeds or developing embryos. He regards the rarity of seed transmission to be due to the inability of most viruses to infect megaspore or microspore mother cells of infected plants as well as to their inability to infect developing embryos because of the lack of plasmodesmatal connection with the endosperm.

2. Spread and Build-Up of the Pathogen

The rate of spread and build-up of the pathogen will vary according to the prevailing seasonal conditions. Given a series of successive seasons favorable for the growth and development of the pathogen in relation to the host, then a progressive build-up of the pathogen as a seed contaminant may be anticipated. The principle of seasonal conditions acting as a limiting factor controlling the rate and extent of seed contamination holds generally for seed-borne pathogens as a whole. If the host plant is regarded as a match box and the pathogen as a match, then seasonal conditions leading to seed contamination may be regarded as the act of striking the match. So long as the seasonal conditions are unsuitable, host and pathogen will tend to exist alongside each other; no outbreak of disease will occur, there will be no seed contamination, and the host plant will tend to flourish in spite of the pathogen. Whether there will be a gradual tendency towards the build-up of seed contamination over the seasons will depend, in the first place, upon the climatic conditions prevailing over the area as a whole and, secondly, upon the specific climatic condition from season to season. This is illustrated by the seed health survey made for fiber flax from 1940 to 1955 in the United Kingdom, the results of which are discussed in the section dealing with the value of seed health surveys.

The pattern of the build-up of seed contamination in a crop may be even, but it may also be erratic and variable. Contamination may occur in pockets which have served as foci for the outbreak and spread of disease. This may be due to the uneven contamination of the seed sample sown or to the soil conditions favoring or disfavoring the outbreak and incidence of disease. That soil conditions of temperature and moisture can exert a very significant effect on the incidence of seedling blight of oats, caused by *H. avenae,* has been clearly demonstrated (Muskett, 1938). When flaxseed was sampled for the United Kingdom seed health survey, it was found that in bulks of seed which had not been thoroughly mixed, the incidence of contamination could vary greatly in different parts of the same bag of seed (Muskett and Colhoun, 1947). An erratic pattern of seed contamination is also likely to occur when the pathogen is originally contracted from the soil, as in the case of *Phoma* sp., causing flax foot rot. Here the pathogen may be contracted in the first place from soil, and the attack becomes evident by the occurrence of odd plants here and there in the crop affected with the disease (Pethybridge *et al.,* 1921). When once the seed has become contaminated, the disease may break out in epidemic form in the crop if the seed is sown under suitable seasonal conditions.

3. *Persistence of the Pathogen*

By persistence of the pathogen is meant the time during which the pathogen will remain viable with, on, or in the seed and assumedly capable of causing disease. It refers to the period during which the seed is stored rather than to the persistence of the pathogen in soil after the seed has been sown. Normally, the conditions required for the germination of the seed and the growth of the host plant will largely assimilate those for the pathogen, and it may be assumed that, after overwintering, the pathogen will become active soon after the seed is sown. There are instances, such as that of ergot, where the sclerotia may remain dormant if buried too deeply in the soil. In the northwest of the United States the brand spores of dwarf bunt of wheat, *T. caries,* may remain viable in the soil for up to 7 years (Wilson, 1955). The time of persistence will clearly depend upon such factors as the nature of the pathogen itself, the condition in which it occurs as a contaminant, and the method of seed storage after harvesting the crop. In the case of a simple mechanically admixed contaminant, such as dodder, the problem is clearly one of comparative seed longevity, while for ergot it may depend upon the relative longevity of sclerotium and seed. In such cases there is a dearth of very accurate knowledge of persistence time which, in any case, will vary with environmental conditions.

It is known that the nematode *A. tritici* in ear cockles of wheat kept dry will remain viable for up to 10 years (Goodey, 1923). In herbarium material the brand spores of *T. caries* were found to be viable after 18 years and those of *Ustilago avenae* after 13 years (Fischer, 1936). Although the brand spores of *Ustilago nuda* are relatively short-lived, barley seed infected with loose smut produced some smutted heads after storage for 11 years (Porter, 1955). *H. avenae,* which is normally carried as mycelia in the seed coats of oats, will retain its viability for a period of up to 10 years in Canada and for at least 7 in Northern Ireland. *Alternaria tenuis,* a mold commonly contaminating seed oats, tends to die out in the early years of the storage period, but with its death *H. avenae* is more readily isolated from an increasing percentage of seeds (Machacek and Wallace, 1952). It has been suggested that molds such as *A. tenuis* may behave antagonistically to *H. avenae,* thus interfering with its ready detection by growth until they have died out. The persistence of *Fusarium* spp. in seed oats does not appear to be so marked because it has been found in Northern Ireland that both mycelia and spores tend to have lost their viability after seed storage for some 3 years. Seed-borne pathogens of flax may persist from 1 to 6 years, as illustrated by the following examples: *C. linicola* (2 to 6 years), *P. lini* (1 to 5 years), *B. cinerea* (1 to 3 years) and *Phoma* sp. (2 to 3½ years) (Colhoun and Muskett, 1948). In blind seed disease of ryegrass, caused by *G. temulenta,* the surface-borne conidia lose their viability after 6 months, while the mycelia carried in the seed tissues will persist for up to 20 months (Calvert and Muskett, 1945). Generally speaking, surface-borne spores of pathogens, as might be expected, tend to lose their viability more rapidly than does mycelium, which is seated within the seed coat and seed tissues.

It may be concluded that the persistence of a seed-borne pathogen under normal conditions of seed storage will vary from a few months to as long as 10 years or more, according to its being surface-borne as thin-walled conidia, as chlamydospores, as sclerotia, as mycelium within the tissues of the seed coat or outer caryopsis, or internally as mycelium within the more deep-seated tissues of the seed. Little evidence is available in regard to the time of persistence of the virus in the case of the relatively few viruses which are seed-transmitted although Middleton (1944) obtained as many virus infected squash plants from seed which was 3 years old as from freshly harvested seed. Working with a seed transmitted virus of muskmelon, Rader *et al.* (1947) obtained 93 and 28% infected seedlings from two experimental lots of freshly harvested seed and only 3 and 6% after the seed had been stored for 3 years.

C. The Prevention of Autonomous Dispersal by Seeds

1. Testing for Seed Contamination

If autonomous dispersal of a pathogen by seed is to be prevented, then the possession of accurate knowledge as to whether and to what extent a seed sample is contaminated will be both desirable and helpful. Some indication as to the likelihood or not of the seed's being contaminated can often be determined by a system of crop inspection. If, for instance, loose smut is seen to occur in crops of wheat and barley, the assumption is that the seed saved from these will be contaminated with the loose smut pathogen. It can then be determined whether or not to use the seed for sowing or to ensure its treatment before sowing in order to control the disease. But crop inspection, although it is the only practicable method available in some cases, cannot be expected to give such a definite or accurate estimate as the direct examination of seed for pathogenic contamination. Methods for the testing of seeds for purity and germination have been evolved and practiced internationally for the last half century, but similar methods for the determination of seed health are of comparatively recent introduction, and those which are available are only just beginning to be used in general practice. This is due to the fact that until recently the need for determining seed health, which in some cases may be quite as important as purity and germination, was insufficiently realized and, at the same time, suitable techniques for carrying out the work were not available.

Notice is taken in routine seed testing of the presence of mechanically admixed pathogens such as dodder, ergot, bunt balls, ear cockles in wheat, etc., but this is more or less included in the purity analysis of the seed sample and cannot be considered as part of a real health test. Suitable techniques for the health testing of seeds must be capable of dealing as inexpensively as possible with large numbers of seed samples and should provide accurate and speedy results in no longer time than is required for carrying out a test for germination. This will allow for the results of purity, germination, and health testing to be made available at one and the same time. The aim of a health test must be to provide an accurate estimate of the percentage of seeds in any given sample which is contaminated with the pathogen in a viable condition. In devising such tests attempts have frequently been made to use the methods employed in modern seed testing, with or without some modification, to cover the need for testing for health. But whereas this line of approach may on occasion provide some approximate information as to whether a particular pathogen is or is not present, or it may indicate in a general way whether the seed sample is healthy or unhealthy, it is not scientific and does not fulfill the conditions to be aimed at in health testing as stated above.

During the period of the second world war thousands of tons of fiber flaxseed produced in the United Kingdom were of the highest quality in so far as the standards of purity and germination were concerned, but a large proportion of the seed was very heavily contaminated with *C. linicola*. This was not and could not be revealed by the normal methods of seed testing and was only determined by use of a special technique devised for the purpose of testing for seed health. An approach to accurate testing for seed health has been made by using sterilized damp filter paper or agar medium upon which the seeds are plated out in Petri dishes and examined for the growth and development of fungal pathogens (Muskett, 1938, 1948; Muskett and Malone, 1941). More recently the use of filter paper has given way to the use of the agar medium method. The Ulster method, using a 2% malt extract agar medium (Muskett and Malone, 1941), and the modified Ulster method, when the seeds are surface sterilized with a dilute solution of sodium or calcium hypochlorite before testing (Muskett and Malone, 1956), have been found to give most reliable results in the case of a large variety of crop seeds and have recently been adopted as the standard international methods for the health testing of seeds of flax and oats. For flax the Ulster method is used for determining seed contamination with *C. linicola, P. lini, B. cinerea, Phoma* sp., *Fusarium lini,* and *Alternaria linicola* as well as with molds in general, while for oats the modified Ulster method is used for determining seed contamination with *H. avenae, Fusarium* spp., and other molds.

For the contamination of ryegrass seed with *G. temulenta*, the water droplet method (Muskett, 1948) can be used for surface-borne conidia, but a modification of the Ulster method is necessary if the amount of internal infection is to be assessed (Calvert and Muskett, 1945). Headway has been made in developing techniques for the direct examination of seeds of barley and wheat for the presence of internal mycelia of the loose smut fungi, and this is exemplified by the whole embryo method (Simmonds, 1946; Russell, 1950). In any consideration of the problem of seed examination for contamination or infection with pathogenic fungi, due recognition must be given to the pioneer work of Doyer (1938) in the Netherlands.

2. *The Value of Seed Health Surveys*

When suitable techniques are available for the rapid and accurate assessment of seed health, it is possible to employ them not only for routine seed testing but also for carrying out planned seed health surveys for any particular district or region. The value of such surveys is wider than the mere checking-up of seed health, for there is always the possibility of discovering areas where seed free from contamination may be grown or where contamination is so severe as to warrant the discontinuance of seed production. Such a health survey was carried out for fiber flaxseed produced in the United Kingdom from 1940 to 1955

(Muskett, 1958). The Ulster method was used to examine more than 25,000 samples of seed drawn from production centers situated in the various counties of the United Kingdom and shown on the outline map (Fig. 2). As a result of this survey, extending over 15 years, it was

FIG. 2. Map showing localities of flaxseed producing areas, expressed as counties, in the United Kingdom, 1940–1955.

shown that fiber flaxseed produced in eastern and southeastern England is relatively free from contamination with *C. lini, P. lini,* and *Phoma* sp. and that there was no build-up of contamination in these areas. In the wetter and cooler regions west and north of the Pennines, conditions are more favorable for these pathogens, and seed contamination tends to build up and increase. Table I shows the survey results obtained for seed contamination with *C. lini*. Seed contamination with *B. cinerea* is general throughout the United Kingdom, with a tendency to be higher in upland and coastal areas. The incidence of *Fusarium lini* and *Alternaria linicola* in seed produced in the United Kingdom is negligible. If ever the need arises in the future for a planned program of flaxseed production in the United Kingdom, the results obtained from this health survey indicate quite clearly that seed production should be confined to the east and southeast of England. Another result arising from this investigation indicates the possibility of clearing stocks of contaminated seed by growing the seed in areas where it is known that contamination of the progeny is not likely to occur. There can be little doubt that the extension of seed health surveys over wider areas and to include a range of agricultural and horticultural crops would furnish results of equal value to those obtained in the United Kingdom for fiber flaxseed and add substantially to the greater understanding of problems relating to seed health.

3. Seed Disinfection

In preventing the autonomous dispersal of seed-borne fungal and bacterial plant pathogens, seed disinfection is a most valuable tool, and with the introduction of modern disinfectants with increased facilities for carrying out the work on a large scale, much more is being done to prevent such dispersal. The introduction of organo-mercury compounds for general use with the seeds of cereals marked a significant advance, and there is now hardly a country in the world where the use of these disinfectants is not known and applied on a large or small scale. The use of thiram as a disinfectant for the seeds of flax, peas, and beans, etc. marked a further advance in so far as this product is relatively non-poisonous (Muskett and Colhoun, 1943). The problem of seed disinfection will not be finally solved until a nonpoisonous product suitable for universal use has been discovered.

The hot water treatment for the internally-borne smut pathogens of wheat and barley is still efficacious, but the need for great care in carrying it out works against its general use. Trends in recent research indicate that more attention is being given to the possibility of disinfecting seeds by physical means. This is to be welcomed, since, although the efficacy of some of the very poisonous chemicals now being used for plant protection is not doubted, equal efficacy from avoiding the use of poisonous substances would deserve serious consideration. Further, seed disinfection must not be regarded as a substitute for the production of

TABLE I

UNITED KINGDOM FLAX SEED HEALTH SURVEY 1940–1955:
PERCENTAGE OF SEED CONTAMINATED WITH *Collectotrichum linicola*

	1940	1941	1942	1943[a]	1944	1945	1946	1947	1948	1949	1950	1951	1952	1953	1954	1955
England																
Suffolk	—	—	—	0.01	0	0	0	0	0	0	0	0	0	0	—	—
Kent	—	—	—	0	0.01	0	0	0	0	0	0	0	0	0	—	—
Norfolk	—	—	—	0	0.01	0	0.015	0	0	0	0	0	0	0	0.04	—
Cambridge	—	—	—	0.01	0	0	0	—	—	—	—	—	—	—	—	—
Sussex	—	—	—	0.12	0.01	0	0	0	0	0	0	0	0	0.01	0.3	0
Lincoln	—	—	—	0.01	0	0	0	0	0	0	0	0	0	0	0.23	—
Northampton	—	—	—	0.01	0.01	0	0	0	0	0	0	—	0	0	0.02	—
Yorkshire E.R.	—	—	—	0.01	0.02	0	0	0.03	0	0	—	0.04	0	0	0	0.01
Yorkshire N.R.	—	—	—	0	0.02	0.02	—	—	—	—	—	—	—	—	—	—
Derbyshire	—	—	—	0	0.07	0	0.025	—	—	0	0	0	0	0	0	—
Wiltshire	—	—	—	0.11	0.02	0.37	0.32	0.41	0.13	0.01	0	0	0	0.12	0.7	0
Somerset	—	—	—	1.8	0.05	1.67	0.26	1.05	0.29	0	0.17	0.82	0	0.44	—	—
Dorset	—	—	—	0.16	0.24	2.5	—	—	—	—	—	—	—	—	—	—
Wales																
Pembroke	—	—	—	7.6	0.35	3.2	0.05	0.14	—	—	—	—	—	—	—	—
Scotland																
Aberdeen	—	—	—	1.7	7.5	8.1	—	—	—	—	—	—	—	—	—	—
Fife	—	—	—	3.3	0.19	0.05	—	—	—	—	—	—	—	—	—	—
Perth	—	—	—	2.6	2.2	1.1	—	—	—	—	—	—	—	—	—	—
Northern Ireland																
Down	1.6	11.7	7.1	4.7	3.2	0	0.21	1.6	0.6	0.13	0.8	—	—	—	—	—
Antrim	5.5	17.5	14.3	6.1	1.7	0.37	0.1	0.33	1.5	0	—	—	—	—	—	—
Armagh	—	20.8	16.3	8.0	4.0	0.1	—	—	—	—	—	—	—	—	—	—
Londonderry	5.4	13.3	26.1	4.0	—	—	—	—	—	—	—	—	—	—	—	—
Tyrone	2.5	17.7	18.1	8.4	4.7	1.7	0.29	0.72	0.81	—	—	—	—	—	—	—
Fermanagh	—	30.3	15.2	20.9	4.1	—	—	—	—	—	—	—	—	—	—	—

[a] After 1943 stocks of fresh, noncontaminated seed were steadily introduced from east and southeast England to areas in the north and west. This accounts for the general decline in contamination from 1943 onward.

healthy noncontaminated seed; it must not be used as a tool to make bad seed good but rather to make good seed better.

4. The Prevention of Seed Dispersal

Control by the prevention of seed dispersal appears to be the obvious answer to the problem if such action were possible or even desirable. The farmer himself frequently adopts this practice, for, if he suspects the seed he intends using to be contaminated and likely to produce a diseased crop, and if there is no other remedy, he will either destroy it or use it for some purpose other than sowing. Success may also attend the prohibition of sowing contaminated seed with the provision of some allowance for tolerance. When fiber flaxseed was being produced in the United Kingdom during the second world war, an epidemic outbreak of foot rot caused by seed-borne *Phoma* occurred in 1943. Since the routine method of seed disinfection with thiram (introduced in 1940) was found to be only about 50% effective for this pathogen, it was decided to discard all seed for sowing which was contaminated to the extent of more than 5%. This action was successful, and although seasonal variation may have played a part, evidence gained in the following seasons showed clearly that the principle of allowing only slightly contaminated seed which had been disinfected to be sown prevented any further serious outbreaks of this disease (Muskett and Colhoun, 1947).

The storage of seed for a period before dispersal in order to allow the pathogen to die out has also suggested itself as a control measure. It is sometimes practiced for celery seed affected with *Septoria apii*, the cause of leaf spot, in the belief that the pathogen is no longer viable in overyeared seed. Apart from the difficulty of getting conidia taken from such seed to germinate, no further evidence seems to be available on this point. Work with flax shows that seed-borne pathogens will die out after normal storage of the seed for some years. Seed of this age, however, will have lost some of its germination capacity and much of its energy of germination, so that this method of control cannot be recommended (Colhoun and Muskett, 1948). The same argument holds for seed oats, where it takes at least 3 years for *Fusarium* spp. to die out and up to 10 years for *H. avenae*. All trace of viability of *G. temulenta* in ryegrass seed disappears after 20 months' storage—a shorter period, and, therefore, more hopeful.

Much can be done by preventing the dispersal of badly cleaned seed. This is exemplified not only in the case of dodder, ergot, wheat ear cockles, and flax rust but also where badly contaminated or infected seed is lighter and smaller and, therefore, capable of being taken out of the sample by more rigorous cleaning. Such is the case with *C. linicola* and *P. lini* of flax as well as with some other fungal contaminants (Lafferty, 1921). Middleton (1944) found in the case of virus diseases of squash that light seed produced up to 37% of infection and heavy seed only 2%; he states that most infected seeds can be removed by careful winnowing. All attempts to prevent the dispersal of fungal and bacterial pathogens by preventing seed dispersal must be given the broadest consideration.

Epidemiological studies have shown that climatic conditions may be a limiting factor in determining the spread and build-up of seed-borne pathogens, and it should be remembered that it is possible to disperse contaminated seed to districts and areas where growth conditions are such that they will lead to the eradication of contamination and to the harvesting of clean, noncontaminated seed.

IV. Plants and Plant Parts

A. *General*

Plants and plant parts which are dispersed as planting stock or farm and garden produce and plant debris which may accumulate as waste in the course of cropping, etc. are considered under this heading. Crop debris and decaying vegetable matter which remain in the soil and help to build up its humus content have been dealt with under the heading of soil. Traffic in plants and parts of plants grows apace, and the problem of combating the autonomous dispersal of plant pathogens through the medium of planting material and plant products assumes growing complexity. Whether the commodity be complete plants, tubers, bulbs, corms, runners, cuttings, or produce for consumption, the need is that it shall be healthy and free from viable pathogens and, in particular, from those which are likely to cause disease or diseases unknown or unrecorded in the place of its introduction. It is the real danger of the spread of disease in this way which has occupied the minds of legislators and administrators, as well as plant pathologists, ever since it has been understood how disease epidemics can arise through the traffic in plants.

The introduction of potato blight (*Phytophthora infestans*) into Europe, with its resultant disastrous effect, as illustrated by the famine in Ireland from 1845 to 1847, is but one example, and the appearance in Europe *circa* 1900, of American gooseberry mildew, caused by *Sphaerotheca mors-uvae*, with its temporary retarding effect upon the cultivation of gooseberries, is but another. Since the problem of adhering soil has already been considered, the pathogens discussed here are those with which plants and plant parts themselves are likely to be infected.

B. *Autonomous Dispersal by Plants and Plant Parts*

1. *The Contamination of Plants and Plant Parts*

The contamination of plants and plant parts means their infection with pathogenic organisms. The rate and pattern of contamination will follow largely that of the disease with which the crop may become infected. Such contamination will, in most cases, be contracted during the growing of the crop although it may occur during storage, particularly in the case of plant produce.

2. *Spread and Build-Up of the Pathogen*

a. *Planting Stocks and Plant Products.* The spread and build-up of the pathogen will take its pattern from the season and the conditions of growth and storage. While the degree of its spread and build-up is of great importance, the actual presence of the pathogen is equally important. The fact that it is present at all in a viable condition will allow for its establishment and spread in a new area if the environment is congenial. If potatoes or gooseberries are to be moved for planting to a new area, where it is known that the diseases with which they are likely to be affected are likely to cause harm, then it is important that they should be free not only from mass infection but from all infection. Accumulated knowledge confirming the existence and importance of physiologic races of pathogens such as *S. endobioticum* (Moore, 1957), *P. brassicae* (Ayers, 1957), and *Venturia inaequalis*, the cause of apple scab (Keitt *et al.*, 1948), indicate the danger of the introduction not only of the pathogen, but of a new physiologic race capable of causing severe crop disease. Although the transmission of pathogenic viruses has been shown to be relatively uncommon in the case of true seeds, the reverse holds for crops which are vegetatively propagated. The probability of complete systemic infection with the virus which results in the permeation of all the plant tissues means that infection will remain in that plant or clone as long as it is cultivated. The ready spread and build-up of pathogenic viruses in vegetatively propagated plant material is, therefore, of special significance and has led to the growing demand for planting stocks which are free from virus contamination. The spread and build-up of contamination in planting stocks and plant products ceases to be of interest when it has reached the stage where the host has been killed or rendered of such poor quality as to be worthless; it then becomes plant debris.

b. *Plant Debris.* Although plant debris may not be generally subject to the same extensive movement as planting stocks and plant products, its accumulation may be a significant factor in securing autonomous dispersal. This is of special local importance in spreading disease from field to field and from farm to farm. Heaps of discarded potato tubers affected with blight caused by *P. infestans* will, if the winter is mild, carry the pathogen through to the next season, when it will sporulate and serve as a source of inoculum for neighboring crops. Crop debris from Brassicae affected with clubroot (*P. brassicae*) may be distributed with manure, while *B. cinerea*, the fungus responsible for gray mold, becomes readily established in decaying plant parts. Prunings from perennial crops also constitute a serious danger and even fallen rose leaves affected with black spot, *Diplocarpon rosae*, ensure the dispersal and survival of the pathogen. As useful as the compost heap in a garden may be for providing a supply of organic manure, it nevertheless consists of a mass of decaying plant debris, and the danger of the dispersal of plant pathogens, in compost may be very real. The ready growth of nonspecialized facultative parasites, such as *P. ultimum* and *R. solani* in debris rich in leaf mold, is also likely to occur and must be reckoned with when such material is used for plant propagation.

3. Persistence of the Pathogen

a. *Planting Stock and Plant Products.* Since planting stocks are normally not stored for long periods and are meant to be used with the least possible delay, the ability of the pathogen to survive over the winter or a dormant period will determine its reaching the new planting site in a viable condition. In the case of transplants such as tomatoes, chrysanthemums, and Brassicae, the adaptability of the pathogen to persist is not of great importance because only a few hours or days at the most are likely to intervene before the stock is replanted in its new site. This means that, except in occasional cases, where the pathogen may be killed during the period of transit or storage, the risk of its dispersal is always present. Even in cases where a fungus or bacterium is carried as delicate mycelium or in a nonresting state within the tissues of the host, such as *Peronospora destructor*, the cause of downy mildew of onion, or *Corynebacterium sepedonicum*, the cause of potato bacterial ring rot, the conditions of storage will normally allow for the survival of the pathogen. In most cases the pathogen will be present as resting mycelia, resting spores, or sclerotia, and thus adapted to withstand adverse conditions. Examples of the persistence of the pathogen as resting spores are provided by *P. brassicae, S. subterranea,* and *S. endobioticum* as well as pathogenic bacteria which form such spores. The cleistocarps of *S. mors-uvae* will survive for long periods until conditions are suitable for the release of ascospores. *B. cinerea* and *R. solani* normally form resistant sclerotia which will retain their viability for years. *Streptomyces scabies,* the cause of common scab of potato, will certainly persist in the tuber from one growing season to another. Viruses are persistent in planting stocks and are readily carried over during the normal period of storage.

Plant products, although used for consumption or decoration, can also serve as agents for autonomous dispersal. Apple scab (*V. inaequalis*), potato bacterial ring rot (*C. sepedonicum*), and virus diseases are cited as examples where the pathogen may survive and persist on or in such produce.

b. *Plant Debris.* The conditions for survival and persistence of the pathogen in planting stocks and plant products also hold largely for plant debris, which may for many years provide a source of inoculum. Perennial crops are cited as an example where fallen leaves and prunings enable a pathogen to persist until the next growing season when they may be instrumental in assuring dispersal. In apple scab and black spot of roses, fallen leaves may provide a potent source of seasonal inoculum while in apple canker, caused by *Nectria galligena,* and American gooseberry mildew the prunings from trees and bushes may behave similarly.

C. *The Prevention of Autonomous Dispersal*

1. *Inspecting and Testing for Infection and Contamination*

As with soil and seeds, reliable methods for testing plants and plant products for contamination or infection with a pathogen provide a valuable tool in helping to prevent its dispersal. In the case of material affected with fungal or bacterial diseases the task may be relatively simple since the symptoms of disease will normally be observed, and symptomatology, aided by examination for the presence of the pathogen, will provide the information required. It is not a difficult task to determine whether *Brassica* seedlings are affected with *P. brassicae,* gooseberry transplants with *S. mors-uvae,* or seed potato tubers with *S. scabies,* *S. subterranea, S. endobioticum, R. solani,* or *Pe. carotovorum,* and an examination of the stock, supplemented, if possible, by field inspection and some knowledge of the growing crop will provide an accurate assessment of plant health. These are the methods normally employed in the granting of health certificates for the export of planting stocks and plant products. At the receiving end it is not uncommon for some form of plant quarantine to be set up whereby incoming planting stock can be grown on in isolation and under constant observation for the purpose of health determination.

The contamination of planting stocks with viruses presents a different and more difficult problem because there is frequently no outward sign to indicate whether or not the stock is affected. Symptoms present in growing stocks, such as transplants, may allow of some assessment being made, but in dormant stocks such as potato tubers, bulbs, corms, and leafless trees, etc., there is usually nothing to indicate virus infection. It is for this reason that inspection of the growing crop from which the stock is derived is practiced as a normal procedure for gauging the likely state of health of the produce. Systems of crop inspection have now come to be practiced on a world-wide scale. No better example can be cited than that of the seed potato crop where so much has been done to prevent the dispersal of crop pathogens by this method. But even so, the problem of determining health by crop inspection alone is made difficult by the varying symptom pictures presented by different potato varieties affected with the same virus, by infection with a virus complex, and by the existence of symptomless carrier varieties of potato.

With increasing knowledge and development of new techniques, however, it has been possible to elaborate testing methods whereby a more certain and accurate approach to the problem can be made. The importance of this direct approach is being rapidly appreciated, and these new techniques are being used on an ever-increasing scale to supplement or replace visual inspection in the field. Briefly, testing methods for virus contamination fall into the three categories of grafting, the sap inoculation of indicator plants, and serology. Although not so widely used for the more easily recognizable infections such as leaf roll and severe mosaic, they are now in common use for milder infections not readily determined by eye inspection. Tuber core grafting (Murphy and McKay, 1926) can be used for potato leaf roll, while stem grafting is employed for the determination of contamination with viruses X, A, B, and C; a scion of the stock to be tested is grafted onto a variety such as Craig's Defiance, which is field-immune to all 4 viruses. Sap inoculation from potato stocks of indeterminate health is made onto such indicator plants as *Nicotiana tabacum* (White Burley), *Nicotiana glutinosa, Datura stramonium, Solanum demissum* (C.P.C. 2103.1 for virus Y and P.1.175404 for virus A), and *Gomphrena globosa* whereby characteristic symptom pictures of such sap-transmissible virus infections as are caused by viruses X, Y, and A are obtained. The introduction of serological methods (Markham *et al.*, 1948; Matthews, 1957) marks yet another advance, since by using either the precipitin or agglutination methods, a rapid technique is made available for the detection of viruses X and S. Grafting techniques have also been evolved for use with stocks of strawberries and raspberries. Healthy wild strawberry plants (*Fragaria vesca*), if inarch grafted with a strawberry variety of unknown health, will act as indicators and provide a symptom picture of the virus carried (Harris, 1932). Similarly, by a modification of Harris's method, adapted to bottle grafting (Garner, 1947), and by using certain raspberry varieties as indicator plants, the health of raspberry stocks may be determined. The extended use of the electron microscope may prove a further boon to testing for health if, by further simplification, rapid and easily applied techniques become available for the direct observation of the virus. In preventing the dispersal of pathogenic plant viruses, testing methods are not only useful for the examination of planting stock if and when required, but are proving invaluable as routine methods for the conduct of health surveys and for use in the building up of foundation stock of planting materials known to be free from virus contamination.

2. Decontamination

a. *Planting Stocks and Plant Products.* The ideal method for preventing the dispersal of plant pathogens by plants and plant products is the obvious one of growing healthy crops. This may be achieved by cultivation in areas where conditions are unfavorable for the incidence of disease or by introducing plant protective measures against the onset of disease. But in spite of all that can be done there will be instances and seasons when planting stocks and produce will carry some kind of infection which will call for the application of some process of practicable decontamination. The form of treatment most commonly applied is chemotherapeutical and is exemplified by the dipping of young apple trees into Bordeaux mixture before export or distribution for the control of *V. inaequalis* (Cass-Smith, 1940), the steeping of raspberry canes into a weak solution of an organo-mercurial to control *Erwinia tumefaciens*, the cause of crown gall (Gleisberg, 1928), the immersion of vine cuttings into a 25 to 30% solution of ferrous sulfate to control *Elsinoe ampelina*, the cause of vine anthracnose (Ravaz, 1927), and the steeping of bulbs of tulips and narcissi into a solution of formaldehyde or a mercury salt to prevent the transmission of bulb-borne diseases (Newton *et al.*, 1932; Hawker, 1935).

The evidence suggests that some such treatments have been adopted as emergency measures without the undertaking of adequate experimental work, but there can be no doubt as to the need for further research on this problem. The disinfection of seed potato tubers for the control of tuber-borne fungal pathogens has received considerable attention, and the use of solutions of hot or cold formaldehyde, acidulated mercuric chloride, and organo-mercurials have all been recommended. The dipping of tubers into a solution of an organo-mercurial within 24 hours after digging has given promising results for the control of late blight caused by *P. infestans*, dry rot caused by *Fusarium coeruleum*, common scab caused by *S. scabies*, some forms of black scurf caused by *R. solani* and skin spot caused by *Oospora pustulans* but not of powdery scab caused by *S. subterranea*, (Greeves, 1937; Cairns *et al.*, 1936; Greeves and Muskett, 1939; Foister and Wilson, 1943; Graham *et al.*, 1957).

The large scale plant for washing and disinfecting seed potatoes in Scotland, to which reference has already been made, operates on the principle outlined above and aims at the production of high grade seed free from soil and viable tuber-borne pathogens. Although fumigation is commonly practiced for the decontamination of stocks affected with insect pests, it has not found favor in use on other pathogens. Heat therapy, applied as a hot water treatment, will free narcissus bulbs from infection with the nematode *Anguillulina dipsaci* (Ramsbottom, 1918a, b). The bulbs are immersed in water for 3 hours at 110° F. It has also been used to free mint (*Mentha* sp.) runners from rust caused by *Puccinia menthae* by immersing them for 10 minutes in mid-February in water at 105 to 115° F. (Ogilvie and Hickman, 1937).

Mention is made of the ingenious theory advanced by Jensen (1887) to account for the introduction of the living blight fungus (*P. infestans*) into North America and Europe. Having found that the mycelium in potato tubers is killed at a temperature of 25° C., he concluded that during the first three centuries of potato cultivation the tubers were disinfected by heat in old sailing vessels while passing through the tropics. With the introduction of the steamship (*circa* 1830 to 1840) the time taken to pass through the tropics was much reduced—with the result that the tubers were not decontaminated, and the pathogen survived the voyage in a viable condition (Jones *et al.*, 1912). Heat therapy has also been applied for planting stocks contaminated with viruses. Kunkel (1935) reported the recovery of peach trees from yellows disease when kept for 14 days or more at 35° C., while Kassanis (1949) freed potato tubers from the leaf roll virus by keeping them at 37° C. in a moist atmosphere for a period of from 10 to 30 days. Bawden (1950) suggests that this method of treatment is not likely to be suitable for general application, but, at the same time, its possible value for freeing small quantities of valuable planting stock from virus contamination must be kept in mind.

The risk of dispersal through plant products also exists—especially for such produce as potato tubers intended for consumption but which could be used for seed. It is, therefore, most desirable to ensure that incoming produce is used for the purpose intended and not allowed to be distributed willy-nilly through areas where it could be a danger to the health of cultivated crops.

b. *Plant Debris.* The destruction of plant debris, either by burning or treatment with some means to render innocuous any pathogens it may carry, is the obvious way of combating the spread of disease through the medium of plant refuse, etc. Waste produce from stores and markets, prunings from fruit bushes and trees, discarded tubers, and roots thrown out in the course of sorting or grading the crop all come under this heading. Reference has already been made to the danger of the compost heap as a reservoir of viable plant pathogens. In the case of perennial crops of trees and bushes the fallen leaves may provide a source of inoculum each year for the next season, and where it has been found impracticable to collect and remove them, some such treatment as the spraying of the orchard floor with a suitable fungicide for the control of apple scab or the heavy mulching of the soil for the control of black spot of roses has been recommended.

3. *The Prevention of Plant and Plant-Part Dispersal*

Where doubt exists as to the possible contamination of plant parts or products and where decontamination is impossible or impracticable, their dispersal in any area where the contamination is likely to become established and cause serious outbreaks of disease should be prevented. It is due to the failure to recognize or to realize the danger of dispersing contaminated material, either through sheer ignorance or through the lack of epidemiological knowledge, that the need has arisen for so much plant-protective legislation and the introduction of that most expensive and ideally unnecessary luxury, the plant quarantine. Quarantine is discussed in some detail by Gram in Chapter 9 of this volume.

Much of the early quarantine legislation had to be framed in the light of very incomplete knowledge, and like poor King Canute in his abortive attempt to persuade the flowing tide to ebb, the earlier legislators got their feet very wet. The Destructive Insects and Pests Act for England and Wales became law on Independence Day, 1907. Its first task was to stem the tide of entry of American gooseberry mildew into the country, since England was believed to be almost free from the disease. Inspection, made possible through the act, showed the disease to be already common in some of the country's southern counties. For some time it has been very doubtful whether legislation framed to prevent the passage of a pathogen from one country to another can be effective when there is only a land border between the two, and with the increase in ease of speed and travel the value of an intervening ocean would now seem to be almost just as doubtful. The complicated boundaries which have had to be evolved of necessity to preserve the political integrity of the strains and races of mankind do not appear to serve the same or any other purpose in the case of microorganisms (Muskett, 1950).

Whereas, in the past, it has seemed the bounden duty of an importing country to prevent the inlet of produce which might be suspect, with increasing knowledge the emphasis has shifted to the exporting country, which should prevent the export of such produce. In fact the time should come and may come (it has come in the case of seed potatoes) when exporting countries will vie with each other for the good health of their products. It is much easier and more sensible for a producing country to vouch for the health of its produce than to place the onus for determining health onto the expensive inspectorate of an importing country, which very often can only say that the incoming material is free from all disease and contamination to the best of its belief.

Nor must the introduction of the pathogen as such be regarded as the bogey incarnate unless there is a grave risk of its introduction's causing serious crop disease. Reference has already been made to the possible desirability of sending stocks of contaminated planting material to be grown in areas likely to clear their contamination. The inhabitants of Switzerland do not object to persons sick with tuberculosis entering their country to effect a cure; the climate of Switzerland encourages the recovery of the host and discourages the activity of the pathogen. The immediate need is for less legislation on a small national scale and for more research into epidemiological problems and disease control, with the object of putting into practice the knowledge so gained. The findings of science must be treated as a whole; they must not be taken piecemeal and prostituted for political, financial, or national ends. It is only in this way that one of the objects of the Second International Plant Protection Convention of 1951 can be attained. That object is that all plant-protective legislation should be framed with a view to encouraging international trade, and not to hindering such trade. When more research has been achieved and the accrued knowledge allows for a more truthful interpretation of the facts, it is essential that the findings be safeguarded and that their correct interpretation be preserved. If this cannot be done, the last state of things may be worse than the first.

REFERENCES

Adams, J. F. 1921. Observations on wheat scab in Pennsylvania and its pathological history. *Phytopathology* **11**: 115–124.
Ainsworth, G. C. 1934. Virus disease investigations. *Ann. Rept. Cheshunt Expt. Sta.* **1933**: 54–64.
Ainsworth, G. C., and L. Ogilvie. 1939. Lettuce mosaic. *Ann. Appl. Biol.* **26**: 279–297.
Ayers, G. W. 1957. Races of *Plasmodiophora brassicae*. *Can. J. Botany* **35**: 923–932.

Baunacke, W. 1922. Untersuchungen zur Biologie und Bekämpfung der Rüben-nematoden *Heterodera schachtii* Schmidt. *Arb. biol. Reichanstalt Land- u. Forstwirtsch. Berlin-Dahlem* **11**: 185–288.

Bawden, F. C. 1950. "Plant Viruses and Virus Diseases," 3rd ed. Chronica Botanica, Waltham, Massachusetts. pp. 298–299.

Bennett, F. T. 1931. *Gibberella saubinetii* (Mont.) Sacc. on British cereals. II. Physiological and pathological studies. *Ann. Appl. Biol.* **18**: 158–177.

Blair, I. D. 1943. Behaviour of the fungus *Rhizoctonia solani* Kuhn in the soil. *Ann. Appl. Biol.* **30**: 118–127.

Bliss, D. E. 1951. The destruction of *Armillaria mellea* in citrus soils. *Phytopathology* **41**: 665–683.

Bremer, H. 1924. Untersuchungen über Biologie und Bekämpfung des Erregers der Kohlhernie *Plasmodiophora brassicae* Woronin. 2. Mitteilung. Kohlhernie und Bodenazidität. *Landwirtsch. Jahrb.* **59**: 673–685.

Cadman, C. H. 1956. Studies on the etiology and mode of spread of Scottish raspberry leaf-curl disease. *J. Hort. Sci.* **31**: 111.

Cairns, H., T. N. Greeves, and A. E. Muskett. 1936. The control of common scab (*Actinomyces scabies* (Thaxt.) Guss) of the Potato by tuber disinfection. *Ann. Appl. Biol.* **23**: 718–742.

Calvert, E. L., and A. E. Muskett. 1945. Blind Seed Disease of Rye-grass (*Phialea temulenta* Prill. et Delacr.) *Ann. Appl. Biol.* **32**: 329–343.

Cass-Smith, W. P. 1940. Black spot or scab of Apples. Serious new outbreaks recorded in the Albany and Manjimup districts. *J. Dept. Agr. W. Australia* **17**: 56–67.

Colhoun, J. 1946. Observations on the effects of Browning (*Polyspora lini* Laff.) of Flax on Seed Production. *Ann. Appl. Biol.* **33**: 255–259.

Colhoun, J. 1953. A study of the epidemiology of clubroot disease of Brassicae. *Ann. Appl. Biol.* **40**: 262–283.

Colhoun, J. 1957. A technique for examining soil for the presence of *Plasmodiophora brassicae* Woron. *Ann. Appl. Biol.* **45**: 559–565.

Colhoun, J., and A. E. Muskett. 1948. A study of the longevity of the seed-borne parasites of flax in relation to the storage of the seed. *Ann. Appl. Biol.* **35**: 429–434.

Crowley, N. C. 1957a. Studies on the seed transmission of plant virus diseases. *Australian J. Biol. Sci.* **10**: 449–464.

Crowley, N. C. 1957b. The effects of developing embryos on plant viruses. *Australian J. Biol. Sci.* **10**: 443–448.

Dowson, W. J. 1957. "Plant Diseases Due to Bacteria," 2nd ed. Cambridge Univ. Press, London and New York. pp. 176–177.

Doyer, L. C. 1938. "Manual for the Determination of Seed-Borne Diseases." The International Seed Testing Association, H. Veenman & Zonen, Wageningen, Holland.

Ellis, E. H. 1929. *Armillaria mellea* in a mine-working. *Trans. Brit. Mycol. Soc.* **14**: 305–307.

Ezekiel, W. N. 1940. *Rept. Texas Agr. Expt. Sta. 1939*, pp. 84–86.

Fedorintchik, N. S. 1935. Agricultural methods for the control of soil-inhabiting organisms, parasitic on plants. *Bull. Plant Protect. Leningrad* **5**: 61–66.

Fellows, H. 1941. Effect of certain environmental conditions on the prevalence of *Ophiobolus graminis* in the soil. *J. Agr. Research* **63**: 715–726.

Findlay, W. P. K. 1951. The development of *Armillaria mellea* rhizomorphs in a water tunnel. *Trans. Brit. Mycol. Soc.* **34**: 146.

Fischer, G. W. 1936. The longevity of smut spores in herbarium specimens. *Phytopathology* **26**: 1118–1127.

Foister, C. E., and A. R. Wilson. 1943. Dry rot in seed potatoes. A summary of some recent experiments. *Agriculture London* **50**: 300–303.

Fuchs, O. 1911. Beitrage zur Biologie der Rübennematoden *Heterodera schachtii*. Z. *landwirtsch. Versuchw. Deut. Oesterr.* **14**: 923–949.

Garner, R. J. 1947. "The Grafter's Handbook." Faber and Faber, London.

Garrett, S. D. 1938. Soil conditions and take-all disease of wheat. III. Decomposition of the resting mycelium of *Ophiobolus graminis* in infected wheat stubble buried in the soil. *Ann. Appl. Biol.* **25**: 742–766.

Garrett, S. D. 1940. Soil conditions and take-all disease of wheat. V. Further experiments on the survival of *Ophiobolus graminis* in infected wheat stubble buried in the soil. *Ann. Appl. Biol.* **27**: 199–204.

Garrett, S. D. 1944. Soil conditions and take-all disease of wheat. VIII. Further experiments on the survival of *Ophiobolus graminis* in infected wheat stubble. *Ann. Appl. Biol.* **31**: 186–191.

Garrett, S. D. 1956. "Biology of Root-Infecting Fungi." Cambridge Univ. Press, London and New York. p. 85.

Gibbs, J. G. 1939. Factors influencing the control of clubroot (*Plasmodiophora brassicae*). *New Zealand Sci. Technol.* **A 20**: 409–412.

Gleisberg, W. 1928. Wurzelkropf an Himbeeren. *Obstet. Gemusebau.* **74**: 163–164.

Goodey, T. 1923. Quiescence and Reviviscence in Nematodes with special reference to *Tylenchus tritici* and *Tylenchus dipsaci. J. Helminthol.* **1**: 47–52.

Graham, D. C., S. N. S. Srivastava, and C. E. Foister. 1957. The control of *Rhizoctonia solani* on potato. *Plant Pathol.* **6**: 149–152.

Greeves, T. N. 1937. The control of blight (*Phytophthora infestans*) in seed potatoes by tuber disinfection. *Ann. Appl. Biol.* **24**: 26–32.

Greeves, T. N., and A. E. Muskett. 1939. Skin spot (*Oospora pustulans* Owen & Wakef.) of the potato and its control by tuber disinfection. *Ann. Appl. Biol.* **26**: 481–496.

Harris, R. V. 1932. Grafting as a method for investigating a possible virus disease of the strawberry. *J. Pomol. Hort. Sci.* **10**: 35–41.

Harrison, B. D. 1956. Soil transmission of Scottish raspberry leaf-curl disease. *Nature* **178**: 553.

Harrison, B. D. 1958. Raspberry yellow dwarf, a soil-borne virus. *Ann. Appl. Biol.* **46**: 221–229.

Hartman, R. E. 1951. Potato wart in America. *Plant Disease Reptr.* **35**: 268–271.

Hawker, L. E. 1935. Further experiments on the *Fusarium* bulb rot of *Narcissus*. *Ann. Appl. Biol.* **22**: 684–708.

Jensen, J. L. 1887. Moyens de combattre et de detruire le *Peronospora* de la pomme de terre. *Mem. Soc. Natl. Agr. France* **131**: 31–156.

Johnson, F. 1945. The effect of chemical soil treatments on the development of wheat mosaic. *Ohio J. Sci.* **45**: 125–126.

Johnson, J. 1937. Factors relating to the control of ordinary tobacco mosaic. *J. Agr. Research* **54**: 239–273.

Jones, L. R., N. J. Giddings, and B. F. Lutman. 1912. Investigations of the potato fungus, *Phytophthora infestans. U. S. Dept. Agr. Bull. No.* **245.**

Kassanis, B. 1949. Potato tubers freed from leaf-roll virus by heat. *Nature* **164**: 881.

Keitt, G. W., C. Leben, and J. R. Shay. 1948. "*Venturia inaequalis,*" IV. Further studies on the inheritance of pathogenicity. *Am. J. Botany* **35**: 334.

Kerr, A. 1953. A method of isolating soft-rotting bacteria from soils. *Nature* **172**: 1155.

King, C. J., C. Hope, and E. D. Eaton. 1934. Further observations on the natural distribution of the cotton root-rot fungus. *Phytopathology* **24**: 551–553.

Kunkel, L. O. 1935. Heat treatment for the cure of yellows and rosette of peach. *Phytopathology* **25**: 24.

Lafferty, H. A. 1921. The browning and stem-break disease of cultivated flax (*Linum usitatissimum*) caused by *Polyspora lini* n. gen et sp. *Sci. Proc. Roy. Dublin Soc.* **16** [N. S.]: 248–274.

Mabbott, T. W. 1956. Potato root eelworm—A report on an experiment to free seed potatoes from adhering soil and cysts. *Scot. Agr.* **36**: 73–74.

Macfarlane, I. 1952. Factors affecting the survival of *Plasmodiophora brassicae* Wor. in the soil and its assessment by a host test. *Ann. Appl. Biol.* **39**: 239–256.

Machacek, J. E., and H. A. H. Wallace. 1952. Longevity of some common fungi in cereal seed. *Can. J. Botany* **30**: 164–169.

McKinney, H. H. 1946. Soil factors in relation to incidence and symptom-expression of virus diseases. *Soil Sci.* **61**: 93.

McNamara, H. C. 1926. Behaviour of cotton root-rot at Greenville, Texas, including an experiment with clean fallows. *J. Agr. Research* **32**: 17–24.

Markham, R., R. E. F. Matthews, and K. M. Smith. 1948. Testing potato stocks for virus X. *Farming:* **1948:** (February) 40–46.

Matthews, R. E. F. 1957. "Plant Virus Serology." Cambridge Univ. Press, London and New York.

Middleton, J. T. 1944. Seed transmission of squash-mosaic virus. *Phytopathology* **34**: 405–410.

Moore, W. C. 1957. The breakdown of immunity from wart disease. *Outlook on Agr.* **1**: 240–243.

Murphy, P. A., and R. McKay. 1925. Further experiments on the sources and development of blight infection in potato tubers. *J. Dept. Lands Agr. Ireland.* **25**: 10–21.

Murphy, P. A., and R. McKay. 1926. Methods for investigating the virus disease of the potato, and some results obtained by their use. *Sci. Proc. Roy. Dublin Soc.* **18**: 169–184.

Muskett, A. E. 1937. A study of the epidemiology and control of *Helminthosporium* disease of oats. *Ann. Botany (London)* **1** [N. S.]: 763–784.

Muskett, A. E. 1938. Biological technique for the evaluation of fungicides. I. The evolution of seed disinfectants for the control of *Helminthosporium* disease of oats. *Ann. Botany (London)* **2** [N. S.]: 699–715.

Muskett, A. E. 1948. Technique for the examination of seeds for the presence of seed-borne fungi. *Trans. Brit. Mycol. Soc.* **30**: 74–83.

Muskett, A. E. 1950. Presidential address—Seed-borne fungi and their significance. *Trans. Brit. Mycol. Soc.* **33**: 1–12.

Muskett, A. E. 1958. Studies on seed health. I. Flax. *Ann. Appl. Biol.* **46**: 430–445.

Muskett, A. E., and J. Colhoun. 1943. The prevention of seed-borne diseases of flax by seed disinfection. *Ann. Appl. Biol.* **30**: 7–18.

Muskett, A. E., and J. Colhoun. 1947. "Diseases of the flax plant." W. & G. Baird, Belfast. pp. 99–105.

Muskett, A. E., and J. P. Malone. 1941. The Ulster Method for the examination of flax seed for the presence of seed-borne parasites. *Ann. Appl. Biol.* **28**: 8–13.

Muskett, A. E., and J. P. Malone. 1956. Detection of seed-borne parasites in seeds. *Nature* **177**: 465–466.

Neal, D. C. 1929. The occurrence of viable cotton root-rot sclerotia in nature. *Science* **70**: 409–410.

Neal, D. C., and L. G. Maclean. 1931. Viability of strand hyphae of the cotton root-rot fungus. *J. Agr. Research* **43**: 499–502.

Newton, W., R. J. Hastings, and J. E. Bosher. 1932. *Botrytis tulipae* (Lib.) Lind. II. Bulb dips. *Sci. Agr.* **13**: 110–113.

Ogilvie, L., and C. J. Hickman. 1937. Progress report on vegetable diseases VIII. *Ann. Rept. Agr. Hort. Research Sta. Long Ashton Bristol* **1936**: 139–148.

Padwick, G. W. 1935. Influence of wild and cultivated plants on the multiplication, survival and spread of cereal foot-rotting fungi in the soil *Can. J. Research* **12**: 575–589.

Pethybridge, G. H., and H. A. Lafferty. 1918. A disease of flax seedlings caused by a species of *Colletotrichum* and transmitted by infected seed. *Sci. Proc. Roy. Dublin Soc.* **15** [N. S.]: 359–384.

Pethybridge, G. H., H. A. Lafferty, and J. G. Rhynehart. 1921. Investigations on flax diseases (second report). *J. Dept. Agr.* (Ireland) **21**: 167–187.

Porter, R. H. 1955. Longevity of *Ustilago nuda* in barley seed. *Phytopathology* **45**: 637–638.

Pryor, D. E. 1946. Exploratory experiments with the big-vein disease of lettuce. *Phytopathology* **36**: 264–272.

Rader, W. E., H. F. Fitzpatrick, and E. M. Hildebrand. 1947. A seed-borne virus of musk melon. *Phytopathology* **37**: 809–816.

Ramsbottom, J. K. 1918a. Investigations on the narcissus disease. *J. Roy. Hort. Soc.* **43**: 51–64.

Ramsbottom, J .K. 1918b. Experiments on the control of the eelworm disease of narcissus. *J. R. Hort. Soc.* **43**: 65–78.

Ratcliffe, G. T. 1934. Cotton root rot as affected by crop rotation and tillage in San Antonio, Tex. *U. S. Dept. Agr. Tech. Bull.* **436.**

Ravaz, L. 1927. A propos de l'anthracnose. *Progr. Agr. et vit.* **87**: 57–60.

Rea, H. E. 1939. The control of cotton root rot in the blackland region of Texas. *Texas Agr. Expt. Sta. Bull.* **573.**

Reddick, D., and V. B. Stewart. 1919. Transmission of the virus of bean mosaic in seed and observations on thermal death point of seed and virus. *Phytopathology* **9**: 445.

Rogers, C. H. 1937. The effect of three- and four-year rotations on cotton root rot in the central Texas blacklands. *J. Am. Soc. Agron.* **29**: 668–680.

Rogers, C. H. 1942. Cotton root rot studies with special reference to sclerotia, cover crops, rotations, tillage, seeding rates, soil fungicides and effects on seed quality. *Texas Agr. Expt. Sta. Bull.* **614.**

Russell, R. C. 1950. The whole embryo method of testing barley for loose smut as a routine test. *Sci. Agr.* **30**: 361.

Ruttle, M. L. 1934. Studies on barley smuts and on loose smut of wheat. *N. Y. State Agr. Expt. Sta. (Geneva, N. Y.) Tech. Bull. No.* **221.**

Samuel, G., and S. D. Garrett. 1945. The infected root-hair count for estimating the activity of *Plasmodiophora brassicae* Woron. in the soil. *Ann. Appl. Biol.* **32**: 96–101.

Schaffnit, E. 1922. Der Kartoffelkrebs. *Deut. Obstb. Ztg.* **68**: 212–213.

Simmonds, P. M. 1946. Detection of the loose smut fungi in embryo of barley and wheat. *Sci. Agr.* **26:** 57.

Smith, H. C. 1954. Microbiological effect of partial soil sterilization with formalin upon reintroduced damping-off fungi. To be published.

Taubenhaus, J. J., and W. N. Ezekiel. 1930a. Recent studies in *Phymatotrichum* root rot. *Am. J. Botany* **17:** 554–571.

Taubenhaus, J. J., and W. N. Ezekiel. 1930b. Studies on the overwintering of *Phymatotrichum* root rot. *Phytopathology* **20:** 761–785.

Taubenhaus, J. J., and W. N. Ezekiel. 1936. Longevity of sclerotia of *Phymatotrichum omnivorum* in moist soil in the laboratory. *Am. J. Botany* **23:** 10–12.

Thorne, G. 1923. Length of the dormancy period of the sugar beet nematode in Utah. *U. S. Dept. Agr. Circ. No.* **262.**

Walkinshaw, C. H., and R. H. Larson. 1958. A soil-borne virus associated with the corky ringspot disease of potato. *Nature* **181:** 1146.

Wallace, G. B. 1935. *Armillaria* root rot in East Africa. *E. African Agr. J.* **1:** 182–192.

Wilson, H. K. 1955. "Grain Crops," 2nd ed. McGraw-Hill, New York, p. 139.

CHAPTER 4

Dispersal of Inoculum by Insects and Other Animals, Including Man

L. BROADBENT

Rothamsted Experimental Station, Harpenden, Hertfordshire, England [*]

I. INTRODUCTION

Some pathogens are carried externally by animals, others internally; some are carried passively, others appear to have an active biological association with their vectors, as the animal carriers are called. Much is known about the spread of several pathogens by man and by insects, but very little about those dispersed by other animals. Most of this chapter is devoted to the spread of viruses, for although there are some diseases of great economic importance caused by animal-dispersed bacteria and fungi, relatively few are plant pathogens.

Knowledge of the methods by which pathogens are dispersed is usually essential before effective control measures can be devised. Two types of spread must be considered: (1) the introduction of the pathogen

[*] *Present address:* Glasshouse Crops Research Institute, Rustington, Littlehampton, Sussex, England.

into a healthy crop, which event may occur over considerable distances, and (2) the spread from plant to plant within a crop.

But let us examine first the pathogens to find out how they are adapted to transmission by animals. Viruses are by definition obligate parasites, and few survive for long outside living cells. Most lose infectivity in extracted plant sap within hours or days, but some, like tobacco mosaic and potato X viruses, can persist on clothing or in plant debris for many months, and are so infectious that they can be carried externally on animals, clothing, or machinery. This is exceptional behavior, and most viruses are transmitted only when an animal, usually an arthropod, feeds first on an infected plant and then on a healthy one. The relationship between arthropod and virus is often close, as we shall see, although it has involved no obvious changes in the animal's morphology.

Bacteria, like viruses, are unable to penetrate plant cuticles and depend for entrance on natural openings or injuries. They depend less on animals for transport, as most are splashed in rain drops, are carried on or in seeds, or in soil, or occasionally are blown by wind. Some have several forms of transport, including animals, but at least one, the cause of cucumber wilt, appears to be entirely dependent on insects. Some bacteria occur in flowers and are spread by pollinating insects; some are contained in slime that oozes from lesions, and insects become contaminated with these as they move about the plant or they may even be attracted to the slime. Others, like some viruses, are transmitted by feeding insects, and some are retained within the animal's body for a considerable period. Most of these do not form resting spores or similar structures, and must survive periods when plants are absent, or weather is unsuitable for growth in diseased plant tissues, or more rarely, in soil or insect vectors. Unlike the fungi, bacteria are not adapted for wind dissemination, nor have they developed really efficient methods of insect transmission as the viruses have.

Most fungal conidia are of the dry spore type and are blown away by the wind, but some have slime spores carried in a sticky liquid, which is dispersed by water or animals, usually insects. These are mostly microfungi, and only a few are pathogenic to plants. This subject was dealt with exhaustively by Leach (1940), who drew attention to the close resemblance in many respects between insect dispersal of pathogens and insect pollination. Insects that both protect a pathogen and provide a means for it to enter a plant obviously provide an effective and prudent method of spread. There are some examples of apparent symbiosis because the insect appears to benefit from its association with the fungus.

II. DISPERSAL BY MAN

Vegetative propagation from infected plants is an all too efficient means of increasing the number, and often the geographical range, of infected plants, and in adopting it widely man has perhaps played his biggest part in dispersing pathogens. The spread of viruses is particularly important because many varieties of plants carry virus without showing symptoms. Dispersal by seeds and plant parts is discussed in Chapter 3 of this volume and need not be pursued further here. Fungal resting spores are also probably transported by man over long distances, as are infective insect vectors, but little is known about such spread; it is probably less important, compared with the moving of infected plants, because the pathogen has few chances of surviving and spreading to other susceptible plants.

Dispersal of a pathogen on a worker's body or clothes, or on machinery or draught animals must usually be local, in contrast to man's dispersal of infected tissues over long distances. Few viruses are transmitted in expressed plant sap outside the laboratory because they are rarely concentrated enough to persist and cause infection. Tobacco mosaic virus, however, is so stable that it can infect after 2 years on equipment, and potato X virus can persist for up to 6 weeks on clothing, so these can spread from one crop to another, as well as within crops, during cultivations or inspections (Johnson, 1937; Todd, 1958). Tobacco mosaic virus is spread widely among tomatoes while the plants are being tied up or side shoots are being removed; it is so persistent that it can survive when plants are composted or when tobacco is cured, and may be introduced into an uninfected tomato or tobacco crop on the hands of smokers. Potato spindle tuber virus is spread by the knives used to cut tubers into seed pieces, a prevalent practice in America, and also by tractors passing through healthy potato crops after infected ones (Merriam and Bonde, 1954). Tulip flower-break and *Cymbidium* mosaic are 2 other viruses spread on cutting knives, but *Narcissus* mosaic is not; neither is the infectious potato X virus, possibly because tuber parenchyma has too low a virus content to be a source of inoculum and also resists infection by inoculation (Bawden *et al.*, 1948). Fruit growers who graft infected budwood scions on to rootstocks provide an efficient, and for some viruses of top-fruit, the only known means of spread.

Bacteria, too, can be spread on cutting knives: *Corynebacterium sepedonicum* (Spieck. and Kotth.) Skapt. and Burkh, which causes ring rot of potato, spreads rapidly when stocks with a proportion of infected seed tubers are cut and planted immediately, but less readily when the cut surfaces are allowed to dry before planting (Bonde, 1939b). The sacks used to store or transport potatoes can also provide sources of infection. Several other bacteria are spread on knives; for example, *C. michiganense* (E. F. Smith) Jensen, causing bacterial canker of tomato (Ark, 1944), and *Pseudomonas solanacearum* E. F. Smith, causing bacterial wilt of bananas (Sequeira, 1958).

Many fungal spores are disseminated on hands, clothing, and machinery, but they are relatively unimportant in the epidemiology of the diseases, and there has been little work on this type of spread. Fungi, and soil-borne pathogens of all kinds, can easily be transported on boots, implements, and the roots of transplanted plants; two well-known examples are *Plasmodiophora brassicae* Woron., causing clubroot of crucifers, and *Synchytrium endobioticum* (Schilb.) Perc., causing potato wart disease—fungi that, although they cannot live as saprophytes in the soil, can exist as resting spores for many years in the absence of host plants. *Verticillium albo-atrum* Reinke and Berth, causing wilt of hops and many other plants, persists for only a short time as a saprophyte in soils and is spread mainly by diseased plant residues carried alone or in soil. Wilt often follows the lines of cultivation down the rows of hop gardens, and is also spread around by the hop pickers (Keyworth, 1942).

III. Dispersal by Other Mammals and Birds

Very little is known about the dispersal of pathogens by wild animals. Dispersal by draught animals attached to cultivation machinery can reasonably be attributed to man. Pathogens that can persist on clothing or machinery might easily be carried on an animal's hair or a bird's feathers, and rabbits and dogs spread potato X virus in potato crops when they brush past infected plants and break the leaf hairs (Todd, 1958). Birds have not been described as vectors of plant viruses, but there seems no reason why they should not carry some on their feathers or beaks. Game birds, such as partridge, often run within crops before flying and might well be responsible for some of the unaccountable introduction of virus X into healthy potato crops.

Dogs, mice, birds, and indeed, frogs, and anything else that moves in flax crops when the plants are wet spread *Sphaerella linarum* Woll., spores of which ooze from infected flax plants in a gelatinous matrix (Christensen *et al.*, 1953). Some of these animals may also spread the fungus to healthy crops over a distance, and small mammals and birds may also disseminate other similar fungi in this fashion. Birds carry the chestnut blight fungus, *Endothia parasitica* (Murr.) Anderson and Anderson; this spreads locally by air-borne ascospores discharged from perithecia in wet weather, but outbreaks in new areas and the consequent rapid spread through North America were probably caused by insectivorous birds (Heald and Studhalter, 1914). Old cankers of chestnut blight are often infested with boring insects, for which birds, especially woodpeckers, search and then become contaminated with pycnospores. Several birds, shot while in the branches of infected trees, were carrying *Endothia* spores; two woodpeckers each had more than half a million spores on its plumage. Leach (1940) pointed out that woodpeckers feed on tree cambium as well as on insects, and so could easily infect healthy trees during feeding.

Little work has been done on the passage of pathogens through the intestines of animals other than insects. Many nonpathogenic fungi are coprophilous, and some are adapted to passage through animals. The resting spores of two plant pathogenic fungi are spread in dung to clean fields, after potatoes infected with *S. endobioticum* (wart disease) or brassica plants infected with *P. brassicae* (clubroot) have been fed to stock (Gibbs, 1931).

IV. DISPERSAL BY SMALL ANIMALS, OTHER THAN INSECTS

The eriophyid mite *Phytoptus ribis* Nal. has long been known to transmit black currant reversion virus, but recently eriophyids were also found to be vectors of several other viruses. Wheat streak mosaic and wheat spot mosaic viruses are transmitted by all active stages of *Aceria tulipae* Keifer that are reared on infected plants. The mites remain infective for several days and through molts; adults are unable to acquire virus, but nymphs become infective after 30 minutes on infected plants. Wheat streak mosaic virus is carried by wind-borne mites, which breed mainly on wheat, and do not survive long off living plants. Several species of grass are susceptible to the virus, but the disease is found on wheat only when sown near other wheat crops or volunteer wheat; plants that emerge after adjacent crops have matured are not infected (Slykhuis, 1955; Staples and Allington, 1956). Mites also transmit fig mosaic and peach mosaic viruses; they inhabit closely adhering peach leaf-bud scales, which are characteristic of the retarded buds of infected trees in summer, so the virus apparently modifies the tree in favor of the vector (Wilson *et al.*, 1955).

Mites have seldom been shown to transmit bacteria or fungi; since they usually occur in rotting tissues of various bulbs and of carnation buds, it is assumed that they transmit the pathogens responsible, but this needs confirming. They also often occur in the tunnels formed by bark beetles, and may possibly play a secondary role in spreading Dutch elm disease and blue-stain fungi. As Leach (1940) points out, many of the mites are carried by flies and other winged insects that feed on decaying tissues. These insects themselves might carry pathogens, but the fact that mites are wingless does not preclude them from being vectors. Nevertheless, more critical experiments are needed before their significance as vectors can be assessed.

Leach also quoted a few papers which show that slugs occasionally transmit fungus spores from diseased to healthy plants, but they are probably of little importance as vectors.

Like some insects several nematode species eject the contents of the esophageal gland when feeding and in doing so might transmit pathogens. Indeed, Steiner (1942) concluded that soil nematodes are important as vectors of bacteria and viruses, but no virus, soil-borne or other, has yet been shown to be carried by nematodes.[*] No doubt pathogens can enter through nematode feeding punctures, but although various associations between nematodes and pathogens have been described, little critical work has been done on them.

A few bacterial and fungal diseases seem to be more prevalent when nematodes are common than when they are not, and some depend on nematodes for their spread. One bacterium that apparently infects only when carried by nematodes is *Corynebacterium fascians* (Tilf.) Dowson, which, with the eelworms *Aphelenchoides ritzema-bosi* (Schwartz) Steiner and *A. fragariae* (Ritzema Bos) Christie, causes the hyperplastic "cauliflower" disease and enations of strawberry (Crosse and Pitcher, 1952). The nematodes are ectoparasitic and carry the bacteria to the meristematic tissues, through which the plant is infected, but which are normally inaccessible to bacteria because they are tightly enclosed within stipules. Similarly, *C. tritici* (Hutchinson) Burkh. does not infect wheat in the absence of *Anguina tritici* (Steinbuch) Filipjev (Cheo, 1946). Galls containing nematodes (cockles) are formed in place of seeds, and are then dispersed by man; bacteria carried within them can remain viable for months. The same eelworms are almost always associated with the fungus *Dilophospora alopecuri* Fr., which causes leaf spotting and deformed heads of wheat and other cereals (Atanasoff, 1925). The nematodes emerge from the cockles in moist soil and live as ectoparasites on cereal plants until they invade the ovaries. The fungus infects the nematode galls and its spores become attached by bristle-like appendages on the mucous covering of the eelworms, which can also acquire spores from germinating pycnidia in the soil. The spores appear to infect only when placed in wounds near the growing point.

Nematodes even though not spreading pathogens may nevertheless

[*] The following paper was published after this chapter was written: Hewitt, W. B., D. J. Raski, and A. C. Goheen. 1958. Nematode vector of soil-borne fanleaf virus of grapevines. *Phytopathology* **48**: 586–595.

help them to infect plants. For instance, several root knot nematodes increase the incidence of carnation wilt by providing wounds for the entry of *Pseudomonas caryophylli* Starr and Burkh. into roots (Stewart and Schindler, 1956).

V. DISPERSAL BY INSECTS

After the discovery in the mid-19th century that fungi and bacteria cause many diseases, it was sometimes postulated that insects might disperse them, but the first experimental evidence was not obtained until 1891, when Waite showed that bees and wasps carry *Erwinia amylovora* (Burrill) Winslow *et al.*, the fire blight bacterium of pears, from diseased to healthy blossoms while searching for nectar. By 1920 several virus, bacterial, and fungal diseases were known to be caused by pathogens transmitted by insects, but relatively little work was done on the subject because plant pathologists and entomologists rarely worked together and seldom trespassed into one another's subjects. Later, viruses attracted workers from both disciplines, and consequently more is now known about their transmission by insects than that of other pathogens. Leach and his co-workers in the United States have pioneered work on the spread of fungi and bacteria by insects, and Leach's book (1940) has stimulated interest in this, partly because some of the diseases, such as Dutch elm disease and chestnut blight, are of considerable economic importance.

Insects are often associated with fungal and bacterial diseases, but it is sometimes difficult to prove that they are vectors. They are, however, well equipped to act as such, because most of them depend on plants for food, they are generally active, and their body bristles enable them to carry many spores or bacteria externally. In addition, many plant pathogens can survive, and some even multiply, inside insects, and insects that regurgitate during feeding seem particularly well adapted to act as vectors.

A. *Method of Transmission*

1. *Viruses*

Not all insects that feed first on a diseased plant and then on a healthy one transmit viruses. Virus must be introduced into a living cell before infection occurs, and so the Homoptera, with piercing and sucking mouth parts, are particularly effective vectors. Most of them feed without causing major damage to plant cells, unlike the Heteroptera, which often have toxic saliva. Damage around the feeding puncture may be one reason why so few Heteroptera transmit viruses.

Some viruses are rarely or never insect-transmitted; some are transmitted by one or a few species of insect; and others by many, but no claim that a virus is transmitted by more than one major group of insects has yet been confirmed, except where the virus is carried as a contaminant on the body, as is tobacco mosaic virus by leaf-miner flies (Costa et al., 1958). This virus can also be transmitted occasionally by grasshoppers (Walters, 1952). Some of the differences in behavior depend on the virus, for the same insect species may show very different efficiency in transmitting different viruses.

There is at present no satisfactory system of virus classification, but insect-transmitted viruses can be divided into three imprecise groups according to their behavior in the vector: (1) viruses that are acquired in brief feeding periods (often less than a minute) on infected plants; the vectors usually cease to be infective within an hour, and the efficiency of transmission is increased if they are prevented from feeding for a few hours before feeding on the infected plant (Watson, 1938). This group comprises the "nonpersistent" viruses of Watson and Roberts (1939). (2) "Persistent" viruses are acquired only after longer feeding periods on infected plants, and once infective, the insect vector often remains so for many days or weeks. (3) some viruses, such as beet yellows, have vectors that remain infective for several hours, and have been called "semipersistent" (Sylvester, 1956).

Nonpersistent viruses are transmitted by aphids, which also transmit some persistent ones. All those known to be transmitted by leaf hoppers, white flies, bugs, thrips, and most biting insects are persistent. They usually have a noninfective or "latent" period, that is, the insect is unable to transmit virus for some hours or days after feeding on an infected plant, whereas nonpersistent viruses are transmitted immediately after the acquisition feed. Some viruses that are transmitted only after a noninfective period in the vector may need to multiply within the insect to reach a transmissible amount, but with others the period may simply be the time needed for virus to pass through the gut wall into the blood and thence to the salivary glands. These noninfective periods differ greatly in length with different viruses and insects.

Several leaf-hopper-transmitted viruses multiply within their vectors and some are transmitted through the eggs, which provide the viruses with an alternative means of survival than in infected plants (Fukushi, 1934; Black, 1950). But not all persistent viruses multiply and remain infective within the insect, and beet leaf hoppers, *Circulifer tenellus* (Baker), lose the capacity to transmit beet curly top virus as they age (Freitag, 1936).

Many viruses are transmitted by one or very few leaf hopper species, but the causes of such specificity are largely unknown. In some it may be connected with the insect's feeding habit and the distribution of the virus within the plant; for instance, beet curly top virus seems to be restricted to the phloem, and lucerne dwarf virus to the xylem (Bennett, 1934; Houston *et al.*, 1947). Vectors are then restricted to phloem or xylem feeders, and a reason why insects often transmit virus only to some plants in a series may be that the hopper does not always reach the tissues in which the virus can develop. Some jassids are known to find the phloem more readily than others, possibly because they follow a pH gradient from the epidermis to the phloem (Fife and Frampton, 1936; Day *et al.*, 1952).

All instars of most insect vectors are able to acquire and transmit virus, but sometimes the noninfective period of persistent viruses is longer than the development period of larvae or nymphs, and then only adults can be vectors. Tomato spotted wilt virus, however, cannot be acquired by adult thrips, but these can transmit virus when they acquire it as larvae (Bald and Samuel, 1931). Some instars may be more efficient vectors than others; for instance, adults of the mealy bug *Pseudococcus citri* (Risso) transmit cacao swollen shoot virus more readily than young nymphs (Posnette and Robertson, 1950).

Most persistent viruses are not readily sap-transmitted, possibly because they are in too low concentration in plant extracts or because they need to be put into specific tissues, but those transmitted by biting insects are unusual in persisting in their insect vectors for considerable periods and also being easily sap-transmissible. Flea-beetle vectors of turnip yellow mosaic virus and the cucumber beetle vectors of squash mosaic virus regurgitate infective juice from the foregut during feeding; they not only infect plants fed on immediately after an acquisition feed, but continue to be infective for several days (Markham and Smith, 1949; Freitag, 1956; Martini, 1958).

The noninfective period in aphid vectors of persistent viruses differs with different test plants and environments. When potato leaf roll virus is acquired from potato by *Myzus persicae*, the aphid is not infective for about 2 days, but this period is decreased to several hours when the source is *Datura stramonium* L. and sometimes to less than an hour with *Physalis floridana* Rybd. (Smith, 1931; Kassanis, 1952; Kirkpatrick and Ross, 1952). Although it might be expected that some persistent viruses multiply in aphids, as in leaf hoppers, the evidence for potato leaf roll and other viruses is inconclusive (Day, 1955; Harrison, 1957).

Because aphids transmit nonpersistent viruses much more readily when starved before the acquisition feed, those that have flown a long way are in a favorable state to transmit if they feed on an infected plant when they land in a crop. Some of these viruses can be acquired or transmitted extremely quickly, often by aphids that probe the epidermis to test the suitability of a plant as a source of food; thus potato Y virus can be acquired in 5 seconds, but probes lasting up to 1 minute are more likely to make an aphid infective (Bradley, 1954). When the aphids' stylets remain inserted for 20 minutes or longer, most aphids are not infective, and many cease to be infective within 15 minutes of leaving the infected plant, even when fasting. Virus is carried near the tips of the stylets and aphids rarely become infective after the stylets penetrate beyond the first layer of cells (Bradley and Ganong, 1955). The stylet tips are well-adapted for carrying virus-containing sap, and van Hoof (1958) suggested that virus might be acquired more readily from epidermis than from parenchyma because aphids pierce the epidermis through the cell wall, but the parenchyma through the intercellular spaces. Both he and Bradley found that aphids could acquire virus from the parenchyma, so the suggestion of Bawden *et al.* (1954) that nonpersistent virus occurs predominantly in epidermal cells may not be the only reason for the effectiveness of short acquisition feeds.

Although many nonpersistent viruses are transmitted by several species of aphid, there is still considerable vector specificity. Thus *Myzus ornatus* Laing, *Myzus ascalonicus* Donc., and *Aulacorthum solani* (Kltb.) transmit dandelion yellow mosaic virus and not lettuce mosaic, whereas *M. persicae* transmits lettuce mosaic virus but not dandelion mosaic (Kassanis, 1947). Even when several species can transmit, some do so more readily than others. The cause of such differences has not been determined although the presence of different virus inhibitors in the aphid's saliva or different abilities to adsorb viruses onto the stylets have been postulated (Watson and Roberts, 1940).

Aphid populations are usually heterogeneous and individual vectors often differ in their efficiency; some strains of *M. persicae* are very poor, some very good vectors of a particular virus, but it is not known whether an efficient strain for one virus would also be efficient for others (Stubbs, 1955; Björling and Ossiannilsson, 1958). Not all individuals of the leaf hopper *Cicadulina mbila* Naude transmit maize streak virus. Those that cannot (the inactive) pick up the virus while feeding on an infected plant, but virus does not get into their blood. Inactive insects become able to transmit virus after their intestine is pierced by a needle to allow virus to enter the blood (Storey, 1933). Attributes of the virus particles that are changeable seem to determine transmissibility by a given species of aphid. The spinach strain of cucumber mosaic virus was transmitted readily by *M. persicae* during 1945–1954, but not at all in 1957, although it was still transmitted as regularly by 2 other species of aphids as in

earlier years. Other strains of this virus were as readily transmitted by
M. persicae in 1955 (Badami, 1957). Other viruses have ceased to be
insect-transmitted after being propagated by mechanical transmission
for several years (Black, 1953), and an instance of gaining transmissibility is provided by potato C virus, which was not aphid-transmitted
when derived from potatoes in 1945 and 1955, although apparently
closely related to the aphid-transmitted Y virus. After propagation by
mechanical inoculation in *Nicotiana glutinosa* L. and *N. tabacum* L.
for 10 years it could be transmitted by *M. persicae*. However, when
passed through potato and back to tobacco, it ceased to be aphid-
transmitted. This suggests that the attributes of a virus that allow it to
be insect-transmitted can be affected by the host plant in which it is
multiplying (Watson, 1956).

2. *Bacteria*

Unlike viruses, very few of which are carried externally as contaminants by insects, most insect-transmitted bacteria are carried incidentally. A few insects, which probably have been long associated with
the bacteria concerned, appear to have a symbiotic relationship with
them, and still fewer seem specially modified morphologically to carry
bacteria and ensure their survival.

Like all bacteria carried incidentally *Erwinia amylovora*, which
causes fireblight of apples and pears, is not dependent on insects, as
both primary and secondary infections occur by rain splash. Nevertheless, insects play a prominent part in dissemination, and primary infection occurs when flies, ants, and others carry bacteria from bark canker
exudate to the blossoms (Thomas and Ark, 1934). Bees and wasps carry
bacteria from flower to flower on their mouth parts, but infection occurs
only when the sugar concentration of the nectar is low (Keitt and
Ivanoff, 1941). Aphids, bugs, and bark beetles carry the bacteria externally and infect shoots when feeding, but bacteria may live for several
days in the intestines of flies, and eggs may be contaminated as they are
laid; bacteria can persist also in puparia and contaminate emerging
adults.

Larvae of cabbage root fly (*Erioischia brassica* Bouché) carry
Erwinia carotovora (L. R. Jones) Holland, both externally and internally;
bacteria are acquired from fly eggs which are contaminated as they are
laid or from decaying plant material or the soil, and they can overwinter in the pupae. They cause stump and heart rot of cabbages and
other brassicas (Johnson, 1930). Similar pathogens cause soft rot of
onions, carried by the onion fly (*Delia antiqua* Meig.) and celery rot,
transmitted by two leaf miners (Leach, 1927).

Erwinia tracheiphila (E. F. Smith) Holland, which causes bacterial wilt of cucurbits, is apparently entirely dependent on the beetles *Diobrotica vittata* Fabr. and *D. duodecimpunctata* Oliv. for overwintering and transmission (Rand and Enlows, 1920). The beetles are particularly effective vectors because during feeding they wound the vascular bundles to which the bacteria are largely confined.

Lepidoptera have seldom been described as vectors of plant pathogens, but the moth *Cactobrosis fernaldialis* (Hulst) is the main vector of the bacterium *Erwinia carnegieana* Lightle *et al.*, which destroys giant cacti in Arizona. Bacteria can be isolated from adult moths, and egg surfaces and larvae carry them externally and internally. Larvae move away from severely diseased tissues and carry the pathogen through the cork, which would otherwise seal off the necrotic area (Boyle, 1949). When potato tubers are cut into "seed pieces," the formation of cork prevents entry of *Erwinia atroseptica* (van Hall) Jennison, causing "blackleg," or seals off necrotic lesions, but insects that feed on the potato below ground aid its entry, and by burrowing in the tubers, prevent the formation of wound cork (Bonde, 1939a). Some of these insects have a symbiotic relationship with the bacteria: species of *Delia* develop normally on infected tubers, but not on sterile ones (Leach, 1931). The bacteria occur in many cultivated soils, but are unable to penetrate undamaged roots or tubers. Bacterial rot of apples, caused by *Pseudomonas melophthora* Allen and Riker, follows feeding by the apple maggot (*Rhagoletis pomonella* Walsh). Bacteria are carried externally and internally by the adults; apples are inoculated when the eggs are laid, and the bacteria are carried in by the burrowing larvae, which prefer rotting tissues (Allen *et al.*, 1934).

A close symbiotic relationship has been reported between the olive fly (*Dacus oleae* Rossi) and several bacteria, including *Pseudomonas savastonoi* (E. F. Smith) Stevens, which causes the olive knot disease (Petri, 1910; Stammer, 1929). Anatomical modification of the adult insects ensures the perpetuation of bacteria through successive generations: the anal tract of the female contains bacteria in several sacs, opposite which is a slit in the membrane separating the tract from the vagina. When an egg passes along the vagina, the slit opens and the egg presses against the openings of the sacs; some bacteria enter the micropyle and later the developing embryo. They are inserted into oviposition wounds, which, according to Petri, are the source of most olive knot in Italy. The insect is not present in California, and there the bacteria spread more slowly.

These examples illustrate two important facts. First, few bacteria cause systemic infection. Insect vectors often not only make the initial infection, as with viruses, but also often spread the bacteria from place to place over plants. Second, many bacteria are carried internally by insects, a fact which may be of evolutionary significance in helping to tide them over unfavorable periods.

3. Fungi

Some fungi differ from viruses and bacteria because they can actively penetrate plant epidermis. Others depend on natural openings such as stomata, while still others, such as bacteria, enter through wounds. Relatively few fungi are spread by insects, but some are so well-adapted to insect transmission that they may have been associated for a long time.

Some insects, especially pollinators which feed without wounding the plant, act merely as vectors of fungi, but the pathogen is often well-adapted for this form of spread. For instance, *Botrytis anthophila* Bond., spread by bees, sporulates only on the anthers of red clover, and *Ustilago violacea* (Pers.) Roussel, spread by nocturnal moths, replaces the pollen of campions, pinks, and other Caryophyllaceae with sticky smut spores; the petals are unaffected and the flowers remain attractive to insects. Mycelium penetrates the ovary but does not destroy the developing seed, which later produces a systemically infected plant whose flowers all produce spores. A small hymenopteran, *Blastophaga psenes* (L.), ensures an unusual method of pollination called caprification and causes an internal rot of figs by carrying spores of *Fusarium moniliforme* var. *fici* Caldis from infected to healthy fruits (Caldis, 1927). The adult male insects emerge from their galls and penetrate to the female insects in their galls in the male inedible figs. The fertile females emerge through the eye of the fig and so collect pollen from the staminate flowers. Male figs, some of which may be infected with the fungus, are hung on female trees when the insects are due to emerge; these enter the receptacles of the female edible figs to oviposit, pollinating and inoculating the fruit with fungus while doing so. They cannot oviposit in the female fig, however, because the styles are much longer than those of the male flowers. Without pollination the fruit of some varieties drops before it is mature.

Some insects carry fungi on their mouth parts and introduce them into plants when feeding. *Nematospora gossypii* (Ashby and Now.), causing stigmatomycosis of cotton, probably depends entirely on cotton stainers and related bugs (*Dysdercus* spp.) which introduce into the bolls needle-like ascospores that are thin enough to allow passage through the stylet canals to and from the stylet pouches of the insect

(Frazer, 1944). Plant bugs are noted for the injury they cause when feeding, and Leach (1940) suggests that the necroses may not all be caused by toxic saliva, but may often be caused by associated fungi of the *Nematospora* type.

Other fungi are carried into the plant by boring insects; the bark beetles that carry *Ceratostomella ulmi* Buism., causing Dutch elm disease, are mainly in the genus *Scolytus*, and the fungus sporulates freely in their egg galleries. Adults are covered by, and ingest, spore-containing slime with which they inoculate the twigs of healthy trees, upon which they prefer to feed before breeding beneath the bark of trees that have been weakened by the fungus during previous years (Clinton and McCormick, 1936). Several brown- and blue-stain diseases of conifers are caused by species of *Ceratostomella* and related fungi, which stain but do not rot the wood and are similarly transmitted by bark beetles (Craighead, 1928). These beetles (*Ips* and *Dendroctonus* spp.) breed only in trees that are dead or weakened by other agents; they do not weaken trees by inoculating them with fungus, as do *Scolytus*. When they attack living trees, however, the fungus blocks the transpiration stream and the trees soon die. Although fungi are ingested by the larvae, Leach (1940) considers them unimportant as food, but important because they weaken the tree, decrease its water content, and make it more suitable for beetles. Three species of scolytids infest different parts of white fir (*Abies concolor* Lindl. and Gord.) in California; the fungus *Spicaria anomola* (Corda) Harz. is associated with those at the top of the tree and in the branches, and causes a light brown stain. *Trichosporicum symbioticum* Wright causes a darker stain and is associated with a third species at the bottom of the tree, although both fungi will grow anywhere on the tree when inoculated. Both kill the cambium as they advance, as do many scolytid-carried fungi, preventing an inflow of resin into the brood galleries of the beetles (Wright, 1938).

The importance of these beetle vectors to the lumber industry was demonstrated by Verrall (1941). Since chemical fungicide treatment of lumber became common, dispersal of air-borne spores has become unimportant, but the ambrosia beetles that attack hardwoods and the bark beetles that attack softwoods are undeterred by the protective surface of chemicals and inoculate the timber below it. Boring insects are not confined to wood. Larvae of the corn borer, *Pyrausta nubilalis* Hübn., distribute several pathogenic fungi and bacteria within maize plants. They weaken adjoining tissues and make them more susceptible to fungal attack, and their frass provides medium for fungal development (Christensen and Schneider, 1950).

A fungus that enters through feeding wounds is *Chilonectria cucurbi-*

tula (Curr.) Sacc., which causes burn blight of pines. Numerous spores exude whenever mature perithecia are moistened, and they are common on the foliage of attacked trees. Adult spittle insects (*Aphrophora saratogensis* Fitch) are contaminated as they crawl about on small twigs near the tops of trees during the autumn, and the fungus enters through their feeding punctures. The next year the fungus girdles the twigs, then moves down the cortex, killing the tree during the next 3 years (Gruenhagen *et al.*, 1947). Wasps and other insects spread *Sclerotinia fructigena* Aderh. and Ruhl. when they feed, for spores usually enter only through wounds. The fungus spreads rapidly through fruit, causing brown rots of apples, pears, plums, and peaches, and sporulates on the surface, so the insects readily become contaminated.

Feeding is not the only way in which insects wound plants, and some fungi are introduced when eggs are deposited in plant tissues. *Urocerus gigas* (L.) and *Sirex cyaneus* F., the wood wasps, inoculate *Stereum sanguinolentum* (Fr.) Fr. in conifers and cause heart rot (Cartwright, 1938). The insects are well adapted for this, and carry the fungus in sacs at the anterior end of the ovipositor, so the egg is contaminated as it is laid. Larvae eat hyphae and carry the fungus in their hypopleural organs (Parkin, 1942). A less intimate relationship exists between crickets of the genus *Oecanthus* and *Leptosphaeria coniothyrium* (Fuckel.) Sacc., causing tree-cricket canker of apple and cane blight of raspberry (Gloyer and Fulton, 1916). The female eats a small hole in the bark, deposits her egg, and then closes the hole, either with a fecal pellet or a chewed piece of bark, usually diseased. Spores and hyphae of this and many other fungi are carried internally and externally by the insects and contaminate the wound.

In an entirely different category of vectors are the fungus feeders, mainly Diptera and Coleoptera, which feed on the sweet sticky secretions that contain the spores; they are contaminated by these, and later leave them on healthy flowers or plants. Examples are the *Sphacelia* stage of the ergot fungus, *Claviceps purpurea* (Fr.) Tul., and the pycniospores of thistle rust. Wind-borne ascospores of *C. purpurea* infect rye and other Gramineae in spring; the fungus invades the ovary and develops conidia (*Sphacelia*) in a secretion which is seemingly attractive to insects. Several insects visit rye to feed on the pollen and secretion, and are contaminated externally, or they ingest the spores, which may be excreted or regurgitated later on a healthy spikelet. Craigie (1927) showed the importance of flies in producing "hybrids" of rust fungi by carrying pycniospores from one pycnidium to another.

Fungus feeders that have caused considerable economic loss during recent years are the nitidulid and scolytid beetles that spread the oak wilt fungus, *Endoconidiophora fagacearum* Bretz. This fungus forms mycelial mats under the bark, which splits above them; beetles are attracted, presumably by the odor, and both they and their larvae feed on the fungus. The fungus is heterothallic, and the beetles serve as spermatization agents by transmitting endoconidia from mats of one type to those of the other, thus stimulating the production of perithecia and ascospores. The two thallus types are rarely intermingled and depend on insects for cross fertilization. The insects also inoculate fresh wounds with spores as they walk over them (Jewell, 1956; Dorsey and Leach, 1956).

B. *Geographical Distribution*

The spread of plants around the world has widely distributed many pathogens and vectors; these are not always carried simultaneously to a new area, and a pathogen introduced alone will not spread unless a "local" insect can act as a vector. Thus tristeza disease of citrus trees became prevalent in South America soon after infected trees were imported from South Africa because *Aphis citricidus* Kirk, an efficient vector, was already prevalent. As this aphid does not occur in California, tristeza spreads less rapidly there than in South America (Wallace *et al.*, 1956).

Viruses may be introduced into a new area unwittingly in insect-free and apparently healthy plants, and may then be transmitted by new vectors to plants which react with a severe disease. A newly introduced insect may also cause trouble by transmitting an indigenous virus from plants which are little affected to others which react severely.

The discovery of Dutch elm disease in the Netherlands in 1919 and the rapidity with which it assumed the status of a major disease suggests that the fungus had not long been associated with bark beetles, which had been known for centuries to infest weakened trees. It was probably not widespread in Europe earlier because the disease is obvious and also, when *Scolytus multistriatus* Marsh. was taken to the United States before 1909, the fungus was not introduced. A later introduction in the 1920's included the pathogen, and this beetle is now the most important vector in the United States (Leach, 1940). *Ceratostomella ulmi* might have replaced less efficient fungi with which the beetles were originally associated although, as there are nonpathogenic strains, a pathogenic one may have arisen by mutation. Similarly, saprophytic fungi are always associated with nitidulid beetles in wounds on healthy oak trees where they serve as food for both adults and larvae. They have not been found without the beetles, with which they are apparently symbiotic. Jewell (1956) suggested that *Endocondiophora fagacearum* had recently become a symbiont, for oak wilt does not occur in many areas where both oaks and beetles abound.

As in organisms, mutation in viruses, coupled with geographical isolation, appears to lead to the development of distinct strains. Thus Brazil, Argentina, and North America have their characteristic strains of beet curly top virus, each with a different species of leaf hopper as vector (Smith, 1957). A strain of curly top similar to the North American strain occurs in Turkey, and Bennett and Tanrisever (1957) postulated that the virus originated in Europe and was carried with beet to several parts of the New World, where it acquired different vectors.

Some polyphagous insects are restricted to a few plants during part of the year; thus *Myzus persicae* overwinters only on *Prunus* spp. in many areas and on horticultural crops in others. Although the aphids cannot acquire potato viruses from such plants and some fly long distances, the potato virus diseases are often most prevalent in crops near peach orchards or gardens because aphid vectors are most numerous there (Davies, 1939; Davis and Landis, 1951).

Changes in cropping can affect the number of vectors in a specific area: millions of *Prunus serotina* Ehrh. were planted in the north Netherlands as forest shade trees during the 1940's and proved to be excellent winter hosts for *M. persicae* in an area where peach is scarce (Hille Ris Lambers, 1955). This species also increased greatly in the Imperial Valley of California when the amount of sugar beet was increased. This in turn increased the incidence of cantaloupe mosaic in melons even though the aphids do not colonize the melons (Dickson *et al.*, 1949). Leaf hopper vectors of beet curly top virus multiplied greatly during the depression of the 1920's on the weeds of abandoned farms in the western United States. The natural sagebrush, and well-cultivated grass, are not favorable covers for hoppers, but overgrazing during this period turned many ranges into semidesert in which the hoppers flourished (Piemeisel, 1932).

Predators and parasites play a major part in altering an insect population from one year to another and also from one area to another. It is often difficult to assess their influence because so many insects are involved. Few studies have been made in the detail attempted by Hille Ris Lambers (1955), who found that the aphid-predator-parasite-hyperparasite population in a potato crop included over 50 species. After aphids have become numerous on crops such as potato, they often suddenly disappear. Hansen (1950) and Hille Ris Lambers noted that this decrease occurs earlier when aphids are more numerous than usual, and they attributed this to insect enemies. While agreeing that parasites and predators always help to determine the ultimate size of the population, other workers consider the major cause of the decline to be the departure of winged aphids (Moericke, 1941; Doncaster and Gregory, 1948). As potato plants mature they become less suitable sources of food for aphids, most of which become winged and fly away. This often occurs when parasites and predators are most numerous, so remaining aphids are quickly eliminated. Occasionally, however, the enemies are very numerous early, when aphids are colonizing the potatoes, and then a large summer aphid population may fail to develop (Broadbent and Tinsley, 1951). In many parts of Europe there is a tendency toward a biennial rhythm, a year with many aphids being followed by one with few, because predators and parasites multiply greatly in seasons when aphids are numerous during the summer, and may then overwinter and help prevent the aphid infestation from developing the following spring. Only when their enemies have decreased in number from lack of food can the aphids again multiply unchecked (Hille Ris Lambers, 1955).

The influence of parasite distribution over a wider area was noted by Stubbs (1956), who contrasted the rapid spread of carrot motley dwarf virus in Australia, where the vector, *Cavariella aegopodii* (Scop.) is very numerous, with the slow spread in California, where the aphids are few because they are severely parasitized. He suggested that the vector is more in equilibrium with its environment in California than in Australia, where it may have been introduced rather recently.

C. Seasons, Climate and Weather

Geographical differences in vector populations are usually determined by the differences in climate if the requisite plant hosts and the vector have been widely distributed. Climate affects the seasonal cycles of insects, but their numbers and activity also differ from one year to another because of differences in weather. The optimum temperature for aphid reproduction is about 26° C. Consequently they are more numerous in continental than in maritime climates, and in warm, dry summers than in cool, wet ones (Jamalainen, 1948). Cultural practices vary from one country to another, so it is difficult to relate the incidences of virus diseases in different parts of Europe, for example, to differences in aphid numbers, although differences in the same area can be related to the vectors (Steudel, 1950). Weather plays a large part in regulating outbreaks of aphids; rain and cold restrict larval development and, consequently, the number of adults. Fewer winged aphids develop in wet weather, and because these seldom fly when it is cool, fewer new colonies are founded than when the weather is warm and dry (Broadbent, 1949; Markkula, 1953).

In temperate climates emphasis tends to be placed on the regulating effect of cold weather, but aphids are soon killed when temperatures rise a few degrees above the optimum (Broadbent and Hollings, 1951). Van der Plank (1944) found that *M. persicae* forsakes potatoes in Africa, and viruses cease to spread when the mean daily maximum temperature reaches 32° C. The adverse effect of a hot climate on aphids is also used to produce virus-free lettuce seed (Grogan *et al.*, 1952).

In an arid climate rain may have an effect opposite to that in a cool one: outbreaks of Pierce's disease of grapevines in California are most severe during wet periods because host plants of the leaf hopper vectors grow best then (Winkler, 1949).

Humidity also determines the loss in celery from the bacterium *Erwinia carotovora:* the larval leaf miners that inoculate plants remain in the outer leaves during wet weather, and soft rot causes relatively little loss, but when it is hot and dry, the flies deposit eggs near the heart of the plant. Larvae search for a moist place when they hatch, and enter the young leaves, causing heart rot (Leach, 1927).

Some fungi produce spores in a gelatinous matrix only during very humid or wet weather; spores of *Sphaerella linarum* and others that are carried as contaminants on animals' bodies can only be spread, therefore, when the foliage is wet, a condition when infection, too, is more likely to occur than when it is dry, for most spores need a high humidity to germinate and infect.

The seasonal cycle of insects depends on the climate, which often differs considerably in regions not widely separated; in Great Britain, for example, most aphids occur on potatoes during July in the southern half of the country, during August in northern England, and during September in parts of Scotland. The production of seed tubers free from leaf roll and Y viruses in Scotland was unwittingly based on this. The principal vector of these potato viruses, and of many others of economic importance in Europe and elsewhere, is *Myzus persicae;* most potential vectors are usually present in England during July and early August, but virus is not necessarily spread mostly at this time, except from one crop to another. A rapid increase in disease incidence often depends on the activity of vectors within crops when plants are very susceptible to infection, such as when relatively few aphids colonize potato crops in the spring.

The time of maximum population of some aphids depends on their plant hosts as well as on climate. Thus the strawberry aphid *Pentatrichopus fragaefolii* (Cock.) is most numerous in late summer on first-year plants, but in late May or June on older ones (Dicker, 1952). Winged forms are numerous only when the population is maximal, and most virus spread coincides with their activity. On the other hand the apterae (wingless forms) are also numerous at these times. On that account Posnette and Cropley (1954) could not determine which were principally responsible for the spread of virus to adjacent plants. The growth of plants in a crop may so modify the microclimate that the vectors can no longer breed on them. *Circulifer tenellus* infests beet and spreads curly top virus within the crop only when the plants are young because the environment is too humid for the leaf hoppers when the plants cover the soil (Romney, 1943).

Many insects are more active and may carry virus farther when it is warm than when it is cool. Bald (1937) recorded a close positive correlation between temperature, thrips activity, and the number of plants showing spotted wilt 12 days later. In Florida aphids carry pepper veinbanding mosaic virus to peppers only within 150 ft. of the source when the temperature averages 62° C., but much farther at higher temperatures (Simons, 1957). In addition to its effect on movement high temperature may affect the insect's infectivity and the plant's susceptibility: *M. persicae* is a more efficient vector of potato leaf roll virus when reared on infected plants at 27° C. than at 22° C., and the resistance of the potato is lower at 27° C. (Webb, 1956).

D. *Availability of the Pathogen and Susceptibility of the Host*

Virus in an infected plant may be more readily available to a vector at one time than at another. Young plants are usually the best sources of virus because the concentration of many viruses decreases as the plants cease to grow rapidly: thus *M. persicae* transmits potato leaf roll virus to few test plants when the source is old, glasshouse-grown infected plants, but readily from very young ones (Kassanis, 1952).

The distribution of virus within the plant can determine when insects acquire virus and on which parts of the plant they need to feed to do so. Many viruses can be acquired by insects some days before a newly infected plant shows symptoms, for example, cauliflower mosaic (Severin and Tompkins, 1948). Kato (1957) found, however, that Y virus can be recovered by aphids from potato only after symptoms show. Aphids can acquire potato leaf roll virus from the lower leaves of full-grown potato plants much more readily than from the rest of the plant (Kirkpatrick and Ross, 1952), suggesting that virus concentration is not always greatest in the youngest, fast-growing leaves. That unequal distribution is sometimes an attribute of the virus, not of the host, was shown when the spread of 2 viruses in cauliflower crops was studied. Both cauliflower mosaic virus and cabbage black ring spot virus are transmitted mainly by *M. persicae* and *B. brassicae*, and both viruses spread readily when the infected source plants are young; but when they are old, cabbage black ring spot virus spreads less readily than mosaic virus, which occurs in high concentration in all the new leaves produced by infected plants, whereas ring spot virus accumulates mainly in the older, lower leaves, and even there is localized in the parts that show symptoms. Only in recently infected plants does ring spot virus occur in young leaves in sufficient concentration to be acquired by aphids. As most aphids alight on the upper parts of plants, they are more likely to acquire cauliflower mosaic virus than ring spot virus (Broadbent, 1954). Different plant species also differ in their effectiveness as sources of the same virus. Thus, although pepper is a better host plant than chard for *M. persicae* and is more susceptible to southern cucumber mosaic virus, aphids acquire virus more readily from chard than from pepper (Simons, 1955). Not only does the host affect insect-transmissibility, but the virulence of a virus may be changed by passage through different hosts; Wallace and Murphy (1938) reported that beet curly top virus is less virulent in sugar beet after passage through its wild hosts.

A host plant need not be susceptible to infestation by the vector to be susceptible to infection by a virus; nevertheless, colonizing insects are usually more prevalent in crops than transient visitors, so it is not unreasonable to consider the colonizers first when seeking vectors. It is true that insects are often more active within a crop when they vainly seek a suitable host plant, but colonizers have to be active at some period if they are to find new hosts, and their potentiality as vectors often depends on the readiness with which they move again after landing on a host plant. *M. persicae* was identified early as the principal vector of potato leaf roll and Y viruses; experiments showed that *M. solanifolii* and *Aphis nasturtii* are also efficient vectors of Y virus, and *A. nasturtii* of leaf roll, but field studies show that almost all the spread of the persistent leaf roll virus can be attributed to *M. persicae*, perhaps because of the relative inactivity of *A. nasturtii* after settling on the plants (Bawden and Kassanis, 1947; Loughnane, 1943; Broadbent, 1950; Hollings, 1955).

These conclusions are confirmed by the distribution of the virus diseases in Scandinavia. *M. persicae* is confined to the southern coastal areas of Norway and Sweden and so is leaf roll. *A. nasturtii* and *M. solanifolii*, however, occur further north, where Y virus spreads (Lihnell, 1948). In brassica crops, also, in Britain, the colonizing *M. persicae* and *B. brassicae* seem to be the only important vectors of cauliflower mosaic virus although at least 20 other noncolonizing species can transmit the virus (Broadbent, 1957).

Many workers doubted if an insect species could be the important vector of a virus when it is rarely numerous on the crop because they failed to appreciate the importance of the winged forms. Some viruses, usually nonpersistent ones, are spread mainly by noncolonizing insects which bring virus with them from the plants they have just left, or acquire it from infected plants within the crop as they move from plant to plant seeking suitable hosts, as *M. persicae* spreads cantaloupe mosaic among melon crops in California (Dickson *et al.*, 1949). It is often difficult to find which of the insects that infest or transiently feed on plants spread a virus; or, if more than one species can transmit, it is difficult to assess their relative importance. The principal vector may be the least prevalent insect pest, as is the case in the citrus groves of California where the main vector of tristeza virus, *Aphis gossypii* (Glover), forms only about 3% of the aphids visiting trees (Dickson *et al.*, 1956).

Even among vector species it cannot be assumed that all the insects that feed or breed on a diseased plant will be infective. Obviously, the more plants that are infected in a crop, the greater will be the proportion of potential vectors that become infective although almost nothing is known about the proportions or numbers of infective aphids in crops. The proportion differs with different viruses and vectors, depending on the time insects take to become infective and the time they remain so. Between 10 and 24% of winged *M. persicae* and *B. brassicae* bred on cauliflowers infected with cauliflower mosaic virus are infective when they leave the plants; a similar proportion of *M. persicae*, but fewer than 5% of *B. brassicae*, are infective when bred on plants infected with cabbage black ring spot virus.

Several factors affect the susceptibility of host plants to both insects and pathogens; the most important are variety, age, growth conditions, and population density. Different varieties of crop plants differ not only in the ease with which they become infected, but also in the extent to which the virus multiples in them and so in the readiness with which insects become infective when feeding on them. Varieties may react differently to different viruses; for example, resistance of potatoes to virus Y is not correlated with resistance to leaf roll virus although transmitted by the same aphids (Bawden and Kassanis, 1946). Apparent varietal differences in susceptibility may sometimes be caused by differential feeding by the vectors; thus varieties of lettuce, which experimentally are equally susceptible to yellows virus, contract the disease to different extents in the field (Linn, 1940).

Susceptibility to infection often decreases with increasing age of plants, and so, other things being equal, incidence of a disease may depend on the age of the crop when infective vectors are active (Broadbent *et al.*, 1952). Beet is most susceptible and intolerant to the leafhopper-transmitted curly top virus when in the cotyledon stage (Wallace and Murphy, 1938); and Hansen (1950) and Steudel (1952) found that numbers of aphids per beet plant and the incidence of yellows increased with successively later sowings. Cereal yellow dwarf virus severely affects only plants infected young, so normally it is of economic importance in California in barley, but not in the earlier-sown oats and wheat (Oswald and Houston, 1953). Few plants show such extreme resistance as cassava, however, for although *Bemisia* spp. feed on mature leaves, they infect only the immature ones with mosaic virus (Storey and Nichols, 1938).

Some fungi infect only during limited periods, for example, the fungus causing Dutch elm disease spreads readily only during late spring and early summer (Parker *et al.*, 1941). Similarly, nitidulid beetles infect healthy trees with the oak wilt fungus only during May and early June, partly because the beetles are attracted to wounds at this time to lay eggs and partly because trees are susceptible only in the spring (Jewell, 1956).

Most workers, who have studied the influence of plant nutrition on the incidence of virus diseases, have found that the best fed plants are the most likely to become infected. Dung and several inorganic fertilizers increase the incidence of both leaf roll and rugose mosaic in potato crops, and aphids also multiply faster on plants treated with dung, sulfate of ammonia, and superphosphate, but less on those treated with muriate of potash (Broadbent *et al.*, 1952). Response to fertilizers varies with the species of aphid, *A. nasturtii* showing little response to the treatments.

Some plants may be more acceptable to the vectors and more susceptible to virus at one temperature than at another. Narcissi are rarely colonized by aphids, and their viruses usually spread slowly, but when retarded bulbs are grown to flower in late summer instead of in spring they are colonized by *Aphis fabae*, and viruses spread rapidly (van Slogteren and Ouboter, 1941).

Storey (1935) was one of the first plant pathologists to realize that density of the plant population can affect disease incidence: close planting of groundnuts and delayed weeding are practiced by the peasants in East Africa, and greatly decrease the incidence of rosette. Van der Plank and Anderssen (1944) obtained some control of spotted wilt virus, which is brought into tobacco fields soon after transplanting, by increasing the density of plants to 2 or 3 per "hill" and by removing the surplus plants after most of the virus had been brought in. Most insects that bring virus into a crop land at random, so a greater proportion of plants is visited when they are widely spaced than when they are crowded together; consequently, beet yellows, beet mosaic, and cauliflower mosaic incidences are lessened by decreasing the distance between rows or between plants in the row (Blencowe and Tinsley, 1951; Steudel and Heiling, 1954; Broadbent, 1957).

Plant size can also affect the spread of viruses because big plants are more likely to be visited by vectors than are small ones, and once infected, the larger plants form bigger reservoirs of virus. In cauliflower seedbeds 30% of the large seedlings were infected with cauliflower mosaic virus, in contrast to 15% of medium sized seedlings, and 5% of small ones (Broadbent, 1957).

Finally, some vectors multiply more rapidly on infected plants than on healthy ones (Carter, 1939; Hijner and Cordon, 1955). Several species of leaf hoppers that complete their nymphal stages on celery or aster infected with aster yellows virus die when transferred to healthy plants, but live on diseased ones (Severin, 1946); to this extent the insects "use" the virus to create a satisfactory source of food for themselves.

E. Introduction of Pathogens into Crops

Persistent viruses must sometimes be carried by insects over hundreds of miles, but it can rarely be proved that this happens and that no local virus sources exist. Occasionally, circumstantial evidence of spread over moderate distances is obtained; for instance, in 1951 *M. persicae* were numerous on leaf roll infected potatoes in the southwest Netherlands, and following southwest winds during the summer dispersal many aphids were trapped about 60 miles to the northeast, where both aphids and virus disease had been scarce; the subsequent outbreak of leaf roll suggested that the aphids had taken virus with them (Hille Ris Lambers, 1955). Because of the difficulty of obtaining evidence, most of the records refer to virus brought into crops from nearby sources. *Macrosteles fascifrons* (Stål) move into lettuce crops from the borders of fields, taking yellows virus acquired from weeds with them; few moved more than 200 ft. during 4 weeks. The rate of vector dispersion, as measured by the incidence of yellows at different distances from the source, differs from one plot to another, probably depending on plant susceptibility, disturbing cultivations, and the weather (Linn, 1940).

Nonpersistent viruses will rarely be carried far. Observations on the spread of pepper veinbanding mosaic virus from infected *Solanum gracile* showed a steep gradient in incidence of infective peppers, falling from 90% plants infected at 6 ft. to 10% at 50 ft. Nevertheless, a few plants become infected at distances up to 1000 ft. (Simons, 1957). In similar experiments with celery Wellman (1937) found that southern celery mosaic virus was carried by aphids from weeds to over 85% of plants up to 30 ft. away but to only 4% at 120 ft. Distances differed from year to year, but no plant was infected during 3 years in plots 240 ft. away from the source. Storey and Godwin (1953) found that most plants infected with cauliflower mosaic virus occur in the first 50 rows adjacent to dis· eased crops. Such gradients of disease, from a high incidence in outer rows to a low one within a crop, often serve to show that a pathogen is spreading into a crop from a nearby source.

Taylor and Johnson (1954) studied the deposition of winged *Aphis fabae* and their subsequent multiplication on bean crops: the sides facing the wind had more colonies than the center or other edges of the crop. Thus gradients of virus disease parallel the activity of the vectors. When such gradients occur with persistent viruses, the vectors must have stayed in the area where they first landed; with nonpersistent ones, however, such gradients are more to be expected because vectors would lose their infectivity while feeding on plants near the edges of fields and would not infect plants at the center even if they later moved there. Trees, tall hedges, and buildings to the windward side shelter crops from aphids, but on the leeward side cause aphids to land, and lettuce mosaic is often more prevalent in parts upwind to such obstructions (Broadbent *et al.*, 1951). Van der Plank (1948) pointed out the possible significance of crop perimeters in affecting the incidence of virus disease in crops covering different areas; the perimeter forms a greater proportion of a small than of a large field, and he reported that whereas maize streak virus often infects the whole crop in small fields, many plants in large fields escape infection.

The danger that a virus will be introduced into a crop is greater where insect host plants and virus sources are numerous than where they are few. Perennial plants are more dangerous than annuals, because once they are systemically infected, they usually remain potential sources of virus, but biennials can be almost as important as perennials in retaining virus from one year to another. Schlösser (1952) suggested that sugar beet viruses probably originated in the wild *Beta maritima* L., common on the coasts of Britain, and spread throughout Europe during the last 30 years. There can be little certainty about this kind of observation, however, because virus diseases are often overlooked until they are looked for critically.

Many annual weeds are potential sources of virus, but they are usually of little significance. Thus beet yellows virus infects *Chenopodium album* L. and *C. murale* L. in beet and spinach fields, but it rarely spreads from them to cultivated plants (Bennett and Costa, 1954). However, several economically important viruses in the United States are carried to cultivated crops by leaf hoppers from weeds, some of which are annuals. Lucerne dwarf virus, which also causes Pierce's disease of grapevines, can be transmitted from many species of naturally infected plants, and infective leaf hoppers are found in such different habitats as cultivated valleys, high mountains, deserts, and seashores (Freitag and Frazier, 1954).

One of the most studied diseases is curly top of beet, transmitted to several crop plants in western United States by the leaf hopper *Circulifer tenellus,* often during transient feeding when the insects move from overwintering hosts in the desert and foothills to cultivated valleys. Virus persists in some overwintering hoppers, and the insects breed on the virus-susceptible Russian thistle and wild mustard in the deserts during the summer and fall (Wallace and Murphy, 1938). Severin (1939) found 75 species of plants, several perennial that become naturally infected with curly top virus. Three perennials are food plants of the hoppers in uncultivated areas, and virus is carried from them to annuals which germinate after early rains. During 5 years with such rain up to 42% of the subsequent hoppers were infective, whereas during 2 years without early rain, the proportion was less than 6%.

A few aphid-transmitted viruses, too, seem to depend on weeds for their survival: celery yellow spot virus is not transmitted by mechanical inoculation or by several species of aphids from celery to celery, but *Rhopalosiphum conii* (Dvd.) (=*Hyadaphis xylostei* Schrank) from symptomless infected *Conium maculatum* L. transmit virus to celery and hemlock (Freitag and Severin, 1945). Cereal yellow dwarf virus is transmitted by the 5 species of aphid that infest cereals in California. Rain delays the sowing of the cereals, but encourages the growth and subsequent heavy aphid infestation of grasses, many of which are susceptible to the virus. When drought follows, infective aphids move from the drying grasses into young grain fields (Oswald and Houston, 1953). Simons *et al.* (1956) described an interesting relationship between tomato and pepper crops and weeds infected with potato virus Y in Florida. Different strains of the virus occur in three widely separated areas, but not in two others only 50 miles away where suitable weed hosts and vectors are present. Potatoes were, or still are, grown in the affected areas, but not in the free ones, and as the distribution of diseased tomato and pepper crops bears no obvious relationship to potato crops, the authors suggest that the virus was introduced with potatoes and persisted in weeds.

Although it is realized that wild plants are often sources of virus from which epidemics may begin, very little is known about the incidence of disease in them in most parts of the world. A few workers have started to survey the vegetation of prescribed area for virus diseases: Mac-

Clement and Richards (1956) in Canada, testing with mechanical inoculation only, found about one plant in ten infected, many with viruses common in cultivated crops. This suggests that a large proportion of wild plants may be infected with one virus or another. In many areas of Britain, however, there is no evidence that susceptible weeds play a significant part in the epidemiology of common virus diseases of such crops as potatoes, brassicas, and lettuce. Infected tubers or seedlings, or plants in older crops are the main sources, and virus is spread from one crop to another when vectors seek alternative hosts. As they fly or are blown over a distance they tend to be dispersed, and the greater the distance between crops, the greater is the dispersion; consequently, crops near a virus source usually become more heavily infected than those farther away. Virus spread is greatly retarded, also, when susceptible crops are separated from one another by immune plants, especially if the intervening plants are suitable hosts for the vectors.

The economic importance of spread of virus from one crop to another depends largely upon the age and purpose of the healthy crop. Insects usually fly away from maturing crops, and if other susceptible crops in the area are at a similar stage and are to be harvested soon, infection will probably cause little loss. However, if young susceptible crops, plants for vegetative propagation, or biennials for seed the next year are being grown, infection may have serious consequences. Spread of virus from one crop to another is particularly important in potatoes; in many parts of the world aphids disperse from them in midsummer, about 2 months before the crop is harvested. Other crops of the same age are visited and infected with virus even if not colonized by the aphids. The plants are usually too old to show symptoms, but seed tubers are infected and give poor yields the next year. In some countries a high proportion of the crops are infected, and so much virus is carried into new stocks that it is unprofitable to keep them for a second year. In Britain and the United States, however, most commercial potato crops are now fairly healthy, so virus spread from one crop to another is not great. Many horticultural crops such as lettuce are grown in small plots in Britain, and serious losses occur when lettuce mosaic virus is carried by aphids from maturing to young crops and there is no break in the succession of crops (Broadbent et al., 1951). The susceptible crop need not be colonized by the vectors, for aphids can infect most bean plants adjacent to clover fields with yellow bean mosaic although they rarely breed on them (Crumb and McWhorter, 1948).

If biennials to be kept for seed become infected, they may form an important source of virus for the annual crop: a cycle of infection begins that can only be broken by growing the seed plants elsewhere, as was done with cabbage seed in the United States and cauliflower seed in England (Pound, 1946; Glasscock and Moreton, 1955). Much work has been done on beet seed crops, for yellows virus not only halves the yield of sugar beet seed, but the plants can be a major source of virus for the root crops. Watson *et al.* (1951) found that distance from a seed crop within a seed area has a pronounced effect on the incidence of mosaic in sugar beet crops but not of yellows: mosaic is usually confined to fields within 100 yd. of a seed crop. Virus is carried to the seed plants from the root crops during the autumn, and the vectors (*M. persicae*) also overwinter on them, carrying yellows to young root crops for miles around in the spring. Healthy seed crops are now produced in Britain by spraying stecklings with appropriate insecticides or raising them in cover crops or away from root crops.

F. *Spread within Crops*

Plants become infected and act as sources of inoculum within crops because (1) they grow from infected seed, (2) they grow from infected tubers or some other plant part either planted or remaining from a previous crop, (3) they become infected in the seedbed and are later transplanted, or (4) they are infected by incoming vectors. If virus is not brought into a crop from outside, the number of plants that becomes infected is often directly proportional to the number of initially infected plants, so the health of the crop at the beginning of the season is important (Broadbent *et al.*, 1951; Zink *et al.*, 1956).

Spread of viruses by insects within crops is usually over short distances, often to neighboring plants, more often along rows than across them, and sometimes in the direction of the prevailing wind (Murphy and Loughnane, 1937; Doncaster and Gregory, 1948). Spread often results in foci of infected plants around those initially infected, whether the virus is persistent or nonpersistent, or the vectors are aphids, beetles, or other insects. There has been much discussion about the relative importance of winged and wingless forms of aphids as vectors. Many workers have assumed that virus is spread from one crop to another by winged aphids, but that subsequent spread to nearby plants within the crop is by wingless ones (e.g., Davies and Whitehead, 1935; Klostermeyer, 1953; Rönnebeck, 1954). Direct observation of the movements of small insects is difficult, and has rarely been attempted. Those who watch flying aphids record that they fly laterally from plant to plant, or over short distances, or they fly upward and are swept away by the wind (Bjørnstad, 1948; Dickson *et al.*, 1949). Others have shown that wingless aphids walk from plant to plant in potato crops (Davies, 1932; Czerwinski, 1943), particularly when their leaves are in contact. Weather greatly affects the movement of wingless aphids, which move most often when it is hot, and especially when plants wilt (Spencer, 1926).

Experiments on the time when viruses spread in potato crops show that much of the season's spread occurs early, when the colonizing winged aphids are active and before a wingless population develops (Murphy and Loughnane, 1937; Doncaster and Gregory, 1948; Bjørnstad, 1948; Broadbent et al., 1950). Doncaster and Gregory thought that wingless aphids might be responsible for the further spread of virus within the crop when the plants touch each other, because winged aphids rarely colonize potatoes during the summer dispersal. But it cannot be assumed that the winged ones do not visit potatoes because they do not colonize them, so they might also spread virus later in the season. The very significant correlation between trapped M. persicae and the spread of both leaf roll and Y viruses suggests that most spread is by winged forms (Broadbent, 1950; Hollings, 1955). The lower correlation coefficient for rugose mosaic (Y) agrees with the evidence from Scandinavia that M. persicae is not the only vector of this virus.

Watson and Healy (1953) used statistical methods to relate trap catches or field counts of aphids to the spread of beet yellows and mosaic viruses in sugar beet crops, and concluded that winged M. persicae are most important in spreading beet yellows virus, despite the usual predominance of Aphis fabae on the plants. It is probable that winged forms of both M. persicae and A. fabae spread beet mosaic virus from sources outside the crop, but little within it. Winged A. fabae are apparently not concerned in spreading yellows virus, presumably because they often remain on the first plant they colonize, whereas M. persicae moves from one plant to another for a few days, depositing nymphs in small batches.

Additional evidence that the winged forms are primarily responsible for spreading virus in potato crops was obtained by surrounding healthy plants with sticky boards to prevent aphids from walking away from adjacent infected plants (Broadbent and Tinsley, 1951). But some of the most conclusive evidence has come from experiments with insecticides. Emilsson and Castberg (1952) controlled aphids with parathion, but did not control the spread of potato Y virus, and Schepers and associates (1955) sprayed potatoes frequently with nicotine, preventing the development of any wingless aphids, yet there was considerable spread of both leaf roll and Y viruses, and the distribution of infected plants in sprayed and unsprayed plots was similar. Later trials with demeton, when no wingless forms developed, had little effect on virus Y, but the spread of leaf roll virus was greatly decreased. It was stopped, and that of Y virus decreased to about half with insecticides in Britain when virus was not introduced from outside the crop. Presumably aphids visit fewer plants in a crop treated with insecticide, and infect fewer with Y virus before they are killed; they die before becoming infective with leaf roll virus. Steudel and Heiling (1954) assumed that demeton affects the wingless forms only, and that much of the spread must be by wingless forms because spraying decreases the incidence of beet yellows. However, as most winged M. persicae visit several plants, spraying with a persistent insecticide will decrease the number visited and the incidence of yellows whether spread is by wingless or winged forms or both.

One of the reasons why some aphid species are important vectors whereas others, equally efficient in laboratory tests, are not, is that some lose their power of flight more readily than others. Young winged forms of some species are much more active than older ones because the wing muscles degenerate after the aphids find suitable hosts and start to reproduce (Johnson, 1953). The more suitable the host, the sooner the aphids settle and lose the power to fly, so aphids that are apparently well-adapted to their hosts, such as Aphis fabae on beet, are unlikely to be able to fly by the time they become infective with beet yellows whereas M. persicae, which does not colonize so readily, will still move occasionally from plant to plant. When aphids are newly mature, even host plants are visited and abandoned several times, and so good colonizers can be efficient vectors of nonpersistent viruses.

Although the evidence suggests that wingless aphids are of little importance as vectors, they do walk from one plant to another, and in hotter climates than northern Europe may move frequently and contribute largely to the spread of persistent viruses (Bald et al., 1950). Walking aphids might not be expected to transmit nonpersistent viruses readily because they are seldom infective after spending some hours undisturbed on an infected plant (Watson, 1938); however, many were infective after a short period of walking and probing on infected plants, and presumably those which walk off a plant have spent some time walking on it first (Bradley, 1953). More information has been obtained on this by catching winged and wingless aphids soon after they voluntarily leave cauliflower plants infected with cabbage black ring spot virus or cauliflower mosaic virus and placing them singly on young seedlings. Similar proportions of winged and wingless aphids transmit virus. We cannot conclude, therefore, that wingless forms do not spread virus if they move, but only that they move infrequently in cool climates, as Fisken (1957) found in Scotland, and then perhaps inoculate adjacent plants, many of which have been infected already by winged forms.

Relatively little work has been done on the epidemiology of insect-borne fungi or bacteria. Rankin et al. (1941) surveyed 3000 square miles of New York state for Dutch elm disease and found at least 100,000 dead and dying trees. More than a third of *Scolytus multistriatus* beetles collected from elms carried *Ceratostomella ulmi*, but despite the prevalence of the pathogen and vectors, spread was slow, suggesting that the beetle is an inefficient vector or that other factors present limit infection. Two such factors are that beetles readily infect trees during June and early July, but usually fail to do so later, and infection often fails to become systemic (Parker *et al.*, 1941). Local spread of the disease from isolated infected elms was also studied by Zentmyer *et al.* (1944). Three-quarters of new infections occurred within 100 ft. of the source, and the maximum distance was presumed to be 180 ft., although the authors state that beetles sometimes carry fungus more than 2 miles. Spread was much more rapid than in New York, 40% of all trees within 75 ft. of the source becoming infected during 2 years. Statistical analysis showed that the probability that a tree would become infected decreased directly with the logarithm of the distance from the source; this result applies to the spread of most pathogens, whether insect- or air-borne. Zentmyer *et al.* postulated that wind influences local spread as well as long distance because more trees were infected to leeward of the source of inoculum. The distribution of trees makes this argument extremely dubious, however, because there were several trees within 30 ft. of the source to leeward, none to windward.

Little is known about the movements of insect vectors within crops, except what can be postulated from the distribution of diseased plants. Direct studies of insect movement are likely now to become easier than they were, for we know more certainly what questions to ask, and can employ new techniques, such as marking insects or plants with radioactive isotopes, in answering them.

REFERENCES

Allen, T. C., J. A. Pinckard, and A. J. Riker. 1934. Frequent association of *Phytomonas melophthora* with various stages in the life cycle of the apple maggot, *Rhagoletis pomonella*. *Phytopathology* **24**: 228–238.

Ark, P. A. 1944. Studies on bacterial canker of tomato. *Phytopathology* **34**: 394–400.

Atanasoff, D. 1925. The *Dilophospora* disease of cereals. *Phytopathology* **15**: 11–40.

Badami, R. S. 1957. Studies on the transmission and multiplication of cucumber mosaic virus. Ph.D. thesis. Univ. London.

Bald, J. G. 1937. Investigations on 'spotted wilt' of tomatoes. III. Infection in field plots. *Bull. Council Sci. Ind. Research Australia* **106**: 1–32.

Bald, J. G., and G. Samuel. 1931. Investigations on "spotted wilt" of tomatoes. *Bull. Council Sci. Ind. Research Australia* **54**: 1–24.

Bald, J. G., D. O. Norris, and G. A. Helson. 1950. Transmission of potato virus diseases. VI. The distribution of the aphid vectors on sampled leaves and shoots. *Australian J. Agr. Research* **1**: 18–32.

Bawden, F. C., and B. Kassanis. 1946. Varietal differences in susceptibility to potato virus Y. *Ann. Appl. Biol.* **33**: 46–50.

Bawden, F. C., and B. Kassanis. 1947. The behaviour of some naturally occurring strains of potato virus Y. *Ann. Appl. Biol.* **34**: 503–516.

Bawden, F. C., B. Kassanis, and F. M. Roberts. 1948. Studies on the importance and control of potato virus X. *Ann. Appl. Biol.* **35**: 250–265.

Bawden, F. C., B. M. G. Hamlyn, and M. A. Watson. 1954. The distribution of viruses in different leaf tissues and its influence on virus transmission by aphids. *Ann. Appl. Biol.* **41**: 229–239.

Bennett, C. W. 1934. Plant-tissue relations of the sugar beet curly-top virus. *J. Agr. Research* **48**: 665–701.

Bennett, C. W., and A. S. Costa. 1954. Observation and studies of virus yellows of sugar beet in California. *Proc. Am. Soc. Sugar Beet Technologists* **8**: 230–235.

Bennett, C. W., and A. Tanrisever. 1957. Sugar beet curly top disease in Turkey. *Plant Disease Reptr.* **41**: 721–725.

Björling, K., and F. Ossiannilsson. 1958. Investigations on individual variations in the virus-transmitting ability of different aphid species. *Socker Handl.* **14**: 1–13.

Bjørnstad, A. 1948. Virussjukdommer på Potet i Norge. *Nord Jordbrugsforskn.* **1948**: 586–590.

Black, L. M. 1950. A plant virus that multiplies in its insect vector. *Nature* **166**: 852–853.

Black, L. M. 1953. Viruses that reproduce in plants and insects. *Ann. N. Y. Acad. Sci.* **56**: 398–413.

Blencowe, J. W., and T. W. Tinsley. 1951. The influence of density of plant population on the incidence of yellows in sugar beet crops. *Ann. Appl. Biol.* **38**: 395–401.

Bonde, R. 1939a. The role of insects in the dissemination of potato blackleg and seed-piece decay. *J. Agr. Research* **59**: 889–917.

Bonde, R. 1939b. Bacterial wilt and soft rot of the potato in Maine. *Maine Agr. Research Sta. Bull.* **396**: 675–694.

Boyle, A. M. 1949. Further studies of the bacterial necrosis of the giant cactus. *Phytopathology* **39**: 1029–1052.

Bradley, R. H. E. 1953. Infectivity of aphids after several hours on tobacco infected with potato virus Y. *Nature* **171**: 755.

Bradley, R. H. E. 1954. Studies on the mechanism of transmission of potato virus Y by the green peach aphid, *Myzus persicae* (Sulz.) *Can. J. Zool.* **32**: 64–73.

Bradley, R. H. E., and R. Y. Ganong. 1955. Evidence that potato virus Y is carried near the tip of the stylets of the aphid vector *Myzus persicae* (Sulz.) *Can. J. Microbiol.* **1**: 775–782.

Broadbent, L. 1949. Factors affecting the activity of alatae of the aphids *Myzus persicae* (Sulzer) and *Brevicoryne brassicae* (L.). *Ann. Appl. Biol.* **36**: 40–62.

Broadbent, L. 1950. The correlation of aphid numbers with the spread of leaf roll and rugose mosaic in potato crops. *Ann. Appl. Biol.* **37**: 58–65.

Broadbent, L. 1954. The different distribution of two brassica viruses in the plant and its influence on the spread in the field. *Ann. Appl. Biol.* **41**: 174–182.

Broadbent, L. 1957. "Investigations of Virus Diseases of Brassica Crops." Cambridge Univ. Press, London and New York.

Broadbent, L., and M. Hollings. 1951. The influence of heat on some aphids. *Ann. Appl. Biol.* **38**: 577–581.

Broadbent, L., and T. W. Tinsley. 1951. Experiments on the colonization of potato plants by apterous and by alate aphids in relation to the spread of virus diseases. *Ann. Appl. Biol.* **38:** 411–424.

Broadbent, L., P. H. Gregory, and T. W. Tinsley. 1950. Roguing potato crops for virus diseases. *Ann. Appl. Biol.* **37:** 640–650.

Broadbent, L., T. W. Tinsley, W. Buddin, and E. T. Roberts. 1951. The spread of lettuce mosaic in the field. *Ann. Appl. Biol.* **38:** 689–706.

Broadbent, L., P. H. Gregory, and T. W. Tinsley. 1952. The influence of planting date and manuring on the incidence of virus diseases in potato crops. *Ann. Appl. Biol.* **39:** 509–524.

Caldis, P. D. 1927. Etiology and transmission of endosepsis (internal rot) of the fruit of the fig. *Hilgardia* **2:** 287–328.

Carter, W. 1939. Populations of *Thrips tabaci*, with special reference to virus transmission. *J. Animal Ecol.* **8:** 261–276.

Cartwright, K. St. G. 1938. A further note on fungus association in the Siricidae. *Ann. Appl. Biol.* **25:** 430–432.

Cheo, C. C. 1946. A note on the relation of nematodes (*Tylenchus tritici*) to the development of the bacterial disease of wheat caused by *Bacterium tritici*. *Ann. Appl. Biol.* **33:** 446–449.

Christensen, J. J., and C. L. Schneider. 1950. European corn borer (*Pyrausta nubilalis* Hbn.) in relation to shank, stalk, and ear rots of corn. *Phytopathology* **40:** 284–291.

Christensen, J. J., L. Henderson, and M. Aragaki. 1953. Dissemination of *Septoria linicola*. *Phytopathology* **43:** 468.

Clinton, G. P., and F. A. McCormick. 1936. Dutch elm disease—*Graphium ulmi*. *Conn. Agr. Expt. Sta. Bull.* **389:** 701–752.

Costa, A. S., D. M. de Silva, and J. E. Duffus. 1958. Plant virus transmission by a leaf-miner fly. *Virology* **5:** 145–149.

Craighead, F. C. 1928. Interrelation of tree-killing bark beetles (*Dendroctonus*) and blue stains. *J. Forestry* **26:** 886–887.

Craigie, J. H. 1927. Discovery of the function of the pycnia of the rust fungi. *Nature* **120:** 765–767.

Crosse, J. E., and R. S. Pitcher. 1952. Studies in the relationship of eelworms and bacteria to certain plant diseases. I. The etiology of strawberry cauliflower disease. *Ann. Appl. Biol.* **39:** 475–486.

Crumb, S. E., and F. P. McWhorter. 1948. Dusting beans against aphid vectors failed to give economic control of yellow bean mosaic. *Plant Disease Reptr.* **32:** 169–171.

Czerwinski, H. 1943. Untersuchungen und Beobachtungen über die Blattlaus *Myzodes persicae* Sulz. als Verbreiter des Kartoffelabbaues auf dem Versuchsfeld des Instituts für Acker-und Pflanzenbau Berlin-Dahlem und dem Versuchsgut Thyrow. *Angew. Botan.* **25:** 301–350.

Davies, W. M. 1932. Ecological studies on aphides infesting the potato crop. *Bull. Entomol. Research* **23:** 535–548.

Davies, W. M. 1939. Studies on aphides infesting the potato crop. VII. Report on a survey of the aphis population of potatoes in selected districts of Scotland (25 July–6 Aug. 1936). *Ann. Appl. Biol.* **26:** 116–134.

Davies, W. M., and T. Whitehead. 1935. Studies on aphides infesting the potato crop. IV. Notes on the migration and condition of alate *Myzus persicae* Sulz. *Ann. Appl. Biol.* **22:** 549–556.

Davis, E. W., and B. J. Landis. 1951. Life history of the green peach aphid on peach and its relation to the aphid problem on potatoes in Washington. *J. Econ. Entomol.* **44:** 586–590.

Day, M. F. 1955. The mechanism of the transmission of potato leaf roll virus by aphids. *Australian J. Biol. Sci.* **8:** 498–513.

Day, M. F., H. Irzykiewicz, and A. McKinnon. 1952. Observations on the feeding of the virus vector *Orosius argentatus* (Evans), and comparisons with certain other Jassids. *Australian J. Sci. Research* **B5:** 128–142.

Dicker, G. H. L. 1952. Studies in population fluctuations of the strawberry aphid, *Pentatrichopus fragaefolii* (Cock.). *Ann. Rept. East Malling Research Sta. Kent* **1951:** 166–168.

Dickson, R. C., J. E. Swift, L. D. Anderson, and J. T. Middleton. 1949. Insect vectors of cantaloupe mosaic in California's desert valleys. *J. Econ. Entomol.* **42:** 770–774.

Dickson, R. C., M. McD. Johnson, R. A. Flock, and E. F. Laird. 1956. Flying aphid populations in southern California citrus groves and their relation to the transmission of tristeza virus. *Phytopathology* **46:** 204–210.

Doncaster, J. P., and P. H. Gregory. 1948. The spread of virus diseases in the potato crop. *Agr. Research Council Rept.* **7:** *London, H. M. S. O.*

Dorsey, C. K., and J. G. Leach. 1956. The bionomics of certain insects associated with oak wilt with particular reference to the Nitidulidae. *J. Econ. Entomol.* **49:** 219–230.

Emilsson, B., and C. Castberg. 1952. Control of potato aphids by spraying with parathion and the effect on the spread of virus Y. *Acta. Agr. Scand.* **2:** 247–257.

Fife, J. M., and V. L. Frampton. 1936. The pH gradient extending from the phloem into the parenchyma of the sugar beet and its relation to feeding behaviour of *Eutettix tenellus. J. Agr. Research* **53:** 581–593.

Fisken, A. G. 1957. Studies in the ecology of potato aphids in eastern Scotland with special reference to *Myzus persicae* (Sulzer). Ph.D. thesis. Univ. St. Andrews.

Frazer, H. L. 1944. Observations on the method of transmission of internal boll disease of cotton by the cotton stainer-bug. *Ann. Appl. Biol.* **31:** 271–290.

Freitag, J. H. 1936. Negative evidence on multiplication of curly-top virus in the beet leafhopper, *Eutettix tenellus. Hilgardia* **10:** 305–342.

Freitag, J. H. 1956. Beetle transmission, host range, and properties of squash mosaic virus. *Phytopathology* **46:** 73–81.

Freitag, J. H., and N. W. Frazier. 1954. Natural infectivity of leafhopper vectors of Pierce's disease virus of grape in California. *Phytopathology* **44:** 7–11.

Freitag, J. H., and H. H. P. Severin. 1945. Transmission of celery-yellow-spot virus by the honeysuckle aphid, *Rhopalosiphum conii* (Dvd.). *Hilgardia* **16:** 375–384.

Fukushi, T. 1934. Studies on the dwarf disease of rice plant. *J. Fac. Agr. Hokkaido Imp. Univ.* **37:** 41–164.

Gibbs, J. G. 1931. Dissemination of clubroot in the dung of farm stock. *New Zealand J. Agr.* **42:** 193–198.

Glasscock, H. H., and B. D. Moreton. 1955. Cauliflower mosaic in East Kent. *Agriculture* (London) **62:** 270–274.

Gloyer, W. O., and B. B. Fulton. 1916. Tree crickets as carriers of *Leptosphaeria coniothyrium* (Fckl.) Sacc. and other fungi. *N. Y. State Agr. Expt. Sta. Geneva N. Y. Tech. Bull.* **50:** 3–22.

Grogan, R. G., J. E. Welch, and R. Bardin. 1952. Common lettuce mosaic and its control by the use of mosaic-free seed. *Phytopathology* **42:** 573–578.

Gruenhagen, R. H., A. J. Riker, and C. A. Richards. 1947. Burn blight of jack and red pine following spittle insect attack. *Phytopathology* **37**: 757–772.

Hansen, H. P. 1950. Investigations on virus yellows of beets in Denmark. *Trans. Danish Acad. Tech. Sci.* **1**: 1–68.

Harrison, B. D. 1957. Transmission of leaf roll virus. *Rept. Scot. Hort. Research Inst. 1956 (1957)*, 30.

Heald, F. D., and R. A. Studhalter. 1914. Birds as carriers of the chestnut-blight fungus. *J. Agr. Research* **2**: 405–422.

Hijner, J. A., and F. M. Cordon. 1955. De vergelingsziekte der Bieten. III. Enige onderzoekingen over de vermenigvuldiging van perzikbladluizen op Suiker-bietenbladeren. *Mededeel. Inst. Suikerbietenteelt Bergen-o-Z* **23**: 251–270.

Hille Ris Lambers, D. 1955. Potato aphids and virus diseases in the Netherlands. *Ann. Appl. Biol.* **42**: 355–360.

Hollings, M. 1955. Aphid movement and virus spread in seed potato areas of England and Wales, 1950–53. *Plant Pathol.* **4**: 73–82.

Houston, B. R., K. Esau, and W. B. Hewitt. 1947. The mode of vector feeding and the tissues involved in the transmission of Pierce's disease virus in grape and alfalfa. *Phytopathology* **37**: 247–253.

Jamalainen, E. A. 1948. Potatisvirosernas betydelse i Finland. *Nord. Jordbrugsforskn. 1948*: 568–570.

Jewell, F. F. 1956. Insect transmission of oak wilt. *Phytopathology* **46**: 244–257.

Johnson, B. 1953. Flight muscle autolysis and reproduction in aphids. *Nature* **172**: 813.

Johnson, D. E. 1930. The relation of the cabbage maggot and other insects to the spread and development of soft rot of Cruciferae. *Phytopathology* **20**: 857–872.

Johnson, J. 1937. Factors relating to the control of ordinary tobacco mosaic. *J. Agr. Research* **54**: 239–273.

Kassanis, B. 1947. Studies on dandelion yellow mosaic and other virus diseases of lettuce. *Ann. Appl. Biol.* **34**: 412–421.

Kassanis, B. 1952. Some factors affecting the transmission of leaf-roll virus by aphids. *Ann. Appl. Biol.* **39**: 157–167.

Kato, M. 1957. Recovery of Y-virus by aphids from infected potato plants. *Bull. Natl. Inst. Agr. Sci. (Japan)* **C32**: 65–88.

Keitt, G. W., and S. S. Ivanoff. 1941. Transmission of fire blight by bees and its relation to nectar concentration of apple and pear. *J. Agr. Research* **62**: 745–753.

Keyworth, W. G. 1942. *Verticillium* wilt of the hop (*Humulus lupulus*). *Ann. Appl. Biol.* **29**: 346–357.

Kirkpatrick, H. C., and A. F. Ross. 1952. Aphid-transmission of potato leaf-roll virus to solanaceous species. *Phytopathology* **42**: 540–547.

Klostermeyer, E. C. 1953. Entomological aspects of the potato leaf roll problem in central Washington. *Wash. State Coll. Agr. Expt. Sta. Tech. Bull.* **9**: 1–42.

Leach, J. G. 1927. The relation of insects and weather to the development of heart rot of celery. *Phytopathology* **17**: 663–667.

Leach, J. G. 1931. Further studies on the seed-corn maggot and bacteria with special reference to potato blackleg. *Phytopathology* **21**: 387–406.

Leach, J. G. 1940. "Insect Transmission of Plant Diseases." McGraw-Hill, New York. 615 pp.

Lihnell, D. 1948. Något om förekomsten och spridningen av virussjukdomar på potatis i Sverige. *Nord. Jordbrugsforskn.* **1948**: 571–577.

Linn, M. B. 1940. The yellows disease of lettuce and endive. *Cornell Univ. Agr. Expt. Sta. Bull.* **742**: 1–33.

Loughnane, J. B. 1943. *Aphis rhamni* (Boyer), its occurrence in Ireland and its efficiency as a vector of potato viruses. *Eire Dept. Agr. J.* **40**: 291–298.

MacClement, W. D., and M. G. Richards. 1956. Virus in wild plants. *Can. J. Botany* **34**: 793–799.

Markham, R., and K. M. Smith. 1949. Studies on the virus of turnip yellow mosaic. *Parasitology* **39**: 330–342.

Markkula, M. 1953. Biologisch-ökologische Untersuchungen über die Kohlblattlaus, *Brevicoryne brassicae* (L.) (Hem., Aphididae). *Ann. Zool. Soc. Zool. Botan. Fennicae Vanamo* **15**: 1–113.

Martini, C. 1958. The transmission of turnip viruses by biting insects and aphids. *Proc. 3rd Conf. Potato Virus Diseases, Wageningen-Lisse, 1958* pp. 106–113.

Merriam, D., and R. Bonde. 1954. Farm machinery spreads spindle tuber. *Maine Farm Research* **1**(4): 7–8.

Moericke, V. 1941. Zur Lebensweise der Pfirsichlaus (*Myzodes persicae* Sulz.) auf der Kartoffel. Thesis. University Bonn.

Murphy, P. A. and J. B. Loughnane. 1937. A ten year's experiment on the spread of leaf roll in the field. *Sci. Proc. Roy. Dublin Soc.* **21**: 567–579.

Oswald, J. W., and B. R. Houston. 1953. Host range and epiphytology of the cereal yellow dwarf disease. *Phytopathology* **43**: 308–313.

Parker, K. G., P. A. Readio, L. J. Tyler, and D. L. Collins. 1941. Transmission of the Dutch elm disease pathogen by *Scolytus multistriatus* and the development of infection. *Phytopathology* **31**: 657–663.

Parkin, E. A. 1942. Symbiosis and siricid wood wasps. *Ann. Appl. Biol.* **29**: 268–274.

Petri, L. 1910. Untersuchungen über die Darmbakterien der Olivenfliege. *Zentr. Bakteriol. Parasitenk. Abt. II* **26**: 357–367.

Piemeisel, R. L. 1932. Weedy abandoned lands and the weed hosts of the beet leaf hopper. *U. S. Dept. Circ.* **229**: 1–23.

Posnette, A. F., and R. Cropley. 1954. Field studies on virus diseases of strawberries. II. Seasonal periods of virus spread. *Ann. Rept. East Malling Research Sta. Kent.* **1953**: 154–157.

Posnette, A. F., and N. F. Robertson. 1950. Virus diseases of Cacao in West Africa. VI. Vector investigations. *Ann. Appl. Biol.* **37**: 363–377.

Pound, G. S. 1946. Control of virus diseases of cabbage seed plants in western Washington by plant bed isolation. *Phytopathology* **36**: 1035–1039.

Rand, F. V., and E. M. A. Enlows. 1920. Bacterial wilt of cucurbits. *U. S. Dept. Agr. Bull.* **828**: 1–43.

Rankin, W. H., K. G. Parker, and D. L. Collins. 1941. Dutch elm disease fungus prevalent in bark-beetle-infested elm wood. *Phytopathology* **31**: 19.

Rönnebeck, W. 1954. Erfolgsaussichten der chemischen Bekämpfung von Virusüberträgern im Kartoffelfeld. *Z. Pflanzenkrankh. u. Pflanzenschutz* **61**: 113–129, 184–196.

Romney, V. E. 1943. The beet leafhopper and its control on beets grown for seed in Arizona and New Mexico. *U. S. Dept. Agr. Tech. Bull.* **855**: 1–24.

Schepers, A., A. J. Reestman, and D. Hille Ris Lambers. 1955. Some experiments with Systox. *Proc. 2nd Conf. Potato Virus Diseases, Lisse-Wageningen, 1954.* pp. 75–83.

Schlösser, L. A. 1952. Zur Frage der Wanderung europäischer Rübenvirosen. *Phytopath. Z.* **20**: 75–82.

Sequeira, L. 1958. Bacterial wilt of bananas: dissemination of the pathogen and control of the disease. *Phytopathology* **48**: 64–69.

Severin, H. H. P. 1939. Factors affecting curly-top infectivity of the beet leafhopper, *Eutettix tenellus*. *Hilgardia* **12**: 497–530.

Severin, H. H. P. 1946. Longevity, or life histories, of leafhopper species on virus-infected and on healthy plants. *Hilgardia* **17**: 121–137.

Severin, H. H. P., and C. M. Tompkins. 1948. Aphid transmission of cauliflower mosaic virus. *Hilgardia* **18**: 389–404.

Simons, J. N. 1955. Some plant-vector-virus relationships of southern cucumber mosaic virus. *Phytopathology* **45**: 217–219.

Simons, J. N. 1957. Effects of insecticides and physical barriers on field spread of pepper veinbanding mosaic virus. *Phytopathology* **47**: 139–145.

Simons, J. N., R. A. Conover, and J. M. Walter. 1956. Correlation of occurrence of potato virus Y with areas of potato production in Florida. *Plant Disease Reptr.* **40**: 531–533.

Slykhuis, J. T. 1955. *Aceria tulipae* Keifer (Acarina: Eriophyidae) in relation to the spread of wheat streak mosaic. *Phytopathology* **45**: 116–128.

Smith, K. M. 1931. Studies on potato virus diseases: IX. Some further experiments on insect transmission of potato leaf-roll. *Ann. Appl. Biol.* **18**: 141–157.

Smith, K. M. 1957. "A Textbook of Plant Virus Diseases" 2nd ed. Churchill, London.

Spencer, H. 1926. Biology of the parasites and hyperparasites of the aphids. *Ann. Entomol. Soc. Am.* **19**: 119–157.

Stammer, H. J. 1929. Die Bakteriensymbiose der Trypetiden (Diptera). *Z. Morphol. Oekol. Tiere* **15**: 481–523.

Staples, R., and W. B. Allington. 1956. Streak mosaic of wheat in Nebraska and its control. *Nebraska Univ. Agr. Expt. Sta. Research Bull.* **178**: 1–41.

Steiner, G. 1942. Nematodes and the life association of the soil. *Proc. Soil Sci. Soc. Florida* **4** (B): 7–10.

Steudel, W. 1950. Über Auftreten und Ausbreitung der virösen Rübenvergilbung im Eldorfer Versuchsfeld und die Beziehungen zum Massenwenchsel der Überträger in 2 Extremjahren. *Nachrbl. Biol. Zent-Anst. Braunsweig* **1**: 166–171.

Steudel, W. 1952. Der Einfluss der Saatzeit auf Auftreten und Ausbreitung der Vergilbungskrankheit der Beta-rüben. *Nachrbl. deut. Pflanzenschutzdienstes Stuttgart* **4**: 40–44.

Steudel, W., and A. Heiling. 1954. Die Vergilbungskrankheit der Rübe. *Mitt. biol. Bundesanstalt Land-u. Forstwirtsch. Berlin-Dahlem* **79**: 1–132.

Stewart, R. N., and A. F. Schindler. 1956. The effect of some ectoparasitic and endoparasitic nematodes on the expression of bacterial wilt in carnations. *Phytopathology* **46**: 219–222.

Storey, H. H. 1933. Investigations of the mechanism of the transmission of plant viruses by insect vectors. *Proc. Roy. Soc.* **B113**: 463–485.

Storey, H. H. 1935. Virus diseases of East African plants. III. Rosette disease of groundnuts. *E. African Agr. J.* **1**: 206–211.

Storey, H. H., and R. F. W. Nichols. 1938. Studies of the mosaic diseases of *Cassava*. *Ann. Appl. Biol.* **25**: 790–806.

Storey, I. F., and A. E. Godwin. 1953. Cauliflower mosaic in Yorkshire, 1950–1951. *Plant Pathol.* **2**: 98–101.

Stubbs, L. L. 1955. Strains of *Myzus persicae* (Sulz.) active and inactive with respect to virus transmission. *Australian J. Biol. Sci.* **8**: 68–74.

Stubbs, L. L. 1956. Motley dwarf virus disease of carrot in California. *Plant Disease Reptr.* **40**: 763–764.

Sylvester, E. S. 1956. Beet yellows virus transmission by the green peach aphid. *J. Econ. Entomol.* **49:** 789–800.

Taylor, C. E., and C. G. Johnson. 1954. Wind direction and the infestation of bean fields by *Aphis fabae* Scop. *Ann. Appl. Biol.* **41:** 107–116.

Thomas, H. E., and P. A. Ark. 1934. Fire blight of pears and related plants. *Calif. Agr. Expt. Sta. Bull.* **586:** 3–43.

Todd, J. M. 1958. Spread of potato virus X over a distance. *Proc. 3rd Conf. Potato Virus Diseases, Wageningen-Lisse, 1958* pp. 132–143.

van der Plank, J. E. 1944. Production of seed potatoes in a hot, dry climate. *Nature* **153:** 589–590.

van der Plank, J. E. 1948. The relation between the size of fields and the spread of plant disease into them. *Empire J. Expt. Agr.* **16:** 134–142.

van der Plank, J. E., and E. E. Anderssen. 1944. Kromnek disease of tobacco; a mathematical solution to a problem of disease. *Bull. Dept. Agr. S. Africa* **240:** 1–6.

van Hoof, H. A. 1958. An investigation of the biological transmission of a non-persistent virus. Thesis, Wageningen. pp. 1–96.

van Slogteren, E., and M. P. de B. Ouboter. 1941. Investigations on virus diseases of narcissus. *Daffodil Yearbook* **1940:** 1–18.

Verrall, A. F. 1941. Dissemination of fungi that stain logs and lumber. *J. Agr. Research* **63:** 549–558.

Waite, M. B. 1891. Results from recent investigations in pear blight. *Botan. Gaz.* **16:** 259. Quoted from Leach (1940).

Wallace, J. M., and A. M. Murphy. 1938. Studies on the epidemiology of curly top in southern Idaho, with special reference to sugar beets and weed hosts of the vector *Eutettix tenellus*. *U. S. Dept. Agr. Tech. Bull.* **624:** 1–46.

Wallace, J. M., P. C. J. Oberholzer, and J. D. J. Hofmeyer. 1956. Distribution of viruses of tristeza and other diseases of *Citrus* in propagative material. *Plant Disease Reptr.* **40:** 3–10.

Walters, H. J. 1952. Some relationships of three plant viruses to the differential grasshopper, *Melanoplus differentialis* (Thos.). *Phytopathology* **42:** 355–362.

Watson, M. A. 1938. Further studies on the relationship between *Hyoscyamus* virus 3 and the aphis *Myzus persicae* (Sulz.) with special reference to the effects of fasting. *Proc. Roy. Soc.* **B125:** 144–170.

Watson, M. A. 1956. The effect of different host plants of potato virus. C in determining its transmission by aphids. *Ann. Appl. Biol.* **44:** 599–607.

Watson, M. A., and M. J. R. Healy. 1953. The spread of beet yellows and beet mosaic viruses in the sugar-beet root crop. II. The effects of aphid numbers on disease incidence. *Ann. Appl. Biol.* **40:** 38–59.

Watson, M. A., and F. M. Roberts. 1939. A comparative study of the transmission of *Hyoscyamus* virus 3, potato virus Y and cucumber virus 1 by the vectors *Myzus persicae* (Sulz.), *M. circumflexus* (Buckton) and *Macrosiphum gei* (Koch). *Proc. Roy. Soc.* **B127:** 543–576.

Watson, M. A., and F. M. Roberts. 1940. Evidence against the hypothesis that certain plant viruses are transmitted mechanically by aphides. *Ann. Appl. Biol.* **27:** 227–233.

Watson, M. A., R. Hull, J. W. Blencowe, and B. M. G. Hamlyn. 1951. The spread of beet yellows and beet mosaic viruses in the sugar-beet root crop. I. Field observations on the virus diseases of sugar beet and their vectors *Myzus persicae* Sulz. and *Aphis fabae* Koch. *Ann. Appl. Biol.* **38:** 743–764.

Webb, R. E. 1956. Relation of temperature to transmission of the potato leafroll virus. *Phytopathology* **46**: 470.

Wellman, F. L. 1937. Control of southern celery mosaic in Florida by removing weeds that serve as sources of mosaic infection. *U. S. Dept. Agr. Tech. Bull.* **548**: 1–16.

Wilson, N. S., L. S. Jones., and L. C. Cochran. 1955. An Eriophyid mite vector of the peach-mosaic virus. *Plant Disease Reptr.* **39**: 889–892.

Winkler, A. J. 1949. Pierce's disease investigations. *Hilgardia* **19**: 207–264.

Wright, E. 1938. Further investigations of brown-staining fungi associated with engraver beetles (*Scolytus*) in white fir. *J. Agr. Research* **57**: 759–774.

Zentmyer, G. A., P. P. Wallace, and J. G. Horsfall. 1944. Distance as a dosage factor in the spread of Dutch elm disease. *Phytopathology* **34**: 1025–1033.

Zink, F. W., R. G. Grogan, and J. E. Welch. 1956. The effect of the percentage of seed transmission upon subsequent spread of lettuce mosaic virus. *Phytopathology* **46**: 662–664.

Chapter 5

Dispersal by Air and Water—The Take-Off

C. T. Ingold

Department of Botany, Birkbeck College, University of London, England

I. Introduction

The dispersal story of a fungus can usually be divided into three major episodes: first, liberation of spores or their actual escape from immediate contact with the parent tissue; secondly, their dispersal in a viable condition to a greater or lesser distance; and thirdly, the coming to rest of the spores on solid substrata, on some of which germination and successful establishment may occur. This chapter is concerned essentially with the first episode although the second cannot completely be ignored, because the efficiency of take-off can be judged only in relation to subsequent dispersal. In particular it is important to consider the turbulence or nonturbulence of the air into which spores are liberated. Before discussing this matter, however, the various types of spore liberation will be considered.

This account will be largely concerned with organisms of importance in plant pathology although reference will often be made to saprophytic types in which particular dispersal mechanisms have been more fully studied than in essentially similar pathogenic forms. However, certain examples, highly interesting in the general context of dispersal in fungi but of no phytopathological importance, will be ignored. Thus the beautiful discharge mechanisms of *Pilobolus, Ascobolus,* and *Coprinus* spp. will receive no mention, nor will the wide range of dispersal types displayed in Gasteromycetes be considered (Ingold, 1953).

The conspicuous part of a fungus is essentially concerned with the production and liberation of spores, the feeding part being usually hidden away as a branched mycelium in the nutritive substratum. If we hope to understand a reproductive structure in a fungus, the question must be asked: "How are the spores set free?" It is extraordinary how often, even for the commonest fungi, no really satisfactory answer can be given to this question.

It is convenient to recognize two contrasting types of spore liberation. In the first, the spores are actively and violently discharged. In the second, liberation is passive in the sense that the energy concerned comes from outside the fungus, the dislodgment of the spores being due to the kinetic energy of wind or rain.

II. Violent Spore Discharge

In connection with the violent discharge of projectiles the size of fungal spores (mostly less than 50μ in diameter) or small spore groups, certain basic mathematical expressions should be considered.

According to Stokes' Law, the rate of fall of a minute spherical particle in a fluid is given by

$$V = \frac{2}{9} \frac{\rho - \delta}{\mu} ga^2$$

where $V =$ the terminal velocity of fall in the medium
$\rho =$ the density of the falling sphere
$\delta =$ the density of the fluid
$g =$ the acceleration due to gravity (981 cm./sec.)
$\mu =$ the viscosity of the medium (1.8×10^{-4} in the case of air).
This can be simplified to

$$V = \frac{2}{9} \frac{ga^2}{\mu} \tag{1}$$

since for fungal spores the density is approximately 1.0, and since the density of the air can be neglected. Turning to the question of the horizontal discharge of a spore we find, according to Barlow (in Buller, 1909) that

$$H = \frac{gD}{V} \tag{2}$$

where H is the initial horizontal velocity of discharge and D is the distance of horizontal throw. Combining (1) and (2), we get

$$D = H \left(\frac{2}{9} \frac{a^2}{\mu} \right) \tag{3}$$

Thus for a given initial velocity of discharge, the distance of horizontal throw is proportional to the square of the radius of the spherical projectile.

The path of a spore projected horizontally is

$$y = \frac{V^2}{g} \left[-\log_e \left(1 - \frac{x}{D} \right) - \frac{x}{D} \right] \tag{4}$$

y being the vertical distance of a point on the curve below the level of the point of departure, and x the horizontal distance from the vertical axis through this point. This curve (Fig. 1) has been referred to by

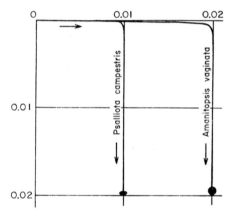

Fig. 1. The sporabolas of two spores shot horizontally from the hymenium. The spores, drawn to scale, are shown below. The scale is in centimeters. (After Buller, 1909.)

Buller (1909) as a "sporabola." It is of interest to compare distances of horizontal discharge (D) and of vertical upward discharge (U):

$$U = D - \frac{g}{k^2} \log_e \left(1 + \frac{k^2 D}{g} \right) \tag{5}*$$

k being given by $9\mu/2a^2$.

* My gratitude is expressed to Dr. R. Tiffen of Birkbeck College, London, for deriving this expression.

For particles the size of fungal spores U is almost as large as D. For example, in the common coprophilous pyrenomycete *Sordaria fimicola*, the spore projectiles are relatively large and an eight-spored mass may be shot horizontally to a distance of 10 cm. This projectile consists of eight spores, each $22 \times 13\mu$ and surrounded by a sheath of mucilage 3μ wide. The total mass has a radius of 21.6μ. Substituting in (5) it is found that $U = 9.82$ cm. In fact it has not been found possible experimentally to demonstrate a consistent difference between the distance of horizontal (10.0 cm.) and vertical discharge.* The difference is still less where smaller projectiles, those normally encountered in plant pathology, are concerned.

Violent discharge of the characteristic or "perfect" spores is the rule in two great groups of fungi, Ascomycetes and Basidiomycetes, although there are many individual examples in both groups in which discharge of ascospores or basidiospores is no longer active. Outside these two groups there are few examples of violent discharge, for in the Phycomycetes generally and in nearly all conidial fungi, including the conidial stages of Ascomycetes and the vast hordes of Fungi Imperfecti, liberation of spores is essentially passive. In this chapter violent discharge will be considered first.

A. *Ascomycetes*

In the majority of Ascomycetes the ascus is explosive although in many genera, widely scattered in any classification, this explosive character has been lost during the course of evolution or, perhaps, has never existed. *Eurotium, Tuber, Chaetomium,* and *Ceratocystis* (*Ophiostoma*) are familiar examples.

The typical ascus is a cylindrical, turgid, elongated cell with a thin cell wall (two-layered in certain Ascomycetes), a thin lining layer of protoplasm, and a large central vacuole containing cell sap in which the ascospores (usually eight in number) are suspended toward the upper end of the ascus. The water relations of the ascus are presumably like those of most other living cells.

During the later stages of maturation the glycogen reserve (staining chestnut brown in iodine) disappears and is probably converted into sugar, which raises the osmotic pressure of the ascus sap. Unfortunately, careful plasmolytic determinations of the osmotic relations of maturing asci have not been made, nor is there any critical information about the osmotic pressure in ripe asci.

The ascus eventually bursts in a definite manner, most frequently

* Unpublished experiment by the author.

either by the flinging back of a small apical lid (operculate Ascomycetes) or by changes at the apex, producing a minute pore (inoperculate Ascomycetes). Depending on the size and form of the apical opening in relation to the size and form of the spores, the latter are discharged simultaneously (or apparently so) or in obvious succession.

Compared with the basidium, which can rarely throw a spore more than 0.2 mm. and never more than 1 mm., the range of the ascus is great —being rarely less than 1 mm., usually of the order of 5 to 10 mm., and sometimes (e.g., in *Ascobolus immersus* and *Pleurage fimiseda*) as great as 500 mm. This very much affects Ascomycetes in relation to liberation of spores into turbulent air. Close to the ground or close to a host surface there is normally a layer of almost still, nonturbulent air commonly of the order of 1.0 mm. thick (Gregory, 1952). Most Ascomycetes are capable of shooting their spores through this laminar layer into the turbulent air beyond.

The structure of the fruit body in Ascomycetes in relation to violent spore discharge varies. Three major types can be recognized: (1) the Discomycetes type, in which the discharge occurs from extensive exposed hymenia; the Pyrenomycetes type, in which the asci are enclosed within a flask-shaped, true perithecium, or in a biologically similar pseudothecium, where the asci must elongate singly up the neck canal to the ostiole before discharge; and the Erysiphales type, in which the asci are completely enclosed within a cleistothecium, the wall of which must first be ruptured before an ascus can emerge to scatter its spores. These types will now be considered separately.

1. *Discomycetes Type*

The organization of the apothecium in relation to spore discharge has been considered in some detail by Buller (1933). Although the examples he analyzed are not directly the concern of the plant pathologist, the principles of organization are fully applicable to genera of phytopathological importance such as *Sclerotinia, Phialea,* and *Trichoscyphella.*

One example, *Aleuria vesiculosa* (Fig. 2), a fairly common species on dunged soil, will be considered. The apothecium is cup-shaped and usually several centimeters in diameter, with a palisade-like lining layer of asci at various stages of development intermixed with paraphyses. When an ascus bursts, an apical lid hinges back, the ascus wall contracts longitudinally and laterally, and the ascospores are shot to a distance of several centimeters. If contents of the asci were discharged at right angles to the hymenium, it is clear that many spores would

simply be shot onto an opposite hymenial surface. This would be particularly true of those species with apothecia of a more vase-shaped
form. However, this type of wastage does not occur, since the spores

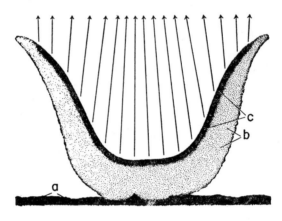

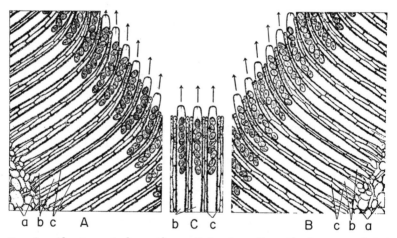

Fig. 2. *Aleuria vesiculosa.* Above: L.S. of small apothecium. *a*, substratum;
b, hypothecium; *c*, hymenium. The arrows show the direction of spore discharge.
Below: parts of the hymenium from the sides (A and B) and the bottom (C) of
the apothecium. (After Buller, 1934.)

are shot freely into the air above the apothecium because of the photo-
tropism of the individual ascus.

A special feature of most apothecia is the phenomenon of puffing,
During a period of quiescence many asci ripen, but remain in a con-

dition of unstable equilibrium. In this state a touch or perhaps a sudden change in humidity, as occurs when an apothecium is breathed upon, is enough to cause all these ripe asci to discharge simultaneously, sending into the air a visible cloud of hundreds of thousands of ascospores which drifts away like smoke. Buller has shown that this simultaneous bombardment sets the whole body of air just above the apothecium in motion, with the result that the spores are carried considerably farther than the distance to which a single ascus, discharging alone, could shoot its spores. Puffing may be of biological significance in the more efficient launching of the spores. Further, the cessation of discharge during periods of stillness tends to prevent the liberation of spores when the air is in a nonturbulent condition, that is, at such times when subsequent effective dispersal is less likely to occur.

2. Pyrenomycetes Type

Many Pyrenomycetes, especially in the genera *Nectria, Epichloe, Rosellinia, Mycosphaerella, Ophiobolus, Venturia, Endothia,* etc., are parasites of higher plants, but again it is more convenient to consider, in the first instance, spore liberation in a saprophytic type, namely *Sordaria fimicola* (Ingold and Hadland, 1958). The structure of this common coprophilous species is illustrated in Fig. 3. The flask-like perithecium is filled with asci at various stages of development, and any free space between them is occupied by mucilage. In Pyrenomycetes generally no gas phase is present within an active perithecium. While remaining attached at its base, a ripe ascus elongates up the neck canal, which is lined by downward-projecting periphyses. When its tip protrudes slightly through the ostiole, the ascus bursts, shooting its spores to a distance of 1 to 10 cm. Another ascus then elongates, and so on, the discharge of asci occurring one at a time in orderly succession. There is obviously no opportunity for "puffing" to take place. Empty asci retract into the perithecium, and soon liquify and disappear. In *S. fimicola* the distance of discharge is relatively great, a feature of many coprophilous fungi, mainly because of the large size of the spores and because of the fact that they tend to stick together. The whole contents of the ascus often forms a single projectile of eight spores. It has already been pointed out that the distance to which a minute spherical body is shot horizontally, with a given initial velocity (corresponding to the muzzle velocity of a gun), is directly proportional to the square of its radius. In most plant pathogens the spores are relatively small, and the distance of discharge rarely exceeds 1 cm. and is more often half this distance. However, such a distance of discharge is normally enough to launch the spores into turbulent air.

A slight variant of the type of discharge in *Sordaria* is found in Pyrenomycetes, with long thread-like spores such as those found in Clavicipitales (e.g. *Claviceps, Epichloe,* and *Cordyceps*). Here the spores from an ascus are shot away in succession. The process in *Cordyceps* is shown in Fig. 4. When the tip of the ascus protrudes from

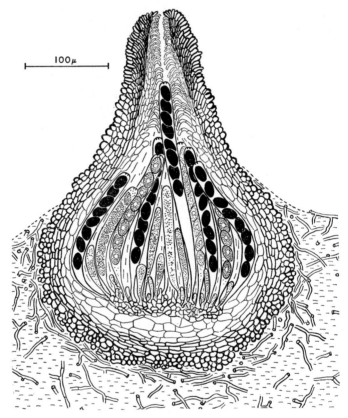

100μ

Fig. 3. *Sordaria fimicola.* L.S. perithecium growing on nutrient agar.

the perithecium, the ascus dehisces by a pore, but at once a thread-like (300μ × 2μ) ascospore is forced into the pore, stoppering the ascus momentarily. It is then shot away like a dart from a blowpipe, and again the ascus is stoppered by the next spore. This process is repeated until, within the space of a few seconds, all eight spores are discharged.

Another departure from the more general *Sordaria* type is to be found in *Endothia parasitica, Gnomonia rubi* and probably in many other species with long-necked perithecia. In these species the asci are small and are produced in great numbers within the perithecium. At ma-

turity they become detached and are squeezed in single file up the rather
long neck canal. When the tip of an ascus emerges through the ostiole,
it bursts, discharging its spores into the air, and the next ascus below
pushes out the empty envelope of the first one. This process can be seen
in operation in *Gnomonia rubi* (Fig. 5), where the neck of the peri-

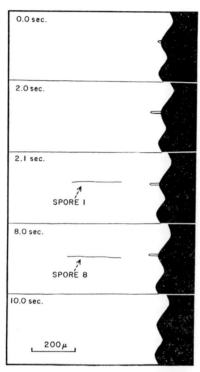

Fig. 4. *Cordyceps militaris.* Profile of two projecting perithecia as seen when
a stroma is laid on its side and viewed under low power of microscope. At 0.0 sec.
the tip of an ascus is beginning to project from its ostiole. At 2.0 sec. it has
reached its maximum extension. At 2.1 sec. the first spore flashes into view, then
rapidly falls out of sight. At 8.0 sec. the last spore has been discharged. At 10.0 sec.
the empty ascus has retracted into the perithecium.

thecium is sufficiently transparent for microscopic observation of the
column of ascending asci (Dowson, 1925). This type of perithecial
behavior clearly allows very rapid spore liberation under suitable conditions, and less than a second may elapse between the discharge of
successive asci. Such a speed of action would be impossible in *Sordaria,*
where the interval between the bursting of successive asci is usually to
be reckoned in minutes.

From this type of spore liberation it is but a short step to the condition in *Ceratocystis* (*Ophiostoma*), where the asci not only become detached on ripening, but the ascus wall undergoes liquefaction. The naked asci, as discrete eight-spored droplets, still pass in single file up the perithecium neck, but as they emerge through the ostiole, no

FIG. 5. *Gnomonia rubi.* Neck of the perithecium in optical section showing passage of asci along neck canal. Above the ostiole the spores and empty membrane of a discharged ascus are shown. (After Dowson, 1925.)

discharge occurs, and they simply run together into a larger drop, poised at the end of the long, black neck. This step in evolution appears to be correlated with the transition from wind to insect dispersal.

3. *Erysiphales Type*

In the powdery mildews (Erysiphales) the cleistothecium is essentially a hibernating structure with a continuous hyphal wall around the ascus or asci within. In the spring, when conditions are favorable, the expanding asci must first rupture this wall before emerging to discharge their spores. This process is illustrated in Fig. 6 for *Sphaerotheca mors-uvae* (Salmon, 1914).

In some powdery mildews the ascus as well as the ascospores may be violently discharged. This has been described, for example, in *Podosphaera leucotricha* (Woodward, 1927). The expanding ascus ruptures the cleistothecium wall in an irregular manner. However, this

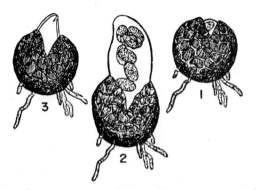

FIG. 6. *Sphaerotheca mors-uvae.* (1) swelling ascus is just bursting through cleistothecium wall; (2) fully swollen ascus is about to discharge its spores; (3) an instant later. (After Salmon, 1914.)

wall itself is elastic. As the enlarging ascus protrudes, it tends to slip out of the stretched cleistothecium shell. The jaws of this shell suddenly spring together, ejecting the whole ascus several centimeters into the air. The ascus itself then bursts, scattering the spores.

B. *Basidiomycetes*

In Basidiomycetes violent spore liberation is characteristic of Hymenomycetes, Tremellales, Uredinales, and certain Ustilaginales. In Gasteromycetes, in which the whole hymenomycete equipment of spore liberation appears to have been lost, the basidium is no longer a spore gun, and consequently, novel methods of spore liberation have been developed along diverse lines. However, Gasteromycetes, being essentially saprophytic, are no concern of the plant pathologist.

The basidium of the Hymenomycetes consists of a single cell bearing apical sterigmata, usually four, with a basidiospore at the end of each. The basidiospore is poised asymmetrically on its sterigma, and when the basidium is ripe, its four spores are discharged in succession. On the spore, very near its junction with the sterigma, is a minute projection— the hilum. It is this hilum that gives the highly characteristic appearance to discharged basidiospores, allowing them to be spotted readily on slides exposed by the aerobiologist. Just before a basidiospore is to be shot away, a drop of liquid makes its appearance at the hilum, and grows to a certain definite size; then the spore is discharged, usually to a distance of 0.1 to 0.2 mm., carrying the drop with it (Fig. 7). Immediately after the discharge of the four spores the basidium is apparently still turgid. Thereafter it slowly shrinks and finally seems to undergo autolysis.

Although studied fairly extensively, the mechanism of basidiospore discharge remains a mystery. It has been suggested (and for this there

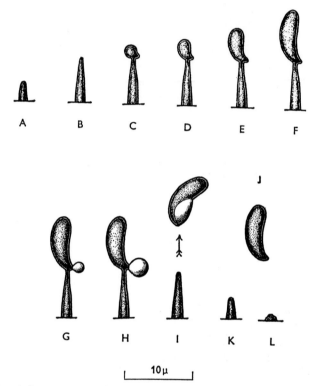

A   B   C   D   E   F

J

G   H   I   K   L

10 μ

FIG. 7. *Calocera cornea.* A–L, stages in the development of the basidiospore at the end of the sterigma and subsequent spore discharge. (After Buller, 1922.)

is good observational evidence in the rust *Gymnosporangium juniperi-virginianae*) that at maturity a cross-wall separates spore and sterigma. Discharge might thus be due to the sudden rounding-off at this region of the junction between a turgid spore and a turgid basidium (Prince, 1943).

If this is so, basidiospore liberation is essentially like conidium discharge in *Conidiobolus* or *Sclerospora*. However, because the sterigma is so narrow at its junction with the spore and because in the fully mature condition observation can only be made in air (since mounting in water at once breaks the connection) it is impossible to be sure whether a cross-wall exists at the moment of discharge. Again, if the discharge is due to rounding-off at the interface between spore and sterigma, the beautiful asymmetry of its position on the sterigma would seem to have no significance, nor would the process of drop secretion at the hilum, which so regularly heralds discharge.

Another theory is that the basidiospore is discharged from its sterigma by a water-squirting mechanism. According to this view, the turgid basidium bursts at the end of the sterigma, discharging a liquid jet which carries the spore with it. Against this view is the fact that immediately after a spore has disappeared, the vacant sterigma appears to be closed at its apex, and no exudation of fluid normally takes place from it. Indeed if this type of discharge is to occur, the sterigma must become sealed immediately so that the turgidity of the basidium may be maintained for the discharge of the remaining spores. As a slight modification of this view, it has been suggested that the drop is exuded not from the spore itself but at the junction of the spore and the sterigma. It is supposed that, having grown to a certain size, the drop is shot away, carrying the spore with it. This view is supported to some extent by Müller's study of spore discharge in the mirror yeast *Sporobolomyces*, in which the aerial conidium is discharged in a manner that appears to be identical with basidiospore discharge in Hymenomycetes. Müller (1954) in a cinematographic study showed that, although normally the spore and its exuded drop disappear simultaneously from the end of the sterigma, occasionally the drop suddenly disappears (presumably having been discharged) leaving the spore behind on the sterigma. However, in this connection it must be remembered that the careful observations of Buller (1922, 1924, 1931, 1933) all go to show that the drop exudes from the spore itself and not from the junction of spore and sterigma.

It has also been suggested that the surface energy of the exuded drop might be mobilized in some way to effect spore discharge (Ingold, 1939). This view has the merit of bringing the exuded drop and the asymmetrical poising of the spore into the picture, but unfortunately there is no real evidence to support it, nor is it at all clear how this energy could be mobilized. It has been calculated, however, that there is enough surface energy available, if it could be utilized, to discharge the spore to the observed distance.

The essential features governing fruit-body construction in Hymenomycetes are the very short distance of basidiospore discharge and the fact that, since basidiospores are sticky, they cannot normally be dislodged by wind once they have settled on a surface. Upward-facing hymenial surfaces are very rarely encountered in Hymenomycetes. Spores shot vertically to a distance of only 0.1 to 0.2 mm. would not usually reach the turbulent air above the laminar layer in contact with the hymenium, and would fall almost at once on the hymenial surface and become permanently stuck. In fact the hymenium in the sporophores of Hymenomycetes is mostly vertical, although it is sometimes horizontal and downward-facing, or it may occupy an intermediate, but still downward-facing, position. It should, perhaps, be remarked here that the position assumed by the hymenium in most toadstools and bracket

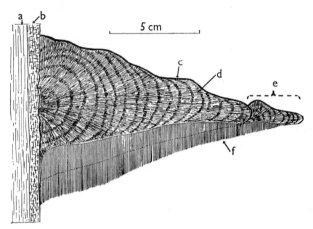

Fig. 8. *Ganoderma applanatum*. Vertical section of a small sporophore in its second year growing on ash. *a*, wood; *b*, bark; *c*, upper "crust" of fungus; *d*, zoned fibrous cap tissue formed in first year; *e*, additional cap tissue produced in second year; *f*, hymenial tubes (the dotted line indicates the boundary between the tubes formed in the first year (above) and in the second (below).

fungi also tends to protect them from rain. This is of importance, since water on the surface disorganizes the hymenium, at least temporarily, in striking contrast to that of Discomycetes, which are not injured by the temporary presence of free water.

Since, for the plant pathologist (especially if he is a forester) the bracket polypores are probably of more significance than agarics, spore liberation in the larger Basidiomycetes will be considered in some detail in a polypore and more briefly in agarics, although the general principles in both are essentially similar.

As a first example, *Ganoderma applanatum* will be taken. This fungus, with an almost world-wide distribution, is a wound pathogen of mature broad-leaved trees causing a heart rot. The mycelium occurs in the wood and the rigid sporophore forms a bracket or shelf broadly and firmly attached to the tree trunk. This woody fruit body is a perennial structure, the small specimen illustrated in Fig. 8 being 2 years old. Examples of 5 or 6 years of age are frequently to be found. The upper surface is extremely hard. On the underside the hymenial tubes grow down from

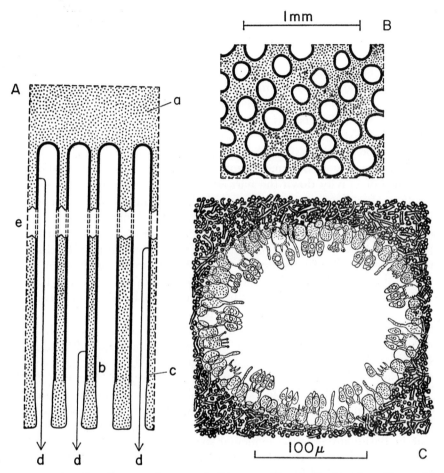

FIG. 9. *Ganoderma applanatum.* A. Diagram of longitudinal section of hymenial tubes. *a*, cap tissue; *b*, hymenial tube; *c*, active hymenium shown by thick black line; *d*, trajectory of discharged spore; *e*, gap in the diagram corresponding to about 20 mm. in the actual specimen or 574 mm. at the scale of this figure. B. Transverse section in region of hymenial tubes. The thick black line around each pore is the hymenium. C. Drawing of a single hymenial tube seen in transverse section.

the sterile cap tissue, and these are long (up to 3 cm. in the specimen figured) and extremely narrow (0.1 to 0.2 mm. diameter) (Fig. 9). During the growing season (May to September) they elongate, the meristematic growing region being at the orifice of each tube. Growth ceases in autumn and winter, and is resumed in late spring. The arrest of growth has structural implications, and the result is that if a sporophore is broken vertically, successive annual layers of growth are clearly visible. Growth of the tubes is controlled by gravity so that each individual tube develops in a perfectly vertical manner. This, combined with the rigidity of the fruit body and its firm attachment to a stout trunk, ensures that the tubes maintain their perfect verticality. This seems to be essential for effective spore liberation. Active hymenium lines each tube throughout most of its length, so far at least as the last two or three annual layers are concerned. In still older parts of the tubes the hymenium ceases to be functional, and the pores may become blocked with sterile hyphae.

The spores in this species are discharged horizontally to a distance of approximately 0.05 mm. (Ingold, 1957). They then fall under the influence of gravity down the narrow tube. If the tube were the merest fraction of a degree out of the vertical, clear fall would seem to be impossible and the spores would presumably become stranded on the hymenial surfaces lower down the tube. There is, however, just the possibility that the spores, which have been shown usually to carry a positive static electric charge (Gregory, 1957), are maintained in midstream during their fall down the hymenial tube by static electric forces.

On emerging into the free air below the tubes, the spores are carried away by the wind. It is to be noted that by their very situation on the tree trunk, the sporophores are in a position to drop their spores directly into the turbulent air. As if to achieve this end, ground-inhabiting species such as bolets and most agarics are forced to raise their spore-producing surfaces above the substratum on stipes. As Gregory (1952) has pointed out, the Ascomycetes can shoot their spores through the surface laminar layer of air into the turbulent layer above, but the basidium is not a sufficiently powerful spore gun to achieve this, so that in Basidiomycetes the hymenial surfaces tend to be so placed that the discharged spores drop into turbulent air. This concept is illustrated diagrammatically in Fig. 10.

In *Ganoderma applanatum* spore liberation is on a gigantic scale, and Buller has estimated that a large sporophore may liberate millions of spores a minute, maintaining this rate more or less for the whole 6 months of its annual spore-fall period.

Ganoderma applanatum is an extreme example which serves to emphasize the principles of basidiospore escape from a sporophore. Apart from species of *Ganoderma* and *Fomes*, bracket polypores have annual sporophores, and usually the pores are wider and shorter than those of *Ganoderma*. Thus in *Polyporus squamosus*, a common species

causing a heart rot of broad-leaved trees (especially elm), the pores are
1 to 2 mm. wide and only about 1 cm. long. These features may be
correlated with the comparative lack of rigidity in the fruit body
(Buller, 1909).

In the agaric, although the principles involved in spore liberation
are essentially the same as in a polypore, there are certain special

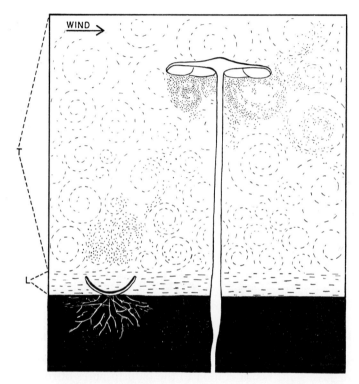

Fig. 10. A cup-fungus (*Peziza* sp.) and an agaric (*Collybia radicata*). The
ground is shown black. Above this is a thin layer of laminar air (L) and on top
of this turbulent air (T). The *Peziza* has just discharged a puff of spores through
the laminar air into the turbulent region. From the pileus of the *Collybia* spores
are dropping into the turbulent air.

features. In the ordinary fleshy toadstool or mushroom, hymenium covers
the gills (or lamellae), which hang down from the under surface of the
cap (pileus), which is itself raised above the ground on a stipe. In the
early stages the stipe may (e.g., in *Pholiota* spp.) or may not (e.g., in
Psalliota spp.) be positively phototropic, but if this tropism does operate in the young sporophore, it is finally lost and the stipe becomes
negatively geotropic. This gives an approximate vertical orientation to

the gills depending from the cap. But there is also a fine adjustment. The individual gill is itself positively geotropic. If there is slight displacement from the vertical, each gill (near its insertion on the cap) undergoes growth movements which bring it again into the vertical plane. This is a special feature of agarics, but absent in polypores, in which readjustment of existing hymenial surfaces does not seem to be possible.

The type of spore, poised asymmetrically on a sterigma, which is violently discharged following drop secretion from a hilum has been termed a "ballistospore" (Derx, 1948). The basidiospores of Hymenomycetes are ballistospores; those of Gasteromycetes and of *Ustilago* are not. Further, certain ballistospores, especially those of the shadow yeasts

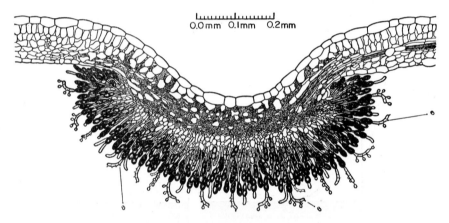

FIG. 11. *Puccinia malvacearum.* A sorus of germinating teliospores on the under side of a leaf of hollyhock (*Althaea rosea*). (After Buller, 1924.)

(Sporobolomycetaceae) cannot easily be regarded as basidiospores. We must now give some consideration to the ballistospores of rusts (Uredinales), which are clearly basidiospores, and to those of *Tilletia caries,* which can be classified as such only by a rather tortuous argument.

In rusts, the teliospore, usually after a winter's rest, germinates to produce a curved transversely septate basidium (promycelium) bearing four basidiospores (sporidia) on its convex side. The organization of the telium in relation to the discharge of basidiospores in rusts has been illustrated by Buller (1931) in *Puccinia malvacearum* (Fig. 11). It is clear that the curvature of the basidium and the position in which basidiospores arise is of importance in relation to the free escape of the discharged spores.

In smuts the occurrence of ballistospores has been demonstrated, particularly in *Tilletia caries,* but it is clear that in *Ustilago* spp. violent discharge does not take place. Buller (1933) has shown that when the brand spore of *T. caries* germinates on a moist surface a short promycelium is formed. This becomes septate and soon grows away from the surface, probably because of negative hydrotropism. From the end cell a tuft of six to twelve needle-shaped spores (primary conidia) is formed. These have been regarded by most mycologists as the basidiospores. While still attached, or after passive liberation, they conjugate, forming *H*-shaped pairs. From one member of each pair a short sterigma is produced bearing an asymmetrically poised, sickle-shaped spore (secondary conidium) which is a typical ballistospore being violently discharged following drop excretion at the hilum (Fig. 12). If an

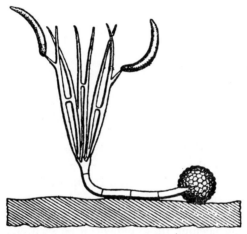

Fig. 12. *Tilletia caries.* Germinating chlamydospore producing a promycelium bearing a crown of six filamentous primary conidia which, following pairwise conjugation, are producing secondary conidia which are ballistospores. (After Buller, 1933.)

H-shaped pair of conjugated primary conidia is planted on a nutrient medium, such as malt agar, a fine, branched mycelium may be formed from which, in due course, a number of sickle-shaped ballistospores may arise on aerial sterigmata. In the field the ballistospore may germinate in contact with a host plant and cause infection, but on nutrient agar, and possibly under certain conditions in nature, a saprophytic mycelium is formed from which further ballistospores are produced. It is of interest to note that in *Tilletia caries* the record discharge distance for a ballistospore has been observed, namely, 1.0 mm.

C. *Other Types of Discharge*

We must now consider a number of examples in which the essential mechanism of discharge involves the sudden rounding-off of turgid spores. Probably the most important example from the point of view of plant pathology is the aecium of rusts (Uredinales) from which the aeciospores are commonly shot to a distance of 5 to 15 mm. Nevertheless in some species no violent liberation occurs. Although the force of propulsion is clearly provided by the sudden change in form of turgid spores, the details of the process are not absolutely clear. The mature aecium is usually a cup-like structure with a firm wall (pseudoperidium) of thickened cells. At the base of the cup is a close-set palisade of basal cells, each producing an ever-growing file in which aeciospores and intercalary cells alternate. Actually the basal cell cuts off a single terminal cell at a time; this divides to form a larger cell above, which becomes the spore, and a smaller below, which is the intercalary cell. Often this cell is delimited not by a wall parallel with the flat top of the basal cell, but by a curved wall at an angle to this plane. The result is that the intercalary cell arises in a corner-wise position—rather as a companion cell is carved off from a sieve tube. The intercalary cell remains thin-walled, while the wall of the associated aeciospore thickens. Most workers have regarded this cell as an ephemeral structure, which soon breaks down, but it has been suggested (Savile, 1954) that it remains turgid until the maturation of its companion spore.

As the aeciospore develops, its wall differentiates into three layers, and at the same time the future germ pores are organized. In some rusts where a pore is to be formed, the wall is much thicker locally and probably different chemically, producing a minute spherical plug, which becomes more or less free from the rest of the wall. In the spore deposit from a discharging aecium, these plugs can be seen either still adhering to the spores or lying free (Fig. 13). When the plug is eventually displaced, it leaves a very thin region in the spore membrane through which a germ tube may emerge if the spore eventually germinates.

It has been suggested that these spore plugs may play an essential part in aeciospore discharge—a part which can be illustrated by a simple model. "A tennis ball compressed over a marble on a table will be thrown farther upward when the confining pressure is suddenly removed than it will be if compressed against the table alone with the same force, and then released" (Dodge, 1924). The suggestion is that in the closely packed aecium the spore is indented by the pore plugs, but in the end the spore suddenly rounds off and is discharged. The pore plug acts as the marble in the model. The major difficulty of this theory is that in some rusts the aeciospores are actively discharged in spite of the absence of pore plugs. It may be, however, that the turgid, intercalary cells persisting among the mature spores act in the same way.

If the spore deposit from a discharging aecium is observed, it will be seen to consist not only of single spores but also of groups of two, three, or more. Occasionally a clump of up to one hundred spores may be shot away as a single projectile.

It is perfectly clear that the mechanism of violent discharge in the rust cluster-cup can operate only under conditions of complete turgidity. Even a slight reduction in turgor leads to a cessation of discharge. No

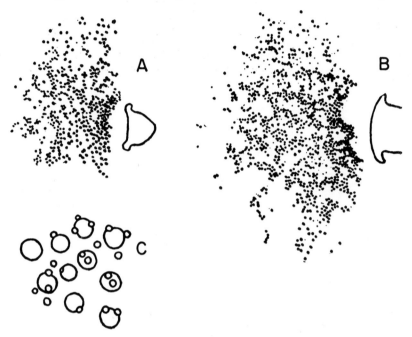

Fig. 13. *Gymnosporangium myricatum* A. and B. Spore prints formed after dissecting an aecium and laying it down on a glass slide in a damp chamber. Prepared from a photograph. C. Outline of spores showing plugs that still remained attached to spores after their flight and also free plugs. (After Dodge, 1924.)

spores are shot from aecia on wilting leaves. However, under damp conditions spores from the outermost layer of the aeciospores in the cluster-cup are violently discharged. These spores are followed by more, and so the cup tends to empty, but the spore supply is renewed from the base.

One of the best-known examples of spore discharge as a result of rounding-off of turgid structures is to be seen in *Entomophthora coronata* (= *Conidiobolus villosus*), which sometimes parasitizes aphids (Martin, 1925). The single conidium is borne on an erect conidiophore, the tip of which bulges into the spore as a dome-shaped columella. At the interface between the two turgid structures, stresses are set up which

are relieved by the sudden eversion of the re-entrant part of the conidium. As a result, the spore springs into the air to a distance of a few
centimeters.

The same type of discharge has been reported in *Sclerospora philippinensis,* causing downy mildew of maize (Weston, 1923). In this
fungus, however, the tip of the conidiophore branch does not project
into the conidium, but there is a flat surface of contact between the
two. It seems that it is by rounding-off in this region that spore discharge occurs (Fig. 14). In S. *philippinensis* the spore is shot to only
a very short distance—about 1 mm. This is probably due to the relatively small area of contact between the reacting structures.

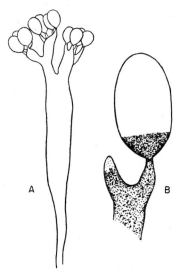

Fɪɢ. 14. *Sclerospora philippinensis.* A. Conidiophore bearing eleven conidia.
B. Part of conidiophore more highly magnified; from the tip on the left the conidium
has been discharged, that on the right being still attached. (Weston, 1923.)

It has been reported that the rounding-off mechanism of violent
discharge operates in some powdery mildews (Erysiphales). Hammarlund (1925) fitted capillary tubes over single conidiophores and watched
spore liberation microscopically. He maintained that the mature conidium is shot to a distance of several spore lengths due to sudden
rounding-off at the junction with the next spore in the chain. This
observation, however, lacks confirmation, possibly because no later
worker has used such an elegant technique as that employed by
Hammarlund.

Although in *Sclerospora,* as we have seen, spores are discharged by

a rounding-off mechanism, generally in downy mildews (Peronospor-
aceae) violent discharge is not very common. However, in a few other
species it does occur, but by a mechanism quite unlike that found in
maize mildew. Pinckard (1942) has described a case of this kind. In
Peronospora tabacina (blue mold of tobacco) as the branched conidiophore dries, violent twisting movements occur which may flick the
finely attached spores into the air (Fig. 15). It might be supposed that

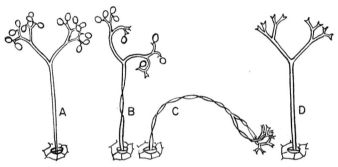

FIG. 15.   *Peronospora tabacina.* A. Conidiophore in damp air with attached
conidia. B and C. Changes on exposure to dry air. D. Recovery on return to damp
conditions. (After Pinckard, 1942.)

even without these movements, the ripe spores would readily be detached by wind, and thus the biological significance of this hyposcopic
discharge would be in doubt. However, Waggoner and Taylor (1958),
as a result of spore-trapping carried out over tobacco seed-beds heavily
infected with blue mold, found that spores were trapped mainly in the
morning, when hyoscopic twirling of the drying conidiophores would
be expected to occur. The absence of spores in the air during midday
hours, when strong hyposcopic movements would be at a minimum, was
taken to imply that forcible discharge is a necessity for spore liberation.

III. PASSIVE SPORE LIBERATION

In a large number of the fungi pathogenic to higher plants, the spores
are not violently discharged, and spore liberation appears to depend
on wind, rain splash, or the activity of insects.

In considering the classification of conidial fungi (Hyphomycetes or
Moniliales) Mason (1937) laid emphasis on the biological importance
of the difference between dry-spore types (Xerosporae) and slime-spore
forms (Gloiosporae). In the former the conidia could be liberated by
wind, but in the latter wind could not bring about liberation, and water
or insects would seem to be indicated as agents in dispersal. However,
from the point of view of dispersal the difference between Mason's two

types is not always clear-cut. Thus in some dry-spore fungi even the strongest winds fail to dislodge spores from their conidiophores, while some slime-spore species form their conidia in spore drops which eventually evaporate, leaving dry spores which can be blown off the conidiophore either singly or in groups. A common example is *Trichoderma viride*, a saprophyte in soil or on wood.

In a number of dry-spore species which rely on wind for spore liberation, the ripe dispersive units (propagules) are borne some distance above the surface of the host on erect structures. This is so in such diverse fungi as downy mildews (Peronsporaceae), gray mold (*Botrytis cinerea*), powdery mildews (Erysiphales), *Omphalia flavida* (gemmifers with gemmae), *Cladosporium fulvum*, and many others. The advantage seems to be that the propagules are exposed directly in turbulent air above the nonturbulent layer, perhaps 50 to 100μ thick, and which so often exists as a skin over the host surface. However, there are many dry-spore pathogenic fungi in which the spores are not raised to an appreciable extent above the surface of the diseased tissue. In this connection special mention must be made of most uredospores of rusts and brand spores of smuts. In these fungi the spores are, without doubt, freely liberated into the air in spite of the absence of violent discharge or of conidiophores raising the spores into a favorable position for liberation. It seems that the spores of such fungi, provided that they are sufficiently loose and powdery when mature, can be liberated freely when the diseased leaf, stem, or inflorescence on which they occur vibrates in the wind. This is the ancient principle of the sling shot. Indeed, it would seem quite likely that long conidiophores only acquire an importance when fungi are very close to ground level or when the part of the host attacked is rigid. These remarks only serve to underline our basic ignorance of this question. Further, we do not know in many cases whether spores become detached more readily under dry or under damp conditions.

In slime-spore fungi there is often doubt about the manner of their dispersal, although the agents concerned are likely to be insects, or water, or both. Among slime-spore fungi well-known to the phytopathologist are *Fusarium* spp., *Colletotrichum* spp., the conidial stage of *Nectria* spp., most members of Sphaeropsidales, the pycnial stage of rusts, the *Sphacelia* stage of ergot, and *Graphium* spp. In the last three examples insect dispersal of the minute sticky spores has been established, but in the others rain splash is probably the main factor involved in the take-off of the spores from the parent tissue. A well-known example of dispersal of rain splash is *Colletotrichum lindemuthianum*, the cause of anthracnose of *Phaseolus* spp. (dwarf and runner beans). The fungus attacks the aerial parts of the host, producing dark, sunken lesions bearing pink acervuli. The slime spores from these are scattered by splashing rain onto healthy foliage and pods.

At this point brief mention should be made of the take-off from the host of bacteria pathogenic to higher plants. In bacteria, apart from certain Actinomycetes, there is no parallel with dry-spore conidial fungi. However, in their dispersal there is a close parallel with slime-spore fungi. In a number of bacterial plant diseases, at some stage slimy masses of bacterial cells occur on the affected host, and the dispersal of these is due either to insects (as in *Bacterium amylovorum*, causing fireblight of pear and apple) or to rain splash. An example of the latter is *Xanthomonas citri*, the cause of citrus canker. The bacteria exude from scabby spots on leaves, young twigs, and fruits, and rain splash carries infection from diseased to healthy tissue.

The problem of the basic mechanics of splash dispersal has recently been investigated by Gregory and his co-workers (1959). The technique used was to allow water drops of definite size to fall onto a watery spore suspension exposed as a film of known thickness on a glass slide. The size and scatter of the reflected droplets was studied and they were examined to determine whether they carried spores. As a test organism *Fusarium solani*, a slime-spore species, was generally used. It was found that a drop 5 mm. in diameter falling from a height of 7.4 m. onto a spore-containing film 0.1 mm. thick produced over 5000 reflected droplets of which more than 2000 carried spores. The droplets ranged in size from 5μ to 2400μ. On the average the distance which they were scattered horizontally was 10–20 cm.

It is to be noted that the larger reflected droplets fall back within a small fraction of a second onto the substratum. The smaller ones, however, may remain longer in the air and be rapidly reduced further in size by evaporation. Thus, as a result of rain splash, slime spores may become suspended in turbulent air and be dispersed in the same manner as dry spores. Although the lists of species recorded by aerobiologists invariably show a great preponderance of dry-spore fungi, there is always a slime-spore element and rain splash may be the principal factor involved in the contribution of this to the air spora.

A study, involving high-speed photography, was also made of splash liberation of conidia from a twig bearing abundant conidial stromata of *Nectria cinnabarina*. Large drops (5.0 mm. diameter) falling from a height into the twig each broke into thousands of droplets all of which carried spores.

Much further quantitative study, particularly in the field, is needed in connection with the problem of splash dispersal, but the work of

Gregory and his colleagues provides an inspiring model for future research.

IV. Meteorological Conditions in Relation to Spore Liberation

Liberation of fungal spores may be conditioned by external factors— especially humidity, rain, temperature, wind, and light.

A. *Humidity and Rain*

These two factors, although usually correlated, are sometimes separable in their effects. As we have seen, rain may have a special effect in splash liberation of certain spores, but, further, some fungi require actual wetting if spore discharge is to take place. This is particularly true in Pyrenomycetes. Thus, for example, in *Nectria galligena* (Munson, 1939; Bulit, 1957), in *Venturia inaequalis* (Keitt and Jones, 1926; Hirst *et al.*, 1955) and in *Endothia parasitica* (Heald and Studhalter, 1915) the discharge of ascospores is closely correlated with rainfall (Fig. 16).

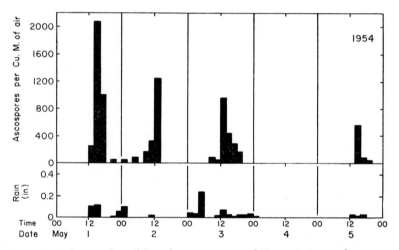

Fig. 16. Relation of rainfall and concentration of *Venturia inaequalis* ascospores per cubic meter of air every 2 hours during May, 1954. (After Hirst *et al.*, 1955.)

In some species (e.g., *Hypoxylon pruninatum*, Gruenhagen, 1945) it has been shown that a saturated atmosphere is not sufficient in itself to initiate spore discharge but that the perithecial stroma must first be wetted before discharge will begin. Although this relationship in Pyrenomycetes between spore discharge and rainfall is the normal one, there are exceptions. Thus *Daldinia concentrica* (Ingold, 1946) can discharge its spores under the driest of conditions, obtaining the water necessary for continued discharge from a water reserve in the stromatal tissue, and *Epichloe typhina* (Ingold, 1948) can also discharge its spores even when the stroma is unwetted and the surrounding air is dry, relying on the water brought to it in the transpiration stream of the host.

High atmospheric humidity and rain are important for continued spore discharge not only in Ascomycetes but also for liberation of basidiospores and for the escape of aeciospores in rust. However, in a number of dry-spore fungi, low humidity may be important for the take-off. In unpublished work in my own department it has recently been established that the sporangioles of the mold *Thamnidium elegans* and the conidia of *Trichothecium roseum* become detached by wind much more readily if it is dry than if it is damp, and the same may be true of other dry-spore fungi.

B. *Temperature*

The effect of temperature on spore liberation is probably largely associated with its influence on spore maturation. Thus in Ascomycetes, in the range normally encountered, an increase in temperature results in an increase in the rate of spore discharge (Ingold, 1939). The same is true of Basidiomycetes. In *Lenzites betulina* Buller (1909) has demonstrated that, although spore discharge can occur over the range 0° to 29° C., the rate of liberation is much lower at the extremes than in the middle region.

It has recently been shown (Ingold and Hadland, 1958) that temperature also may affect the distance of spore discharge. Thus in *Sordaria fimicola* the average distance of discharge of eight-spored projectiles is 6.30 cm. at 21 to 24° C. but only 5.23 cm. at a temperature of 7 to 10° C.

C. *Wind*

Wind is probably a major factor in connection with the take-off of many parasitic fungi although quantitative information is sadly lacking. Mean-wind speed increases in a regular manner with height, and this may be expressed by the formula (Geiger, 1950)

$$v_2 = v_1 z^\alpha$$

where

v_1 = wind velocity at unit (1 meter) distance above the ground
v_2 = wind velocity z units above the ground

and

α = an exponent which varies to some extent but near the ground is usually in the range of 0.2 to 0.3

This is, of course, a statistical "law," true on the average, but not necessarily giving a correct picture at any given moment. Theoretically at ground level the wind velocity is zero. Even under gale conditions a layer, perhaps only a few molecules thick, is still, or, if it is in motion, is nonturbulent. This "laminar layer" during the day is often a millimeter or less in thickness, but during the night with the disappearance of thermal turbulence, it may be reckoned in meters. However, although this laminar layer is normally present, it may locally and temporarily be invaded by violent eddies which may pick up dry spores and whirl them upward.

In connection with wind as a spore-liberating agent, the position of the spore-producing surfaces on diseased plants and the disposal of the spores on the conidiophores may be of great importance. It is to be hoped that wind-tunnel experiments will in the future add much to knowledge of the influence of wind on the escape of spores.

D. *Light*

Light is a minor factor in connection with the take-off of the spores of pathogens. Like temperature, it probably exerts its influence, if any, in conditioning spore maturation. It will be discussed later in connection with periodicity of discharge.

V. Periodicity of Spore Liberation

From the point of view of the spread of plant diseases, the time of day when the spores of a pathogen are set free may be of importance. If the spores are liberated when atmospheric turbulence is high, their wide dispersal is favored, but this is likely to be an advantage only if they are of the type that can survive the relatively dry conditions often associated with turbulence. For delicate, short-lived spores it may be vital to the spread of the pathogen that liberation occur at a time of day when the air is damp and when potential infection drops, as the result of dew or rain, are likely to persist on the host leaves. Thus any daily cycle of spore liberation must be carefully studied by the plant pathologist.

Broadly speaking, this question of periodicity has been investigated in two different ways. First, the actual liberation of spores has been studied, often in the laboratory, and second, the daily cycle of spore-content in the air in the neighborhood of infected plants has been followed.

In considering any daily cycle of spore liberation in a particular case it must be borne in mind that each of the four major factors influencing the take-off of spores, namely, temperature, humidity, light, and wind, tends to exhibit a daily cycle of behavior. Light, temperature, and wind velocity tend to be maximal in daytime, while humidity tends to be high at night associated with lower temperature and decreased atmospheric turbulence. Again, it is, perhaps, important to realize that periodic appearance of spores in a spore trap does not necessarily mean that they have been set free in a periodic manner. Let us consider, say, the apothecium of a Discomycete on the ground discharging spores at a uniform rate. During the night in fair weather there may be a thickish layer of still or laminar air close to the ground, and spores discharged into this would soon fall to the ground and would not be caught in a spore trap operating at the standard height of 1 m. During the day, with the onset of turbulent conditions and the reduction of the laminar layer to a bare millimeter or so, spores would be brought into the region sampled by the trap. Thus a periodicity might be recorded quite unconnected with spore liberation. Probably, however, there is normally a close correlation between liberation and trapping, provided the distance between the source and the trap is not too great.

Another general point which should be made is that periodic rhythm in spore liberation may be conditioned by periodic spore production or by the periodic operation of conditions which favor the escape of spores from a reservoir in the parent tissue.

In the powdery mildew of clover, caused by *Erysiphe polygoni*, it has been shown (Yarwood, 1936) that each conidiophore normally produces and abstricts one conidium each day and that this rhythm depends on the natural alternation of light and darkness. Spore liberation tends to occur during the daytime and in greatest abundance about noon. Childs (1940) has also reported a diurnal cycle of spore maturation in a number of other powdery mildews, including species of *Sphaerotheca* and *Podosphaera*, and Yarwood (1957) has found a similar state of affairs in species of *Micosphaera* and *Uncinula*. However, in *Erysiphe graminis* on barley (Yarwood, 1936) no diurnal cycle was observable.

In *Taphrina deformans* a periodicity has been found (Yarwood, 1941) with spores discharged in greatest numbers in the evening. For the basidiomycete *Corticium filamentosa*, which forms its basidia on leaves of *Hevea*, nocturnal spore discharge has been demonstrated (Carpenter, 1949). Nocturnal discharge of ascospores occurs in *Daldinia concentrica* (Ingold, 1946; Ingold and Cox, 1955). This is an endogenous rhythm which continues for a number of days in continuous darkness at constant temperature. Under these conditions, however, the rhythm is finally lost, but is immediately restored on return to the normal periodic alternation of light and darkness.

In the saprophytic pyrenomycete, *Sordaria fimicola*, the periodicity of spore discharge has also been rather fully studied, and it may be that the picture obtained will prove to be generally applicable to nonstromatal species (Ingold and Dring, 1957). In *Sordaria* there is no sign of an endogenous rhythm; the cycle is entirely dependent on the cycle of light changes in the day. Under conditions of illumination of 12 hours light (100 f.c.) and 12 hours dark in each day, spore discharge is at a low level during the period of darkness. With the onset of light, discharge rate rises to a maximum and thereafter falls, but not to the level of discharge in darkness. The change from light to dark always involves a rapid decline in rate. It has been shown (Ingold, 1958) that it is the short rays of light (400 to 500 mμ) which are effective in stimulating discharge.

It should be remarked, however, that in the investigations using *Daldinia* and *Sordaria*, temperature has been kept constant and the water supply has been in no way limiting.

Mention has already been made of the periodicity in trapping of the spores of *Peronospora tabacina*. Waggoner and Taylor observed a maximum of spores in the morning, and associated this with the daily decrease of humidity in the early hours operating the hyposcopic mechanism of dispersal.

Work in Britain (Hirst, 1953) and in Nigeria (Cammack, 1955) shows that diurnal periodicity of spores in the air is the rule with such diverse types as the brand spores of *Ustilago*, the conidia of powdery and downy mildews, and the uredospores of rusts, although it remains to be seen if this is due to periodicity of spore liberation, to rhythm in the turbulent conditions of the air bringing spores to the spore trap orifice, or to a combination of both.

Much remains to be determined about the daily cycle of spore liberation, but from what is known the periodicities observed do not appear to have much selective value for the pathogen in the sense that the fungus achieves a greater infection as a result of restricting its spore output to certain times a day.

We are left with a general picture of spore liberation in which one of the principal features is the lack of exact knowledge. However, plant pathologists generally are becoming increasingly interested in the quantative aspect of dispersal, including the take-off, in the pathogens they study, and in the next decade we may hope to see the development of a much more detailed picture.

REFERENCES

Bulit, J. 1957. Contribution à l'étude biologique du *Nectria galligena* Bres. agent du chancre du pommier. *Ann. inst. natl. recherche agron. Sér.* **C7**: 67–89.

Buller, A. H. R. 1909. "Researches on Fungi," Vol. I. Longmans, Green, London. pp. 1–287.

Buller, A. H. R. 1922. "Researches on Fungi," Vol. II. Longmans, Green, London. pp. 1–492.

Buller, A. H. R. 1924. "Researches on Fungi," Vol. III. Longmans, Green, London. 1–611.

Buller, A. H. R. 1931. "Researches on Fungi," Vol. IV. Longmans, Green, London. pp. 1–329.

Buller, A. H. R. 1933. "Researches on Fungi," Vol. V. Longmans, Green, London. pp. 1–416.

Buller, A. H. R. 1934. "Researches on Fungi," Vol. VI. Longmans, Green, London. pp. 1–513.

Cammack, R. H. 1955. Seasonal changes in three common constituents of the air spora of Southern Nigeria. Nature 176: 1270–1272.

Carpenter, J. B. 1949. Production and discharge of basidiospores by Pellicularia filamentosa (Pat.) Rogers on Hevea rubber. Phytopathology 39: 980–985.

Childs, J. F. L. 1940. Diurnal cycle of spore maturation in certain powdery mildews. Phytopathology 30: 65–73.

Derx, H. G. 1948. Itersonilia, nouveau genre de Sporobolomycètes à mycélium bouclé. Bull. Botan. Gardens Buitenzorg Ser. III 18: 465–472.

Dodge, B. O. 1924. Aecidiospore discharge as related to the character of the spore wall. J. Agr. Research 27: 749–756.

Dowson, W. J. 1925. A die-back of rambler roses due to Gnomonia rubi Rehm. J. Roy. Hort. Soc. 50: 55–72.

Geiger, R. 1950. "The Climate Near the Ground." Harvard Univ. Press, Cambridge, Massachusetts.

Gregory, P. H. 1952. Fungus spores. Trans. Brit. Mycol. Soc. 35: 1–18.

Gregory, P. H. 1957. Electrostatic charges on spores of fungi in air. Nature 180: 330.

Gregory, P. H., E. J. Guthrie, and M. E. Bunce. 1959. Experiments on splash dispersal of fungus spores. J. Gen. Microbiol. 29: 328–354.

Gruenhagen, R. H. 1945. Hypoxylon pruinatum and its pathogenesis on poplar. Phytopathology 35: 72–89.

Hammarlund, C. 1925. Zur Genetik, Biologie und Physiologie einiger Erysiphaceen. Hereditas 6: 1–126.

Heald, F. D., and R. A. Studhalter. 1915. Seasonal duration of ascospore expulsion of Endothia parasitica. Am. J. Botany 2: 429–448.

Hirst, J. M. 1953. Changes in atmospheric spore content: diurnal periodicity and the effects of weather. Trans. Brit. Mycol. Soc. 36: 375–393.

Hirst, J. M., I. F. Storey, W. C. Ward, and H. J. Wilcox. 1955. The origin of apple scab epidemics in the Wisbech area in 1953 and 1954. Plant Pathol. 4: 91–96.

Ingold, C. T. 1939. "Spore Discharge in Land Plants." Oxford Univ. Press, London and New York.

Ingold, C. T. 1946. Spore discharge in Daldinia concentrica. Trans. Brit. Mycol. Soc. 29: 43–51.

Ingold, C. T. 1948. The water-relations of spore discharge in Epichloe. Trans. Brit. Mycol. Soc. 31: 277–280.

Ingold, C. T. 1953. "Dispersal in Fungi." Oxford Univ. Press, London and New York. pp. 1–197.

Ingold, C. T. 1957. Spore liberation in higher fungi. *Endeavour* **16:** 78–83.

Ingold, C. T. 1958. On light-stimulated spore discharge in *Sordaria*. *Ann. Botany (London)* [N.S.] **22:** 129–135.

Ingold, C. T., and V. J. Cox. 1955. Periodicity of spore discharge in *Daldinia*. *Ann. Botany (London)* [N.S.] **19:** 201–209.

Ingold, C. T., and V. J. Dring. 1957. An analysis of spore discharge in *Sordaria*. *Ann. Botany (London)* [N.S.] **21:** 465–477.

Ingold, C. T., and S. Hadland. 1958. The ballistics of *Sordaria*. *New Phytologist* **58:** 46–57.

Keitt, G. W., and L. K. Jones. 1926. Studies on the epidemiology and control of apple scab. *Wisconsin Univ. Agr. Expt. Sta. Research Bull.* **72.**

Martin, G. W. 1925. Morphology of *Conidiobolus villosus*. *Botan. Gaz.* **80:** 311–318.

Mason, E. W. 1937. Annotated Account of Fungi Received at the Imperial Mycological Institute. List 2, Fasc. 3 (Gen. Pt.), I.M.I., Kew, Surrey.

Müller, D. 1954. Die Abschleuderung der Sporen von *Sporobolomyces*—Spiegelhefe—gefilmt. *Friesia* **5:** 65–74.

Munson, R. G. 1939. Observations on apple canker I. The discharge and germination of spores of *Nectria galligena* Bres. *Ann. Appl. Biol.* **26:** 440–457.

Pinckard, J. A. 1942. The mechanism of spore dispersal in *Peronospora tabacina* and certain other downy mildew fungi. *Phytopathology* **32:** 505–511.

Prince, A. E. 1943. Basidium formation and spore discharge in *Gymnosporangium nidus-avis*. *Farlowia* **1:** 79–93.

Salmon, E. S. 1914. Observations on the perithecial stage of American gooseberry mildew [*Sphaerotheca mors-uvae* (Schwein) Berk.] *J. Agr. Sci.* **6:** 187–193.

Savile, D. B. O. 1954. Cellular mechanics, taxonomy and evolution in the *Uredinales* and *Ustilaginales*. *Mycologia* **46:** 736–761.

Waggoner, P. E., and G. S. Taylor. 1958. Dissemination by atmosphere turbulence: spores of *Peronospora tabacina*. *Phytopathology* **48:** 46–51.

Weston, W. H. 1923. Production and dispersal of conidia in the Philippine *Sclerosporas* of maize. *J. Agr. Research* **23:** 239–278.

Woodward, R. C. 1927. Studies on *Podosphaera leucotricha* (Ell. Ev.) Salm. *Trans. Brit. Mycol. Soc.* **12:** 173–204.

Yarwood, C. E. 1936. The diurnal cycle of the powdery mildew *Erysiphe polygoni*. *J. Agr. Research* **52:** 645–657.

Yarwood, C. E. 1941. Diurnal cycle of ascus maturation of *Taphrina deformans*. *Am. J. Botany* **28:** 355–357.

Yarwood, C. E. 1957. Powdery Mildews. *Botan. Rev.* **23:** 235–301.

CHAPTER 6

Dispersal by Air and Water—The Flight and Landing

HARALD SCHRÖDTER

Agrarian Meteorological Research Station,
Aschersleben, Germany

The problem of dissemination of plant diseases, whose propagules (such as fungal spores) cannot move by themselves, is more amenable to theoretical treatment than any other problem in phytopathology. This is especially true for air-borne pathogens. Once in the air, the way these propagules travel, the horizontal and vertical distance covered, and the time in transit all depend exclusively on external forces of a physical

169

nature. Thus, the problem assumes a physical rather than a biological character.

A knowledge of these forces is a prerequisite for theoretical treatment of the agent's flight. Some concepts in this area of phytopathology are unclear. Often, only two forces or effects of forces are considered, i.e., velocity of wind (horizontal aerial movement) and velocity of fall that the agent would have in calm air. Thus, for instance, Christensen (1942) calculated that a spore of *Ustilago zeae*, when brought 1 mile upward at a wind velocity of 20 m.p.h., can travel a distance of 2500 miles in about 9 days. Such calculations, however, have little practical and no theoretical value. Such an observation cannot explain how the spore got so high up. Since the wind acts horizontally and the velocity of fall vertically, no possibility of upward movement is considered; yet spores and pollen are found even in the highest atmospheric strata. First, one has to find out which external forces are responsible for transportation of the causative agents and how the individual force components affect the agent. Then a theory of agent flight can be established.

I. Transportation Forces

In discussing the determining factors for transportation of the agents through air, one need not consider molecular forces and electrostatic effects. Although they could exert an effect on the movement of the causative agents, they are so much overshadowed by other influences as to be negligible.

Gravitation affects each small particle in the air; together with buoyancy and internal friction of the air it acts constantly to give each particle its own falling velocity (in calm air). The horizontal movement of the air, called wind, is superimposed over this direction of movement. Finally, turbulence results in the vertical movement of air and contained particles. The resultant of all these forces then determines what pathway the particles follow from take-off to landing. These forces and their effects will be examined individually and briefly.

A. Gravitation

According to Newton's law of gravitation, an attracting force k acts between two bodies with masses m_1 and m_2 that are at a distance r from one another:

$$k = G \frac{m_1 m_2}{r^2} \text{ [dyn]} \tag{1}$$

whereby G is the universal gravitation constant, which is independent of the state of both bodies. The terrestrial force of gravity is the resulting attraction between the mass of the earth and bodies found on or near it. This gravitation imparts to each body a downward accelerated movement during free fall. In the atmosphere the effect of gravitation is partly compensated by buoyancy and by the opposing force of internal friction of the air. The net effect of these forces, as mentioned, is the velocity of fall inherent in each particle.

B. Velocity of Fall

A sphere-shaped particle with radius r that moves in the (calm) air with velocity v experiences, according to Stokes' law, a resistance of the size

$$k = 6\pi\eta vr \text{ [dyn]}. \tag{2}$$

The reference is valid in this form only under the condition that the radius of the particle is larger than the free path of the corresponding gas with viscosity η. Since the average free path in the air only measures 0.1μ and the diameter of spores generally is about 10μ, this condition can be considered as adequately fulfilled. Thus, as the particle is accelerated by gravitation (diminished by the insignificant amount of air buoyancy), there is an increase in frictional resistance. Thus, an equilibrium is established between the weight k' of the particle and the frictional resistance k so that the particle falls with constant velocity. Since the weight of the sphere-shaped particle is given by

$$k' = \frac{4}{3}\pi r^3 sg \tag{3}$$

where s represents the density of the particle and g terrestrial acceleration, fall velocity of sphere-shaped particles can be calculated from the equilibrium condition (buoyancy neglected)

$$\frac{4}{3}\pi r^3 sg = 6\pi\eta vr. \tag{4}$$

It is

$$v_k = \frac{2sg}{9\eta}r^2. \tag{5}$$

In phytopathology we are mostly concerned with agents that are not spherical, but ellipsoid, as is the case (at least approximately) in fungal spores. Falck (1927), who concerned himself very thoroughly with velocity of falling fungal spores in calm air, attempted to correlate experimentally the velocity of falling ellipsoid particles with the velocity of spherical particles of the same volume and found the relation

$$v_e = \frac{v_k}{\sqrt[3]{a/b}} \tag{6}$$

whereby v_e represents velocity of falling ellipsoid particles, v_s velocity of falling spherical particles of equal volume, and a and b the axes of the ellipsis. From equation (5)

$$v_e = \frac{2\,sg}{9\eta\,\sqrt[3]{a/b}}\,r^2 \tag{7}$$

is derived. When the volume of the spherical and ellipsoid particles are equal,

$$v_k = \frac{4}{3}\pi r^3 = \frac{4}{3}\pi ab^2 = v_e. \tag{8}$$

Radius r can be written as

$$r = \sqrt[3]{ab^2}. \tag{9}$$

Inserted into equation (7), the equation for velocity of falling ellipsoid particles is

$$v_e = \frac{2sg}{9\eta}\,\sqrt[3]{a} \times b\,\sqrt[3]{b^2}. \tag{10}$$

Thus, the velocity of falling ellipsoid fungal spores in calm air depends essentially only on the size relationship of axes a and b of the ellipsoid (s,g, and η can be considered constant in this observation) and establishes a physiological value determined by form.

The velocities of fall determined according to equation (10) by Schrödter (1954) for various groups of spores lie between less than 1 mm./sec. and a few cm./sec. This is in accord with reports by Ingold (1953), according to whom the very small spores of *Lycoperdon pyriforme* have the small fall velocity of 0.05 cm./sec., whereas the large conidia of *Helminthosporium sativum* fall 2.8 cm./sec.

The falling velocity (in calm air) of different propagules is an important characteristic in their dispersal. This fact is not always properly recognized. Although Gregory (1952) admits that the velocity of fall of spores has some influence on the total distance of dissemination, he neglects this influence as long as the spores can be found in the turbulent air movement. He thus overlooks the fact that the gravitational fall is always going on. Even in turbulent air when the net movement of the particle is upward, gravitational fall continues. Among other things, Fortak (1957b) while discussing the problem of the extraterritorial sphere of influence of dust transportation from land to open sea, shows how greatly the fall velocity of the air-borne particle affects its dispersal. His results show a numerically strong dependence on the sedimentation parameter. Our discussion of the flight of the propagule will clarify even more the great significance of fall velocity in dissemination.

C. Horizontal Air Movement

Horizontal air movement is one of the most important factors in the dispersal of plant pathogens and of plants and seeds as well (Wildeman, 1947). The wind, a term mostly used for horizontal air movement, is considered most important in epidemiology.

Wind is moving air. The cause of this movement lies ultimately in temperature contrasts as they occur everywhere on the globe of the earth. Aside from gravitational fall, spores and other suspended particles move with the air. There is not just a horizontal air movement in the atmosphere. The paths of individual air particles as well as of the suspended matter are actually extremely entangled and "disorganized." The horizontal component of the air movement determines the direction and the velocity of movement of spores in air. The direction of spore dissemination and the velocity, which in turn affects the distance that the propagules travel, give the pathologist information as to where new disease outbreaks are likely to occur. This is why horizontal air movement assumes importance in general epidemiologic observations and examinations. From numerous works that have been concerned with this part of the problem only those by Newhall (1938), Oort (1940), Bonde and Schultz (1943), and Waggoner (1952) are mentioned as examples. The direction of the horizontal spread of agents is not only dependent on the general, i.e., average or moderately large wind direction, but also in great measure on the local regional relationships that affect the air current (Bochow, 1955). A convincing example for this is given by studies of Zogg (1949) about epidemiology of *Puccinia sorghi*, conducted on the occasion of a maize rust epidemic in a river valley 100 km. long.

Under the influence of gravitation and wind alone (as horizontal air movement) a spore can never fly higher than its point of departure lies (with the exception of a forced upward movement of air while running over an obstacle). Within this framework very narrow limits are put on the dispersal of propagules. Observations prove, however, that spores rise high in the atmosphere and that dissemination over great distances is possible. Considerable height differences can be overcome by spores and a decisively significant vertical force seems to be present. This force lies in a property that characterizes all movements in the atmosphere, namely, in atmospheric turbulence.

D. Atmospheric Turbulence

If we study the flowing fluids with different density δ and diverse viscosity η in tubes of various diameters d, it can be seen that the stream is "laminar" in small velocities and "turbulent" in high ones. It can be further seen that the transition from laminar to turbulent state does not occur in a gradual increase of velocity, but suddenly, i.e., in transgressing a limiting value of velocity. This limiting velocity v is not constant, however. Rather, the transition from laminar to turbulent flow occurs when a critical value of the so-called "Reynolds number" is exceeded. The Reynolds number R is given in

$$R = \frac{\delta}{\eta} \times vd. \tag{11}$$

In atmospheric currents the value of the length d is always so large that even when velocity v is low, the value of the Reynolds number is high. Thus, the laminar type of current practically does not occur in the atmosphere, certainly not in the layers that are significant for the disseminations of propagules. This fact is very important for all epidemiologic observations, since it dooms to failure every attempt to connect dissemination of pathogens with wind unless turbulence is considered.

The "dynamic turbulence" is closely connected with the so-called "shearing" between air strata of various horizontal velocities. These are always present in the atmosphere. We have only to imagine that the wind velocity near the earth's surface is smaller than at a higher altitude. Because of turbulence in air, air particles and suspended matter travel from one stratum into the other and an exchange takes place in a vertical direction (the horizontal turbulence exchange should not be considered here). This vertical transportation of air quanta as a result of dynamic turbulence disappears when the wind does not change with altitude because the above mentioned shearing then also disappears. However, this does not mean that the exchange in a vertical direction then disappears altogether. Only such turbulence is equal to zero as derives its energy from the current.

Another very important vertical change occurs, namely, the one that is correlated with the thermic increase of the atmosphere as well as with its thermic stratification and the heat supply of the earth. It is a known fact that warm air is lighter than cold air. An air quantum that is warmer than its surroundings has buoyancy (according to the principle of Archimedes) and moves vertically upward while another comparatively colder air quantum takes its place. Above all, the thermic differences of the ground are very significant for "thermic turbulence." Individual occurrences of a vertical exchange of greater or smaller turbulence bodies can barely be observed through dynamic turbulence. Only its total effect becomes visibly manifest and the occurrences of a thermic turbulence exchange can be observed in numerous individual manifestations. In addition to vibration of the air over an overheated surface the most marked manifestation is the appearance of large swelling clouds that can be especially seen during the height of summer, and into which great quantities of air ascend from the overheated earth surface. Naturally, the same amount of air descends again between the clouds. Significantly, the thermically caused upward movement of spore-laden air occurs quickly and over a relatively small land surface, while it subsides slowly and over great areas. Thus, Firbas and Rempe (1936) did not find the expected distribution according to size and fall velocity in pollens caught at a height of 2000 meters during an airplane flight. The strong and rapid anabatic wind stream seems to carry along the total mass of pollen bodies; there is no possibility that the differential size and fall velocity can have any effect on distribution. Night flights thus brought forth the originally expected results.

As far as epidemiology is concerned it is unimportant whether these occurrences in the atmosphere are "thermic" or "dynamic" turbulence. Their effect is the same, i.e., there is a possibility of a vertical agent transfer through vertical exchange of air quanta. Through the exchange calculations of Schmidt (1925) all these turbulence reactions were organized into one uniform scheme. The surpassing significance of the vertical mass exchange for epidemiology of plant diseases, shown by Schrödter (1954), requires that a short abstract of the theory of vertical mass exchange be given before the theory of the flight of the pathogen. In this way the problem of agent dispersal can be fully understood.

During the exchange process all those properties of air masses are exchanged that had remained preserved during vertical movement, i.e., the ascending or descending air quanta retain their respective property until they are mixed with the surrounding air—and in this mixture they give up their respective surplus property to the surrounding air or they cover the deficit with the surplus from the surrounding air. Thus, the organic or inorganic particle content of the air belongs to the interchangeable properties. The number of particles of an air quantum remains practically unchanged during sufficiently rapid vertical movement as long as there occurs no mixture with other air masses.

Imagine a horizontal surface at some place in the atmosphere that, because of turbulence, is constantly carried upward or downward by air quanta. Thus it is unimportant whether the surface is quiet or whether it moves with the average current of the atmosphere. After a sufficiently long period of time, because of the continuity condition, the sum of the air quanta ascending through a given area per unit time should equal the sum of the air quanta descending through this area per unit time. The total "mass flow" M of the exchange is thus given by

$$\frac{1}{2} M = \sum m_u = \sum m_o \qquad (12)$$

when we designate the quanta ascending through the imaginary plane surface with the subscript u and the descending quanta with the subscript o. If we then consider the number of spores contained in an air quantum as an interchangeable property, each ascending quantum m_u contains the spore quantity $m_u s_u$ and each descending quantum m_o the quantity $m_o s_o$. The total transfer that occurs through the surface unit in the time unit is thus given by

$$S = \frac{1}{ft} \left(\sum m_u s_u - \sum m_o s_o \right) \tag{13}$$

whereby f represents the plane surface and t the time.

It seems at first glance that $S = 0$ because of equation (12). This, however, is not so. According to equation (12) M only represents the flow of mass, and nothing is said about the property that is transferred with the mass. As we know, the spore content of air depends on height. Near the surface, where spores develop and are ejected, the number is naturally larger than in the higher strata of the atmosphere. This fact is expressed in a certain vertical distribution of the spore content of air. If we imagine that the spore content contains s-1 units above the surface and $s + 1$ units below the surface (in other words it changes by 2 units with height) and if we shift one quantum from below to above and as a replacement one quantum from above to below, we gain above $(s + 1)$ $-(s - 1) = + 2$ units and lose below $(s - 1)$-$(s + 1) = -2$ units. Although the condition of equation (12) is fulfilled, actually a flow of property s took place, i.e., s is not equal to zero. S equals zero only when it does not depend on altitude. The change of property s with altitude, i.e., its vertical distribution, is the decisive factor.

If we count altitude z, within which no mixture occurs, from the imaginary surface f on, whereby above f, $z > 0$, we can describe the distribution of s near the surface f through development in a series. Using only the first member of this series, we have

$$s = s_f + \frac{\partial s}{\partial z} \times z + \frac{\partial^2 s}{\partial z^2} \times \frac{z^2}{2} \tag{14}$$

whereby s is the sum of s_f, the value of s in the surface f plus the first and second derivatives of s with respect to z taken in surface f. For a first approximation we may ignore the second derivative and we may write for values s_u and s_o in equation (13)

$$s_u = s_f + \frac{\partial s}{\partial z} \times z_u$$

$$s_o = s_f + \frac{\partial s}{\partial z} \times z_o. \tag{15}$$

If, with equation (12) in view, we substitute the values of equation (15) into equation (13) we have

$$S = \frac{1}{ft} \left(\sum m_u z_u - \sum m_o z_o \right) \frac{\partial s}{\partial z} \tag{16}$$

for the spore flow through the imaginary surface. The parenthetic expression is always negative since we consider z_u as negative and z_o as positive. According to calculation, however, this parenthetic expression represents the sum of all air quanta m that pass through the imaginary surface, either upward or downward, each multiplied by the distance z traveled without the mixture ("mixing length" in the sense of Prandtl) at which it was from the surface. It is thus

$$S = - \frac{\sum mz}{ft} \times \frac{\partial s}{\partial z} \tag{17}$$

or

$$S = -A \times \frac{\partial s}{\partial z} \tag{18}$$

whereby we obtain A, the exchange coefficient:

$$A = \frac{\sum mz}{ft} \left[\frac{\text{gm.}}{\text{cm. sec.}} \right]. \tag{19}$$

With equation (18) the flow of the interchangeable material, in this instance the spore content of air, is represented as the product of two factors, of which one $(\partial s/\partial z)$ depends only on the vertical distribution of the interchangeable property, the other (A) only on the movement processes, i.e., on the mass exchange. Hence the designation "exchange coefficient," which measures the turbulent movement processes in the atmosphere. Its special value for our observations lies primarily in the fact that according to equation (19) the exchange coefficient A is independent of the exchanged property. Numerically, the exchange coefficient in the atmosphere is subject to considerable changes. Its smallest value is near the soil, because naturally the soil, as a firm boundary surface, impedes any vertical movement. The exchange coefficient thus depends on altitude. In orders of magnitude A has the value of 1 gm. cm.[-1] sec.[-1] from 1 to 10 meters altitude, the value of 10 at 10 to 100 meters altitude, and of 50 at 100 to 500 meters altitude. In single instances A can take on values of 200 or more.

In epidemiology the exchange coefficient characterizes the total turbulent processes in the atmosphere which are responsible for the transfer and dispersal of propagules. To determine whether an effect of dynamic or thermic turbulence is involved in vertical transfer is no longer necessary. What deciding role turbulent mass exchange plays in the spread of the pathogen must yet be demonstrated.

II. The Flight

The forces having an effect on the particles in the air have been discussed. The theory of agent flight should show how the transfer in the air as well as the dispersal of propagules occurs. The term "dispersal" is defined here to mean the overcoming of distance in space from the time of the last departure to the first landing. The problem is considered only at the x–z plane of a rectangular coordinate system, in which the x-axis lies in the average wind direction and the z-axis vertically, i.e., only two-dimensionally. Such a precise definition of the term "dispersal" is to be understood geometrically and not biologically. The concept of dispersal as used elsewhere in the literature has several meanings, depending on whether the flight plane, the spore concentration in a unit volume of air, or the infection possibility is considered. This ambiguity not only leads to lack of clarity, but can also result in false notions and conclusions. Thus, in his observations, Gregory (1952) follows not the path of the spore cloud, but the changes of concentration per air volume along this path as a consequence of turbulence. These, however, are two completely different problems. Contrary to all expectations he concludes that the spores cannot be carried far from the source of infection but that under normal turbulent conditions 99.9% of the spores are deposited within the first 100 meters from the source. He concludes this from theoretical assumptions based on the equation by Sutton (1947) about turbulent diffusion and on experimental observations, from the viewpoint of the change in concentration of spores and its effect on the possibility of infection. This has nothing to do with the distance that the mass of spores can travel.

Epidemiologically, both problems are equally important: the absolute distance as well as the maximum distance in which a significant concentration of spores is still present. The concept "dispersal," however, is used in this part of the study exclusively for the first of both these questions and is thus completely unequivocal.

Schmidt (1925) was already concerned with the theoretical aspect of the spread of plant seeds through turbulent air currents. More recently Rombakis (1947) tackled this problem again and proved that the results obtained by Schmidt (1925) could be improved in various ways. The elegant solution of the problem developed by Rombakis (1947) was used by Schrödter (1954) for the problem of spread of disease-producing agents. The theory of spore flight, described below, is based on the studies of Rombakis (1947). The somewhat extensive derivation of the formulas leads to an understanding of the problems of line of flight, range of flight, and duration of flight, which can then be applied to problems of epidemiology.

A. *Line of Flight*

The studies by Schmidt (1925) define as "average dispersal" of particles that limit in which 99% of all disseminated seeds have again reached the earth surface. Had the percentage been set at 80%, based on purely biological considerations, the dispersal would be but 13% of the values calculated by Schmidt (1925). Although he did not consider the effect of gravitation in the basic differential equation, he added it later to the solution. The theory given by Rombakis (1947), on the other hand, is based on considerations to be applied here to fungal spores.

The local change of spore thickness s with the time t has to be equal to the convergence of spore flow w, i.e., it has to be

$$\frac{\partial s}{\partial t} = \frac{\partial w}{\partial z}. \tag{20}$$

The spore flow w is made up of the current

$$w_1 = -\frac{A}{\delta} \times \frac{\partial s}{\partial z} \tag{21}$$

that is caused by exchange, corresponding to equation (18) in which δ is air density, and of the current

$$w_2 = -cs \tag{22}$$

caused by fall movement under the influence of gravitation, whereby c means the fall velocity of spores in calm air. The total spore current is thus given by

$$w = w_1 + w_2 = -\frac{A}{\delta} \times \frac{\partial s}{\partial z} - cs. \tag{23}$$

Substituting this expression into equation (20) gives the complete differential equation for dispersal of spores

$$\frac{\partial s}{\partial t} = \frac{A}{\delta} \times \frac{\partial^2 s}{\partial z^2} + c\frac{\partial s}{\partial z} \tag{24}$$

which, contrary to Schmidt (1925), includes the fall effect due to gravitation. On condition that at time $t = 0$ and at place $x = 0$, $z = 0$ a number

N of spores is dispersed in the open space $z > 0$, the number n' of spores, found above z at time t, is given by

$$n' = \int_z^\infty n \, dz = \frac{2N}{\sqrt{4\pi at}} \times \exp\left(-\frac{c^2 t}{4a}\right) \int_z^\infty \exp\left(-\frac{z^2}{4at} - \frac{c}{2a} \times z\right) dz$$

(25)

where $a = A/\delta$.

The following definition of "probable flight line" leads to an unequivocal solution that is independent of any arbitrary limitation: A point P at the altitude z at time t should be considered a point of probable flight line when it is also probable that a spore is found above as well as below this point. This means that the line is determined, above as well as below which 50% of all spores are found and dispersed. This percentage, contrary to that chosen by Schmidt, is not an arbitrary number but the condition for the equation of two probabilities. The probable line of flight is thus defined by

$$\frac{n'}{N} = \frac{1}{2}$$

(26)

and from equation (25) it follows that

$$\frac{1}{2} = \frac{2}{\sqrt{4\pi at}} \times \exp\left(-\frac{c^2 t}{4a}\right) \int_z^\infty \exp\left(-\frac{z^2}{4at} - \frac{c}{2a} \times z\right) dz.$$

(27)

The value of an integral corresponding to that in equation (27) can be written in general form as

$$\int_\alpha^\infty \exp\left(-\xi^2 - 2\beta\xi\right) d\xi = \frac{1}{2}\sqrt{\pi}\,(\exp \beta^2)[1 - \Phi(\alpha + \beta)].$$

(28)

In equation (28) the expressions α and β correspond to

$$\alpha = z/\sqrt{4at}$$

and to

$$\beta = \sqrt{c^2 t/4a}$$

in equation (27). Thus equation (27) can be rewritten to give

$$\frac{1}{2} = 1 - \Phi\left(\frac{z}{\sqrt{4at}} + \sqrt{\frac{c^2 t}{4a}}\right)$$

(29)

or

$$\Phi\left(\frac{z}{\sqrt{4at}} + \sqrt{\frac{c^2 t}{4a}}\right) = \frac{1}{2}.$$

(30)

This transcendental equation has the root

$$\frac{z}{\sqrt{4at}} + \sqrt{\frac{c^2t}{4a}} = 0.4769 \tag{31}$$

from which it follows that

$$z = 0.4769 \sqrt{4at} - ct. \tag{32}$$

In a coordinate system, a wind of average velocity U travels the distance x in time t, or

$$x = Ut \tag{33}$$

and we can write equation (32) as

$$z = 0.4769 \sqrt{\frac{4Ax}{\delta U}} - \frac{c}{U} \times x. \tag{34}$$

This is the equation of the probable flight line.

The question about the shape of the flight line of spores can be answered when equation (34) is squared and transposed to the form

$$\frac{c^2}{U^2} \times x^2 + 2 \frac{c}{U} xz + z^2 - (0.4769)^2 \times \frac{4A}{\delta U} x = 0. \tag{35}$$

An equation of the second degree of general form

$$a_{11}x^2 + a_{22}z^2 + 2a_{12}xz + 2a_{11}x + 2a_{23}z + a_{33} = 0 \tag{36}$$

describes a parabola of which the determinant is

$$D = \begin{vmatrix} a_{11}a_{12} \\ a_{12}a_{22} \end{vmatrix} = 0. \tag{37}$$

Since, in the case of equations (35) and (36), $a_{11} = (c/U)^2$, $a_{12} = c/U$ and $a_{22} = 1$, we may write the determinant

$$D = \begin{vmatrix} \left(\dfrac{c}{U}\right)^2 & \dfrac{c}{U} \\ \dfrac{c}{U} & 1 \end{vmatrix} = 0 \tag{38}$$

which fulfills the condition given in equation (37). The line of flight is thus a parabola. Since the inclination of the axis of a parabola is given by

$$\tan (2\alpha) = \frac{2 \tan \alpha}{1 - \tan^2 \alpha} = \frac{2a_{12}}{a_{11} - a_{22}} \tag{39}$$

the inclination of axis for the line of flight parabola is

$$\tan \alpha = - \frac{c}{U}. \tag{40}$$

The line of flight of spores is a parabola. The inclination of its axis is the vector determined by the velocity of fall of spores in quiet air and the average wind velocity (compare with Fig. 1).

As mentioned previously, the course of a single particle is unusually complicated and practically not reproducible because of the "disorganized" movement due to turbulence. The probable flight line does not describe the course of an individual particle, which is per se epidemiologically uninteresting. Rather, the probable flight line is a curve repre-

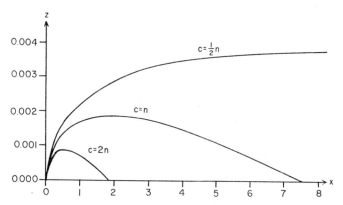

Fig. 1.   Form of flight line with varying velocity of fall (c), equal mass exchange and equal wind velocity (z-axis increased 1000 times).

senting the average path of ejected spores, 50% of which occur below and 50% above this line as the mass of spores expands under the influence of wind, turbulent mass exchange, and fall caused by gravitation. We can best characterize this probable flight line by describing it as the course of the center of gravity of the transferred spore cloud. Figure 1 shows how great the significance of fall velocity is in this problem. Lines of flight are compared, using varying values of c with corresponding values of A and U. Velocity of fall must be considered in relation to the turbulent mass exchange when discussing the problem of dispersal. Thus, if fall is neglected, no solution of the problem can be reached.

B. Range of Flight

Especially interesting from an epidemiological point of view is the question of how far the spores of pathogens can fly. This can be answered from theory when an unequivocal definition is also given for the range of flight while developing the theory given above. Rombakis (1947) deduces this definition from the one of probable flight line. The "probable flight range X" is, accordingly, from the distance of the source of spores to where the probable line of flight again cuts the earth surface.

Between the spore source ($x = 0$, $z = 0$) and this cutting point ($x = X$, $z = 0$) only 50% and not 99% of the spores (as per Schmidt's definition) get to the ground. According to the definition of flight line it is also probable that a spore flies to the point $x = X$ or travels an even greater distance. If, however, we consider a point $x = X + m$, we know that more than half of the spores are disseminated up to this point. When we consider a point $x = X - m$, we know that more than half of the spores disperse above this point.

When, according to this definition in equation (34), we say $z = 0$ and $x = X$, the determining equation for the probable range of flight is

$$0 = 0.4769 \sqrt{\frac{4A}{\delta U}} X - \frac{c}{U} X \tag{41}$$

or, in terms of X,

$$X = \frac{4AU}{\delta c^2} (0.4769)^2 \tag{42}$$

which simplifies to the equation of probable range of flight

$$X = 0.91 \frac{AU}{\delta c^2}. \tag{43}$$

The probable range of flight is, therefore, directly proportional to the vertical mass exchange caused by turbulence and to horizontal wind velocity, and inversely proportional to the square of velocity of fall in calm air.

The significance of this formula, especially the deciding role that fall velocity plays is clearest in some examples given in Table I, when the ranges of flight are compared one with another in these four examples.

TABLE I

FLIGHT RANGE (X), WITH DIFFERENT VALUES OF MASS EXCHANGE (A), WIND VELOCITY (U), AND VELOCITY OF FALL (c)

	A gm./cm. sec.	U m./sec.	c cm./sec.	X km.
1.	10	4	2	7.6
2.	20	4	2	15.2
3.	20	8	2	30.3
4.	20	8	1	121.3

As seen in examples 1 and 2 of that table, the range of flight is doubled when the mass exchange is doubled. The same holds true for doubling the horizontal wind velocity (examples 2 and 3 of the table). If, on the other hand, the velocity of fall is cut in half (examples 3 and

4), the range of flight becomes fourfold, since the fall velocity is squared in the formula. Thus, contrary to Gregory (1952) and Ingold (1953) the velocity of fall is an extremely important factor in determining the range of flight and cannot be neglected in the problem of dissemination. This can be also seen clearly in Fig. 1. If the curve given in Fig. 1 is plotted on coordinates where the ratio of the scales of ordinate : abscissa ratio is 1:1 (rather than 1:1000), we obtain a flat, slowly ascending curve that

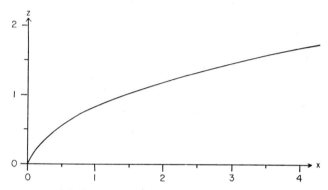

FIG. 2.   Form of flight line in a mass exchange of 10 gm./cm. sec., a horizontal wind velocity of 1 m./sec. and a fall velocity of 1 cm./sec. (with an equalized standard distribution of co-ordinate axes).

appears almost straight even at a small distance from the origin (Fig. 2). Even in small turbulence the effect of fall is almost imperceptible. This may be the reason for underestimating its significance. However, Rempe (1937) showed the effect of gravitation on the distribution of pollen sizes at various altitudes.

The range of flight can be great even under normal wind and turbulence, as is shown in Table I. How great these can be was calculated by Schrödter (1954) for various spore sizes (Table II). Although large spores can fly as far as a few kilometers, they still fall on the ground within visible distances. The very small spores, on the other hand, should be described as "suspension particles" within the air plankton.

TABLE II

PROBABLE FLIGHT RANGE OF SPORES OF DIFFERENT SIZES WITH A WIND
VELOCITY OF 2 m./sec. AND A MASS EXCHANGE OF 10 gm./cm. sec.

Spore size (length/width) μ	Velocity of fall (cm./sec.)	Flight range (km.)
Small spores (5:3)	0.035	12,400
Medium spores (14:6)	0.138	800
Large spores (20:16)	0.975	16

In numerous epidemiological studies attempts have been made repeatedly to solve the problem of how far spores of pathogens can fly. The question often assumes great importance, especially in studies on the epidemiology of *Phytophthora infestans*. Without question, spore flight has an important significance in the difficult problem of forecasting epidemics (Raeuber, 1957). Schrödter (1954) has applied the theory on the dissemination of *Phytophthora infestans* to the epidemiology of potato blight and has compared predictions based on the previously given theory with practical observations.

According to Schrödter's (1954) calculations, *Phytophthora* spores have a falling velocity of 1.3 cm./sec. Thus the flight range given in Table III for various wind and turbulence conditions is given on the basis of equation (43).

TABLE III

PROBABLE FLIGHT RANGE (X) OF SPORES OF *Phytophthora infestans* UNDER
VARIOUS WIND AND TURBULENCE CONDITIONS

A gm./cm. sec.	U m./sec.	X km.
0.1	2	0.09
1	4	1.8
10	6	27
20	8	72
50	10	225

It is difficult to carry out direct observations on how far spores of *Phytophthora infestans* fly. Generally, therefore, the distance was judged from observed infections in the respective studies. Such data should be considered as underestimates of the distance spores can fly, because such observations tell only how far they can fly in concentrations sufficient to produce an infection while retaining their germinative capacity. Such observations also assume that environmental conditions favor the development of the organism at the spot where the spores reach the ground. While these matters are of epidemiological interest, they have nothing to do with the actual flight range. But comparison of the observations with theory is possible only under these conditions.

That spores of *Phytophthora infestans* can be carried very far by the wind because of their light weight was stressed by Fischer and Gäumann (1929). Hänni (1949) also concludes that they can be carried over vast distances, but assumes this to occur only after the passage of considerable time, and direct dissemination by the wind to occur only over relatively short distances. While Bonde and Schultz (1943) established flights of 200 meters, Hänni (1949) observed flights of 1 km. In spores caught at various points over a large area Raeuber (1957) could establish that the rhythm of the daily number caught remains the same over several kilometers, from which fact a slight mobility and a corresponding broad dispersal can be concluded. Thomas (according to van der Zaag, 1956) could catch spores at 4.8 km., while Hyre (cited by van der Zaag, 1956) caught them even at a 14 km. distance from the spore source. Van der Zaag (1956) concludes from observations on an island several kilometers from land that spores can fly at least as far as 11 km. without losing their capacity to germinate. From his observations Godfrey (cited by van der Zaag, 1956) reports distances of 24 km., while Harrison (cited by van der Zaag, 1956) suggests even those of 48 to 64 km. (Table IV).

TABLE IV

OBSERVED FLIGHT RANGES FROM THE LITERATURE OF SPORES OF
Phytophthora infestans

Observations of author (Reference)	Flight range (km.)
Bonde and Schultz	0.2
Hänni	1
Raeuber	> 2
Thomas	4.8
van der Zaag	> 11
Hyre	14
Godfrey	24
Harrison	48–64
Fischer and Gäumann	very far

If values given in Table IV are compared with data in Table III, we note, notwithstanding the restriction mentioned above, that the observed flight ranges are consistent with those calculated on the basis of theory. Although data in Table IV vary from 200 meters to more than 60 km., it would be useless to dispute over what is the true flight range. Such differences can be caused by differences in the degree of turbulence of the atmosphere and by differences in horizontal wind velocity. At any rate, comparison of Tables III and IV shows that theory and observation agree.

C. Height of Flight

During their flight through the air, propagules have frequently been found at high altitudes, even in the highest strata of the atmosphere. Thus we may ask what is the ceiling of the flight line parabola. The "maximum probable flight altitude" can be derived from the data given so far: by analogy with the previous definitions it is the maximum height that the center of gravity of the spore cloud can achieve. Thus, although one spore can fly above this altitude, less than 50% of spores are dispersed above this point of the maximum probable flight line.

According to this definition (Rombakis, 1947) the condition $dz/dt = 0$ is valid for the highest point of probable flight line. If we use this condition in equation (32), we get

$$\frac{dz}{dt} = 0.4769 \ \sqrt{4a} \times \frac{1}{2 \ \sqrt{t}} - c = 0. \tag{44}$$

Solving this equation for t, we get

$$t = \frac{(0.4769)^2}{4} \times \frac{4a}{c^2}. \tag{45}$$

If we now substitute the value of t, [equation (45)] in equation (32) under the condition $dz/dt = 0$, we obtain the highest point of the flight line:

$$z_{\max} = 0.4769 \times 4a \times \frac{0.4769}{2} \times \frac{4a}{c} - c \times \frac{(0.4769)^2}{4} \times \frac{4a}{c^2} = (0.4769)^2 \times \frac{a}{c} \tag{46}$$

and with it, because $a = A/\delta$, the equation of maximum probable flight altitude

$$z_{\max} = 0.2274 \times \frac{A}{\delta c}. \tag{47}$$

The maximum probable flight altitude is accordingly directly proportional to the size of turbulent mass exchange and inversely proportional to velocity of fall. It is independent of horizontal wind velocity.

Here for the first time is a definition of the size of dispersal, completely independent of wind as a horizontal air movement. Naturally, the independence is not so remarkable per se because the horizontal wind velocity, as we have seen with analysis of the effective transportation forces, contributes no component to a vertical movement. Thus we derive from the equation that there is an epidemiologically specially significant dimension in the question of wind dispersal which is independent of the wind as such but entirely dependent on turbulence.

Since the velocity of fall is not squared in equation (47) as it is in equation (43), its effect on the altitude of flight, considered numerically, is smaller than on the range of flight. However, considering as a ratio the extent of the atmosphere horizontally in relation to its vertical thickness we can visualize the atmosphere. From this point of view, the effect of velocity of fall must be at least as great on flight altitude as on flight range.

The flight altitudes that can be attained by spores in various mass exchanges and at different velocities of fall are given in Table V, and likewise, the maximum probable flight altitude for spores of *Phytophthora infestans* calculated from equation (47). Apparently spores, especially small ones, can attain considerable altitudes.

The accuracy of the theory can be tested by the results of catching spores during an airplane ascent. As Table V shows, we would expect spores to be distributed in altitude according to their size or velocity of fall. The pollen studies already mentioned by Rempe (1937) partly show the actually expected result, and indeed, show it with a single kind of pollen. Thus, for instance, during one night *Betula* pollen, caught at

TABLE V

VARIATION IN MAXIMUM PROBABLE FLIGHT ALTITUDE OF SPORES OF DIFFERING
SIZE WITH VERTICAL MASS EXCHANGE

Spore size (length/width) (μ)	Fall velocity (cm./sec.)	Maximum flight altitude in m. with a mass exchange A			
		10	20	50	100
		(gm./cm. sec.)			
Small spores (5:3)	0.035	541	1082	2705	5410
Medium spores (14:6)	0.138	137	274	685	1370
Large spores (22:16)	0.975	19	38	95	190
Spores of *Phytophthora infestans*	1.3	15	29	73	145

around 1000 meters altitude had an average diameter of 23μ, and that caught near the ground had an average diameter of 27μ. During the day, however, pollen of all kinds and sizes was uniformly distributed at all altitudes. At a height of 2000 meters Firbas and Rempe (1936) did not find the expected distribution of pollens according to size and fall velocity. As far as *Phytophthora* is concerned, Hänni (1949) describes observations suggesting that spores have risen to altitudes of several hundred meters. According to Table V, however, the maximum probable flight height under the turbulence occurring near the soil is likely to be less than 100 meters. Apparently there are discrepancies between theory and observation. Hänni's (1949) studies, however, clarify the apparent difficulty. These studies were carried out in mountain areas where the turbulence is characteristic but differs from that encountered in planes. Orographically conditioned vertical currents could develop, amounting to as much as 200 gm./cm. sec. or more in a small area and for a limited period of time. Under these conditions an ascent of spores of *Phytophthora infestans* to several hundred meters in altitude is not a problem. An explanation for the observations by Firbas and Rempe (1936) has been given in discussing turbulence as a transportation force. The strong vertical air movements, as they are known from the huge swollen clouds, allow the value A in formula (47) to increase markedly. Then the effect of velocity of fall on the size distribution of particles disappears for a limited time in a limited volume. Stakman *et al.* (1923), in spore-trapping experiments in airplanes, found no spores. This indicates that these spores normally reach heights of less than 100 meters, as Table V shows. The results by Raeuber (1957), who caught spores at trapping stations at several locations near the ground as well as at an altitude of 22 meters, should also be used as confirmation of theoretical results. Not only is the rise and fall of the numbers caught daily at an altitude of 22 meters analogous to that occurring at ground stations, but also the total number of spores caught at this altitude was one-third of those caught at the normal ground stations directly below and one-tenth of the spore number caught at the true source of spores.

Thus we can determine the probable flight altitude of the spores and see that theory and observation substantially agree with one another.

D. *Duration of Flight*

The question of how long the time is from the take-off of spores to their landing again has seldom been asked. The flight time is difficult to observe and can scarcely be determined experimentally. To be sure, calculations have been made, such as those by Christensen (1942), who estimated that a spore of *Ustilago zeae*, flying 1 mile above the ground, would come back to the ground only in 9 days. Such a calculation considers only the downward motion under the influence of gravitation and not the vertical movement resulting from the influence of turbulence. The question of duration of flight, then, can only be answered theoretically and one should refer to the derivation by Rombakis (1947). For the sake of completeness reference should be made to Schmidt's (1925) treatment of this problem.

Here, too, the duration of flight is understood as a "probable flight duration" since it naturally follows from definitions for flight line, flight range, and flight altitude. If we designate the duration of flight with τ, we can proceed from the simple condition that $t = \tau$ must be at the place of $z = 0$, $x = X$, where the spore lands. Then, however, according to equation (32)

$$0.4769 \sqrt{4a\tau} - c\tau = 0 \tag{48}$$

or after squaring,

$$c^2\tau^2 = (0.4769)^2 \times 4a\tau \tag{49}$$

when

$$\tau = (0.4769)^2 \times \frac{4a}{c^2} \qquad (50)$$

and substituting A/δ for a, we obtain, as equation of probable duration of flight,

$$\tau = 0.91 \times \frac{A}{\delta c^2}. \qquad (51)$$

We obtain the same result by dividing equation (43), i.e., the equation of probable flight range, by the horizontal wind velocity U.

The probable duration of flight is thus directly proportional to the vertical mass exchange and inversely proportional to the square of the velocity of fall. It is independent of the horizontal wind velocity.

Again we have a significant quantity for dispersal that does not depend on the wind as such. The duration of stay in the air is determined only by the vertical movement components, to which horizontal wind velocity does not contribute anything. From equations (47) and (51) we see that the maximum probable flight altitude is achieved in time $t = \frac{1}{4} \tau$, and the curve of the flight line has a steep ascent and a flat descent.

Table VI gives the values of the flight duration under various turbulence conditions for various spore sizes, to which the respective values for spores of *Phytophthora infestans* are added.

TABLE VI

PROBABLE FLIGHT DURATION OF SPORES OF VARIOUS SIZES UNDER VARYING VERTICAL MASS EXCHANGE

Spore size (length/width)	Fall velocity cm./sec.	Flight duration under mass exchange A			
		10	20	50	100
Small spores (5:3)	0.035	72 days	144 days	1 year	2 years
Medium spores (14:6)	0.138	5 days	9 days	23 days	46 hours
Large spores (22:16)	0.975	2¼ hours	4½ hours	11 hours	22 hours
Spores of *Phytophthora infestans*	1.3	1¼ hours	2½ hours	6¼ hours	12½ hours

We can see, therefore, that the flight in the air can last for 1 hour or 1 year, depending on size of spores and on turbulence. From Schrödter's (1954) calculations we see that the flight duration at small exchange values near the ground can be but a few minutes for large spores. On the other hand, a tiny spore 4μ in length and 1μ in width has a velocity of fall of 0.006 cm./sec. and can remain in the air more than 33 years at an average mass exchange of 50 gm./cm. sec. From a practical point of view such spores should only be considered as suspension particles for which the probability of reaching ground is very small, unless another external circumstance provides a back transfer to the earth's surface. The duration of stay in air as computed from equations cannot be checked by observation.

The duration of flight is significant from an epidemiological point of view in connection with the problem of viability of spores. Consider the spores of *Phytophthora infestans* as an example. According to a short summary by Raeuber (1957) the spores retain their viability in dry air for a very limited time. When, on the other hand, we conclude from the data in Tables III and VI that these spores can cover a distance of 72 km. in only 2½ hours at a mass exchange of 20 gm./cm. sec. and a wind velocity of 8 meters/sec., we understand it to be a broad dispersal not only of spores, but also of infection. Because such conditions are fulfilled mostly in windy and rainy weather (i.e., under high atmospheric humidity) one can hardly count on a loss of viability in so short a time. In connection with the viability of propagules the duration of flight is thus also an epidemiologically important problem, about which theory can give adequate information.

Rombakis (1947) himself points to the fact that objections could be raised against the "exchange theory" when the particles to be transported leave their source individually, one after the other, and not as a group in large concentration at one time. Even under these two conditions identical results can be obtained by deductions from statistical physics.

III. CONCENTRATION IN THE AIR

The second important problem to be tackled deals with the variation in number of propagules per unit volume of air. We know from experience that the number of spores contained in a cubic meter of air changes with altitude. We know from spore-trapping experiments that the spore concentration is largest on the ground and that it decreases with altitude. From the theory of vertical mass exchange we know further that it is this vertical change of the spore content which should be considered a property of the air that elicits the "flow of property" in a vertical direction. Such a mass exchange occurs not only vertically, but also horizontally. Thus we are dealing with occurrences that are very similar to the diffusion of gases. Diffusion is known to be a direct consequence of molecular movement, i.e., a compensation of density differences due to the random character of molecular movement. In a turbulent mass exchange we also have analogous disorganized movement and can consider the occurrences as a kind of diffusion in which, instead of molecules, larger air quanta are involved. The effect of such a turbulent diffusion is readily observed, e.g., the spread of a trail of smoke from a factory chimney. Like the trail of smoke from the factory chimney, the spore cloud coming from an infection source is dispersed in a horizontal and vertical direction, and as the cloud increases in volume, the spore concentration must become less and less.

A theoretical treatment of diffusion of small particles, emitted from a point source into a turbulent medium, was carried out by Ogura and Miyakoda (1954). Edinger (1955) also concerned himself with the dispersal by turbulent diffusion of particles too large to participate in Brownian movement. Turbulent diffusion in the air stratum near the ground was treated in detail by Sutton (1953). In the spread of plant pathogens the air stratum near the ground is the true place of observation. Therefore, the following is based on Sutton's presentation.

A. *Turbulent Diffusion*

The theory of turbulent diffusion in relation to the present problem contains a series of mathematical difficulties. Contrary to the problem of spore flight, which is concerned only with vertical mass exchange, the present problem is concerned with vertical and with horizontal mass exchange as well. A complete derivation will be sacrificed in this chapter, and instead a description of what is necessary for understanding of the basic equation for concentration change will be given. One should refer to Sutton (1953) and the literature cited for further details.

We limit ourselves to diffusion from a point source and use a coordinate system with the x-axis in the direction of the average wind, the y-axis at a right angle to the average wind, and the z-axis vertical. Thus at $z = 0$ we have the earth's surface. The average wind is considered to be steady and dependent only on altitude, so that the conditions $u = u\ (z)$, $v = w = 0$ are valid for the average velocity components in the direction of the axes. In addition, we assume that only small temperature gradients are present, that the ground neither absorbs nor emits the propagules being dispersed, and that during diffusion no propagules are deposited from the cloud. The particles are assumed to be so small as to have negligible falling motion. Although velocity of fall is significant for dispersal, we can, for the time being, assume that only short distances are under consideration and that the effect of fall is a needless complication to understanding the basic principle. A theoretical exposé that takes sedimentation into consideration, as in agent flight, is given later in another context (see Section V).

The problem is the solution of the differential equation for diffusion, which is given in a general form by

$$\frac{ds}{dt} = \frac{\partial}{\partial x}\left(a_x \frac{\partial s}{\partial x}\right) + \frac{\partial}{\partial y}\left(a_y \frac{\partial s}{\partial y}\right) + \frac{\partial}{\partial z}\left(a_z \frac{\partial s}{\partial z}\right) \tag{52}$$

in which s is the concentration in the x,y,z directions at time t, and a_x, a_y and a_z represent the parameters of diffusion in the direction of the coordinate axes. This equation is related to equation (24) for the case $c = 0$, i.e., the equation (24) is a special case of equation (52), when $a = A/\delta = $ const., and is the vertical component of this diffusion. If we consider a continuous point source, then neglecting the term

$$\partial/\partial x(a_x \cdot \partial s/\partial x)$$

we have

$$u_{(z)} \frac{\partial s}{\partial x} = \frac{\partial}{\partial y}\left(a_y \frac{\partial s}{\partial y}\right) + \frac{\partial}{\partial z}\left(a_z \frac{\partial s}{\partial z}\right). \tag{53}$$

The difficulties connected with the solution of this differential equation were overcome by Sutton (1953) with the help of Taylor's theorem.

If σ is the standard deviation of distances, traveled at a time T by particles originally concentrated in the x-z plane, then we have

$$\sigma^2 = 2w'^2 \int_0^T \int_0^t R(\xi)\, d\xi\, dt \tag{54}$$

in which $R\ (\xi)$ is the correlation coefficient between eddy velocities (w') at time t and $t + \xi$. According to Sutton (1953) $R\ (\xi)$ is given by expressions of the form

$$R_x(\xi) = \left(\frac{\eta}{\eta + u'^2\xi}\right)^n \tag{55}$$

in which η represents the coefficient of kinematic viscosity and n is a number for which Sutton (1953) gives the value $n = \frac{1}{4}$. The solution of the diffusion problem would be to find a function for the distribution of the concentration, that for a given $R\ (\xi)$—in addition to other conditions—also fulfills equation (54). From equations (54) and (55) it follows that

$$\sigma_x^2 = 2u'^2 \int_0^T \int_0^t \left(\frac{\eta}{\eta + u'^2\xi}\right)^n d\xi\, dt. \tag{56}$$

In integrating we may neglect terms of the order of η since they are small compared to $u'^2 T$, thus obtaining

$$\sigma_x^2 = \frac{1}{2} C^2 (uT)^{2-n} \tag{57}$$

in which C^2 represents the general coefficient of diffusion given by

$$C^2 = \frac{4\eta^n}{(1-n)(2-n)u^n}\left(\frac{u'^2}{u^2}\right)^{1-n}.$$ (58)

For $n = 1$ equation (57) has the form

$$\sigma^2 = 2Kt$$ (59)

which corresponds to Einstein's law for Brownian motion.

For turbulent diffusion over an aerodynamically rough surface not only kinematic viscosity η must be taken into account but also macro-viscosity, caused by rough ground and called N by Sutton (1953). Since η is surpassed by N many times in size, η can be substituted by N in equation (58) so that the general diffusion coefficients acquire the form

$$C_y^2 = \frac{4N^n}{(1-n)(2-n)u^n}\left(\frac{u'^2}{u^2}\right)^{1-n}.$$ (60)

If Q is the strength of the source, i.e., the quantity of diffusing substance given up by the source in time unit, then according to Sutton (1953) the function sought for concentration within the continuous point source is

$$s(x,y,z) = \frac{2Q}{\pi C_y C_z u x^{2-n}} \times \exp - \left[x^{n-2}\left(\frac{y^2}{C_y^2} + \frac{z^2}{C_z^2}\right)\right].$$ (61)

Since the significance and origin of dimensions C_y and C_z are sufficiently known, we can use this function, derived from the theory of turbulent diffusion, in the observations that follow about the concentration change along the course of flight.

B. *Horizontal Concentration Change*

A spore cloud, arising from a sufficiently high point source, has the shape of a horizontal cone. The tip lies at the source of the spores, and the base points toward the downwind. A section through this cone, at a right angle to the average wind direction, has the shape of an ellipsis, since the turbulent dispersal of spores is smaller in vertical direction than in the horizontal one. Wilson and Baker (1946) demonstrated this experimentally by using small puffs of ammonium chloride. Brunt (1934) established the ratio of horizontal to vertical components of turbulence as 1.59:1 by means of a double wind vane. By catching spores, Wilson and Baker (1946) found a similar ratio 1.55:1. The diffusion coefficients C_y and C_z in equation (61) are given by Sutton (1953) as $C_y = 0.4$ and $C_z = 0.2$; thus, they also show the elliptical shape, but with different axes. But, under the conditions of equation

(61) Sutton (1953) proved that these values for diffusion coefficients describe the concentration change with distance with sufficient accuracy. Therefore, for simplicity's sake, these values are used.

The form of the spore cloud changes when the ground, as a limiting surface, prevents downward dispersal. In most cases the spore sources lie on the ground or close to it. Therefore we shall consider first the horizontal change in concentration at the ground. The spore source is located at the point $x = y = z = 0$. Consider the change in concentration along the x-axis downwind, i.e., the concentration change with increasing x when $y = z = 0$. Assume a continuous point source with arbitrary but firm values for strength Q and the average wind velocity u. This gives the decrease of concentration in the direction of the wind (along x-axis) based on equation (61) (Fig. 3). Since we chose arbitrarily the

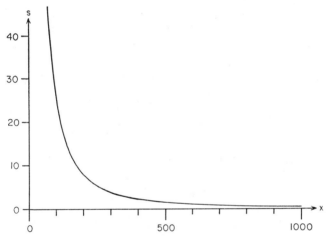

FIG. 3.   Horizontal change of concentration (s) on the ground with increasing distance (x) from a continuous point source of spores, in the downwind direction.

values of Q, u, and x, as long as they are consistent with one another, Fig. 3 shows the shape of a curve for the general case.

We can see from Fig. 3 that as the distance increases, the concentration rapidly decreases to small values. This explains Kerling's (1949) statement, for example, that even though the infection of peas by *Mycosphaerella pinodes* spreads in the direction of the prevailing wind, the strength of attack decreases with distance from the source of inoculum. We also understand the results of studies by Bateman (1947) about pollen dispersal and by Parker-Rhodes (1951), about Basidiomycetes of Skokholm Island; Parker-Rhodes obtained deposits of pollen or of spores only over short distances. We now understand how Gregory

(1952) concluded that 99.9% of spores should fall to the ground within the first 100 meters.

Buller and Lowe (1910) established that the ratio between the number of microorganisms deposited on a horizontal surface and the number of microorganisms found in a certain air volume fluctuates greatly. Durham (1944) came to the same conclusion: there is no close connection between the number of the spores deposited and the actual spore concentration. Just as the spore concentration rapidly decreases to small values with distance, so do the chances of catching spores on a sticky surface decrease. Small wonder that investigators have concluded that the spores precipitate when the effect of turbulent diffusion is not taken into consideration. Figure 3 and equation (61), used for calculations, show how untrue this is. In this example and in accordance with hypotheses, no particles have precipitated yet from the spore cloud, but dispersal in a horizontal and a vertical direction have taken place, and turbulent diffusion is responsible for this. This diffusion is actually not constant, even though we have considered it so for simplicity's sake. Reckoning with this we can also understand, at least partly, the results of Bateman (1950), according to which species are not spread in a normal frequency around their source, but the distances are greater and under certain conditions show a digression above the expected value.

Figure 4 shows how the concentration changes in a plane normal to the average wind direction, along the y-axis, where $z = 0$, i.e., the concentration is observed on the ground. The change in concentration in the crosswind direction can be observed only at a limited distance from the spore source. Because the downwind concentration according to equation (61) is heavily dependent on distance, two distances were chosen, $x = b$ and $x = 2b$, in order to describe the distribution of the concentration in the average crosswind direction and the change of this distribution in the average downwind direction.

As Fig. 4 shows, the concentration decreases sharply along the y-axis on either side of the point $y = 0$. If we double the distance along the x-axis where we observe the concentration change and measure it at the value $x = 2b$ instead of $x = b$, then the maximum concentration is much lower, as expected. In the vicinity of $y = 0$ the spore concentration is lower than at a distance of $x = b$. But at a greater distance in the crosswind direction, $y = \pm 50$, the spore concentration is visibly higher than at distance $x = b$. The increasing lateral dissemination through turbulent diffusion leads (at a given distance from point $y = 0$) to the increase of concentration in the periphery at the cost of the concentration in the center; the quantity of dispersed spores remains the same since according to assumption, no precipitation from the spore cloud occurs. The curves offer the picture of a random distribution as we know it from the typical bell shape of Gauss' normal distribution. The difference between the distributions for $x = b$ and $x = 2b$ could be expressed by their different standard deviations. This parameter could be used as a measure for dissemination. Thus, for instance, the decrease in concentration with lateral distance would follow the normal curve and $\pm\, 3\sigma$ units would include 99.73% of this total. A limiting value could be established on the basis of phytopathological considerations, below which the probability of infection is negligible. This measure for "dispersal" could be of extraordinary value for epidemiological questions.

Sutton (1947) pointed out that the particles in a cloud, subject to turbulent diffusion, are distributed normally about the center with a

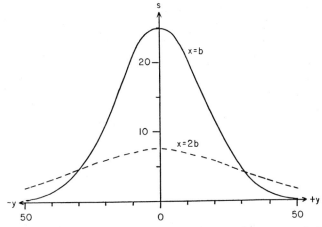

FIG. 4. Horizontal change of concentration (s) in the crosswind direction on the ground at two distances, $x = b$ (———) and $x = 2b$ (– – –), from a continuous point source of spores, located at the point $x = y = z = 0$.

certain standard deviation. This increases steadily when the cloud is expanded into free air through turbulence. He calculated the standard deviation for smoke and gases under various turbulence conditions. Gregory (1945) used Sutton's equation successfully for the question of spore dispersal. He was one of the first in phytopathology to use the modern meteorological presentations about turbulent diffusion for the problem of agent distribution. Empirical formulas for spore dispersal were established several times. For example, Wilson and Baker (1946) described the dispersal of *Sclerotinia laxa* through fruit trees by means of equation (62)

$$y = \frac{A}{x^p} \tag{62}$$

where y is the ratio between the percentage of blossom infection in trees at a distance from the source and the percentage of blossom infection of trees serving as a source. The horizontal distance from the source is x, while A and p are constants that, according to Wilson and Baker (1946), depend on wind velocity and possibly also on other factors. Although Wilson and Baker (1946) recognize that turbulence as well as wind velocity play an important role, their empirical equation (62), with which they could obtain very good results, could not clarify the actual effect of turbulence on dispersal. Gregory's (1945) equations are no longer of purely empirical nature. The dimensions contained in them are defined from physical considerations.

The comparison between theory and observation involved certain difficulties. These arose primarily from our inability to measure spore concentration because of the lack of adequate instruments. Schrödter (1952a) used the Zeiss-Konimeter for measuring the spore content of the air, but the air volume samples taken with this apparatus were too small to yield positive data. On the other hand, the "Cascade Impactor" (May, 1945) made such studies possible. Previous experiments, however, were based mainly on the number of spores adhering to a sticky surface or on the number of infected plants around an infection source. As was shown above, such data could give no information about the actual spore concentration in the air because they depend on too many factors. But since the spore concentration among these factors also represents a significant dimension in unit volume of air, such results can give information, if not quantitatively at least qualitatively, about the seasonal variation in spore content of the air, as established by Horne (1935) and Hyde and Williams (1946). With this sedimentation method Durham (1942) established that a great "spore shower" occurred in October, 1937, over the whole eastern area of the United States, in which the deposit on horizontal surfaces was up to 800–1200 per cm.^{2} a day at several localities.

Observations give little information about the magnitude of Q, nor can a measure of C_y or C_z be derived from them, although data on wind velocity u are mostly available. Yet these values are necessary for using equation (61). Stepanov (1935) set free 1.2×10^9 spores of *Tilletia caries* at an altitude of 1 meter so as to catch them at varying distances leeward from the spore source on sticky surfaces. If the data by Lambert (1929) on dispersal of aecidiospores of *Puccinia graminis* are observed, or those by Buchanan and Kimmey (1938) on the horizontal dispersal of infection with *Cronartium ribicola*, or by Bonde and Schultz (1943) on infection dispersal by *Phytophthora infestans*, in which case the spore source or the infection focus was exactly known, the same characteristic curve is found as in Fig. 3 for horizontal change of spore concentration. Thus it is possible on the basis of certain assumptions to find a direct relationship between theory and the results of such studies.

For this comparison we have chosen the data of Stepanov (1935) and of Wilson and Baker (1946) on the horizontal change in the number of *Lycopodium* spores with distance from the source. To obtain numerical values for use in equation (61) we must assume that the spore numbers established in these studies are equal to the number of spores per unit volume. We further consider the diffusion coefficients $C_y = 0.4$ and $C_z = 0.2$ as valid also for these experiments. Since strength Q is only known hypothetically through Stepanov's (1935) data (a measure for the spore quantity dispersed per time unit is lacking), we choose the

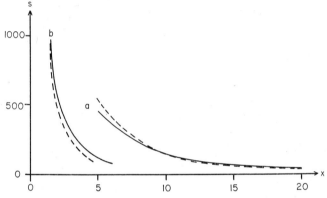

Fig. 5. Comparison between observed values (– – –) and values calculated according to equation (61)–(———) of horizontal concentration change. (Observed values (*a*) according to Stepanov, (*b*) according to Wilson and Baker.)

value of Q so that values for concentrations calculated by means of equation (61) for the first distance, data x, is approximately the size of a measured numerical value. This comparison is therefore only approximate.

The result is shown in Fig. 5. The dotted curve (a) corresponds to Stepanov's data (1935), the dotted curve (b) to data by Wilson and Baker (1946). The unbroken curves, on the other hand, represent the calculated values according to equation (61) under the above assumptions. The agreement between theory and observation is considered very good. Thus equation (61), obtained from the theory of turbulent diffusion, describes the horizontal concentration change in a sufficiently exact manner. The horizontal concentration change follows a logarithmic law. It is directly proportional to the strength of the source and indirectly proportional to the diffusion in horizontal and vertical directions.

It decreases with distance, not with x^2 as Wilson and Baker (1946) assumed, but with a somewhat smaller exponent given by 2-n. According to Sutton (1953) the value $n = \frac{1}{4}$ can be applied.

C. The Vertical Concentration Change

With the help of equation (61) we can also demonstrate the vertical concentration change just as we can the horizontal concentration change. Here again the vertical concentration change must be observed at a distance from the spore source. Putting the source at the point $x = y = z = 0$ and observing the concentration change with z at positions $y = 0$ and $x = a$, $x = 2a$ and $x = 3a$ with firm values of Q, u, C_y and C_z, we obtain the curves shown in Fig. 6, based on equation (61).

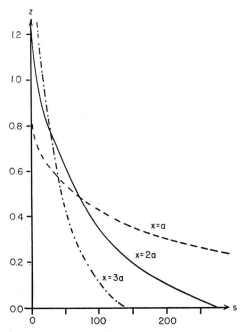

FIG. 6.   Change of concentration of spores (s) with increasing altitude (z) at a given distance from a continuous point source of spores.

Figure 6 shows the decrease in number of spores with height in the expected logarithmic form. In comparing the three curves for distance, $x = a$, $x = 2a$, and $x = 3a$, we recognize that the decrease in number of spores with height becomes less as distance from the spore source is increased, while at the same time the spore concentration rapidly decreases near the ground. Then we obtain the same picture as that already demonstrated in Fig. 4 for the horizontal change in spore concentration in the crosswind direction. Close above the earth's surface the concentration decreases as distance increases, but higher above the earth's surface it increases at first.

For the vertical concentration change, too, it is not easy to find experimental data, with the help of which a comparison between theory and observation is possible. The vertical dispersal of spores has usually been studied with airplanes equipped with spore traps (Stakman *et al.*, 1923). These studies were made in order to investigate how high up spores and pollen could be found. Although no conclusions were drawn as to the change in spore concentration with altitude within a given spore cloud, the studies did demonstrate a general decrease in number of spores with altitude. These results were later confirmed repeatedly. Thus MacLachlan (1935) used an airplane to catch basidiospores of *Gymnosporangium* at different altitudes over a heavily infected area. Craigie (1945) conducted similar experiments to determine the role of air-borne spores in the dispersal of rust to western Canada. At altitudes between 1000 and 5000 ft. surfaces were exposed by airplane for 5 to 15 minutes and the number of spores per unit area was determined for various altitudes extending as high as 14,000 ft. At 1000 ft. 24,200 spores per unit area were found; at 5000 ft., 7560 spores; at 10,000 ft., 108 spores; and at 14,000 ft., 10 spores. Thus, under these conditions the spore concentration decreases logarithmically with height.

This relation was also demonstrated by Rack (1957) for the air stratum near the ground with simple spore traps set at heights of less than 2.5 meters. Only the relative spore content in the air and its change with height can be established from these studies because of the nature of the instrument used. To use these data to compare theory and observation we must again make plausible assumptions about the unknown parameters. The result of this comparison is given in Fig. 7. The agreement between calculated and observed values is good, which indicates that equation (61) describes the vertical change in concentration accurately.

The general validity of this relation between height and spore concentration can also be examined by comparing the curve given in Fig. 6 with the results of MacLachlan (1935) and Craigie (1945). Figure 8 presents the comparison graphically. Data from which each curve is constructed were converted from the original data to the same relative scale to make them comparable in a graph. This was done by determining the ratio of values of S, the spore concentration, at the lowest altitude in each series and multiplying the original data by this ratio. As Fig. 8 shows, the vertical change in concentration calculated by means of equation (61) is qualitatively the same as the observed change in

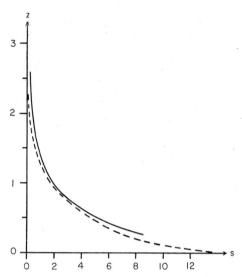

Fig. 7.   Comparison between calculated (– – –) and observed (————) values of spore concentration (s) with altitude. (Observed values from Rack, 1957.)

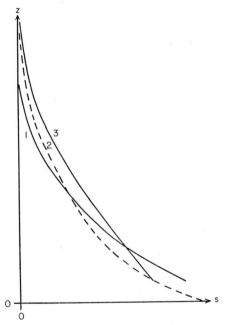

Fig. 8.   Comparison between observed (————) and calculated (– – –) values of spore concentration (s) with altitude. (Curve 1 from observations by Craigie (1945), curve 3 from observations by MacLachlan (1935), curve 2 from Fig. 6, where $x = 2a$.)

spore concentration with height. Both the horizontal and the vertical change in concentration follow a logarithmic law. It is directly proportional to the strength of the source and inversely proportional to the turbulent diffusion in both the horizontal and vertical directions and is also inversely proportional to the $(2 - n)$ power of the distance from the source of spores.

In the special case when the source of spores does not lie on the earth's surface but occurs at a height h above the ground, z does not equal 0, but instead $z = h$. When the spore source is sufficiently high above the ground and observations are made relatively near (horizontal) to the source, the vertical concentration of spores can be computed by means of equation (61). In this case we chose the coordinate system in such a way that the zero point lies at $x = y = 0$, $z = h$, and altitude z from equation (61) is counted from h, positive upward and negative downward. The question arises whether the diffusion coefficient C depends upon height. Sutton (1953) shows the nature of the relation between the diffusion coefficient C at height z in meters above the ground by the empirical formula

$$C = C_0 - 0.075 \times \log_{10} z \tag{63}$$

in which C_0 represents the diffusion coefficient on the ground. As can be seen, C varies but little with altitude and when small altitudes are involved, we can safely assume that C remains constant. For small altitude differences Sutton (1953) showed that the ground did not act as a limiting surface in vertical distribution of concentration, e.g., the smoke coming from a factory chimney at first spreads as though the earth's surface were not a limiting surface. Thus the vertical concentration change is symmetrical about a line parallel with the earth's surface that goes through the source of spores at height point $z = h$. As Fig. 4 shows, such symmetry is to be expected. Studies by Wilson and Baker (1946) indicate that this is true both in theory and in fact (Fig. 9).

Wilson and Baker (1946) studied the change in spore concentration in the air by freeing Lycopodium spores from a source at an altitude of 7.5 ft. and by catching spores on glass plates at various distances from the source. The spore cloud downwind had a sphere-shaped form. Also, as Fig. 9 clearly shows, there was a rapid decrease in spore number in the horizontal direction and a nearly normal distribution in the vertical, with the center of the spore cloud as an axis.

A comparison of these observations with theory is supplied by Fig. 10, calculated on the basis of equation (61). The value of Q is not obtainable from the data of Wilson and Baker (1946). A value of Q was assumed, such that the estimated value of concentration corresponds to the highest spore number observed by them. This assumption is made to permit a qualitative comparison. All other values of concentration are calculated from this value for Q for the same points as were observed by Wilson and Baker (1946).

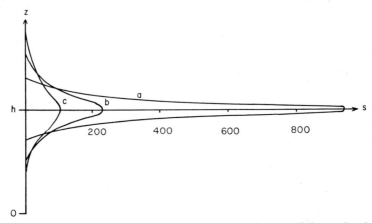

Fig. 9. Number of *Lycopodium* spores (s) caught at a different height (z) and at a different distance ($a = 5$, $b = 10$, $c = 15$ ft.) from a spore source at the altitude of $h = 7.5$ ft. (Data of Wilson and Baker, 1946.)

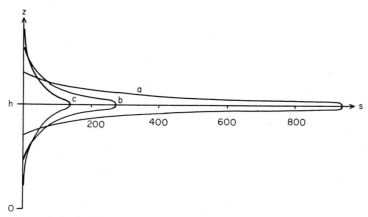

Fig. 10. Calculated spore concentration at different altitudes and at different distances from a source of spores at an altitude $z = h$. (Based on data of Wilson and Baker (1946) in Fig. 9.)

Figures 9 and 10 correspond almost completely. The agreement of observations with theory is unusually good. Thus collecting spores, as Wilson and Baker (1946) and many others have done, can answer questions about spore dispersal when these questions are qualitative rather than quantitative.

D. *The Concentration at Ground Level with Elevated Source*

Sources of pathogenic spores are mostly on the ground or so near the ground that we hardly have to consider their height. This is especially true because we can regard the upper limit of the closed cover of vegetation as the surface of the earth when vegetation is relatively low. For higher vegetation, e.g., fruit trees, this is not true. From an epidemiological point of view the question of spore concentration at any point is of little interest. The change of concentration with the altitude of the source along a parallel to the x-axis was discussed in the previous sections. We will now give our attention to the concentration of spores near the ground when the spores arise from a high source.

Directly under the source the concentration will be naturally zero. Then the concentration will increase at first. However, since the spore cloud becomes more diffuse with distance because of turbulent diffusion, the concentration will finally decrease again. Thus, from a high source of spores the shape of the curve relating distance to spore concentration at the ground is not simple.

If the source is at the point $x = y = 0$, $z = h$, then, according to Sutton (1953), the equation for the concentration at one point of the atmosphere with coordinates x,y,z, is

$$s\ x\ y,z) = \frac{Q \times \exp\left(-\dfrac{y^2}{C_y^2 x^{2-n}}\right)}{\pi C_y C_z u x^{2-n}}$$
$$\times \left[\exp\left(-\frac{(z-h)^2}{C_z^2 x^{2-n}}\right) + \exp\left(-\frac{(z+h)^2}{C_z^2 x^{2-n}}\right)\right]. \quad (64)$$

The dimensions contained in this equation are all known from previous explanations. When $h = 0$, equation (64) simplifies to equation (61). When we ask only how the concentration changes at the ground, and remembering that the source is at height h above, we can set $y = z = 0$ into equation (64) and simplify it to

$$s(x)_{y=z=0} = \frac{2Q}{\pi C_y C_z u x^{2-n}} \times \exp\left(-\frac{h^2}{C_z^2 x^{2-n}}\right). \quad (65)$$

Figure 11 shows the change in spore concentration along the ground, as described by equation (65).

From an epidemiological view the apex of this curve has two interesting aspects. What determines how high the peak of concentration is? At what horizontal distance from the source does this maximum occur, i.e., what does this distance depend on? Under certain circumstances this distance could be considered epidemiologically as a "critical" distance. We designate these two characteristics as s_{max} and x_{max} (Fig. 11).

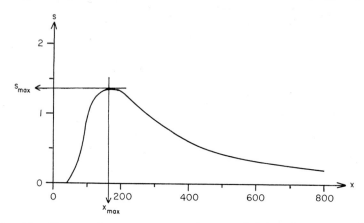

FIG. 11. Change of concentration on the ground (s) with increasing distance (x) from a spore source at height (h) above. (Calculated from equation (65).)

Equation (65) shows that the spore concentration s must attain a maximum when the exponent $h^2/C_z^2 x^{2-n} = 1$, that is, when $x^{2-n} = h^2/C^2_z$. According to Sutton (1953) the maximum concentration at the ground from equation (65) is

$$s_{max} = \frac{2Q}{e\pi u h^2} \times \left(\frac{C_z}{C_y}\right). \tag{66}$$

Thus the maximum concentration at the ground is directly proportional to the strength of the source and inversely proportional to the wind velocity and to the square of the altitude of the source above the ground.

From the condition leading to the derivation of equation (66) from equation (65) we arrive at the distance of the point of maximum concentration from a point under the source

$$x_{max} = \left(\frac{h^2}{C_z^2}\right)^{1/(2-n)}. \tag{67}$$

The distance of maximum concentration is approximately proportional to the height of the source, but it is independent of the horizontal wind velocity. This should not be overlooked in evaluating the "critical" distance.

The accuracy of this theoretical result cannot be tested because no observations are available. The studies of Wilson and Baker (1946) involve only relatively short distances, and extrapolations of curves from their data would be unreliable because the number of spores decreases so rapidly as the distance increases. They can serve conditionally, however, to test the accuracy of the theory if we consider the number of spores observed beneath sources at varying height. From their observations we cannot derive the true values for either s_{max} or x_{max}. However, we can contrast the observed values with curves calculated for this special case from equation (65), and this is done in Fig. 12.

The comparison is most alike when spores are counted at a point 2 ft. beneath the source, i.e., $h = 2$. The agreement is also good when

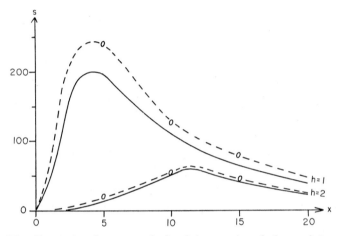

FIG. 12.   Comparison between calculated (———) and observed (– – –) spore concentrations at ground level for sources of spores of varying altitude. (Values observed by Wilson and Baker, 1946.)

$h = 1$. Although there are but three observed values alone, we also know that directly under the source, i.e., at $x = 0$, $z = h - 1$, the number of spores must be zero, thus giving four observed values to which the curve can be fitted.

Thus, when the source is high, the concentration of spores near the ground increases with distance from zero (directly beneath the source) to a maximum at a distance that varies approximately with the height of the source, and then decreases to low values as the distance increases further.

We have seen how the spore concentration decreases to very small values even at a short horizontal distance from the source. Knowing how rapidly spore concentration decreases with distance we can understand why in many spore-trapping experiments, no spores have been detected and also why an astronomical number of spores must be involved in dispersal if successful infections are to occur. Purely biological causes increase the number of spores required. If, at a great distance from the source, there is to be a measurable probability for successful infection, the spore output has to be very large indeed. A consideration of turbulent dispersal alone shows that our calculations must involve sources of strength Q, involving numbers of the magnitude of 10^6 to 10^8 spores. Spore sources of this strength have been observed. In local pollen clouds, visible to the naked eye, Durham (1947) measured concentrations from 2×10^6 to 10×10^6 pollen grains per cubic meter of air. According to Buller (1909) a specimen of *Calvatia gigantea* contained about 7×10^{12} spores. White (1919) reports that *Ganoderma applanatum* can eject 3×10^{10} spores a day for 6 months, while according to Stevens (1911) a single apothecium of *Sclerotinia sclerotiorum* can produce about 3×10^7 spores. According to Ingold (1953) a *Penicillium* colony, with a diameter of 2.5 cm., can develop 4×10^8 conidia; an ear of corn infected by *Tilletia caries* can contain 1.2×10^7 blight spores; the fungus *Daldinia concentrica* can eject more than 10^8 spores a day. Gigantic numbers of spores indeed are needed for dispersal.

IV. LANDING

Duration and range of flight of spores are known from the theory of agent flight. Therefore we know *when* and *where* they land. The discussion was based upon the "statistical mass" of spores and dealt with the center of gravity of the spore cloud. To close the cycle of dispersal, only the velocity with which the spore cloud as a whole gets to the ground can be discussed from the statistical point of view. But the question as to how the single spore lands from the turbulent air is not answered. However, flight and landing are the decisive components for dispersal. Therefore we shall now consider the problem of deposit.

A. *The Problem of Deposit*

In the following discussion the term "deposit" is used in the broadest sense. It encompasses the deposition on surfaces of spores during transport through the air, whether the surfaces are horizontally or vertically oriented, and whether or not the deposition is induced by external circumstances. The processes of deposition cannot be studied adequately under natural conditions, i.e., outdoors. Moreover, in our considerations, the transition has to be made from the total mass of spores to the behavior of individuals or groups of individuals.

The whole complex problem of deposition in phytopathology has heretofore been neglected. A few studies have been concerned with the visible result of deposit processes rather than the deposit process itself. Yarwood and Hazen (1942) made studies on how the conidia of *Erysiphe graminis* are oriented during deposition, and thus touched on an important question. Gregory (1951, 1952) concerned himself with deposition in a more extensive way and made valuable experimental observations on exactly defined surfaces.

Generally speaking, the very same forces that are responsible for the transportation of the propagules through air are also decisive for deposition of spores. Deposition is but a part of the transfer process. It is the transfer of particles from the air to surfaces. Up to now we have observed only the transfer of particles from the surfaces in and through the air. Important forces for deposition are gravitation and fall velocity, under whose influence the spores sediment slowly. Another effective force develops from the horizontal air movement, resulting in the deposition of spores at perpendicular surfaces during their movement in the general current. This process of impaction can deposit spores somewhat forcibly. Turbulence is also an effective force in deposition. Deposition occurs on the upper side of plant organs and on their lower side as well, as a result of motion of particles directed vertically upward as well as downward. Deposition is also expedited by washing out through precipitation. The following section will consider these processes in more detail.

B. *The Terminal Velocity*

In Section II we considered the motion of the spore cloud and interpreted the definitions of probable flight line, flight range, flight altitude, and flight duration that were introduced by Rombakis (1947). Since the "where" and "when" have been treated within the motion complex, we can readily clarify the problem of terminal velocity. To this end, the data by Rombakis (1947) are again helpful. By referring to the derivations given in Section II we can readily obtain a precise definition for end velocity. The "probable end velocity" is the end velocity of the "center of gravity" of the spore cloud.

Turning again to some equations from Section II we have equation (32), from which we obtained the equation of probable flight line

$$z = 0.4769 \sqrt{4at} - ct \qquad (32)$$

and obtained the equation of the maximum probable flight altitude, with the help of equation (32), from the condition

$$\frac{dz}{dt} = 0.4769 \sqrt{4a} \, \frac{1}{2\sqrt{t}} - c = 0. \qquad (44)$$

This equation says merely that the vertical components of velocity at the highest point of the flight line are equal to zero.

If we ask about the end velocity, with which the spore cloud arrives at the ground during the landing process, we naturally refer to a vertically directed component of velocity. Thus, starting from equation (44), we have only to ask about the velocity dz/dt at the end of the time of flight, that is, the time $t = \tau$. The flight duration, τ, is given by

$$\tau = 0.91 \, \frac{A}{\delta c^2} \tag{51}$$

which was derived from equation

$$\tau = (0.4769)^2 \, \frac{4a}{c^2}. \tag{50}$$

If we take equation (44) at the time $t = \tau$ we get

$$\left(\frac{dz}{dt}\right)_\tau = 0.4769 \, \sqrt{4a} \, \frac{1}{2} \frac{1}{\sqrt{\tau}} - c. \tag{68}$$

From equations (50) and (68) equation

$$\left(\frac{dz}{dt}\right)_\tau = 0.4769 \, \sqrt{4a} \, \frac{c}{2 \times 0.4769 \, \sqrt{4a}} - c \tag{69}$$

follows, from which

$$\left(\frac{dz}{dt}\right)_\tau = -\frac{1}{2} c \tag{70}$$

results. This is the "probable end velocity." Thus the spores fall to the ground with a velocity that is independent of all transfer forces except gravitation and is just half as great as the fall velocity due to gravitation in calm air. Since this fall velocity is generally very small, especially as compared with the horizontal wind velocity, we must establish that the landing of the spore cloud is nothing but a slow sedimentation under the influence of gravitation, independent of turbulence and horizontal wind velocity.

C. Sedimentation and Impaction

The conclusion that the landing of a statistical mass of spores occurs by sedimentation cannot be applied to the individual spore, except in calm or laminally streaming air, when all vertically acting forces are eliminated. On clear nights free of wind, when the air near the ground has cooled down by radiation, the laminar or "quasilaminar" layer can rise up to a few meters. Under these conditions the air soon becomes free of spores through sedimentation, as Tyndall (1881) has shown. In free air, where vertically oriented forces of turbulence influence the spores again and again, sedimentation cannot play a very great role as a factor in landing.

Normally during the day the laminar layer exists only as a boundary layer directly at the surfaces where at the most it gains a few millimeters in thickness. Since the boundary between the laminar surface layer and the turbulent air current is not constant, spore-containing whirls can penetrate into the laminar layer, as described by Gregory (1952), and leave behind small volumes of air containing spores in an interchange with air free of spores. Spores thus brought into the laminar layer settle then under the influence of gravitation and deposit before new whirls from the turbulent layer can reach them and take them away. In this case forces other than sedimentation play a primary role.

When the wind brings to the surface of the plant a volume of air containing a certain quantity of spores, the number of spores deposited is difficult to determine. We must first observe the processes on geometrically simple, exactly defined surfaces. Wind tunnel experiments as carried out by Gregory (1951) seem to be especially adapted for this.

Under different wind velocities Gregory (1951) examined the deposition of spores of *Lycopodium clavatum* on cylinders with diameters ranging from 0.018 to 2.0 cm. Deposition increases with increasing wind velocity and with decreasing cylinder diameter. The effect results mainly from "impaction," a principle described by Sell (1931) for liquid drops. If an object (cylinder, plate, etc.) is set in the path of a spore moving with an air current, the spore moves by its own inertia a bit farther toward the object even when the air has already avoided the obstacle. The length of this "course of inertia" determines whether the particle hits the obstacle and is deposited on it, or whether it is deflected around it without deposition. The length of this course of inertia depends on the size of the particle, the velocity of the current, and the form and size of the object placed in the course of flight. These factors at the same time determine to what degree an object is suited for spore deposit. From aerodynamic observations Sell (1931) shows that in the case of cylinders the impaction efficiency is determined by the dimension-free size

$$k = \frac{v_s v_0}{rg} \qquad (71)$$

whereby v_s means fall velocity of the particles in calm air, v_0 the current velocity, r the radius of the cylinder, and g the gravitation acceleration. The connection between size k and impaction efficiency E was determined empirically by Sell (1931). Glauert (1946), who considered a similar problem, determined a coefficient that is practically identical with the one by Sell (1931). The values of impaction efficiency observed experimentally by Gregory (1951) in the wind tunnel are lower than would be predicted by the equations of Sell (1931) and Glauert (1946).

But the values correspond well to those by Langmuir and Blodgett (1949). In their theoretical treatment of the problem, a set of curves is established for the relation between E and k, which is given from the dimension-free size

$$\Phi = \frac{R^2}{k} \qquad (72)$$

in which R represents "Reynold's number," already described in equation (11). For values $\Phi = 10$ to $\Phi = 10^4$ the values of impaction efficiency determined experimentally by Gregory (1951) fall within the range of these curves (except for a few extreme values of k).

Deposition by impaction, which results from the translation energy of the particles headed up by the wind, plays the greatest role in the landing of single spores. Gregory (1950, 1951) showed that the effect is small when small spores approach large obstacles in the presence of small wind velocities. Large spores, on the contrary, are predestined for deposition by impaction, especially on small obstacles at high wind velocity. Many leaf-disease-causing agents dispersed by wind have relatively large spores (*Phytophthora, Helminthosporium*, etc.) while species that inhabit the ground (*Penicillium, Aspergillus*) are mostly characterized by small spores which are not suited for deposition by impaction.

A high impaction efficiency is naturally unsuited to the dispersal of a disease within a dense plant population. According to Johnstone *et al.* (1949), the capacity of a particle to penetrate into a closed vegetation covering is inversely proportional to the impaction efficiency of vegetation, since a high degree of efficiency greatly limits the mobility of spores. According to Gregory (1952) a spore size of 10μ, the most frequent diameter of spores dispersed by wind (e.g., of many ascospores and basidiospores), represents a good compromise between the originally opposed requirements for dispersal and deposition. The large-spored leaf and stem parasites are quite correctly labeled by Gregory (1952) as "impactors," while the small-spored ones seem to be special "penetrators" that are deposited rather by sedimentation.

The usual vertical sticky deposits, used in routine catching of spores and pollens, have only a very small impaction efficiency (Gregory, 1951). The results so obtained, therefore, offer an incomplete picture of dispersal of pathogens. This accounts for the frequent divergence of data on dispersal and for the discrepancies between theory and observation.

According to Gregory (1952) "turbulent deposit" is another factor in the landing of single spores. This effect was noted by Durham (1944) while catching pollen, and he found that the deposit on horizontal surfaces is greater (as would happen from sedimentation) but that a deposit also occurs at the lower side of horizontal surfaces, an effect that cannot be explained by sedimentation. Turbulence transports the spores not only from above to below but also from below to above. Under these forces a deposition occurs on the lower side of surfaces. The turbulent deposit is but a deposit through impaction, at which the particles gain their kinetic energy from the vertical rather than from the horizontal component of the turbulent current. Consequently, only two effects are generally important for the landing of a single spore: sedimentation under the influence of gravitation and impaction under the influence of the movement of the current.

The combined effect of these processes leads to a decrease in spore content of the air. At least in large spores in dry weather there is seldom a consistent increase of spore content in the air. Gregory (1952) concluded that the daily spore ejection of larger spores is in equilibrium with the daily deposit. Meetham (1950) obtained a similar result for smoke impurities in the air, so that the above conclusion seems completely justified. With regard to the theory of agent flight it is questionable, however, whether the assumption of a daily equilibrium between expulsion and deposit can be justified in small (or in the smallest) spores.

D. *The Humidity and Precipitation Effect*

In the theoretical discussion we did not take into consideration that through the influence of external events, a "forcible" limitation of spore dispersal is possible. We supposed the falling velocity of particles to be a constant process. In connection with the problem of deposit we are now concerned with the problem of what the consequences are when these assumptions are not fulfilled. Let us, for instance, observe the fall velocity: clearly it actually cannot be constant. A spore that gradually dries out during flight becomes lighter; a spore that swells in humid air becomes heavier. In condensation the accumulation of water by the transferred particles makes them heavier, and in that way, too, their fall velocity changes quite considerably under certain conditions. Since the fall velocity, on the other hand, exerts a great influence on dispersal, the humidity of air tends to limit the theoretically possible dispersal and result in premature deposit. Thus the usual simple methods of bacteriological air studies (exposing of agar plates) produce different results depending on the relative humidity of air (Uhlig, 1953). Increasing air humidity results in a decrease in spore concentration. According to Silhavy (1954) the numbers of germs are generally low (= strong deposit) at a low temperature with high air humidity; at a high temperature with small relative air humidity, on the other hand, they are generally high (= scanty deposit).

It is not easy to find a connection between spore deposit and relative air humidity, since the number of spores caught depends on other factors as well. In his studies of the epidemiology of *Phytophthora*, Raeuber (1957) found a correlation of $r = +0.54$ between the number of spores trapped and the relative humidity. We must assume, accordingly, that the relative air humidity plays an important role in the process of deposition and for the total complex of dispersal. Although studies about this in phytopathology are rare, the assumption seems justified since it corresponds to the results of aerosol research. Studies by Meetham (1954) dealt with the deposit of smoke particles in the presence of fog. Little indeed is known about the mechanism of this type of deposition.

The influence of rain on dispersal and deposit is better known. In single instances rain alone can transport a pathogen from one plant part to another (Müller-Stoll and Hartmann, 1950). Aside from this, rain means the end of spore dissemination. For small and very small spores that can barely be deposited through other processes, washout of spores by rain represents one of the few possibilities to get to the ground again after a short period of time. In spore-trapping experiments Rack (1957) showed that the relative spore density (number per surface unit) increases with the increasing total precipitation. The duration of precipitation is also decisively significant for the decrease of particle content in the air, as Raynton (1956) could establish. The rapid filtration of radioactive aerosol particles from the atmosphere by precipitation was described by Mügge and Jakobi (1955), while Herman and Gorham (1957) came to the conclusion from studies of mineral constituents in snow and rain that more substances are washed out of the atmosphere with rain than with snow.

The mechanism of spore washout by rain is closely dependent on raindrop size. Raindrops have a diameter up to 5–6 mm. According to Best (1950) their fall velocity lies between 2 and 9 meters per second. The problem of rain washing of particles from the air was studied by Langmuir (1948), whose theory of collection of particles by raindrops is restricted primarily to sphere-shaped particles. On the basis of this, Greenfield (1957) treated the washout of radioactive particles from the atmosphere and showed that the exchange effectiveness between raindrops and particles depends on the particle size. The number of particles washed out is a function of the quantity and duration of precipitation. On the basis of Langmuir's (1948) theory Gregory (1952) concluded that small spores of *Lycoperdon* and the ground-inhabiting Penicillia cannot be collected by drops with a diameter under 1 mm. In drops with a 2 mm. diameter the effectiveness of collection increases to a maximum of 15% but decreases again with larger drops. For basidiospores of *Psalliota campestris* the collection commences with a drop diameter of 0.2 mm., achieves a maximum of 30% with a drop diameter of 2 mm., and decreases again with further increasing drop size. In *Tilletia caries,* in uredospores of *Puccinia,* and in conidia of *Erysiphe graminis* the collection with all possible drop diameters is larger than zero and achieves a maximum of 80% with a drop diameter of 2.8 mm. The maximum collection is achieved with drop sizes of 2 mm. It is about 25% in small spores with a 4μ diameter and 80–90% in large spores (20–30μ diameter).

Whether any other factors influence the strength of rain washout of spores is not known. The effect of wettability on washout is unknown, for example. Gregory (1952) notes that spores of *Ustilago perennans* are moistened by water only with difficulty but are very easily collected by rain. When they have reached the ground, they remain, as Burges (1950) showed, in the upper ground layers like other unmoistened spores, and they are not washed into the ground.

The influence of washout by rain on the deposition of spores can be shown by an example given by Gregory (1952): 2 mm. rain elicited a deposition of spores of *Ustilago* about 200 times as great in 2 hours as would otherwise be deposited during a whole day on equal surfaces exposed to wind but protected from rain.

The rain washout means an abrupt end to their dispersal for the majority of pathogens. It strongly restricts the dispersal under certain conditions, especially for leaf and stem pathogens; the ground-inhabiting organisms, on the other hand, have very small spores and but a small chance of returning to the ground in a short time in the absence of precipitation. For them washout by rain is presumably the normal way of landing.

V. Various Problems

The circle of questions that are connected with flight and landing of agents is now closed. Certain problems remain that seem important.

A. *Particle Stir-Up from the Ground Surface*

In the treatment of spore concentration of the atmosphere we assumed that spores arise from a point source, that the spore ejection is continuous and the fall velocity negligible. This picture is somewhat incomplete even if it leads to a satisfactory theoretical interpretation of the processes. Under certain conditions inoculum accumulates in dust consisting of very fine particles of plant residues that are whirled by the wind into the air. Once it gets into the air, this material can be considered a part of atmospheric dust. Just as it does with dust the wind will also stir up and transport rust spores from an infected field. How does the spore concentration of the air change in such a case? Clearly the concentration must increase from the leeward side to the windward side of such a field, since new spores always are added to those that were first stirred up and carried on. It is clear also that this increase in concentration can last only as long as the field is traversed by air currents, and then a concentration decrease should follow, corresponding to the theory already presented on horizontal concentration change. However, it is also evident that the concentration cannot increase in an unlimited manner even when the spore "activity" is ever so large, because after a certain time a type of equilibrium will be reached. Fortak (1957a) treated this problem in a theory of dust transfer over a dust-active earth surface. Since his results are pertinent to the problem of spore dispersal, we will discuss the applicable aspects here.

If a wind is blowing with velocity u in the positive direction of the x-axis, the fall velocity of a certain particle is s, the exchange coefficient is η (measured in cm.^{2}/sec.) and the number of particles in volume unit is σ, then the differential equation of the vertical mass exchange is

$$\frac{\partial \sigma}{\partial t} + U \frac{\partial \sigma}{\partial x} - s \frac{\partial \sigma}{\partial z} = \eta \frac{\partial^2 \sigma}{\partial z^2}. \tag{73}$$

[Compare this with equation (24) in Section II.] For various conditions Fortak (1957a) gave solutions of this differential equation that are significant for the theory of dissemination in the stirring up from ground or plant surface. Since only particles having a certain fall velocity with constant wind and constant mass exchange are observed under these conditions, we wish to know their concentration.

For simplification Fortak (1957a) introduced new, independent variables such as $T = s^2 t/4\eta$, $X = s^2 x/4\eta U$, and $Z = sz/2\eta$, whose connection with equations (51), (43), and (47) is readily evident in Section II. Equation (73) is simplified with these normal variables to

$$\frac{\partial \sigma}{\partial T} + \frac{\partial \sigma}{\partial X} - 2 \frac{\partial \sigma}{\partial Z} = \frac{\partial^2 \sigma}{\partial Z^2}. \tag{74}$$

On the basis of this solution the particle transfer for each particular case can be described. This is true not only under the above mentioned concentration increase until a sedimentation equilibrium is obtained, but also throughout the entire process of particle filtration, e.g., by forest or hedgerows.

How the course of spore concentration takes shape on the ground when the wind blows over a "spore active" strip, such as a rust-infected corn field, and how it carries along stirred-up spores over an adjoining noninfected area can be treated theoretically.

According to Fortak (1957a) for the special case when $x < d$, d being the width of the infected strip, the solution is

$$\sigma = \frac{C}{s} \times \psi_{0\,(X,Z)} \tag{75}$$

an equation that describes the change of spore concentration in the direction of the wind over the infected strip. For all $x \geq d$, or with the above normal variables written $X \geq s^2 d/4\eta U = D$, thus for the area beyond the infected strip in the direction of the wind, the result is

$$\sigma = \frac{C}{s} [\psi_{0\,(X,Z)} - \psi_{0\,(X-D,Z)}] \tag{76}$$

and for the spore concentration at the surface of the previously spore-free area, we have, when $Z = 0$,

$$\sigma = \frac{C}{s} [4i^2 \operatorname{erfc} \sqrt{X - D} - 4i^2 \operatorname{erfc} \sqrt{X}] \tag{77}$$

in which functions of the type erfc x or ierfc x are known functions from the theory of heat conduction. The factor C represents a measure for the dimension of spore stir-up or spore filtration.

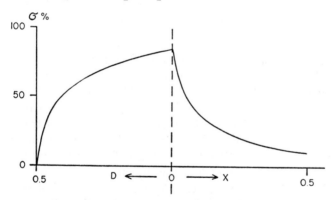

FIG. 13. Change of relative spore concentration σ in wind direction over a "spore active" strip of width $D = s^2 d/4\eta U = 0.5$ and over an adjoining, originally spore-free area $(X > 0)$.

Figure 13 represents the solution of equations (75) and (77) for a certain width of the infected strip. Since the normal variables were again used here, this figure represents regularity in a general form. For individual conditions of wind and turbulence and for a given spore shape or sedimentation type, the change in concentration can be obtained. It is only necessary to transfer the normal variables X and D into the actual distance coordinates x and d. Thus, for instance, in a strip with a width of 240 meters and under normal conditions of wind and turbulence, the relative spore concentration near the ground will take the course shown in Fig. 14, namely, according to curve a with a fall velocity of spores of 1 cm./sec. and according to curve b with a fall velocity of 0.45 cm./sec. In small (lighter) spores the sedimentation equilibrium is achieved later, so that at the end of the strip the relative

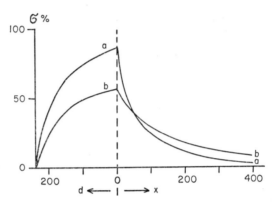

FIG. 14. Change of relative spore concentration σ in wind direction over a "spore active" strip of width $d = 240$m. over an adjoining, originally spore-free area with various fall velocities ($a = 1$ cm./sec., $b = 0.45$ cm./sec.) demonstrated with real distance co-ordinates for normal external circumstances.

concentration is smaller than the case of larger (heavier) spores. On the other hand, the relative concentration decreases more slowly than the distance from a "spore-active" strip. Thus, almost behind the strip the concentration is higher than for larger spores, and a relative concentration of 10% is achieved only at a distance 50% greater from the strip. If a relative concentration of 10% is considered as the lower limiting value for danger of infection, the decrease of fall velocity to about half would increase the danger of infection by 50%. It is shown here too how great is the significance of fall velocity for the dispersal of pathogens.

If we consider that the starting concentration of small spores amounts to many times more than that of large spores, then the differences become even clearer. If, for example, according to conditions underlying Fig. 14 the initial concentration of small spores is twice that of the large ones, the number of small spores per volume unit at a 250 meters distance from the spore-active strip would be three times as great as that of large spores; in case of increase in initial concentration by a tenth power, it would be sixteen times as high as that of large spores. In addition to wind and turbulence conditions, the initial concentration and the fall velocity establish either the size of the area in which there is a given danger of infection or the magnitude of the danger of infection within a certain area.

B. Effect of Filtration of Obstacles (Wind Shelter Strips)

The theory of Fortak (1957a) allows description of particle filtration by wind from strips. Rows of trees or hedges have been employed as protective screens in phytopathology. Thus, according to Klemm (1938) attempts were made in Rumania to prevent the dispersal of corn rust by installation of wind shelter strips that would hinder the transfer of spores. Ruggieri (1948) hoped that the dispersal of *"mal secco"* of citrus trees could be limited with wind shelter strips. On the basis of his own studies, as well as similar projects in the Soviet Union extensively reported by Grebenščikov (1951), Schrödter (1952a,b) pointed out the uncertainty of the outcome of such attempts.

By assuming that the particle absorption started much before the wind defense strips were encountered Fortak (1957a) finds the solution for particle density on the ground within such a strip to be

$$\sigma = \frac{1}{s} [(C_1 + C_2)4i^2 \operatorname{erfc} \sqrt{X} - C_2] \tag{78}$$

and for the particle density on the ground behind the wind shelter strip (at the leeward side of the strip) to be

$$\sigma = \frac{1}{s} [(C_1 + C_2)4i^2 \operatorname{erfc} \sqrt{X} - C_2 4i^2 \operatorname{erfc} \sqrt{X - B}]. \tag{79}$$

C_1 is a measure for the particle stir-up, C_2, on the other hand, a measure for filtration, while the normal variable $B = s^2b/4\eta U$ contains the real width b of the wind shelter strip. Hence, the course of the particle concentration on the ground shown in Fig. 15 follows for a given strip width B with diverse filter effectiveness C_2. Comparison with concentration change outside of the wind shelter strip—and uninfluenced by it (dotted curve in Fig. 15)—shows clearly how quickly the concentration decreases within the wind shelter. However, the repeated increase of concentration directly behind the defense strip is especially interesting. This increase is observed also in practice, as shown by Schrödter's (1952a) spore traps and by Illner's (1957) observations about the question of wind shelter and weed dispersal. Both studies show that the usual shelter strips are scarcely suited to hinder the dispersal of spores or weed seeds.

The question is naturally asked how wide a wind shelter strip has to be if the total content of particles with sedimentation constant s is filtered

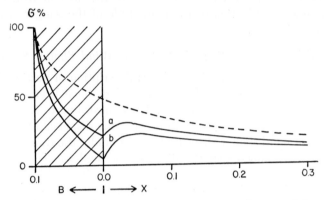

Fig. 15.   Change of relative spore concentration on the ground in and behind wind shelter strips of width B and different filter effect C_2 (a: $C_2 = 0.5 \cdot C_1$; b: $C_2 = 0.8 \cdot C_1$; --- outside of the wind shelter).

out. Based on the theory by Fortak (1957a) width B' of the "total" filtration can be found with the help of equation (78), which can be written under these conditions as

$$0 = (C_1 + C_2)4i^2 \operatorname{erfc} \sqrt{B'} - C_2. \tag{80}$$

Solved according to B' the result is then the searched-for width of the wind defense strip to

$$B' = \left(4i^2 \operatorname{erfc}^{-1} \times \frac{C_1}{C_1 + C_2}\right)^2. \tag{81}$$

Since B or B' are normal variables, known to have been introduced to make the description independent of the wind and turbulence conditions, we have to take into consideration that the real strip width b necessary for complete filtration can be completely different, depending on external circumstances.

Thus, theory shows that the installation of wind shelter strips to avoid spore transfers is completely problematical, which explains the various failures of such attempts. Future studies about the question of wind shelter and spore dispersal will have to pay more attention to the physical side of the problem. For this, a foundation is the theory of dust transfer by Fortak (1957a) in its application to the questions of dispersal of disease-producing agents.

C. Spores in Upper Air

The presence of spores in higher atmospheric strata was noted in connection with the problem of epidemiology of corn rust. From the experimental point of view Stakman et al. (1923) were the first to prove that the forces of turbulence and convection are capable of transporting even the relatively large uredospores of rusts to great altitudes of the atmosphere. Numerous similar studies confirmed this (Dillon Weston, 1929; Craigie, 1945; Kelly et al., 1951). That only very few spores are caught at these altitudes is insignificant. The fact that spores can be transported to these altitudes at all is quite important from an epidemiological point of view.

In general, at 4000–5000 meters altitude with a time of exposure of 5–15 minutes, a result of 2–3 spores per cm.[2] can be expected. The continental "steam cap" reaches nearly up to this altitude, as the studies by Junge (1951) about vertical distribution of aerosols over Europe show, in normal exchange and in undisturbed weather. This does not mean that no spores can be found at greater altitudes. The ascent of the American stratosphere balloon "Explorer II" proved, according to the report by Rogers and Meier (1936), that even in the stratosphere above 11,000 meters some spores are still found. Generally, the distribution of spores is limited to the ground stratum of the troposphere, as Niemann (1955) established in a review about the organic matter of the natural aerosol.

Proctor (1934) and Proctor and Parker (1938) suspected that the stratification in the vertical distribution of microorganisms is connected with the vertical build-up of air bodies. Reifferscheid (1952) also points to the fact that the changing bacterial content of the air obviously is connected with the source area and the biography of air masses, and Kelly and Pady (1954) came to the same conclusion.

All these statements can be understood from the theoretical point of view. As far as the flight altitude is concerned, we only have to refer to the explanations in Section II. As Table V showed, a flight altitude of more than 5000 meters lies completely within the possible range. One has to consider that only the "maximum probable flight height" is concerned here and that according to the definition, spores can also be found with equal probability above this point. The flight altitude depends not only on turbulence conditions but also on fall velocity. Hence, very small spores could theoretically achieve a maximum flight altitude of 15,750 meters according to values calculated by Schrödter (1954) in a mass exchange of 50 gm./cm. sec.

We therefore have to establish that the presence of spores in higher atmospheric strata is not unusual but is to be expected from the theory of agent transfer.

D. *Intercontinental Dispersal Through the Air*

The presence of spores in the high atmosphere is in itself of small interest from a phytopathological point of view. Its significance lies in the fact that it leads to a consideration of whether an intercontinental dispersal of pathogens is possible with air current. Ingold (1953), for instance, asks whether spores can be transferred from America to Europe or vice versa. If we want to consider the problem of intercontinental dispersal theoretically, then we must exclude the question of viability. Whether transfer of spores is possible from one continent to another can be answered in the affirmative, and then even a water surface such as the Atlantic Ocean does not represent an obstacle.

Flight ranges of more than 10,000 km. are quite conceivable (compare with Table II). This is not a purely theoretical result. Mügge and Jakobi (1955) point to the fact that for a broad dispersal of aerosols the so-called "jet-stream" is decisive: a strong west current with which at an altitude of 8–10 km., velocities of 200–400 km./hour are reached. By this "jet-stream," aerosol particles can be transferred in a very short time over very great distances, since through the meandering of this current, rapid transfers into a north-south direction can occur. These and similar currents are probably able to transport spores and pollens (that according to theory and experience are present at these altitudes) over very large distances, even from continent to continent. This assumption is corroborated by various studies and observations. The work of Junge (1951) shows, for instance, that aerosols of extra-European origin occur above the so-called continental moisture cap. Craigie (1945) could make believable the fact that uredospores of rust, found at various points in Canada, must have originated from sources lying very far south, because at the time of trapping these spores, the most northern limit of the area with rust infection was found about 500 miles south of Canadian trapping places. Bergeron (1944) reported about a probable wind transfer of spores and pollens from the area of the lower Yenisey up to southwest Finland. That the ocean does not represent an obstacle can be seen from the fact that according to Niemann (1955) pollen precipitation can be found far up over the ocean. Naturally, spores that have to traverse the ocean can be found only in the highest air strata above it. Spore trappings from the ship's mast, as carried out by Zobell (1942), indicated that the air over the ocean became free of fungal spores. Such results are only evidence of limited strength. Pady (1954) can, on the basis of two transatlantic flights, show a completely different result, which confirms an intercontinental transportation. Accordingly, air masses of polar origin above the ocean can contain about 4 fungal spores per cubic foot, while in air masses of tropical origin, even about 15 fungal spores per cubic foot were found.

All these observations prove that the supposition is justified, not only from this theory, but also from practical experience, that through air currents an intercontinental transfer of spores, even above the ocean, is absolutely possible and probable. Whether this knowledge has a greater practical significance seems doubtful. Even if the propagules retained their viability over such a long period of time, many other conditions would still have to be fulfilled before the intercontinental transfer of spores becomes significant. Through the widening of world trade with plant and plant products man himself has obviously become a major factor in the intercontinental dispersal of plant disease, more effective at any rate than the intercontinental transfer of disease-producing agents through air currents could ever be. This knowledge in no way lessens the great significance that wind and turbulence have for dispersal. This significance does not lie in the theoretically given possibility of over-coming very great distances, but rather in the fact that these factors also determine decisively the dispersal in a limited area. The knowledge of the basic principles of agent dispersal, as they have been demonstrated here, is undoubtedly an important contribution to the understanding of those processes that lead to an occurrence of illness. It herewith establishes the most important foundations of epidemiology.

REFERENCES

Bateman, A. J. 1947. Contamination of seed crops. III. Relation with isolation distance. *Heredity* **1**: 303–336.

Bateman, A. J. 1950. Is gene dispersal normal? *Heredity* **4**: 353–363.

Bergeron, T. 1944. On some meteorological conditions for the dissemination of spores, pollen, etc., and a supposed wind transport of Aloina spores from the region of Lower Yenisey to Southwestern Finland in July 1936. *Svensk Botan. Tidskri.* **38**: 269–292.

Best, A. C. 1950. The size distribution of raindrops. *Quart. J. Roy. Meteorol. Soc.* **76**: 16–36.

Bochow, H. 1955. Der Einfluss der Witterung auf das Auftreten der Kraut- und Knollenfäule (*Phytophthora infestans* (Mont.) de Bary) und die daraus sich ergebenden Möglichkeiten für die Einrichtung eines Warndienstes zur Durchführung prophylaktischer Massnahmen. *Wiss. Z. Univ. Rostock* **4**: 47–66.

Bonde, R., and E. S. Schultz. 1943. Refuse piles as a factor in the dissemination of late blight. *Maine Agr. Expt. Sta. Bull.* **416**: 229–246.

Brunt, D. 1934. "Physical and Dynamical Meteorology." Cambridge Univ. Press, London and New York.

Buchanan, T. S., and J. W. Kimmey. 1938. Initial tests of the distance of spread to and intensity of infection on *Pinus monticola* by *Cronartium ribicola* from *Ribes lacustre* and *R. viscosissimum. J. Agr. Research* **56:** 9–30.

Buller, A. H. R. 1909. "Researches on Fungi," Vol. I. Longmans, Green, London.

Buller, A. H. R., and C. W. Lowe. 1910. Upon the number of micro-organisms in the air of Winnipeg. *Trans. Roy. Soc. Can.* [3]**4:** 41–58.

Burges, A. 1950. The downward movement of fungal spores in sandy soil. *Trans. Brit. Mycol. Soc.* **33:** 142–147.

Christensen, J. J. 1942. Long distance dissemination of plant pathogens. *In* "Aerobiology." American Association for the Advancement of Science, pp. 78–87. Washington, D. C.

Craigie, J. H. 1945. Epidemiology of stem rust in Western Canada. *Sci. Agr.* **25:** 285–401.

Dillon Weston, W. A. R. 1929. Observations on the bacterial and fungus flora of the upper air. *Trans. Brit. Mycol. Soc.* **14:** 111–117.

Durham, O. C. 1942. Air-borne fungus spores as allergens. *In* "Aerobiology." American Association for the Advancement of Science, pp. 32–47. Washington, D. C.

Durham, O. C. 1944. The volumetric incidence of atmospheric allergens. II. Simultaneous measurements by volumetric and gravity slide methods. Results with ragweed pollen and *Alternaria* spores. *J. Allergy* **15:** 226–235.

Durham, O. C. 1947. The volumetric incidence of atmospheric allergens. V. Spot testing in the evaluation of species. *J. Allergy* **18:** 231–238.

Edinger, J. G. 1955. On the dispersal of large particles in the atmosphere. *Bull. Am. Meteorol. Soc.* **36:** 211–215.

Falck, R. 1927. Über die Grössen, Fallgeschwindigkeiten und Schwebewerte der Pilzsporen und ihre Gruppierung mit Bezug auf die zu ihrer Verbreitung nötigen Temperaturströmungs-Geschwindigkeiten. *Ber. deut. botan. Ges.* **45:** 262–281.

Firbas, F., and H. Rempe. 1936. Über die Bedeutung der Sinkgeschwindigkeit für die Verbreitung des Blütenstaubes durch den Wind. *Bioklimat. Beibl.* **3:** 49–53.

Fischer, E., and E. Gäumann. 1929. "Biologie der pflanzenbewohnenden parasitischen Pilze." Fischer, Jena.

Fortak, H. 1957a. Staubtransporte über staubaktiver Erdoberfläche. *Z. Meteorol.* **11:** 19–27.

Fortak, H. 1957b. Zur quantitativen Beschreibung der Passatstaubfälle und verwandter Erscheinungen. *Gerlands Beitr. Geophys.* **66:** 116–128.

Glauert, M. 1946. A method of constructing the paths of raindrops of different diameters moving in the neighbourhood of (1) a circular cylinder (2) an aerofoil, placed in a uniform stream of air; and a determination of the rate of deposit of the drops on the surface and the percentage of drops caught. *Aeronautical Research Comm.* (London). *Repts. Mem.* 2025: 1–12.

Grebenščikov, I. 1951. Über biologische Schädlingsbekämpfung (an Beispielen aus der neueren sowjetischen Literatur). *Urania* **14:** 329–335.

Greenfield, S. M. 1957. Rain scavenging of radioactive particulate matter from the atmosphere. *J. Meteorol.* **14:** 115–125.

Gregory, P. H. 1945. The dispersion of air-borne spores. *Trans. Brit. Mycol. Soc.* **28:** 26–72.

Gregory, P. H. 1950. Deposition of air-borne particles on trap surfaces. *Nature* **166:** 487–488.

Gregory, P. H. 1951. Deposition of air-borne *Lycopodium* spores on cylinders. *Ann. Appl. Biol.* **38:** 357–376.

Gregory, P. H. 1952. Fungus spores. *Trans. Brit. Mycol. Soc.* **35:** 1–18.

Hänni, H. 1949. Beitrag zur Biologie und Bekämpfung der Kraut- und Knollenfäule der Kartoffel, verursacht durch *Phytophthora infestans* (Mont.) de By. *Phytopathol. Z.* **15:** 208–332.

Herman, F. A., and E. Gorham. 1957. Total mineral material, acidity, sulphur and nitrogen in rain and snow at Kentville, Nova Scotia. *Tellus* **9:** 180–183.

Horne, A. S. 1935. On the numerical distribution of micro-organisms in the atmosphere. *Proc. Roy. Soc.* **B118:** 154–174.

Hyde, H. A., and D. A. Williams. 1946. A daily census of *Alternaria* spores caught from the atmosphere at Cardiff in 1942 and 1943. *Trans. Brit. Mycol. Soc.* **29:** 78–85.

Illner, K. 1957. Über den Einfluss von Windschutzflanzungen auf die Unkrautverbreitung. *Angew. Meteorol. Z. Meteorol.* **2:** 370–373.

Ingold, C. T. 1953. "Dispersal in Fungi." Oxford Univ. Press, London and New York. pp. 96–117.

Johnstone, H. F., W. E. Winsche, and L. W. Smith. 1949. The dispersion and deposition of aerosols. *Chem. Revs.* **44:** 353–371.

Junge, C. 1951. Austausch und großräumige Vertikalverteilung von Luftbeimengungen. *Ann. Meteorol.* **4:** 380–392.

Kelly, C. D., and S. M. Pady. 1954. Microbiological studies of air masses over Montreal during 1950 and 1951. *Can. J. Botany* **32:** 591–600.

Kelly, C. D., S. M. Pady, and N. Polunin. 1951. Aerobiological sampling methods from aircraft. *Can. J. Botany* **29:** 206–214.

Kerling, L. C. P. 1949. Attack of peas by *Mycosphaerella pinodes* (Berk. et Blox.) Stone. *Tijdschr. Plantenziekten* **55:** 41–68.

Klemm, M. 1938. Getreiderost und Windrichtung. *Deut. landwirtsch. Presse* **65:** 328.

Lambert, E. B. 1929. The relation of weather to the development of stem rust in the Mississippi Valley. *Phytopathology* **19:** 1–71.

Langmuir, J. 1948. The production of rain by a chain reaction in cumulus clouds at temperatures above freezing. *J. Meteorol.* **5:** 175–192.

Langmuir, J., and K. B. Blodgett. 1949. Mathematical investigation of water droplet trajectories. *Gen. Elec. Research Lab. Rept. R. L.* **225:** 1–47.

MacLachlan, J. D. 1935. The dispersal of viable basidiospores of the *Gymnosporangium* rusts. *J. Arnold Arboretum (Harvard Univ.)* **16:** 411–422.

May, K. R. 1945. The Cascade Impactor: an instrument for sampling coarse aerosols. *J. Sci. Instr.* **22:** 187–195.

Meetham, A. R. 1950. Natural removal of pollution from the atmosphere. *Quart. J. Roy. Meteorol. Soc.* **76:** 359–371.

Meetham, A. R. 1954. Natural removal of atmospheric pollution during fog. *Quart. J. Roy. Meteorol. Soc.* **80:** 96–99.

Mügge, R., and W. Jakobi. 1955. Über die Möglichkeit einer weiträumigen Beeinflussung und radioaktiven Verseuchung der Atmosphäre durch Atombombenversuche. *Physik. Bl.* **11:** 495–506.

Müller-Stoll, W. R., and U. Hartmann. 1950. Über den Cytospora-Krebs der Pappel (*Valsa sordida* Nitschke) und die Bedingungen für eine parasitäre Ausbreitung. *Phytopathol. Z.* **16:** 443–470.

Newhall, A. G. 1938. The spread of onion mildew by windborne conidia of *Peronospora destructor*. *Phytopathology* **28:** 257–269.

Niemann, A. 1955. Der organismische Anteil des natürlichen Aerosols. Das Aeroplankton. *Z. Aerosol-Forsch. u. Therap.* **4:** 105–115.

Ogura, Y., and K. Miyakoda. 1954. The theory of three-dimensional turbulent diffusion. *J. Meteorol. Soc. Japan* **32**: 143–159.

Oort, A. J. P. 1940. De verspreiding van de sporen van tarwestuifbrand (*Ustilago tritici*) dorr de lucht. *Tijdschr. Plantenziekten* **46**: 1–18.

Pady, S. M. 1954. Aerobiological studies of fungi and bacteria over the Atlantic Ocean. *Can. J. Botany* **32**: 202–212.

Parker-Rhodes, A. F. 1951. The basidiomycetes of Skokholm Island. V. An elementary theory of anemophilous dissemination. *New Phytologist* **50**: 84–97.

Proctor, B. E. 1934. The Microbiology of the Upper Air. *Proc. Am. Acad. Arts. Sci.* **69**: 315–340.

Proctor, B. E., and B. W. Parker. 1938. Microbiology of the Upper Air. *J. Bacteriol.* **36**: 175–185.

Rack, K. 1957. Beschreibung und Arbeitsweise eines einfachen Sporenfanggerätes. *Z. Pflanzenkrankh. u. Pflanzenschutz* **64**: 332–340.

Raeuber, A. 1957. Untersuchungen zur Witterungsabhängigkeit der Krautfäule der Kartoffel im Hinblick auf einen Phytophthora-Warndienst. *Abhandl. Meteorol. Hydrol. Dienst deut. Demokratischen Rep.* **6**: (40), 1–38.

Raynton, H. W. 1956. Multiple correlations of particulate air pollution with weather factors at Detroit and Windsor. *Bull. Am. Meteorol. Soc.* **37**: 333–337.

Reifferscheid, H. 1952. Zum Keimgehalt der Luft. *Ann. Meteorol.* **5**: 363–367.

Rempe, H. 1937. Untersuchungen über die Verbreitung des Blütenstaubes durch die Luftsrömungen. *Planta* **27**: 93–147.

Rogers, L. A., and F. C. Meier. 1936. The collection of micro-organisms above 36,000 ft. *Natl. Geograph. Soc. Stratosphere Ser.* **2**: 146–151.

Rombakis, S. 1947. Über die Verbreitung von Pflanzensamen und Sporen durch turbulente Luftströmungen. *Z. Meteorol.* **1**: 359–363.

Ruggieri, G. 1948. Fattori che conditionano o contribuis-cono allo sviluppo del "mal secco" degli agrumi e metodi di lotto contra il medesimo. *Ann. sper. agrar.* (Rome) [N.S.] **2**: 1–51.

Schmidt, W. 1925. Der Massenaustausch in freier Luft und verwandte Erscheinungen. "Probleme der kosmischen Physik," Vol. 7. H. Grand, Hamburg.

Schrödter, H. 1952a. Untersuchungen über die Wirkung einer Windschutzpflanzung auf den Sporenflug und das Auftreten der Alternaria-Schwärze an Kohlsamenträgern. *Angew. Meteorol. Z. Meteorol.* **1**: 154–158.

Schrödter, H. 1952b. Zur phytopathologischen Problematik von Windschutzanlagen. *Nachrbl. deut. Pflanzenschutzdienst (Berlin)* [N.F.] **6**: (32): 91–92.

Schrödter, H. 1954. Die Bedeutung von Massenaustausch und Wind für die Verbreitung von Pflanzenkrankheiten. Ein. Beitrag zur Epidemiologie. *Nachrbl. deut. Pflanzenschutzdienst (Berlin)* [N.F.] **8** (34): 166–172.

Sell, W. 1931. Staubausscheidung an einfachen Körpern und in Luftfiltern. *Forschungsh. Ver. deut. Ing.* **347**: 1–22.

Silhavy, F. 1954. Untersuchungen des Keimgehaltes der Luft in Wien. *Wetter u. Leben* **6**: 16–19.

Stakman, E. C., A. W. Henry, G. C. Curran, and W. N. Christopher. 1923. Spores in the upper air. *J. Agr. Research* **24**: 599–606.

Stepanov, K. M. 1935. Dissemination of infectious diseases of plants by air currents. (translated title). *Bull. Plant. Protection (U.S.S.R.)* Ser. II Phytopathology **8**: 1–68.

Stevens, F. L. 1911. A serious lettuce disease. *N. Carolina State Coll. Agr. Expt. Sta. Bull.* **217**.

Sutton, O. G. 1947. The theoretical distribution of airborne pollution from factory chimneys. *Quart. J. Roy. Meteorol. Soc.* **73:** 426–436.

Sutton, O. G. 1953. "Micrometeorology." McGraw-Hill, New York.

Tyndall, J. 1881. "Essays on the Floating Matter in the Air in Relation to Putrefaction and Infection." London.

Uhlig, W. 1953. Die Bestimmung des Keimgehaltes der Luft. *Wiss. Z. Univ. Berlin* **3:** 487–501.

van der Zaag, D. E. 1956. Overwintering en epidemiologie van *Phytophthora infestans*, tevens enige nieuwe bestrijdingsmogelijkheden. *Tijdschr. Plantenziekten* **62:** 89–156.

Waggoner, P. E. 1952. Distribution of potato late blight around inoculum sources. *Phytopathology* **42:** 323–328.

White, J. H. 1919. On the biology of *Fomes applanatus*. *Trans. Roy. Can. Inst.* pp. 159–167.

Wildeman, E. de. 1947. Les vents et la végétation. *Acad. roy. Belg. Bull. classe Sci.* [5] **32:** 252–257.

Wilson, E. E., and G. A. Baker. 1946. Some aspects of the aerial dissemination of spores, with special reference to conidia of *Sclerotinia laxa*. *J. Agr. Research* **72:** 301–327.

Yarwood, C. E., and W. E. Hazen, 1942. Vertical orientation of powdery mildew conidia during fall. *Science* **96:** 316–317.

Zobell, C. E. 1942. Micro-organisms in marine air. *In* "Aerobiology," American Association for the Advancement of Science, pp. 55–68. Washington, D. C.

Zogg, H. 1949. Untersuchungen über die Epidemiologie des Maisrostes *Puccinia sorghi* Schw. *Phytopathol. Z.* **15:** 143–192.

CHAPTER 7

Analysis of Epidemics

J. E. VAN DER PLANK

Division of Plant Pathology, Dept. of Agriculture, Pretoria, Union of South Africa

I. Introduction

A. Aim of the Chapter

This chapter is analytical rather than descriptive. In conformity with the basic purpose of this treatise the chapter aims at an understanding of the factors and processes that go to make an epidemic, and not at a description of important epidemics, past or present.

B. Some Common Misconceptions

It is stated in the literature that for an epidemic to occur there must be an aggressive parasite that multiplies fast, spreads far and swiftly, and is not particularly selective in its requirements. These are total misconceptions. They are the cause of much confused thinking and must be disposed of forthwith.

Consider swollen shoot of cacao, a systemic virus disease in West Africa, as an example. The virus complex is carried by slow-moving flightless mealy bugs of the family Pseudococcidae, and spreads largely from tree to tree in contact (Posnette, 1953). It is delicate, and survives for less than an hour in the feeding vectors (Posnette, 1953). The number of infected trees on a farm multiplies slowly; under conditions of unrestricted natural spread it took 30 months for the percentage of infected trees to increase from 31 to 75 (Anonymous, 1949). The spread of infection from farm to farm is also slow. In 1947 the largest area of disease in West Africa had reached a radius of only some 10 miles after having spread continuously since 1922 (Posnette, 1947). Yet there can be no doubt that swollen shoot is a major epidemic. The virus complex is endemic in West African indigenous trees of the Sterculiaceae and Bombacaceae. As a sporadic disease, cacao swollen shoot has a long history in West Africa (Posnette, 1953). But some 30 years ago the epidemic began, with the merging of separate but expanding, more or less circular outbreaks, into larger amorphous areas of dead and dying trees, which spread ever more rapidly and devastated whole farms in their spread (Posnette, 1953). The disease has caused political upheavals, and the cacao industry from the western Ivory Coast to central Nigeria has needed drastic measures to save it.

Another example is oak wilt, caused by the fungus *Ceratocystis fagacearum*. The current epidemic of this disease in the United States was rated sufficiently high to get an entire chapter to itself in the limited space of "Plant Diseases," the United States Department of Agriculture's Yearbook for 1953. Yet the parasite has very limited means of spread. It can spread over a distance by some means that are not yet properly understood, but the main spread is from tree to tree. Infection takes place through root grafts, and local barriers such as roads are sometimes enough to stop it (Riker, 1951).

An extreme example is psorosis, a virus disease of citrus. No vector is known. The virus can spread from tree to tree by root grafts, but the natural spread is so slow that it is extremely difficult to demonstrate in orchards. Yet psorosis is currently the greatest killer of citrus trees in California (Moore *et al.*, 1957). Psorosis epidemics, it seems, may take half a century or more to develop.

C. *Epidemics as a Matter of Balance between Opposing Processes*

The human population of a country can increase as a result of a high birth rate; it can also increase as the result of a low death rate. It will increase with a low birth rate provided that the death rate is even lower. As with men, so it is with plant pathogens. Disease can increase to epidemic levels because (to consider only the extremes) the pathogen has a high birth rate or because it has a low death rate. The misconceptions we have just discussed have arisen because attention has been focused on high birth rate epidemics. But low death rate epidemics are also important, particularly with perennial hosts.

High birth rate epidemics are usually caused by fungi which develop uredospores, conidia, oidia, and the like, and produce local lesions in the host. Low death rate epidemics are caused largely but not entirely by systemic pathogens. The explanation is often fairly obvious. The systemic pathogen is safe within the host, and if the host is perennial and the disease not immediately lethal, a long life of the infected host guarantees a long life to the systemic pathogen. With pathogens as well as with men longevity means a low death rate. The terms are practically equivalent.

The line between the two types of epidemic is often somewhat blurred, but at the extremes the distinction between them is clear and has interesting consequences. High birth rate epidemics are usually controlled by fungicides or resistant varieties; low death rate epidemics are mainly controlled by means of sanitation. High birth rate epidemics usually spread fast; low death rate epidemics usually spread slowly. These and other consequences will unfold themselves logically as we proceed. But the terms high birth rate epidemics and low death rate epidemics have been used purely to illustrate a point and now will be dropped in favor of more conventional expressions.

II. The Multiplication of Infections

A. Multiplication within a Crop

1. The Course of an Epidemic

There is no such thing as a typical epidemic. The variety of epidemics in plant pathology is infinite. To mention just two factors, the epidemic varies with the amount of inoculum that is the source of the infection, and this ranges with the different diseases from scarce to abundant; it varies with the rate at which the infections multiply, and this ranges from very slow to very fast. Because of this variety, one example is as good as another. Blight of potatoes, caused by *Phytophthora infestans,* is chosen here as an example because of its place in the history of plant pathology. But even for this one disease the example we have chosen for illustration is not typical of all epidemics. It is based on data from western Europe. If blight in North America had been the example, stress would have been laid on the danger of epidemics starting from piles of culled potatoes and garbage dumps near towns.

Figure 1 is based on data taken from a probit foliage decay line given by Large (1945) for an epidemic of blight on potatoes in England. Observations were started on August 11, when 0.1% of the foliage was infected. This is equivalent to an average of about 1 lesion per plant. The epidemic progressed for about 4 weeks, after which all the foliage had been destroyed by blight. The curve that shows this in Fig. 1 is sigmoid. The figure also shows the rate of increase of infection per cent per day. The rate for this epidemic began at about 48%, when observations were started on August 11, and gradually dropped to zero as the epidemic ran its course.

In the Netherlands the early history of a potato blight epidemic was studied by van der Zaag (1956). We assume that the results hold for England too. Van der Zaag found that the most important primary foci of infection were infected plants growing from infected seed. These plants had a few weak, shriveled shoots with a few lesions from which spores were released during the second half of May. They were most abundant in the very susceptible variety, Duke of York, in which about 1 primary focus per square kilometer was found. Infection spread first around these foci, then generally over the fields, and from field to field and from variety to variety. Our concern here is not with the progress in any particular field but with the epidemic generally.

These findings show how inadequate a picture Fig. 1 gives of an epidemic. There are 3,000,000 or 4,000,000 plants in 1 sq. km. of potatoes, so that there are (in round figures) 3,000,000 or 4,000,000 lesions per square kilometer of potatoes when 0.1% of the foliage is infected. Still in round figures, infection had to multiply 1,000,000 times from the original foci before the level of 0.1% was reached on August 11. Figure 1 describes the one-thousandfold increase (from 0.1 to 100%) that occurred after

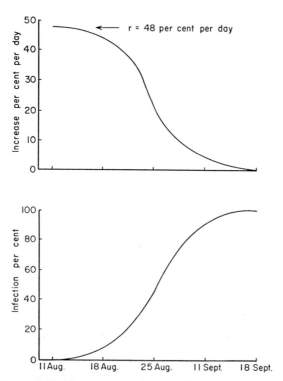

FIG. 1. *Lower half:* The progress of an epidemic of blight (*P. infestans*) in potatoes. (Data of Large, 1945.) *Upper half:* The increase of infection per day expressed as a percentage of the infection already present.

August 11, and ignores the one-millionfold increase that went before. And in terms of time Fig. 1 starts in August instead of May, like the biography of a centenarian that starts after his seventieth birthday.

Consider the matter from the farmer's point of view. For him the most important single characteristic of an epidemic is its date of onset. This decides when he must spray or whether he need spray at all. If the date is early—say, in July in England—heavy losses are likely to occur if the disease is unchecked. But if it is late—say, in September—losses are likely to be small (apart from tuber infection), and spraying would be a waste of material and effort. There are of course some variations in detail (an epidemic may start early and then be checked by a change in the weather) but the general pattern is clear, as can be seen from the analyses of Moore (1943), Large (1952), Beaumont et al. (1953), and Large et al. (1954). The date of onset is determined by what happens before the onset, i.e., by that portion of the epidemic not described in Fig. 1.

Infection increased one-millionfold between the second half of May and August 11, i.e., in about 80 days. This is equivalent to an average increase "at compound interest" at the rate of 17% per day. But the rate would not have remained at a steady average since it is affected by changes in the weather. Apart from that, the potato becomes more susceptible as it becomes older (Grainger, 1956). One can therefore infer that the rate was considerably less than 17% at the start and increased to 48% by August 11.

2. Rate of Multiplication before the Onset of the Epidemic

For convenience we can define the onset of an epidemic as that time when not more than 5% of the susceptible tissue is infected, or, for systemic diseases, when not more than 5% of the plants are infected. Within this rough limit we can decide on any criterion we wish; for example, with potato blight in England and Wales the starting point for the assessment of blight is 0.1% infection, and this level can conveniently be taken to indicate the onset.

The rate of increase of disease has been taken as

$$\frac{dx}{dt} = kx(1 - x) \tag{1}$$

in which k is a constant and x is the proportion of susceptible tissue that is infected, or, for systemic diseases, the proportion of infected plants. The rate at which infection occurs is, according to this equation, proportional to the product of the proportion of infected tissue and the proportion of healthy susceptible tissue, that is, to the proportion of tissue that is still available for infection. Curves of this equation describing the progress of infection with time have the sigmoid shape so commonly found in plant pathology. Large (1945) applied the equation to blight epidemics and concluded that it would give a good fit to actual blight progress curves within the limits of accuracy of the original observations. Nevertheless the reader is warned that after the onset a good fit can come about only as a result of counterbalancing factors, because the incubation period (i.e., the pre-reproduction period after infection) inevitably tends to increase the value of k as the epidemic progresses beyond the onset. That is, after the onset, k is just an empirical constant even in a constant environment. We use equation 1 and sigmoid progress curves almost solely to provide a helpful introduction to the study of multiplication. After the introduction the topic is treated in a way that will nearly obviate the need for considering disease progress curves beyond the onset.

Infection is influenced by the weather, the susceptibility of the host, the virulence of the pathogen, etc. So equation 1 will be rewritten in the form

$$\frac{dx}{dt} = kx(1 - x)f(T,H,S \ldots) \tag{2}$$

in which f $(T, H, S \ldots)$ is a function of the temperature and humidity of the air, the susceptibility of the host, and so on.

Before the onset of an epidemic, x is small and, in the definition already given for the onset, less than 0.05. As a good approximation for the progress of infection up to the onset, the term $(1 - x)$ can be dropped and equation 2 rewritten as

$$\frac{dx}{dt} = kxf(T,H,S \ldots) \tag{3}$$

$$r = \frac{100}{x} \frac{dx}{dt}$$

$$= 100kf(T,H,S \ldots) \tag{4}$$

By definition, r is the rate of increase per cent per day (or per year, if years are the units of time) up to the onset of the epidemic. Within the limits of the approximation just stated r is independent of the progress of the epidemic (up to the onset) and becomes a direct reflection of the environmental conditions, the susceptibility of the host, and so on. A qualification, normally of minor importance, will be discussed in Section II, A, 6.

3. Some Comments about r

One must become familiar with r. It is a fundamental and perhaps the most useful concept of epidemiology. It plays its part not only in multiplication rates, but also in the rate of spread of epidemics in distance (Section IV, A and E), in the theory of forecasting (Section III, B), in sanitation (Section III, C), and directly or indirectly, in much else. The impression may have been given that r is only an approximation. That is incorrect. For convenience r is allowed to make its debut approximately as the percentage rate of multiplication at or before the onset of an epidemic, which is accurate enough for present purposes. But *r* is a concept capable of exact determination (as by equation 5) and applicable throughout the course of the epidemic. The reasons for using it mainly at or before the onset will appear later.

In reporting the results of censuses, human birth rates, death rates, and rates of increase of population are given in terms of 1,000 of population. It is not assumed that the rates are the same for all hours of the day, for all seasons of the year, or for all years of boom and depression, peace and war. The crude rates are simply a convenient way of expressing what is happening. So too *r* can be regarded as a convenient way of reporting the results of censuses of infections before or at the onset. It is not implied that *r* is constant from hour to hour or day to day. It just expresses the tempo of developments up to the onset in an uncomplicated way. But one condition is implied: fractions of a day or, if appropriate, a year must be avoided. When, for example, it is calculated in Section III, C that an epidemic would be delayed 3.7 days, this must be interpreted as "from 3 to 4 days."

In one way *r* has an advantage over crude census rates, which are subject to the influence of varying proportions of the population in the different age groups, particularly to a varying proportion of women of childbearing age. Superficially, the same problem occurs with *r*. With potato blight, for example, it takes from 4 to 6 days or longer after inoculation for spores to be produced. But for most of this period there is no recognizable lesion, and spore formation begins soon after the lesions become visible in the field. Up to the time of the onset of the epidemic relatively few of the lesions seen in the field are not of spore-bearing age; one could without great difficulty count as lesions only those of an age to produce spores. The validity of using lesions of this sort for determining multiplication rates is examined in Section II, A, 6.

The magnitude of *r* reflects the effect of temperature, humidity, rainfall, wind, and other environmental factors on multiplication; it reflects among other factors the resistance or susceptibility of the host, the proportion of spores that germinate, the proportion of germinated spores that manage to enter the host and establish infection, the rate of increase in size of the lesion, the speed at which spores are produced and their number, the abundance of vectors and their mobility, efficiency, and distribution, and the size and number per acre of the host plants. It summarizes the equilibrium of the factors (except *x* itself) that affect the tempo of multiplication. Because of this, few of these factors will be specifically dealt with in this chapter. There is, for example, no discussion of the effect of weather and climate. This may seem strange in a chapter on epidemiology. But it is logical. When a forecaster uses his knowledge of the weather and other relevant factors to forecast an epidemic, he is in fact forecasting a faster rate of multiplication. To him the weather and other factors are important. To us (for the purpose of this chapter) the rate of multiplication is important. This statement carries no implication that the one approach is better than the other. There are several possible approaches to the discussion of epidemics. One chooses what one believes to be the most apt for one's purpose.

4. The Estimation of r

Substitute $r/100$ for kf $(T,H,S$ . . . $)$ in equation 2, integrate, change logarithms to the base 10, and rearrange thus:

$$r = \frac{230}{t_2 - t_1} \log \frac{x_2(1 - x_1)}{x_1(1 - x_2)}. \tag{5}$$

Here x_1 and x_2 are the proportion of susceptible tissue infected (or, for systemic diseases, the proportion of infected plants) at dates t_1 and t_2, and $t_2 - t_1$ is the interval in days (or years, if this is appropriate) between these dates.

For example, according to the data of Large (1945) blight in potatoes at Dartington in 1942 increased from 0.1 to 5.0% in 7 days. Here x_1 and x_2 are 0.001 and 0.05, respectively, and $t_2 - t_1$ is 7 days. From equation 5, $r = 57\%$ per day.

In general, the use of equation 5 assumes that the lesions are randomly distributed. In the particular case of potato blight there is the independent evidence of Gregory (1948) that this is so; but randomness is not the rule. There are often quick departures from randomness, especially when systemic diseases multiply, particularly the systemic diseases of trees. There is a general rule about this: the smaller the size of lesion, the higher the value of x_2 that can be used without incurring a serious error from lack of randomness. A systemically infected plant must be considered as a single lesion (Section IV, F).

As another example, consider cauliflower mosaic. It spreads in non-random fashion to form nests of infected plants (Broadbent, 1957). In a trial with different strains of cauliflower there were 1.7 and 5.9% infected plants on August 21 and September 4, respectively (see Fig. 4 in Broadbent, 1957), so x_1 and x_2 are 0.017 and 0.059, respectively, and $t_2 - t_1$ is 14 days; whence r is 9.2% per day. The epidemic was started artificially by planting an infected plant at the center of each plot of 121 plants, so 5.9% infection represents roughly 7 plants around each infector plant. The evidence is that at this stage the error from nonrandomness is small, so the estimate of r is fairly trustworthy; but at much higher values of x_2 estimates would be too low.

With local lesion disease on plants that grow between t_1 and t_2, allowance must be made for new susceptible tissue. If susceptible tissue increases m times between t_1 and t_2, equation 5 must be rewritten as

$$r = \frac{230}{t_2 - t_1} \log \frac{mx_2(1 - x_1)}{x_1(1 - x_2)}. \tag{6}$$

Chester (1943) gives figures for the multiplication of leaf rust (*Puccinia triticina*) of wheat in Oklahoma. After a severe winter followed by normal weather, infection increases at a steady rate from 1 pustule per 1,000 leaves at the beginning of March to 10 pustules per leaf at the beginning of June. During this period there is a tenfold increase of leaf tissue (Chester, 1946); hence m is 10. The ratio x_2/x_1 is 10,000, and $t_2 - t_1$ is 92 days. An infection of 10 pustules per leaf is equivalent to about 1% infection, according to Fig. 13 of Chester (1950); so x_2 is 0.01 and x_1 is even smaller, and we can ignore the terms $(1 - x_1)$ and $(1 - x_2)$. By equation 6, $r = 12.5\%$ per day.

5. General Comments on the Restriction of Much of This Chapter to Events before the Onset

Physical chemistry advanced far in the theory of dilute solutions. The gas laws were applied to dilute solutions, and dissociation constants were determined in dilute solutions. This was done in the first place to avoid the difficulties of dealing in theory and practice with the behavior of molecules and ions at high concentrations. In the same way this chapter deals to a great extent with the theory of dilute concentrations of disease: of disease up to the onset, defined arbitrarily as the 5% level. Primarily the reason for this is to avoid the objection against using disease progress curves after the onset.

How much information do we lose by confining quantitative discussions to the period up to the onset? The answer is: surprisingly little. Consider these examples. In Section III, C an equation is given that evaluates sanitation in terms of a delay in the onset of the epidemic. If the weather and other conditions stay constant, the delay in the onset is also the delay in reaching the 50% level of disease or the 99% level. If the weather changes, then interest is changed from the factor of sanitation to the factor of weather. By describing the effect of sanitation on the onset, one has in effect described all that needs to be described about the effect of sanitation on the course of the epidemic. In other words, the loss of information from confining attention to the period up to the onset is negligible. Also, it does not matter what criterion one takes for the onset, provided that it is not more than about 5%; it could just as well or better be taken at 0.1%. In Section III, B we discuss the application of r to the theory of forecasting; in most cases forecasts are in practice confined to the onset of an epidemic.

Gradients of infection away from the source figure largely in Sections IV and V. With gradients, too, it can be shown both that it is wise to keep calculations to the period up to the onset of the epidemic and that remarkably little information is lost by doing so. In this chapter we do in fact discuss gradients at higher levels of disease, and correct the data as best we can. But this is only through lack of choice; the data are so scant that one cannot at present afford to be selective.

6. Justification for Using the Law of Compound Interest When There Is an Incubation Period

The meaning given to r is that it is the rate of compound interest (per cent) up to the onset. True compound interest (we are not concerned with bankers' compound interest) is added to accumulated capital as it is earned, and then instantly begins earning itself; the concept of an incubation (i.e., pre-reproduction) period is foreign to the law of compound interest as it is used in science. Are we then justified in applying the law, as represented by r, to plant disease? It seems that we are, and it will be shown that r can be used as an apparent rate.

The meaning of x is the proportion of infected tissue in which incubation is complete. The infection is visible and the lesions are of an age to produce inoculum (according to the suggestion in Section II, A, 3). Consider now the total proportion x' of tissue that is infected, even if incubation is still incomplete. To simplify the argument, we shall confine attention to events before the onset of the epidemic. Instead of equations 3 and 4, let us write for the same set of observations

$$\frac{dx'}{dt} = \frac{r'}{100} x'_{t-P} \tag{7}$$

Here x'_{t-P} is the proportion of infected tissue at time $t - P$, in which P is the incubation period. It is the proportion of tissue in which incubation is complete and therefore has the same meaning as x in the earlier equations. It can be determined that

$$r = r'e^{-\frac{Pr}{100}}. \tag{8}$$

In effect, r is a compound interest rate to which P contributes, outwardly like any other factor, such as the abundance of vectors.

Equation 8 holds only when P and r' are constant. More generally, it can be shown that despite an incubation period the concept of compound interest is valid even if P and r' vary with temperature, humidity, etc.

There is more to it than just that. In the early history of an epidemic (for example, soon after inoculation in an artificial epidemic) r at first varies with time, even if P and r' are constant, and only later settles down to the stable value given by equation 8. The larger the product Pr, the larger are the variations. Similar variations occur when, for example, an epidemic is checked by drought and then builds up again. The previous history of the epidemic, every previous fluctuation, is remembered in the multiplication rate, and this memory factor is the special contribution of an incubation period to the concept of compound interest.

There is a qualification. Previous memory is wiped out each time multiplication stops for a continuous interval at least as long as P, and then starts anew. Hence, the memory factor can cause a drift in the multiplication rate of potato blight from day to day, but not in that of potato leaf roll from year to year.

Variations in the value of r, whether caused by memory or any other factor, are properly cared for by equation 5. This equation estimates the average of the value of r at every instant between any times t_1 and t_2, irrespective of any variations that occur.

But although it is important to know that the memory factor's effect on r is correctly estimated, it is often equally important to know how to eliminate this effect so that other factors can be studied without interference. Except within approximately 2.2 P days after inoculation in an artificial epidemic or 1.2 P days after the end of a major interruption in a natural epidemic, the effect of the memory factor on r can be made small by arranging that the interval between t_1 and t_2 should be as near to 1.2 P days (or a multiple thereof) as is possible without using fractions of a day. For example, if P is 6 days and it is wished to study in an artificial epidemic the separate effect on r of factors other than the memory factor, observations should begin whenever convenient after the thirteenth day from inoculation and then be made at weekly intervals. Very exact knowledge of P is here unnecessary, and in the example just quoted an 8-day interval between t_1 and t_2 would also almost eliminate the memory factor's effect on r.

B. Increase of Disease when the Pathogen Does Not Spread between the Host Plants

Consider bunt of wheat caused by *Tilletia caries* and *T. foetida*. Plants are infected as young seedlings, and do not release spores until the grain has been formed. One plant cannot infect another during the course of the season. There is multiplication of infection, but only as an increase from season to season and not within a single crop. Many other systemic smut fungi behave similarly.

With obligate heteroecism there are similar restrictions. The apple rust fungi *Gymnosporangium* spp. move hither and thither from apples to the alternate hosts and back. During this movement from one host to the other there can be a multiplication of infection, but there is no multiplication directly from apple to apple. Similarly, *Cronartium ribicola* does not spread from pine to pine.

With many of the systemic or quasi systemic vascular wilt diseases the pathogen is not returned in great quantity to the soil until the host dies. The pathogen may build up from season to season, but it does not spread much from plant to plant during the season.

Sometimes there is apparently no spread from plant to plant and no building-up within the host species even over the seasons. Eastern X virus spreads from chokecherry (*Prunus virginiana*) to peach but apparently not from peach to peach (Hildebrand, 1953). The virus of Pierce's disease has a wide range of species of host plants from which it infects grapevines, but it does not seem to spread from grapevine to grapevine (Hewitt *et al.*, 1949). Tomato spotted wilt virus infects tobacco, but the thrips vectors do not breed on this host and there is no evidence of spread from tobacco to tobacco (van der Plank and Anderssen, 1945). Peaches with X disease, grapevines with Pierce's disease, and tobacco with tomato spotted wilt apparently do not contribute to the building-up of an epidemic of these three virus diseases; in them epidemics are secondary (see Section III, D) and are the result of multiplication in other hosts.

Absence of spread from plant to plant can occur at times even with diseases that normally spread. Figure 2A, reproduced from a report by Doncaster and Gregory (1948), shows the distribution of rugose mosaic, caused by virus Y, in an isolated potato field. This field was initially free from virus Y, but was invaded from a source 300 yd. away. The plants which were infected as a result of this invasion did not pass the infection on to their neighbors, and there was no evidence of secondary spread. Absence of secondary spread can be expected when the invasion takes place late in the season or when the presence of vectors is transient. It is possibly not uncommon.

The type of increase without multiplication which has been discussed in the previous five paragraphs can cause an epidemic which superficially resembles other epidemics but which is fundamentally distinct. There is, for example, no reason why the progress curve of the epidemic with time should be sigmoid. Often the approach to control is different. It is therefore important to be able to detect when infection is increasing without spreading from plant to plant.

This can be done in various ways. One can mark infected plants and determine whether they are foci of infection by comparing the number of plants which become infected in an area near them with the number of plants which become infected in a comparable area at a distance away from them. But the most convenient methods use the distribution of

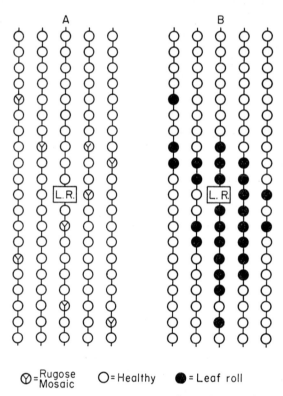

⊘=Rugose Mosaic   ○=Healthy   ●=Leaf roll

Fig. 2. Distribution of rugose mosaic and leaf roll around an infected plant, L.R., grown from a potato tuber infected with leaf roll. For convenience, rugose mosaic and leaf roll are shown in separate diagrams, A and B, respectively. (After Doncaster and Gregory, 1948).

diseased plants in the field or orchard without a knowledge of their history. Figure 2B shows how leaf roll develops in a potato field around an infected plant grown from an infected tuber. There is a nest of diseased plants near this plant. Nests of this sort vary in their compactness and shape from disease to disease, but it is probably safe to assume that with all plant diseases there is a tendency for infected plants to aggregate to some extent near the source of infection. (The tendency is greatest when r' is low in value and the gradients are steep; see Section IV, E and F about scales of distance.) The test for spread of infection is a test for aggregations. Cochran (1936) examined some general tests, and Todd (1940) and Freeman (1953) developed a test for the special case of the death of trees planted at the corners of a square lattice in a rectangular plantation. The simplest test yet devised makes use of doublets (van der Plank, 1946). A doublet consists of 2 adjacent diseased plants. If n plants are examined in sequence, and of these μ are diseased, the expected number of doublets is

$$d = \frac{1}{n} \mu(\mu - 1). \tag{9}$$

A run of 3 diseased plants is counted as 2 doublets; a run of 4, as 3 doublets; and so on. A test of significance has been worked out by G. A. McIntyre of the Commonwealth Scientific and Industrial Research Organisation, Canberra, Australia, and it is hoped it will be published shortly.

As an example, the distribution of leaf-roll-infected potato plants in Fig. 2B is analyzed. There is a total of 100 plants, including the original diseased plant; of these, 28 are infected. If one starts at the top left corner, reads down the first row, up the next, and so on, one counts 19 doublets. The expected number is only $28 \times 27/100$ or 7.56. The infected plants show excessive (nonrandom) aggregation. A corresponding analysis for the 9 potato plants with rugose mosaic in Fig. 2A gives d (observed) 0 and d (expected) 0.72. There is no evidence of nonrandom aggregation. In practice one is usually concerned with collecting evidence for the absence rather than for the presence of spread of infection. Extensive data are needed, and precautions must be taken against extraneous heterogeneity of the field. The method can be used to examine evidence for spread in any direction, and counting can start from any randomly chosen starting point. Missing plants, uneven spacings, or changing directions do not affect the analysis mathematically, although they may affect its interpretation biologically. From what is written in Section IV, F it follows that spread of infection is most easily detected by this method if the disease is a systemic disease of trees.

III. THE AMOUNT OF INOCULUM AT ITS SOURCE IN RELATION TO EPIDEMICS

A. *The Amount of Inoculum and Rate of Multiplication before the Onset*

In the preceding section our concern was with rates of multiplication. The amount of inoculum at the source of the epidemic must now be considered. When infected plants are the starting inoculum—when, for example, epidemics of potato blight start from lesions on infected shoots developing from infected tubers or when potato leaf roll spreads from an infected plant, the sequence of multiplication is homogeneous. Lesions produce lesions, and infected plants produce infected plants. We shall be concerned only with homogeneous sequences. When the source of inoculum is resting spores or anything but infected plants, we consider the sequence as starting from the first plants to be infected directly from this inoculum, i.e., the first infected plants are considered as the inoculum at its source. This restriction to homogeneous sequences simplifies what has to be discussed without affecting the conclusions appreciably.

Suppose I_0 and I are respectively the amounts of inoculum (in terms of the number of lesions or, for systemic diseases, the number of infected plants) at the source and at the onset of the epidemic which was defined in Section II, A, 2.

$$I = I_0 e^{rt/100}. \tag{10}$$

Here t is the time taken up to the onset, and r has the meaning given in earlier equations. To quote an example given previously, if P. *infestans* multiplies a millionfold in 80 days,

$$e^{80r/100} = I/I_0 = 10^6$$

whence $r = 17.3\%$ per day. This is an average rate for the 80 days.

More often one needs to know the effect of a change in the amount of inoculum at the source: a change brought about, for example, by sanitation. One can therefore profitably rewrite equation 10. Suppose the amount of inoculum at the source is reduced from I_0 to I'_0. The delay in the onset of the epidemic, Δt, can then be determined from the equation

$$I_0 = I'_0 e^{r\Delta t/100}$$

whence

$$\Delta t = \frac{230}{r} \log \frac{I_0}{I'_0}. \tag{11}$$

In the equation, r is the rate during the time of the delay. Logarithms are to the base 10.

Suppose $r = 69.3\%$ per day at the onset. How long will the onset be delayed by halving the amount of inoculum at its source?

$$t = \frac{230 \log 2}{69.3}$$

$$= \frac{230 \times 0.301}{69.3}$$

$$= 1.0.$$

The answer is 1 day. Natural compound interest of 69.3% per day, which is added to the accumulated capital at every instant, is equal to 100% "banker's" compound interest, which is added once a day. This numerical problem makes the obvious point that if the amount of infection is doubled every day, halving the amount at its source will postpone the onset by a day. The criterion for the onset must of course be fixed, but, provided that it is fixed within the limit stated in Section II, A, 2, the particular value at which it is fixed has no relevance. (But read also Section II, A, 5.)

Consider another example. Broadbent (1957) tested the use of barriers to protect cauliflower seedlings from mosaic, and found that a barrier of three rows of barley around the seedbed reduced infection from 3.0 to 0.6%. How long would the onset of an epidemic of cauliflower mosaic be delayed in crops planted from protected seedbeds? Use the value $r = 9.2\%$ per day, calculated for cauliflower mosaic in Section II, A, 5.

$$\Delta t = \frac{230}{9.2} \log \frac{3.0}{0.6}$$
$$= 17.5.$$

The onset of the epidemic would be delayed 17.5 days. For properly apt results, r should be measured for the same variety as that used in the barrier experiment, in the same district, at the same time of the year, in the same type of soil, etc.

B. Some Comments on the Theory of Forecasting of Epidemics

The method and effectiveness of forecasting epidemics varies with the value of r in equation 11. Consider the two extremes of forecasts that ignore, and forecasts based entirely on, the amount of inoculum at the source.

1. Forecasts That Ignore the Amount of Inoculum

According to equation 11, the higher the value of r at the onset, the less the error of a forecast of the time of onset that ignores differences in the amount of inoculum at the source. If r is large enough, approximate forecasts become possible without reference to inoculum. An alternative condition would be that the amount of inoculum is so large that it ceases to be a limiting factor. Both conditions possibly exist with, say, apple scab when scabby spring weather follows a fall and a winter favorable to the survival of large amounts of inoculum in dead leaves.

Potato plants become more susceptible to blight as they grow older (Grainger, 1956), and high values of r are possible toward maturity.

It is this fact of a high value toward maturity that makes short-range forecasts of blight feasible on weather data alone. It has been found that there may be a "zero time," a date (July 1 in west Scotland) before which forecasts based on weather data alone are invalid (Grainger, 1950). Interpreted by equation 11, "zero time" is the date on which the magnitude of *r* becomes high enough to blur the effect of variations in the amount of inoculum and make the epidemic specially sensitive to the weather. The more susceptible the variety, the earlier can "zero time" be fixed or, alternatively, if "zero time" is unchanged, the more accurately can forecasts be made.

2. Forecasts Based on the Amount of Inoculum Alone

As the value of *r* at the onset decreases, the effect of variations in the amount of inoculum on the date of the onset increases. With low enough values of *r* the importance of the inoculum factor becomes dominant, and approximate forecasts can be based on it alone. The number of sclerotia of *Sclerotium rolfsii* in the soil can be used to forecast losses of sugar beet from this fungus (Leach, 1938). In general the soil is not a medium conducive to the fast multiplication of pathogens, and methods of forecasting other diseases caused by soil-borne pathogens on inoculum alone are likely to be feasible.

C. An Epidemiological View of the Problem of Sanitation: the First Rule of Sanitation

Equation 11 tells us that, measured as a delay in the onset of an epidemic, the benefit of a given percentage reduction in the amount of inoculum at its source is inversely proportional to *r*, the magnitude of *r* being determined at the time of the delay. This is the first rule of sanitation.

Within the limits of one disease the rule means that sanitation helps most when it is needed least. Before any method of sanitation is recommended for the control of a disease, it should be ascertained that the method will remain effective even during seasons when conditions are such that infection multiplies at its fastest.

In comparing different diseases the rule means that control by sanitation is most apt for those diseases that multiply most slowly. If *r* is large, sanitation is relatively ineffective, and it is usually necessary to use fungicides or, alternatively, to call in the plant breeder to produce a resistant variety, i.e., to bring down the magnitude of *r*. When *r* is small, one is likely to be dealing with a disease that can be controlled by sanitation: by crop rotation, by fumigation of the soil before the crop is planted, by destroying diseased crop residues or using manure free from inoculum, by planting healthy or disinfected seed and nursery stock, by roguing out diseased plants, by isolating fields from sources of inoculum, by destroying weeds or other hosts that can carry infection, or by any other method that reduces inoculum at its source.

For example, systemic diseases tend to have low values of r, and a study of the literature shows that the majority of them are controlled by sanitation in one form or other.

As r increases, sanitation becomes less effective. But where do we draw the line? At the one extreme, with very low rates of multiplication, sanitation is almost completely effective; for example, on present knowledge, a citrus grower can be protected against losses from psorosis by the sanitary measure of using only healthy nursery stock to plant his orchards. Are there, at the other extreme, infections that multiply so fast that sanitation is worthless? The answer depends on the circumstances. Consider this example. A field of potatoes grown from blight-free seed can become infected with blight from infected refuse piles or from infected fields. Take the second alternative. From calculations based on meager data in the literature, it can be estimated that doubling the isolation of a potato field from its neighbors would reduce the amount of blight that the field gets from its neighbors by 83%. (See Section IV, B and D.) If, from Fig. 1, we take r to be 48% per day, this isolation will postpone the onset of an epidemic by 3.7 days. (Here $I_0/I'_0 = 100/(100\text{–}83)$.) On an allowance of an increase of a ton of tubers per acre per week during the critical period of the growing season, isolation to the extent stated would mean a gain of crop in an unsprayed field of about half a ton per acre. Whether this gain would be worth working for depends on the circumstances. On a small farm, isolation is impossible or possible only at the cost of arrangements that are not acceptable to the farmer. But on a large estate some farm planning with an eye to isolation is not ruled out. It is not for our present purpose desirable to pursue this topic at length, but it should be stated that even with a fast multiplying disease like blight of potatoes the possibility of sanitation cannot be excluded before conditions are analyzed.

D. An Epidemiological View of Breeding for Resistance

One especially important deduction from equation 11—and the first rule of sanitation—concerns resistant varieties. Plant breeders like to aim at high resistance or complete immunity; this is desirable, and the effect of immunity is readily understandable: there is no epidemic (and in that case the matter would be outside the scope of this chapter). But commonly the available resistance is only partial; infection occurs, but at a slower rate. The magnitude of r is reduced, and the value of sanitation correspondingly increased. Every quantum of resistance, however small, increases the efficiency of sanitation; and every quantum of sanitation increases the value of the partial resistance. As methods of control, sanitation and partial resistance should go together. When a disease is controlled by sanitation, partial resistance in any measure is an achievement not to be despised. It has been much undervalued in plant pathology, largely as the result of ignoring its connection with sanitation.

E. *Secondary Epidemics*

An epidemic can be defined as secondary if it starts from inoculum derived from another, earlier epidemic. In Section II, B it was observed that epidemics of eastern X disease of peaches, Pierce's disease of grapevines, and tomato spotted wilt on tobacco are secondary because there is apparently no spread of the diseases in the crops mentioned. Infection must come from outside.

In the Netherlands van der Zaag (1956) found that with the potato variety Duke of York there was about 1 primary focus of infection per square kilometer at the start of the season, this focus originating from an infected seed tuber. With the more resistant variety Noordeling, primary foci were much rarer or entirely absent. Further, he tested varietal differences by artificially inoculating leaflets in the field before natural infection was apparent, and then 12 days later counting how many leaflets had become secondarily and naturally infected from these primary artificial sources. For every 1 lesion on Noordeling that developed secondarily around the primary source, there were 180 on Duke of York. From this we infer that the magnitude of r was roughly 180 times as great for Duke of York as for Noordeling. This estimate is rough but adequate; the evidence does not allow an exact estimate of either r or r'. Epidemics in Duke of York take about a month to develop from the primary foci, so, from equation 11, an epidemic in Noordeling would need 180 months to develop. If one adds to this the information about the scarcity of natural primary foci with Noordeling, the period needed would be much greater. Even if one admits the possibility of error, the differences are striking enough to make it reasonably certain that a primary epidemic of blight in Noordeling is improbable in a growing season limited to 4 or 5 months. If Noordeling becomes significantly blighted, it is almost certainly as a result of infection obtained initially from some other variety.

The tendency for disease to spread from more to less susceptible varieties and cause secondary epidemics in them, increases with the extent to which initial inoculum must multiply to cause an epidemic. For any given time up to the onset, the logarithm of the amount of multiplication is proportional to r. If two varieties differ in that in the one r is twice as great as in the other at all times, then by the time the more susceptible variety has multiplied 10^2 times the less susceptible will have multiplied 10 times; by the time the more susceptible has multiplied 10^6 times the less susceptible will have multiplied 10^3 times. As multiplication continues, the difference in level of disease between the varieties increases. The more the multiplication needed before a level of, say, 5% is reached, the greater is the difference in disease between the varieties when the more susceptible has reached that level; hence, other things being equal, the greater the chance that disease in the less susceptible variety will be influenced by inoculum from the more susceptible. With diseases like potato blight, in which relatively little inoculum survives the winter, the danger of susceptible varieties starting secondary epidemics in other varieties is correspondingly great.

Late blight, caused by *Phytophthora infestans,* can survive perennially on tomatoes in countries in which tomatoes are grown all the year round. It can also be brought into the summer-grown tomato plants of colder climates by blight-infected transplants imported from warmer areas. But late blight of tomatoes has also a considerable literature of epidemics secondary to those of potatoes. Neighboring blighted potato fields or potato refuse piles are repeatedly implicated as the source of tomato blight. But in one detail there has been a noteworthy change in the literature since Mills (1940) summarized it. In 1940 races of *Phytophthora infestans* from potato were poorly adapted to tomatoes, and, according to Mills, had to be trained to attack tomatoes by a few passages through tomato leaves. Nowadays there are frequent references in the literature to potato races that readily attack tomatoes, although a distinction between potato and tomato races still exists. On the general evidence of the literature, secondary epidemics on tomatoes are now more easily established from potatoes. There has been, it would appear, a change in the relationship between *P. infestans* and the potato, which has also involved the tomato secondarily and possibly incidentally, and which has perhaps been the cause of the destructive epidemics of tomato blight on a scale unknown before 1946.

There is a type of secondary epidemic brought about by mixed cropping. The apple variety Delicious has considerable resistance to powdery mildew, caused by *Podosphaera leucotricha.* Jonathon is very susceptible and is commonly used as a pollinator for Delicious. In mixed orchards spores from diseased Jonathans may start secondary epidemics on Delicious which are severe enough to require control measures

(Sprague, 1953). Hardwoods grown alone are normally resistant to *Fomes annosus* but may be killed when grown in mixed stands with susceptible conifers in which inoculum builds up (Peace, 1957). These examples show the value of uniformity of resistance in minimizing the risk of secondary epidemics, a point to remember when reading Sections VI, C, 2, f and VI, E.

Secondary epidemics provoked by mixed cropping are often used by plant breeders to eliminate susceptible lines of seedlings. A variety known to be susceptible is interplanted with the material to be sorted out in order to ensure that infection will be present in the breeders' plots. The method is simple and convenient, but there is the danger of confusing the smaller amount of resistance adequate to stop a primary epidemic with the larger amount needed to cope with a secondary epidemic.

IV. THE SPREAD OF EPIDEMICS

A. *Factors That Affect the Rate of Spread*

Section IV describes how an epidemic spreads over a distance. Three factors are considered at the start. A fourth factor, scale of distance, is discussed later in the section.

1. *The Gradient of Infection*

The probability that a healthy plant in a given direction will become infected depends on the distance of that plant from the source of infection. Infection grades away (usually smoothly, but not necessarily so) from the source. Unless otherwise stated, the source will always be taken to be a point—a single plant, for instance—and not a field or strip. Gradients should be determined only when the percentage of infection is low; apparent gradients necessarily become flatter as disease mounts.

2. *The Abundance and Distribution of Susceptible Host Plants*

The probability that a spore or other propagule will travel a given distance is proportional to the number of propagules released at the source. If the number of air-borne spores at the source is multiplied 100 times, then on an average 100 times as many as before will blow past the first milestone, 100 times as many past the second, and so on. When heavy spore showers are detected hundreds of miles from the nearest source, it is reasonably certain that the source is not a single plant but fields of plants, not just a few fields but hundreds of acres of fields. Abundant host plants mean, too, that the leaps the pathogen need make from one host plant to another are small. Their distribution—whether in small fields or large—also affects the pathogen's spread; this is a matter to be discussed in Section V.

3. The Rate of Multiplication

Spread is multiplication at a distance from the source of inoculum; and, for a given gradient, multiplication at a distance is related to multiplication in general. Fast multiplication of disease lesions means fast spread of disease. The connection has long been tacitly accepted, and pathologists commonly use the words "multiplication" and "spread" interchangeably. A tie between multiplication and spread is discussed in Section IV, E (equation 13).

B. Horizons of Infection

Horizons of infection have been discussed by van der Plank (1949b). For argument's sake suppose temporarily that the probability that a lesion (or, for systemic diseases, an infected plant) will form a daughter lesion in unit time on a healthy plant at a distance s is

$$p = \frac{a}{s^b}. \tag{12}$$

Here a and b are constants. We shall not bother about the accuracy of this equation; the relationship shown is just scaffolding, which will be removed later. Suppose that there are infected fields scattered over a large area, and consider any field as center. Suppose that this field is only lightly infected: that the epidemic in it has not gone further than the onset, and that it receives inoculum from other fields in a sector narrow enough for the gradients toward the center to be considered uniform. The probability that a lesion will develop in this field as a result of inoculum received from a parent lesion two units of distance away in the sector is $1/2^b$ times the probability that a lesion will develop from inoculum from a parent lesion one unit of distance away in the sector. But on an average the number of parent lesions two units of distance away is twice the number one unit away (because for a given angle at the center the arc is proportional to its radius). Hence on an average the number of lesions caused by inoculum received from all sources (all parent lesions) two units away is $2/2^b$ or $1/2^{b-1}$ times the number from inoculum received from all sources one unit away. Similarly the number from inoculum received from all sources three units away is $1/3^{b-1}$ times the number from all sources one unit away. If Q is the number of lesions from inoculum received from all sources one unit of distance away the number of lesions from inoculum received from all sources at all distances is

$$Q\left(1 + \frac{1}{2^{b-1}} + \frac{1}{3^{b-1}} + \cdots\right).$$

If $b > 2$, this series is convergent, and there will be a limit from beyond which inoculum will not come.

To simplify calculations, suppose that the distance between fields is relatively large and that the fields are uniformly infected and uniformly distributed. We can, as an adequate approximation, take the distance between the centers of neighboring fields as the unit of distance. If $b = 2.5$, 62% of the daughter lesions caused by inoculum received from other fields will come from fields, beyond the immediate neighbors, 40% from more than 3 fields away, and 32% from more than 5 fields away. If $b = 3$, the respective figures are 39, 17, and 11%; if $b = 4$, the figures are now 17, 3, and 1% respectively. If, for example, one regards inoculum coming from behind the horizon as negligible if it is responsible for less than 10% of the daughter lesions, then if $b = 2.5$, a horizon is established more than 50 fields away; if $b = 3$, about 5 fields away; if $b = 4$, 2 fields away. The horizon draws in sharply as b increases, i.e., as gradients become steeper.

It is not assumed that gradients are the same in all sectors, and the horizon about a field need not be circular.

C. Continuous and Discontinuous Spread of Epidemics

If $b > 2$, the source of a new outbreak will probably be within a horizon. The greater the magnitude of b, the more likely is the source to be near, and the easier it will be to follow the path of an epidemic. The spread will be continuous.

But if $b < 2$, more inoculum will arrive from far than from near (assuming of course that host plants occur over a wide area). Infection will appear as if "from nowhere." There will be what have been called "spot" infections—infections that cannot be traced to their source. The spread will be discontinuous.

Low values of b can be expected if the movement of inoculum is oriented with a restriction on random scattering, as would occur, for example, if the inoculum were carried by birds migrating toward a particular destination. Migratory birds are thought to spread chestnut blight by carrying the sticky pycnospores of *Endothia parasitica* (Heald and Studhalter, 1914; Leach, 1940). "Spot" infections were a feature of the great chestnut blight epidemic in North America, and occurred in addition to local infections caused by wind-blown ascospores; it seems likely that during migrations b was less than 2.

D. The Determination of Gradients; the Scrapping of Equation 12; Dutch Elm Disease; Potato Blight

Equation 12 was used only to build up an argument. In scrapping it one need not replace it by a better equation, but only consider its most useful features. The central inferences from the equation concern the value $b = 2$, or, to scrap the equation, concern a gradient in which the number of lesions formed by inoculum from a source varies inversely as the square of the distance from the source. If one plots the number of lesions against distance on a log-log scale, the inverse-square lines are straight. One can draw as many as one wishes—all parallel. Such are the lines A, B, C, D in Fig. 3. The observed gradient for any disease can then be compared immediately with these lines. If its slope is steeper than theirs, there will be a horizon of infection, and spread will be continuous. Similarly one can draw a number of parallel inverse-cube lines like the lines E and F in Fig. 3. If the observed gradient is steeper than theirs, horizons can be expected to be fairly close. In Fig. 4 the process is continued, and lines G, H, I, and J show the number of lesions inversely as the fourth power of the distance from the source of infection.

Dutch elm disease, caused by *Ceratostomella ulmi*, was chosen to illustrate Fig. 3. There is a fair amount of information about it. Among other things, the spread of disease from a single infected tree in a limited period of time has been observed by several workers to virtually cease within some hundreds of yards from the tree, so one knows in advance that one should expect gradients steeper than the inverse-square lines. On one point there is a difficulty—a difficulty common to most of the literature of diseases that could be used for illustration: gradients should be determined only at low percentages of disease. This limits information to the lower part of the curve; the disadvantage of this is that information there is usually based on relatively few diseased plants and is consequently not powerful statistically. At higher levels of disease one can correct the curve partially (or fully, if the lesions are distributed randomly) by transforming percentages of diseases into calculated numbers of infections per 100 plants. Attention to this was drawn by Gregory (1948), who published a useful table of transformed values. Some examples will explain the transformation. Suppose there were exactly 100 random infections per 100 plants. Not all plants would be infected; on an average, 36.8% would have no infections (they would remain healthy) and 63.2% would have 1 or more infections. The table calculates this in reverse; it transforms 63.2% disease to 100 infections per 100 plants. In Fig. 3 the highest figure for disease is 88.9%, which is transformed to 220 infections per 100 trees. At low percentages the change is small and usually negligible: 5% disease transforms to 5.13 infections per 100 plants.

Figure 3 analyzes the combined data of Zentmyer et al. (1944) for three plots in Connecticut; and the data of Liming et al. (1951) for a

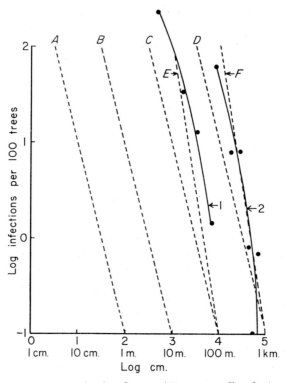

Fig. 3. Amount of Dutch elm disease (*Ceratostomella ulmi*) at varying distances from the source of inoculum. Curves 1 and 2: data of Zentmyer et al. (1944) and Liming et al. (1951), respectively, shown as transformed numbers of infections. A, B, C, and D are inverse-square lines with scales of distances as 1:10:100:1000. E and F are inverse-cube lines with scales of distance in the ratio 1:10.

plot in New Jersey. These data were collected within a year of the emergence in large numbers of the vector beetles from the source of infection which in each case was a single naturally infected tree. There was therefore little time for secondary multiplication to affect the gradients. At the lower levels of disease, which are the safest to observe, the gradients are steeper than the inverse-square lines and are more like the inverse-cube lines. This is what one would expect from general observations on the disease, but the data are too few to warrant detailed statistical analysis.

Figure 4 analyzes records of potato blight, caused by *Phytophthora infestans*. The data of Limasset (1939) were taken from the paper of Gregory (1945). Bonde and Schultz (1943) recorded the number of lesions per 100 plants, so no transformation is needed. These records

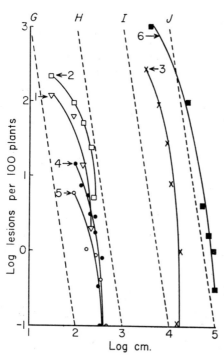

FIG. 4. Amount of potato blight (*P. infestans*) at varying distances from the source of inoculum. Curves 1 and 2: data of Limasset (1939). Curve 3: data of Bonde and Schultz (1943). Curves 4 and 5: data of Waggoner (1952). Curve 6: data of Newhall (1938) for *Peronospora destructor*. Curves 1, 2, 4, and 5 are based on transformed numbers of lesions. G, H, I, and J are inverse fourth-power lines with scales of distance as 1:10:100:1000.

were taken from a field about 100 ft. away from an infected dump pile of about 25 barrels of cull potatoes. Blight was first noted in the pile on June 12, and had infected most of the plants in the pile by June 25. The readings in the potato field that are reproduced in Fig. 4 were taken on July 12. It is thus possible that there had been some secondary multiplication in the field before then, so the gradients, steep as they are, may underestimate the true steepness. The results of Waggoner (1952) in curve 4 were obtained 9 days after artificial inoculation of the center from which sporangia later spread; those in curve 5 from another plot 18 days after inoculation, during 9 days of which the weather was generally unfavorable for infection. In addition, data are presented for the related fungus *Peronospora destructor* to make the records as complete as possible. They are derived from the data of Newhall (1938) for downy mildew lesions per 100 ft. of row, and no transformation was needed. These various records are consistent in suggesting that, as a reasonable approximation at the low amounts of disease in which we are primarily interested, the number of lesions falls off inversely at least as the fouth power of the distance from the source. This result has been assumed in the calculation made for blight in Section III, C. In Fig. 5 (to be discussed later) two more curves are shown for *Phytophthora infestans*. They are slightly steeper than an inverse—sixth-power gradient. The evidence from all the records that the curves at low amounts of disease become steeper than an inverse—fourth-power gradient is statistically significant; but it is inadequate to say how steep they eventually become.

Curve 3 in Fig. 4 is displaced to the right of curves 4 and 5. Displacements will be discussed under the next heading. But one reason for displacement seems evident here: the source of infection for curve 3—the cull pile—was comparatively large and heavily infected, and was at a distance from the field; the sources for curves 4 and 5 were smaller and within the fields.

E. Scales of Distance; a Tie between Multiplication and Spread

For illustration let us return to the chestnut blight fungus spread by migrating birds. There are two relevant features about birds during migration: the flights are longer between pauses, and are oriented toward some particular destination. The second feature—orientation—was cited as probably involved in making spread discontinuous. The first feature —long flights—was ignored. Making flights longer without change of orientation and without serious loss of inoculum during flight would make an epidemic spread on a larger scale (in the word's literal meaning of relative dimensions). But it would not make a continuous spread discontinuous.

Consider the inverse-square lines in Fig. 3. The scale of distance for line D is exactly 1,000 times the scale of line A at any given level of infection. Between any two given levels of infection the change from line A to line D is a change from millimeters to meters, from meters to kilometers. In Fig. 3 displacement to the right means an increase of scale of distance.

Other things (including the strength with which the inoculum is emitted at the source) being equal, longer flights by winged vectors or longer motions by the inoculum generally mean a larger scale of distance and displacement to the right. Restricted motion, which one might expect of inoculum moving through heavy soil, would mean a smaller scale and displacement to the left.

When disease spreads from a single point source of inoculum, one can define the scale of distance on a relative basis by saying that the scale of distance varies directly with the distance between two given levels of disease (which must be defined if necessary). When curves

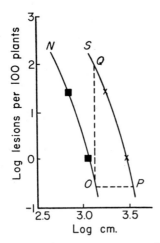

FIG. 5. Amount of potato blight, *P. infestans,* at different distances from the source of inoculum. Data of van der Zaag (1956), given as transformed numbers. Explanation in text.

relating disease and distance are plotted in a log-log graph and the displacement of the curves is fairly regular or when the two levels of disease are selected close together, a change of scale of distance is readily determined graphically.

Consider Fig. 5, which is constructed from data of van der Zaag (1956) for the spread of *Phytophthora infestans* from an incompletely removed source of infection. The data for percentages of diseased plants have been transformed into the number of lesions per 100 plants. To the north of the focus (curve N) the spread was less than to the south (curve S). Since the spread in both directions was from the same source of inoculum, the displacement of curve S to the right of curve N is the result of a changed scale of distance. This is measured by the line OP, which represents an increment of 0.4 in the logarithm of the distance or a 2.5-fold increase in scale of distance at the level of disease at or near points O and P (log 2.5 = 0.4). The argument will have been grasped in the simpler comparison between the straight lines A and D a few paragraphs back, and needs no further elucidation.

The corresponding change in the scale of disease at the distance represented by points O and Q is measured by the line OQ, which represents an increment of 2.5 in the logarithm of the number of lesions or a 316-fold increase in the number ($\log 316 = 2.5$). At this distance there was about 316 times as much disease to the south as to the north as a result of a 2.5-fold change of scale of distance.

The records of Waggoner (1952) for *P. infestans* in his plot at Clear Lake in 1950 on day eighteen show a scale of distance to the NNW about 8 times as great as to the SSE. Since, approximately, disease varied inversely as the fourth power of distance from the source (curve 5 of Fig. 4), there was about 8^4 or 4096 times as much disease over a given distance to the NNW as to the SSE. This result appears to have been due to wind. There is considerable evidence in the literature that wind can strongly alter the scale of distance. One reason why wind affects the scale in different directions is that more inoculum leaves the source in one direction than in another.

To determine a relation between multiplication and spread, referred to in Section IV, A, 3, consider a primary gradient set up in healthy plants surrounding a point source of infection. A primary gradient is one set up by inoculum derived directly from the initial point source without complications from secondary multiplication of disease in the zone of the gradient. For example, curves 1 and 2 of Fig. 3 probably represent primary gradients of Dutch elm disease. Return to equation 7 and consider a boundary condition. While $t < P$, the quantity x'_{t-P}, taken here as the point source, is constant. Because the gradient is set up in plants healthy at the start, i.e., when $t = 0$, the amount of disease at any given time less than P and (for a given gradient) at any given distance from the source, will be proportional to the value of r' prevailing over the period of the observations. Whence, to follow the reasoning in the previous paragraphs,

$$\Delta s = k r'^{(1/b)} \tag{13}$$

where Δs, which determines the scale of distance, is the distance between two given levels of disease in the gradient; k is a constant; b has the same meaning as in equation 12; and changes in r' are assumed to be moderately small.

If the two levels of disease are taken fairly close together, the value of b can, with reasonable accuracy, be taken as constant over Δs. This feature appears in all the curves in Figs. 3 and 4, especially at distances not too near the source. Therefore the use of b here does not revive equation 12, but only the part of it that may legitimately be revived. It is necessary that b should be positive; i.e., there must be an actual decrease of disease with distance away from the source.

Equation 13 holds for those factors (except the incubation period) which effect r but not the gradient. With such a range of factors affecting r—from wind to the susceptibility of the host—and such a range of inoculum—from air-borne spores to water-splashed bacteria and vector-transmitted viruses—any generalization about the effect on gradients is difficult. It is, however, worth noting that in their effect on scale of distance the factors that determines r cannot be distinguished one from another (except the incubation period). Consider, for example, diseases that spread mainly "by contact" between plants that are immediate neighbors. It is common experience that these diseases multiply slowly, and it is generally assumed that they multiply slowly because inoculum can only be spread by contact. In many cases one can use the opposite argument: the diseases appear to spread by contact because they multiply slowly for reasons that need not be known.

A summary of the basic concepts might facilitate an understanding of the relation between multiplication and spread. We have been concerned with a point source of inoculum, hence only with primary gradients, hence not with the incubation period, and hence with r' and not r, as equation 13 shows. If inoculum comes from a source other than a point (e.g., an epidemic's front) the incubation period and r may become involved. A particular solution for the relation between r and the spread of the front of an epidemic of wheat stem rust underlies the Appendix. It is for the special case in which the pathogen's birth rate greatly exceeds its death rate and lesions are small.

F. Inverse Scales of Distance; the Law of Lesion Size

We have been considering changes in the distance scale on which a pathogen can spread. Now let us think of the problem from the opposite view and consider changes in the scale of distance over which a pathogen must spread if it is to transmit disease. As an example we may consider the law of lesion size.

The law is that the highest potential rates of multiplication are with small lesions. A systemically infected plant is regarded as a single lesion extending over the whole plant. (The largest lesion is a systemically infected tree.) In round figures, small local lesions like those of potato blight can multiply one-billionfold in a season, systemic diseases of small herbaceous plants up to ten-thousandfold, and systemic diseases of trees about tenfold in a year. Evidence is given elsewhere (van der Plank, 1958). The word "law" is used to indicate that the relationship was observed, not predicted. Only maximum rates are relevant; it is not relevant to know that in arid climates or immune varieties potato blight does not multiply at all.

Two virus diseases with efficient aphid vectors are cauliflower mosaic and tristeza disease. The number of cauliflower plants infected with cauliflower mosaic multiplies faster than that of orange trees infected with tristeza disease (van der Plank, 1958). Suppose cauliflower plants in a field could be enlarged to 10 times their normal size with all distances increased in proportion: the plants would be 10 times as tall, 10 times as broad, with the distance between them 10 times as great, and in rows 10 times as wide. Suppose one plant in the field is infected. The distance from any relative position on this plant to any relative position on a neighboring plant or any relative position on any plant in the field would be increased 10 times by the process of enlargement. The scale of distance that an aphid would have to travel to transmit the virus would be increased 10 times, and the probability of a transmission would drop, correspondingly, according to the gradient. Similarly, if orange trees in an orchard could be shrunk to one-tenth their size with all other distances shrunk proportionately, the probability of transmission would rise in accordance with a decrease to one-tenth of the scale of distance over which an aphid must travel. So, other things being equal, an aphid has a greater chance of transmitting mosaic between cauliflower plants than between orange trees simply because orange trees are larger. The argument applies not only to vector-transmitted viruses but to any sort of inoculum. It applies not only to systemic disease but to any lesion; a uredospore of a cereal rust fungus must travel over only a very small distance, a few millimeters, to fall clear of an isolated pustule on healthy tissue. Cereal rust pustules can multiply fast because the scale of distance the pathogen must travel is small.

Inverse scales of distance are only one of the factors involved in the effect of size of lesion. The incubation period (to mention another) is often longer in systemic disease; the effect of this period has already been given in equation 8. Forest trees seem to have resistance to virus diseases, systemic bacterial diseases and systemic smut diseases. Operating in the opposite direction is the factor of the size of plant (Section VI, D, I).

V. Epidemics in Relation to the Abundance and Distribution of Host Plants

A. *General*

Agriculture has meant bringing plants together in fields and—to meet the ever growing demand for food—increasing the acreage of these fields. This raises two separate questions with which this section is concerned.

First: how does the bringing together of plants and increasing the acreage affect the prevalence of disease? The general answer is that disease is encouraged. But there are exceptions, and increasing the acreage, if it means enlarging the fields without increasing their number, may at times even reduce the percentage of disease. Also, apart from this exception, the relation between disease and intensified agriculture is not simple. Some diseases are more sensitive to intensified agriculture than others, and increase relatively faster as the acreage is increased.

The second question is: how does the distribution of host plants affect epidemics? For example, if the acreage remains constant, how do the size and distribution of the fields influence infection? The answers can be of the greatest practical importance if epidemics can be reduced by nothing else than planned agriculture. The least exploited method of reducing plant disease is by planning the pattern of farming in directions other than by crop rotation; no attempt is made here to produce a blueprint for such exploitation, but it is hoped at least to indicate that blueprints are entirely feasible.

B. *Disease in Susceptible Plants Scattered among Immune Plants*

Although bringing plants together into fields normally increases the likelihood of disease, epidemics among scattered host plants are not uncommon. For example, *Puccinia malvacearum* attacks only wild and garden plants. Yet it spread through western Europe within 5 years of its first appearance (Gäumann, 1946).

But bringing plants together may sometimes be a necessary condition for an epidemic to start. A good example is provided by the "native" potatoes of the mountains of Basutoland (van der Plank, 1948). The chief vector of the potato viruses, *Myzus persicae*, is abundant, and its winter host, the peach, almost ubiquitous. The varieties have no great resistance to virus disease, and succumb quickly when they are planted in garden plots. But when they grow—as they ordinarily do—as odd plants in the corn fields or in the grass near roadsides, there is little evidence of virus disease, and the varieties have persisted for more than a century in good health.

Mixed cropping has been deliberately used to control disease. Planting squashes and marrows in corn is commonly practiced in South Africa to control an aphid-borne mosaic disease. In Denmark and England beet seedlings intended for seed crops have successfully been protected against virus yellows disease by shield crops of barley (Hansen, 1950; Hull, 1952). In France the idea has been extended. Seedlings of beets are raised in beds which are latticed with longitudinal and cross bands of barrier crops to give subdivisions about 20 yd. long by 5 yd. wide. The barrier bands are about 1 yd. wide. Oats, corn, hemp, and sunflower are generally used (Hull, 1952). In England, Broadbent (1957) showed that narrow barriers of barley rows reduced the incidence of cauliflower mosaic and cabbage black ring spot in cauliflower seedbeds, a matter that has already been mentioned in Section III, A as an illustration of a quantitative problem in sanitation. There is a considerable range in detail as one passes from mixed cropping through shield crops to barrier crops; but all are methods based on the reduction of the effective movement of inoculum, and all share the common feature that they are useful in practice only against a type of disease which we shall call a crowd disease, i.e., a disease that is likely to reach epidemic proportions only when the host plants are crowded together into fields.

C. The "Epidemic Point" in Crowding Plants Together

Before crowd diseases are discussed consider what happens when susceptible host plants are crowded together. It is useful here to return to our introductory concept of epidemics as a matter of balance between the birth and death rates of the pathogen. Bringing plants nearer together increases the movement of inoculum between them; and it increases the birth rate of the pathogen. But it is unlikely to affect the death rate greatly (unless the pathogen or its vector is itself parasitized or preyed upon). When the point is reached at which births exceed deaths the danger of an epidemic begins.

Take as examples three diseases of trees: rosette disease of peaches, swollen shoot of cacao, and tristeza disease of sweet oranges on sour orange rootstocks. All are caused by viruses that kill their hosts and die with them. Rosette virus ordinarily spreads slowly from peach to peach, and its birth rate is low. However, its death rate is high, because it quickly kills its peach host, which usually dies in the same season in which symptoms are first seen, and then dies too. Ordinarily, the death rate exceeds the birth rate, and the disease in peaches is self-eradicating (Hildebrand et al., 1942) although it occasionally flares up and affects a whole orchard (McClintock et al., 1951). Swollen shoot of cacao has the same features as peach rosette, but not in quite such an extreme degree. It spreads slowly, but not quite so slowly; it kills quickly, but not quite so quickly, and infected trees may survive up to 2 years or longer. Tristeza disease has an abundant and efficient vector, Toxoptera citricidus (among others), which occurs in both winged and wingless forms, and infection spreads relatively fast through an orchard in which T. citricidus occurs. The disease kills sweet oranges on intolerant rootstocks but not very fast; the trees go into a decline that may last for several years. Compared, then, with peach rosette, citrus tristeza has a higher birth rate and a lower death rate.

The three diseases form an interesting series with regard to the epidemic point, which we define as the point in crowding plants together at which the birth rate of the pathogen exceeds the death rate.* In peach rosette the epidemic point is usually imaginary: it is usually not reached even when peaches are in continuous orchard formation. The disease of peaches is usually sporadic and self-eliminating, and the virus persists only because it has other more tolerant hosts such as the wild plum, from which it spreads to peaches. If epidemiology is the science of disease in populations, in peaches this behavior is epidemiological hypersensitivity, comparable in its effect on populations with ordinary hypersensitivity in its effect within the plant (Volume I, Chapter 14). Swollen shoot of cacao has a lower epidemic point, which was apparently reached in West Africa between the World Wars, when cacao production was expanding rapidly. Before then the disease in cacao had a long history of sporadic outbreaks (Posnette, 1953); it was only afterwards that the epidemic began to rage. Tristeza seems to have a fairly low epidemic point in countries in which *Toxoptera citricidus* is present; in these countries the virus seems to pervade quickly all susceptible species of citrus, killing those trees which are on unsuitable rootstocks and saturating the rest.

It is reasonable to suppose that with all diseases that cause primary epidemics the host plants are crowded beyond the epidemic point, at least during epidemic years. (The epidemic point will necessarily be lower in years favorable to the disease.) If the epidemic point is passed during the recorded history of man's crowding plants together, there will be a discontinuous change from sporadic disease to epidemic disease, as has happened apparently with swollen shoot of cacao. But where the epidemic point is low it was probably passed long ago, and the process of intensifying agriculture will seem to have a continuous effect—with epidemics becoming continuously more likely to occur.

D. Crowd Diseases; Changes in the Relative Importance of Diseases; a Glimpse of the Future

Crowd diseases are likely to reach epidemic proportions only when the host plants are crowded together; they are diseases with a high epidemic point. The inoculum is likely to have a high death rate (as when, for example, it cannot persist in the soil); or the movement of

---

* This definition is loose because the balance between births and deaths varies with x. A precise definition would need to stipulate some arbitrary value of x at which births should still exceed deaths.

inoculum between separated plants is likely to be small because of a small scale of distance, as reflected in a steep gradient and a low value of r or, more strictly, r'.

By equation 11 the effect of variations in the amount of inoculum reaching a field is greatest when r is least. To make a long story short, consider only diseases like potato blight, the cereal rusts, and those virus diseases not transmitted directly through the soil or dead plant residues. Usually, the systemic virus diseases multiply more slowly than the local lesion diseases (van der Plank, 1958). Therefore, intensified agriculture, by bringing fields nearer together and increasing the movement of inoculum between them, is likely to advance epidemics of systemic virus diseases relatively faster than those of local lesion diseases. To some extent the trend has been observable during the past century of fast-rising food production. Plant pathology started as a branch of mycology, but became increasingly more concerned with virus diseases. One grants that much of this history has been fortuitous; had de Bary's chief interest been in virus diseases, the history would have been different. But the change was not wholly fortuitous.

Further, because diseases especially sensitive to the intensification of agriculture are, as a result of this characteristic, especially amenable to control by isolation and sanitation generally, plant pathologists can expect to be much more concerned with the theory and practice of sanitation in the future than in the past.

E. The Effect of Making Fields Larger

1. Inoculum Coming from Other Hosts

Consider the finding of Wellman (1937) in Florida that cucumber mosaic virus, causing mosaic in celery, comes from other hosts such as *Commelina nudiflora* growing within 75 ft. of the field. For the sake of argument, accept this figure and ignore the possibility of some inoculum arriving from beyond 75 ft. or of vectors flying right over the field without settling in it. The area of a 75 ft. zone about a square field of 0.1 acre is 0.86 acre; about a field of 1 acre it is 1.85 acres; about a field of 10 acres it it 4.95 acres. Thus 10 acres of celery divided into 100 square fields of 0.1 acre, would draw infection from other hosts scattered over 86 acres; divided into 10 square fields of 1 acre, from other hosts scattered over 18.5 acres; and concentrated into 1 square field of 10 acres, from other hosts scattered over only 4.95 acres (van der Plank, 1948). Concentration of the host plants into a single field of compact shape reduces infection from outside to a minimum.

Probably one of the few occasions on which the percentage of disease is reduced while agriculture is intensified is when infection comes from scattered hosts near the fields and acreage is increased by increasing the size of the fields and not their number.

2. Inoculum Moving between Fields

We shall consider here what happens when fields are made larger and correspondingly fewer, so that the total acreage remains constant. To do so we shall revive equation 12, but only to the limited extent that we use it, as in Section IV, D, to illustrate the gradient of disease. Discussion will be limited to what happens before the onset of an epidemic, i.e., to inoculum moving into fields that are not already heavily infected, which is the only case of practical importance.

Assume that the fields are equal in size and uniformly shaped, orientated, and distributed over the country. Making them larger and correspondingly fewer increases the average distance between them in proportion to the square root of their average area, their shape and orientation being unchanged. The average distance, not necessarily on a straight course, that a spore (or other propagule) must travel from any particular relative position in the field of its origin to any particular relative position in the first field it reaches is proportional to the square root of the average area of the fields, that is, it must travel an average distance $k_1 A^{\frac{1}{2}}$ where k_1 is a proportionality constant and A the average area of the fields. The probability that a lesion (or, with systemic diseases, an infected plant) in one field will form a daughter lesion (or infected plant) at any particular point in the first field is, therefore, by equation 12

$$\frac{a}{k_1{}^b A^{\frac{1}{2}b}}.$$

The average distance the spore must travel to cross the first field, that is, the average potential number of daughter lesions along its track across the field, is also proportional to the square root of the average area. The probability of a daughter lesion somewhere along the track can therefore be taken as

$$\frac{ak}{k_1{}^b A^{\frac{1}{2}(b-1)}}$$

where k is another proportionality constant. Similarly, if the spore passes the first field, the probability of a daughter lesion in the second field it reaches is

$$\frac{ak}{k_2{}^b A^{\frac{1}{2}(b-1)}}$$

in the third

$$\frac{ak}{k_3{}^b A^{\frac{1}{2}(b-1)}}$$

and so on where k_2, k_3 . . . are constants. The probability of a daughter lesion in any field other than the field of origin is:

$$p = \frac{ak}{A^{\frac{1}{2}(b-1)}}\left(\frac{1}{k_1{}^b} + \frac{1}{k_2{}^b} + \frac{1}{k_3{}^b} + \cdots\right).$$

The series

$$\frac{1}{k_1{}^b} + \frac{1}{k_2{}^b} + \frac{1}{k_3{}^b} + \cdots$$

may be taken as convergent when $b > 1$ because it is almost identical with the series

$$\frac{1}{k_1{}^b}\left(1 + \frac{1}{2^b} + \frac{1}{3^b} + \cdots\right)$$

which is convergent when $b > 1$. Hence, when constants are collected together as K,

$$p = \frac{aK}{A^{\frac{1}{2}(b-1)}} \qquad (b > 1) \tag{14}$$

within the limit of the initial assumption of uniformity.

As an example of the effect of area, with an inverse-fourth power gradient (which on present data seems a fair approximation to the behavior of *Phytophthora infestans* not too near its source), doubling the average area of fields and halving their number reduces the probability that a lesion will cause the development of a daughter lesion in some other field by 65%; trebling their area reduces the probability by 81%.

If one wishes to show that the number of daughter lesions in other fields follows the same trends, it must also be shown that the multiplication of disease in the field of origin is not appreciably affected by the area of this field. This follows from direct observation. Increasing the area of fields reduces the amount of inoculum that escapes from the field of origin. If this affected the multiplication of disease there, one would expect gradients of disease within the field, the border being significantly less diseased than the center. Small border effects have indeed been observed: e.g., Thomas *et al.* (1944) found that peach yellow-bud mosaic occurred less in the outside row or two, when disease multiplied within and the orchard was not exposed to infection from without, and

Storey and Godwin (1953) found that when cauliflower mosaic multiplied within a field the incidence was somewhat less in the outer rows. But these border effects are small and extend inward for only a few rows or feet. If they had been strong, they would long ago have received general comment, and one may infer that with the exception of very small plots and fields, the area of the field does not greatly affect the rate of multiplication within. The reason is not difficult to find. The vast bulk of inoculum released from a field falls back into the same field. Variations in the small proportion that escapes have a large effect on inter-field movement of disease, but very little on disease within the field of origin itself.

F. *The Paradox; in Praise of Large Fields; the Second Rule of Sanitation*

The paradox is this. Bringing plants together into fields increases the chance of epidemics; bringing them still further together, by increasing the area of the fields and correspondingly reducing their number, may reduce the chance of a general epidemic.

In the literature of plant pathology it is common to read of the danger of bringing together the host plants of a pathogen. The indiscriminate indictment for bringing plants together is unjustified. Food must be grown, and it is time to write in praise of the large field.

Take these two examples: swollen shoot of cacao can be controlled by sanitation, i.e., by cutting out diseased trees. But the scope for this on small farms is limited, and the difficulties have been described by Posnette (1953). "Each farm, consisting usually of less than 5 acres, has to be treated separately although it has no clearly defined boundaries, and from the standpoint of disease control about 50 acres is the smallest area it is practicable to consider as a unit. For treatment to have any permanent value, the unanimous co-operation (or at least the consent) of many individual farmers must be obtained, and no method of achieving this has been found. Consequently, the Ivory Coast, Nigeria, and the Gold Coast [Ghana] have each in turn been forced to abandon their original plans for disease eradication and have had to adopt the expedient of a 'cordon sanitaire' around the heavily infected districts."

At the other end of the scale we read of the trend gardening has taken in the Everglade region of Florida in recent years (Anonymous, 1957). Anyone farming less than a section or two of land—1 or 2 square miles—is considered a little man in the vegetable patch. Celery fields are half a mile long. A celery harvester has been described that weighs 60,000 pounds and carries a crew of nearly 100 persons aboard. Weeds are cleaned out chemically. The writer does not pause to mention such a trifle as disease, but if our inference from Wellman's findings is correct (in Section V, E, 1) celery mosaic from weeds must cease to exist as a practical problem.

If inoculum comes from other hosts—as cucumber mosaic virus in celery fields comes from *Commelina* and other weeds—making fields larger reduces the percentage of infection in the fields. If inoculum moves from field to field, making fields larger and correspondingly fewer reduces the movement. If sanitation is practiced within the field—as by using clean seed if the pathogen is seed-borne, by rotation of crops if the pathogen persists in the soil, by roguing out diseased plants, and by planting disease-free nursery stock—the size of field does not affect the process directly. But making fields larger and correspondingly fewer affects it indirectly by reducing the reentry of inoculum from without. Guarding against the reentry of large amounts of inoculum is part of the process. One can summarize all this in a second rule of sanitation: efforts at sanitation are furthered by making homogeneous fields, orchards, and plantations larger and correspondingly fewer.

The qualification that the fields should be homogeneous is implicit in all our arguments. If, for example, part of a large field is sown with healthy and part with diseased seed, there is no necessary advantage in largeness; it would have been better to separate the two parts. Sanitation needs common sense as well as common rules.

With diseases that spread slowly, such as some root diseases, the second rule may seem to have no urgency. But these diseases spread in time, as experience shows, and the rule applies in time.

G. *The Reduction of Disease by Farm and Country Planning*

What is discussed under this heading in five paragraphs, namely, the planned reduction of disease by the proper spacing and grouping of fields, may well have in the future a chapter and then a treatise to itself. This is sanitation, no different fundamentally from the destruction of alternate hosts such as barberry bushes. But we are concerned here not with other hosts, but with the crop itself. Two examples will illustrate the problem. One of the chief reasons for epidemics of virus yellows of beet in England is the indiscriminate intermingling of the sugar and fodder beets with some 8000 acres of seed crops in areas naturally congenial to the aphid vector (Hull, 1952). Concentrating seed growing into larger fields in fewer regions would reduce the chance of epidemics. In Holland 80% of the surface of the area, De Streek, is down to potatoes, mainly the early-maturing variety Duke of York, which is intensely susceptible to blight. This (presumably) has come about entirely for reasons unconnected with blight, such as the suitability of the soil and climate for early varieties. But the fact remains that the concentration of very susceptible early varieties is excellent planning of a countryside against blight, because the over-all damage is less than when very susceptible early and less susceptible mid-season varieties are intermingled.

The problem is to compute the effect of a change in the spacing and grouping—the pattern—of fields. The simplest way is to put matters on a relative basis, to use the existing pattern as a standard, and to compute how a change in the pattern would change the date of the onset of an epidemic. From the gradients one can determine the percentage change in the number, i.e., the relative number, of daughter lesions that a field acquires from other fields. From the percentage change one can use equation 11 to determine Δt, the delay in the onset of the epidemic, i.e., the relative date. If, to quote for illustration purely random figures, Δt is 6 days, the date of onset might be postponed from July 20 to 26, or from August 1 to 7, or from November 12 to 18, the actual date, as distinct from the delay, will not be estimated in advance. But the estimate of the delay itself is enough for an estimate of the gain in yield (from a knowledge of average dates of onset and average increments of yield with the development of the crop). From this one could judge whether any feasible change in the pattern of fields is worth recommending.

It is not implied that the calculations would be simple, but ways and means of numerical computation can usually be found. The determination of gradients, especially over distances not near the source, may be difficult; among fungi, a start might be made with those that release their spores only in the cool of the night and early morning or during cloudy, wet weather: their gradients are likely to be more easily determined. But collecting an appropriate range of r values for different varieties, different maturities, and different conditions of the weather should not be difficult; for some diseases such as potato blight, data already exist in the literature, from which a range of values could be calculated.

The response of the various diseases will vary. The greatest benefits from a change in the pattern of fields—often a delay of months in the onset—can be expected when the gradient is steep and r is low. (Steep gradients will also simplify the computations because they limit the area that must be scanned.) Diseases such as potato blight, with high values of r but steep gradients, are less apt for inclusion in planning, but cannot be excluded. Diseases with both shallow gradients and high values of r are probably not worth planning for. This lack of universality does not condemn the method any more than the use of fungicides in plant pathology is condemned by their failure (up until now) to help much in controlling the rust diseases of cereals. One chooses a method by what it will do, not by what it does not do.

The general scope for planning is becoming more favorable under both poles of farming, capitalistic and communistic, because mechanization is introducing larger units and more freedom for organization. On the evidence, there is already room for maneuver, at least with some diseases.

H. *Epidemics in Experimental Plots; an Epidemiological View of Field Experiments in Plant Pathology*

In Section III, E we discussed secondary epidemics. Potato varieties, which although not immune are resistant enough to escape epidemics on their own, can become severely infected through the multiplication of inoculum received from susceptible varieties. Apples of the variety Delicious have resistance but not immunity to powdery mildew, and may become infected when interplanted with susceptible Jonathan as pollinators. So, too, when one plants small experimental plots of resistant but not immune varieties in the same variety trial as plots of susceptible varieties, one can expect inoculum to move from the susceptible to the resistant varieties and initiate there a secondary epidemic that otherwise would not have developed. If the purpose of the trial is a demonstration of qualitative differences, no harm is done. But if the purpose is to put a quantitative value on the resistance, this value will be underestimated, possibly grossly, and the trial will give no indication of how the variety would behave in the hands of the farmer, which after all is the point of the trial. Smallness of plot magnifies the error because it magnifies movement of inoculum between plots. Also, resistance itself contributes to the error: the greater the resistance, the smaller the value of r, so, by equation 11, the greater the advancement of the date of onset of the epidemic in consequence of the arrival of a given amount of inoculum from the susceptible varieties, and hence the greater the error in evaluating resistance, if the onset is early enough to affect the result. The first rule of sanitation (Section III, C) prevails in experimental plots as much as elsewhere; here it is in reverse, with an advancement instead of a delay of the onset (i.e., with Δt negative).

Precisely the same argument holds in trials with fungicides. If the fungicide were perfect and conveyed complete protection in all circumstances, no harm would be done by the proximity of unsprayed control plots. But fungicides ordinarily fall short of perfection, and the presence of unsprayed controls necessarily causes the value of the fungicide to the farmer to be underestimated. An example has been given by Christ (1957). A fault on the right side, one may say, but it remains a fault.

There has been a strange change of fashion. In the bad old days experimenters dispensed with adequate replication. Their experiments were often biologically sound, but seldom capable of statistical interpretation. Nowadays we determine with great mathematical nicety the statistical significance of a result that has no reality outside the experimenter's plots. It seems that the statistician and the plant pathologist have each wrongly assumed that the other has examined the techniques of field experiments in plant pathology and approved of them. Better techniques could probably be evolved, perhaps by using plots of unequal size and cutting down subdivisions as much as is possible without interfering greatly with statistical efficiency. But the real solution is to reduce the errors at their source. If, for demonstration purposes, it is necessary to plant a resistant and susceptible variety together, or to have a sprayed and unsprayed plot together, it should be considered as a demonstration and left at that. But if one wishes to evaluate new varieties quantitatively, they should be compared with others of about the same class: susceptible varieties with susceptible varieties, moderately resistant varieties with moderately resistant varieties—each class in its own separate trial. In fungicide trials one fungicide should be compared with another without an untreated control, if the purpose of the trial is to determine which fungicide is the more efficient. This will reduce the error, even if it does not entirely exclude it.

From these remarks one excepts diseases like many root diseases that spread too slowly for plots to interfere with each other.

VI. The Host Plants

A. Conditions for an Epidemic of Disease in Annual Crops

1. The Annual Rise and Decline of Epidemics: Rules about Its Form

Among annuals we include perennials and biennials grown as annuals, such as beet grown for its roots.

Epidemiologically, the problem with annuals is to determine how disease can strike quickly enough to cause substantial damage. Heavy losses can occur quickly enough if small lesions multiply fast enough to compensate for scarcity of inoculum at the start, or if the amount of inoculum at the start is high enough to compensate for a slow rate of multiplication of small lesions, or if each individual lesion causes damage great enough to compensate for low initial inoculum or slow multiplication, or with any of the countless gradations between these ways.

Consider the first two ways. According to equation 11 the higher the value of r, the less the effect on an annual epidemic of variations in the carry-over of inoculum from the previous season, and hence the less the effect of environmental factors other than those operating during the season of the epidemic itself. The climatic and other risks are concentrated and not well spread, and, as a general rule, one can expect large fluctuations from season to season.

The same rule can be put more elaborately: the higher the value of r, the less likely is a nonrandom succession of epidemic years, provided that the variety of the host and the race of the pathogen remain unchanged. The provision is necessary to exclude what happens when a new aggressive race arises and causes successive epidemics until it is countered by new resistant varieties.

Stem rust of wheat, caused by *Puccinia graminis,* illustrates this rule. The explosiveness of its epidemics indicates a high value of r,[*] and the data compiled by McCallan (1946) show a wide fluctuation—from a trace to 23%—in crop losses from year to year in the United States. Leaf rust, caused by *P. triticina,* which on the whole produces less explosive epidemics, does almost as much damage on the average, but within narrower limits, from 1.0 to 9.6% as one would expect from a lower value of r.

Another rule, which needs little explanation, is: the higher the value of r, the steeper the rise, and, usually, the steeper the decline of an annual epidemic. The second part, about the decline, can only be inferred logically for low-priced crops such as corn and wheat. With high-priced crops that justify a large fungicide account one cannot infer that inoculum drops to a low level between seasons, even if r is high.

2. *The Fast Multiplication of Small Lesions with a Low Amount of Inoculum at the Start*

Because of a high value of r, sanitation is not very effective against diseases with these characteristics (Section III,C) unless it is undertaken thoroughly and extensively, as in a nationwide eradication of barberry bushes for the control of stem rust of wheat. Epidemics are typically controlled by using resistant varieties (e.g., against cereal rusts) or fungicides (e.g., against late blight of tomato). Epidemics are typically widespread; they involve more than a few farms and commonly extend over whole countries or states. This accords with what was said in Section IV. Epidemics tend to fluctuate widely from season to season.

3. *The Slow Multiplication of Small Lesions with a High Amount of Inoculum at the Start*

The root knot nematodes (*Meloidogyne* spp.) of tropical and subtropical climates are examples. They survive well from year to year. The

---

[*] One numerical value is calculated in the Appendix.

multiplication rate is relatively low; e.g., one does not expect severe epidemics if the soil is only lightly infected at the beginning of the season. This is indeed the fundamental assumption in soil fumigation, which reduces the population of nematodes but normally falls far short of complete eradication.

Because of a low value of r, diseases in this category can usually be controlled by sanitation, e.g., by fumigation, isolation, clean fallows, or crop rotation. Epidemics are typically local, i.e., they may involve only a part of a single field. Fluctuations from year to year are relatively small; one can normally predict fairly accurately what will happen one year from what happened the previous year.

4. Multiplication of Large Destructive Lesions and Systemic Infections

If each individual lesion or systemic infection is very destructive, relatively slow multiplication of a relatively small amount of inoculum at the start will bring about a destructive epidemic.

Because of slow multiplication, sanitation is commonly effective (Section III, C). Thus, for virus diseases of annuals, sanitation is the commonest recommendation for control. An analysis of recommendations in the 1957 edition of Smith's "Textbook of Plant Virus Diseases" establishes this point. Epidemics tend to be local (Section IV, G). Evidence here is strong; there does not seem to be a single example among annual plants of a disease with large lesions that spreads widely in a year without man's help. One expects disease not to fluctuate wildly from year to year. Evidence here is weak and conflicting. Hull (1952) states that epidemics of virus yellows in sugar beet develop in a spiral over a period of years. Peak outbreaks have never yet occurred in the root crop in England directly after years of light infection, but have taken 2 or 3 years to develop. But Wolf (1935) found no correlation between the amounts of mosaic in consecutive tobacco crops on the same land, even though in 125 out of 229 fields the virus was observed to overwinter in tobacco stubbles.

B. Conditions for an Epidemic in the Annual New Growth of Perennial Crops

There is the same need for speed here; the new growth must be infected quickly enough for the epidemic to be destructive.

Some diseases owe little to the perennial nature of the host; e.g., tuber-borne inoculum does not usually play a significant part in epidemics of early blight in potatoes, caused by *Alternaria solani*. The greatest effect of perenniality occurs when the crop occupies a perennial site such as an apple orchard or vineyard or when the disease affects perennial tissues as well as the annual new growth. Inoculum then commonly overwinters locally; e.g., epidemics of apple scab start from inoculum released in spring from rotting leaves or infected twigs; epidemics of apple and grape powdery mildew start from infected bud scales.

Many of the diseases of the annual new growth of perennial crops are caused by fungi that multiply fast in small lesions. They differ from corresponding diseases of annual crops in often having a larger initial source of overwintered inoculum. Consequently many tend to be particularly destructive, and must be kept under control by the lavish use of fungicides. It is a matter of fact that the greatest sales of fungicides (excluding seed dressings) are for use against diseases in this category. The crops must be productive enough in terms of money to pay the bill.

C. Epidemics of Disease in Perennial Tissues

1. Plants Grown from Seed

The diseases in coniferous forests fall within this group, as well as many diseases of hardwoods, plantation crops, ornamentals, and the like.

In agriculture one is concerned largely with epidemic disease; in forestry, largely with endemic disease. With indigenous pathogens of indigenous trees growing under natural conditions, inoculum has existed over a long period, and a balance is struck between pathogen and host. Disease control is primarily a matter of: a, forestry practice to maintain a reasonably healthy balance; b, selecting suitable sites for species adapted to the locality with stock grown from seed of suitable origin and with the appropriate composition and management of the stand. There may be small local and temporary epidemics, but the general ecological pattern is of a stable community of pathogens and hosts. In the language of this chapter there is no multiplication and no spread; inoculum is perennial, and within limits the area of the forest has little effect. What we have been discussing is inapplicable—which emphasizes the point that this chapter is concerned only with epidemic disease and not disease in general.

With introduced pathogens or introduced hosts a new balance must be struck, and it is commonly very unfavorable to the host. Examples are chestnut blight, Dutch elm disease, and swollen shoot of cacao. Epidemics of disease following new combinations of host and pathogen seem to be much like those of disease in annual plants, except that the time scale is different; one can conveniently plot the progress of the epidemic in years rather than weeks.

2. Dangers of Vegetative Propagation

a. *Special Danger from Systemic Disease.* Although the material used for vegetative propagation can carry the inoculum of local lesions, it is especially dangerous for systemic disease. In "Plant Diseases," the 1953 Yearbook of Agriculture of the United States Department of Agriculture, about 8% of the space given to diseases of plants grown from seed is about viruses. For vegetatively propagated plants the figure is 28%. It is largely because of the property of systemic infection that viruses are so dangerous in plants propagated vegetatively.

b. *Danger from Longevity.* Many of the clones used in agriculture and horticulture are old. The bulk of the citrus fruit of commerce comes from varieties 80 years old or more. Old apple varieties remain highly popular. The potato varieties Russet Burbank, Irish Cobbler, and White Rose, which rank second, fourth and sixth, respectively, in the United States, are all very old. This longevity provides the span needed for a slow epidemic—what in Section I, C was called a low death rate epidemic. It is one of several factors in the accumulation of virus diseases, so that, for example, it is rare to find a single healthy clonal citrus tree, as experience with the Florida budwood certification scheme shows (Norman, 1956).

The longevity factor (the danger of perpetuating the virus) is the one usually considered in references to the danger of virus diseases in vegetatively propagated plants. But it is easy to overrate the importance of the factor. In providing a long span of years long-lived clones are no different from long-lived plants grown from seed.

c. *Danger from the Randomization of Sources of Infection.* Figure 2B shows a nest of leaf-roll-infected potato plants loosely clustered about the plant that was the original source of inoculum. Within the nest, and especially along the rows which are the main direction of spread, there are many nonrandom contacts between diseased plants: contacts that are harmless in the spread of a systemic disease. Within the nest diseased plants are separated from healthy plants outside the nest; the deeper they are within the nest, the greater the separation and the less the chance of transmission. Suppose that the field of potatoes had been harvested and the crop used for seed the next year. There would have been a mixing of seed with a scattering of diseased tubers among healthy ones, so that when the new crop grew there would be new random contacts between diseased and healthy plants that would allow a less hindered spread of infection. The phenomenon is general. When systemic disease spreads from a focus in an orchard to form a nest of diseased trees, there is a similar automatic brake on further spread and a similar release of that brake every time buds are randomly collected as propagating material for a new orchard.

The danger from this source is greatest when r or r' is small, as it usually is with systemic diseases of trees in particular (van der Plank, 1958). For reasons given in discussing scales of distance in Section IV, E the smaller the value of r', the greater the tendency for diseased plants to cluster, hence the stronger the automatic brake and the greater the benefit to the pathogen of a random use of propagating material in establishing a new orchard or field. One could paraphrase this in general terms by saying that the feebler the pathogen's own power of spread, the greater is the relative benefit to it of man's moving propagating material around, and that feeble powers are on the whole likely to be found in systemic pathogens of trees.

d. *Danger from the Infectious Incompatibility of Scion and Rootstock.* One of the worst epidemics on record, that of tristeza disease of citrus in South America, resulted from what in the event proved to have been an unfortunate choice of rootstock. Typically, tristeza was found in sweet orange on sour orange rootstocks although other combinations were involved. Neither sweet orange on sweet orange stock nor sour orange on sour orange stock suffered noticeably. The disease was one of a combination of species, not of single species.

The key to the understanding of tristeza is the difference between transmission by grafting and by vectors. Infected sweet oranges harbor with apparent tolerance a virus component which is readily transmissible to sour orange seedlings by grafting, and causes them to be stunted. But although this component is freely transmitted by vectors such as *Toxoptera citricidus* from sweet orange to sweet orange, it has not been found in adult sour orange trees even when they grow beside infected sweet oranges in a vector-ridden orchard. Sour orange in the orchard is resistant to systemic infection by vectors of this particular component. But when one grows a sweet orange scion on a sour orange rootstock in a tristeza-infected locality, the sweet orange foliage acquires the component by vector transmission, and the sour orange rootstock acquires it from the scion across the graft union. The result, it seems, is tristeza (McClean and van der Plank, 1955).

To generalize, the necessary conditions for infectious incompatibility between species neither of which shows marked symptoms on its own roots are probably that both species should be susceptible by graft transmission, that one or both species should be resistant to systemic infection by vectors, and that one but not both species should be tolerant of the pathogen or particular strain of it. Exocortis of sweet orange on trifoliate rootstocks is probably an example in which both species are resistant to systemic infection by vectors (no vector is known). Incompatibility in such a combination is normally the result of using infected material in the nursery.

e. *Pernicious Nursery Practices; Contamination During Handling.* It would be unrealistic to ignore the part that pernicious nursery practices can play in increasing diseases which on their own increase slowly. Rootstocks have been rebudded after the first buds have failed, sometimes with a different variety. Rose nurserymen have been known to obtain an abundant source of material for rootstocks by cutting stocks off above the bud union and reusing the cuttings after rooting them for a new lot of buds the following season.

Rather different in type because the practices are not in themselves reprehensible is the spread of inoculum while handling the material for propagation. Ring rot, caused by *Corynebacterium sepedonicum,* black leg, caused by *Erwinia phytophthora,* and the virus disease spindle tuber are transmitted by the knife used to cut seed potatoes, and, other things being equal, epidemics are more common when seed is cut and not planted whole.

f. *Genetic Uniformity of Clones.* Apart from mutations, a clone remains genetically uniform. If a pathogen can attack the clone, genetic conditions are uniformly favorable to disease—a point sometimes stressed. On the other hand, if the clone is resistant, conditions are uniformly unfavorable to disease—a point sometimes overlooked. The problem is part of a wider problem discussed in Section VI, E. The danger of secondary epidemics in crops not uniform in resistance has been mentioned in Section III, E.

g. *Disease in Relation to Vegetative Propagation in Nature.* Plants propagated vegetatively are common in nature, ranging from sod grasses to suckering trees. As a group they do not seem to be especially liable to disease. In them vegetative propagation is primarily a matter of longevity and (presumably) of genetic uniformity. In particular, there is no randomization of sources of infection. Members of the clone stay close together, even when propagation material is released from the air, as the bulbils of *Agave.* To put the matter teleologically (purely for the sake of brevity!), nature does not make the mistake of distributing this material as she distributes seeds and fruits. Only man makes this mistake, and gives the pathogen a mobility it would otherwise not have.

The dangers of vegetative propagation usually stressed in the literature are the dangers of perpetuating the pathogen in the clone, i.e., the longevity factor, and the danger of genetic uniformity. If those were the worst dangers, the prospects of improvement would not be hopeful, because the dangers would be inherent in the core of the process of vegetative propagation. But with vegetative propagation in nature as a background one doubts whether they are. An assessment of disease factors in vegetative propagation in agriculture and horticulture seems overdue. In particular, it should be assessed whether vegetative propagation is in fact inherently dangerous or whether we are not making it more dangerous than it need be. If, as one might guess, much of the trouble starts from the randomization of sources of infection, it should not be beyond the ability of man to devise means of curbing that randomness. Partial curbs are already being applied: perhaps the best-known is tuber-uniting of potatoes (cutting seed potatoes and planting the pieces together in sequence). But more could be done, and pathologists might take a broad look at the disease problem in vegetative propagation to see whether they cannot cut it down to size.

D. *Epidemics of Systemic Disease*

1. *Relation with the Size of the Plant*

In Section IV, F a systemically infected plant was regarded as a single large lesion. Between small plants growing close together in narrow rows inoculum has less distance to travel than between large trees proportionately widely spaced. Other things being equal, an individual vector, for example, will transmit disease more easily between the small plants than between the trees. But there in another quite different problem. If large plants are scattered among the small plants without change of spacing, the large plants are a bigger target for the inoculum and are more likely to become infected. Because it is implicit in the concept of systemic disease that only one successful transmission is needed to infect the plant, these large plants will be expected to develop a larger percentage of systemic disease than the small plants among which they are scattered (van der Plank, 1947). Some figures of Broadbent (1957) can be quoted. In cauliflower seedbeds the infection with cauliflower mosaic was 37.5% in large plants, 6.5% in medium plants, and 0.5% in small plants. The corresponding figures for cabbage black ring spot were 13.8, 7.0, and 2.4%, respectively.

2. *Relation with the Number of Plants per Acre*

Suppose plants are being infected with a systemic disease caused by inoculum coming from outside the plants, e.g., plants infected with air-borne or vector-borne inoculum entering the field from another field or plants infected with inoculum from the soil in which they grow. Consider, for example, two fields exposed to a uniform invasion of migrating infective insects. If m_1 and m_2 are the mean number of transmissions of inoculum per plant in the two fields and x_1 and x_2 the proportions of disease developed,

$$1 - x_1 = e^{-m_1}$$
$$1 - x_2 = e^{-m_2}$$

according to the Poisson theorem. Hence,

$$\frac{\log (1 - x_1)}{\log (1 - x_2)} = \frac{m_1}{m_2}.$$

The mean number of transmissions per plant can reasonably be assumed to be proportional to the number of vectors per plant, and, because the vector environment of the two fields is uniform, this is inversely proportional to the number of plants n_1 and n_2 per unit area in the two fields. Thus,

$$\frac{m_1}{m_2} = \frac{n_2}{n_1}.$$

and

$$\frac{\log (1 - x_1)}{\log (1 - x_2)} = \frac{n_2}{n_1}. \tag{15}$$

This relation (in a slightly different outward guise) was used by van der Plank and Anderssen (1945) for the discussion of infection of tobacco with tomato spotted wilt virus. The virus is brought into fields by thrips which apparently settle randomly and do not spread the disease from tobacco to tobacco. The percentage of disease varied with the number of plants per unit area in the manner predicted by equation 15.

If the proportion of infection is low for a given disease and vector, one may simplify matters by an algebraic transformation, and, as an approximation, write

$$\frac{x_1}{x_2} = \frac{n_2}{n_1}.$$

If μ_1 and μ_2 are the number of infected plants per unit area in the two fields, then

$$\mu_1 = n_1 x_1$$
$$\mu_2 = n_2 x_2.$$

So, as an approximation when the proportion of infection is low,

$$\mu_1 = \mu_2. \tag{16}$$

With systemic disease, if inoculum enters the crop randomly and if the proportion of infection is low, the number of infected plants per unit area is constant and independent of the density of the stand (van der Plank, 1947). This relation was observed experimentally by Linford (1943) without a realization of the condition that the proportion of infection must be low. Pineapple plants were spaced 12, 15, and 18 inches apart in the row, giving populations of 21,780, 18,150, and 14,520 plants per acre, respectively. The same number of plants per acre developed yellow spot, caused probably by tomato spotted wilt virus and carried in randomly by thrips. The percentage of infection was low (3.3, 4.6, and 5.2% for the 12, 15, and 18 inches spacing, respectively), so the condition underlying equation 16 is satisfied, and the number of infected plants per acre was 720, 820, and 760, respectively.

In modern agronomy there is a trend toward high plant populations per acre. From the point of view of disease levels this is a trend in the right direction for crops menaced by vascular wilt diseases and other systemic or quasi-systemic diseases. A simple experiment makes a useful demonstration: tomato seedlings growing sparsely spaced in trays are easily infected at suitable temperatures with bacterial wilt when a culture of *Pseudomonas solanacearum* is poured over the soil, but it is much more difficult to infect a high proportion of tightly crowded seedlings.

E. *Effect of Genetic Variability of the Host*

1. *Effect of the Type of Propagation on the Prevalence of Disease; an Economic Factor*

In what type of plant are epidemics of disease most likely to be common? Stevens (1939, 1948) presented evidence that self-pollinated plants and vegetatively propagated plants have most disease, and came to the conclusion that no disease control measures yet put into practice equal in efficiency on a broad scale the natural ability of a cross-pollinated crop to protect itself through variation. He regards uniformity as dangerous. His evidence came both from the volume of publication of diseases in the United States and from McCallan's (1946) list of outstanding diseases in the United States.

The lowest disease ratings were for the group of cross-pollinated plants grown from seed: corn, sugar beet, and sweet corn. (The evidence is for the days before hybrid corn became popular.) But one must be careful about deductions from this. The group is dominated by corn. Corn is indigenous to North America. Disease of indigenous crops caused by native pathogens tends to be on an endemic rather than epidemic level. The outstanding diseases of corn in McCallan's list are root, stalk, and ear rots, and smut. These are recognizable as usually endemic diseases. The difference in disease between cross-pollinated indigenous corn and self-pollinated introduced wheat and oats has still to be traced convincingly to the method of pollination.

The highest disease ratings were for vegetatively propagated plants: potato, apple, sweet potato, peach, strawberry, pear, and cherry. A glance at this list shows the economic fallacy in trying to compare these crops with corn. If the gross return of money per acre were no more for unblemished apples than for corn, epidemics of apple scab would be rare, because no farmer could afford to grow apples except where scab epidemics were rare or until resistant varieties were available. The economic argument is obvious: epidemics are frequent in crops that give high gross returns of money per acre because these are the only crops that can support frequent epidemics. The bearing of this argument on disease in vegetatively propagated crops is clear. If one takes this into account, together with the fact that there are several dangers (discussed in Section VI,C,2) in vegetative propagation that have nothing to do with genetics, one remains unconvinced on any evidence yet presented that there is any substantial genetic reason why plant pathologists should deplore vegetative propagation.

Consider, for example, blight in potatoes. A genetic objection to vegetative propagation might seem plausible if, when blight first struck in the 1840's, the European potato industry had relied on only one or two clones. In point of fact it seems that varieties were then almost indescribably numerous. (Among other reasons the raising of new varieties was the obvious counter to the accumulation of virus diseases in the absence of an organized seed potato industry, and local varieties were often the result of poor roads and no railroads.) These varieties were very diverse in respect to maturity, response to length of day, growth habit, and the size, shape, and color of the tuber. If there was a lack of diversity of resistance to blight, it would be difficult to argue that it came from vegetative propagation.

Admittedly, experience during the last 100 years suggests that there is not adequate resistance within *Solanum tuberosum* for the development of resistant, early maturing varieties. A likely reason is that *S. tuberosum* came from the Andes where blight is not endemic; and breeders are now convinced that for higher resistance they have to go to other species of *Solanum* (also vegetatively propagated) native to the parts of Central America where *Phytophthora infestans* is probably also native. Vegetative propagation seems to have little or nothing to do with the matter.

Admittedly, too, blight in the 1840's caught the potato with its defenses down. But during recent years *Puccinia polysora* has caught cross-pollinated corn in Africa with its defenses down. One reason, which has nothing to do with vegetative propagation, seems evident: before these epidemics potatoes in Europe and corn in Africa had a long history of freedom from these fungi.

One grants that a wide range of genes is desirable in any crop; but is this more difficult to maintain or to draw upon to block an outbreak of disease in a diversity of clones than in a diversity of individuals in a cross-pollinated variety? With this diversity in reserve is there no case for uniformity of resistance to a disease; and must one consider the apparent value of uniform resistance as illusory, even though there are many examples of clones with long-lasting resistance?

2. Rise and Decline of Epidemics Caused by Foreign Pathogens

Many of the greatest epidemics of plant disease have resulted from organisms introduced newly into a country: in Europe, blight of potatoes, powdery and downy mildews of grapes; in America, blight of chestnuts, blister rust of pines, and Dutch elm disease are familiar examples. Some introductions remain obscure because they find conditions uncongenial. Others find conditions to their liking and host plants with only weak defenses against attack. An epidemic follows. When the host plant is a tree that cannot quickly be replaced, the epidemic runs its course, and, in the short period of man's interest, seems to reach a destructive end. That, for example, is the history of chestnut blight in North America. But with short-lived crops adjustments are usually made quickly: the crop may be shifted to another area, fungicides may be used or cultural practices changed, or resistance may be accumulated by selection (conscious or unconscious) with each new generation of the host (provided that there was resistance available for accumulation). After an initial rise, the epidemic declines to a less devastating level.

Potato blight in Europe is an example. After the great epidemics of the 1840's, blight settled down and, even before the discovery of Bordeaux mixture, caused milder losses. In the process the old varieties disappeared and new ones appeared. One can reconstruct something of the early epidemics from old varieties that have survived. There is documentary evidence of the introduction of potatoes into Basutoland in 1833 from the Cape Colony (van der Plank, 1949a). The background makes it probable that the initial source was Europe. These potatoes have continued to grow in the mountains, under conditions not very favorable to blight. Recently many of these varieties were tested for possible use as parents in a breeding program. It was found that they were intensely susceptible to blight; even varieties with a late maturity, which nowadays in Europe almost invariably goes with high field resistance, were very susceptible. If these varieties represent European potatoes before 1840, the calamitous epidemics need no further explanation, and those who grumble about poor progress toward blight resistance do so in ignorance of the very great advance that has already been made in exploiting what genes there are for resistance in *Solanum tuberosum.*

F. *Vulnerability and Resistance of the Host to Disease; a Matter of Natural Selection*

The question of the type of plant in which epidemics are most likely to be common can be probed from another angle: the geographical and ecological position of the plant before it was taken into cultivation. This has been much better understood in forestry than in agriculture.

The fundamental concept is that of vulnerability. A state of vulnerability means that circumstances are favorable for attack and harm by appropriate pathogens. Vulnerability must not be confused with susceptibility. Indeed, in nature they are to a great extent mutually exclusive: a species can be in a very vulnerable state or it can be very susceptible, but it is unlikely for long to be both vulnerable and susceptible. Natural selection will see to that.*

To give an example of geographical vulnerability, North American plants have been vulnerable to North American pathogens, and, if brought into cultivation in their natural habitat, are likely to have some measure of resistance to them. Extended, the argument brings one to the well-known fact that epidemics are more common if either the host or the pathogen has been introduced.

To give examples of ecological vulnerability, ecologically dominant plants—plants in a more or less pure stand—are more vulnerable than those in mixed stands because inoculum can more easily spread between them. Perennial plants are more vulnerable to systemic disease than annuals because systemic disease (usually) persists for the rest of the life of the plant.

Dominant long-lived trees—redwoods, pines, eucalypts, and the like—are, because of their ecological state, highly vulnerable to viruses and on the geological evidence many have been so continuously for mil-

---

* Natural selection is implicit in the whole argument. This is the centenary of the publication by Darwin and Wallace of their essay, and plant pathologists can have little satisfaction in the thought that 100 years have gone by without the greatest concept in biology having left more than a scratch on their subject.

lions of years. That they have survived destruction by harmful viruses implies great resistance, and up until now no virus disease has been recorded in them. The argument for dominant long-lived trees holds also, although sometimes to a lesser extent, for dominant perennials of any sort, such as the dominant grasses of veld and prairie. Great vulnerability can be expected to have required great resistance, which seems to accord with the facts, because there does not seem to be a single record of natural infection (let alone an epidemic) by a harmful virus of any plant species that has achieved ecological dominance and is growing in its natural environment. Exceptions may yet be found, but they are unlikely to alter the general conclusion that there have been epidemics of plant virus diseases only because we have taken into cultivation a lot of annuals and other plants with no background of ecological dominance in nature.

Tolerance must be grouped with resistance here, and the discovery of harmless latent viruses in ecologically dominant perennials would not invalidate the argument in any way.

These examples illustrate the connection between vulnerability and resistance. One point is still very obscure. Geographical vulnerability can explain why epidemics are more common with foreign pathogens or in foreign hosts. But can ecological vulnerability sometimes lead to general resistance, even against foreign pathogens? So far, e.g., the redwoods, pines, and eucalypts have remained free from harmful virus diseases despite international commerce and movement of viruses. It would be a mistake to reject the possibility of general resistance as far-fetched just because one cannot for the moment point to the mechanism.

APPENDIX: A SUGGESTION FOR THE CONTROL OF STEM RUST OF WHEAT

When this chapter was written, it was realized that stem rust of wheat, caused by *Puccinia graminis tritici*, behaved in many ways like blight of potatoes. Rowell (1957), testing a method of inoculating wheat with rust spores carried in oil, had published an S-shaped progress curve for an attack of race 15B on Marquis wheat. From this curve one calculates that r was about 50% per day between July 4 and 10, 1956. But the work of Hayden (1956) had not been seen. Without knowledge of r and the appropriate equations Hayden was not in a position to see fully the capital significance of his results.

When Race 15B reached epiphytotic levels, it was observed that the varieties Lee and Sentry were less severely damaged than Marquis, Mida, Carleton, and Nugget, even though all these varieties (Lee and Sentry included) were fully "susceptible," in the sense that the infection types with Race 15B were 3 or $X +$ to 4. Hayden inoculated these varieties with Race 15B when all had headed except Marquis and Carleton, which were in the boot stage. Relatively little difference in yield resulted between plots inoculated with heavy and light concentrations of spores with all varieties except Lee and Sentry. When exposed to light concentrations of spores, the yield of these two varieties was depressed much less than that of all other varieties. As inoculum was increased from light to heavy, the yield of Lee and Sentry more closely approached that of the four other varieties. (By equation 11 the effects of varying amounts of inoculum at the start are greatest when r is least.) Hayden inoculated plants with Race 15B in the center of plots. The rate of spread of rust from these centers was lowest in Lee among the bread wheats and in Sentry among the durums. (By equations 8 and 13, with a given incubation period and environmental conditions, the rate of spread of a given pathogen is determined by r.) Hayden inoculated plants with spores. On the "susceptible" varieties except Carleton, which was not included in the test, the inoculations produced fewer lesions per culm on Lee among the bread wheats and on Sentry among the durums.

From these results there is little doubt that Lee and Sentry have lower r values, and that these relatively low r values are at least in part the result of a resistance to infection which cannot possibly be reflected in the accepted criterion of "susceptibility": an X, 3 or 4 type of reaction. The resistance of Lee and Sentry to Race 15B is comparable with that of the potato variety Noordeling to *Phytophthora infestans*, discussed in Section III,E. In each case there is a certain apparent tolerance in the sense that the varieties fare better than others in an epidemic, and this tolerance is in reality partial resistance manifested as a low value of r. Partial resistance has long been recognized and is considered to be polygenic and not greatly affected by the race of the fungus. It will be assumed that this is so.

There is nothing original in a suggestion that tolerance in some form or other might profitably be used to lessen losses from rust. The suggestion has often been mooted. But our recommendation is not just tolerance, valuable though it be, but cumulative delay. A rust epidemic adequately delayed is no epidemic at all.

Let us rewrite equation 5 as follows:

$$t_2 - t_1 = \frac{230}{r} \log \frac{x_2(1 - x_1)}{x_1(1 - x_2)}.$$

The time taken for an epidemic in a field to develop from any given level of infection x_1 to any other given level x_2 is inversely proportional to r. But the same idea applies to an epidemic in its whole course from field to field, from country to country. If the values of r of all "susceptible" varieties could be halved, then every step which before took 1 day would now take 2, other things being equal. One pictures the whole epidemic process occurring step by step in the same order as before, but with each step now taking twice the time. An epidemic which before needed 2 months to travel from Mexico to Canada would now need 4, other things being equal. Epidemics starting from infected barberries or wild grasses would be delayed in the same way.

Let us consider the errors. The reasoning is not true of the relatively short time that spores are actually air-borne between fields. Another error comes from lesions' growing old and sterile. This error is on the safe side, i.e., it makes equation 5 undervalue the benefit of reducing r. The condition that other things be equal is unattainable. Here too the error is likely to be on the safe side. Rust epiphytotics occur as a result of particularly favorable combinations of climatic conditions, and these are less likely to extend over, say, 4 months than over 2. Finally, an error comes from the incubation period's effect on the disease progress curve (Section II, A, 2). Here too the error is on the safe side, because if, e.g., factors counterbalancing this effect make the curve for a high-r variety sigmoid, they will make the curve for a low-r variety progressively flatter than sigmoid.

Because the delay is cumulative with the progress of the epidemic, it might seem that on the main North American rust track the benefits of delay would increase from south to north: that Canada would gain more than Mexico. Perhaps this is true. But the south in turn gets inoculum from the north, so the process is not just one way.

Suppose it were agreed that after some specified date no new varieties would be released unless they had relatively low r values. There would be an immediate local benefit to farmers who planted these varieties, a benefit of the same sort as that gained by those who planted Lee and Sentry during the recent epidemics of Race 15B. But hopes would go far beyond that—to the time when low r varieties had accumulated along the rust track and delayed general epidemics out of existence. If all states along the rust track pursued a policy of enlightened local self-interest and released only low r varieties, they could expect both an interim and a final dividend. That is our suggestion.

It would probably be easiest to determine r comparatively. Lee or Sentry might, for example, be used as a standard for testing against Race 15B those varieties that have a "susceptible" reaction to this race. The easiest, but not the only, way of producing suitable new varieties would be to use breeding material "susceptible" to one or other race. But it is not the aim of this appendix to discuss methods of breeding; it is to describe the benefits that could be expected from stable polygenic resistance manifested as relatively low values of r and to state how this resistance could best be used.

REFERENCES

Anonymous. 1949. W. African Cacao Research Inst. Tafo, Gold Coast, Ann. Rept. 1947/8: 21.

Anonymous. 1957. Weed 'em and reap. Monsanto Mag. 37: 29–33.

Beaumont, A., J. H. Bant, and I. F. Storey. 1953. Potato spraying trials in Yorkshire, 1947–51. Plant Pathol. 2: 56–60.

Bonde, R., and E. S. Schultz. 1943. Potato cull piles as a source of late-blight infection. Am. Potato J. 20: 112–118.

Broadbent, L. 1957. Investigations of virus diseases of Brassica crops. Cambridge Univ. Press, London and New York. 94 pp.

Chester, K. S. 1943. The decisive influence of late winter weather on wheat leaf rust epiphytotics. Plant Disease Reptr. Suppl. 143: 133–144.

Chester, K. S. 1946. "The Cereal Rusts." Chronica Botanica, Waltham, Massachusetts. 269 pp.

Chester, K. S. 1950. Plant disease losses: their appraisal and interpretation. Plant Disease Reptr. Suppl. 193: 190–362.

Christ, R. A. 1957. Control plots in experiments with fungicides. Commonwealth Phytopathol. News 3: 62.

Cochran, W. G. 1936. The statistical analysis of field counts of diseased plants. Suppl. J. Roy. Statist. Soc. 3: 49–67.

Doncaster, J. P., and P. H. Gregory. 1948. The spread of virus diseases in the potato crop. (Brit.) Agr. Research Council Rept. Ser. No. 7: 189 pp.

Freeman, G. H. 1953. Spread of diseases in a rectangular plantation with vacancies. Biometrica 40: 287–296.

Gäumann, E. 1946. "Pflanzliche Infektionslehre." Verlag Birkhäuser, Basel. 611 pp.

Grainger, J. 1950. Forecasting outbreaks of potato blight in West Scotland. Brit. Mycol. Soc. Trans. 33: 82–91.

Grainger, J. 1956. Host nutrition and attack by fungal parasites. Phytopathology 46: 445–456.

Gregory, P. H. 1945. The dispersal of air-borne spores. Brit. Mycol. Soc. Trans. 28: 26–72.

Gregory, P. H. 1948. The multiple-infection transformation. Ann. Appl. Biol. 35: 412–417.

Hansen, H. P. 1950. Investigations of virus yellows in beets in Denmark. Trans. Danish Acad. Tech. Sci. 1950: 68 pp. (Abstr. in Rev. Appl. Mycol. 30: 399).

Hayden, E. B. 1956. Progressive development of infection by Puccinia graminis var. tritici Eriks. and E. Henn. (Guyot) on certain varieties of wheat and the relation of stem rust to yield. Univ. Minnesota Graduate School Thesis. 103 pp.

Heald, F. D., and R. A. Studhalter. 1914. Birds as the carriers of the chestnut blight fungus. J. Agr. Research 2: 405–422.

Hewitt, W. B., N. W. Frazier, J. H. Freitag, and A. J. Winkler. 1949. Pierce's disease investigations. Hilgardia 19: 207–263.

Hildebrand, E. M. 1953. Yellow-red or X-disease of peach. *Cornell Univ. Agr. Expt. Sta. Mem.* **323:** 54 pp.

Hildebrand, E. M., G. H. Berkeley, and D. Cation. 1942. Handbook of virus diseases of stone fruits in North America. *Mich. Agr. Expt. Sta. Misc. Publ.* 76 pp.

Hull, R. 1952. Control of virus yellows in sugar beet seed crops. *J. Roy. Agr. Soc. Engl.* **113:** 86–102.

Large, E. C. 1945. Field trials of copper fungicides for the control of potato blight. I. Foliage protection and yield. *Ann. Appl. Biol.* **32:** 319–329.

Large, E. C. 1952. The interpretation of progress curves for potato blight and other plant diseases. *Plant Pathol.* **1:** 109–117.

Large, E. C., R. E. Taylor, I. F. Storey, and A. H. Yule. 1954. Spraying trials in the potato-growing area around the Wash, 1948–53. *Plant Pathol.* **3:** 40–48.

Leach, J. G. 1940. "Insect Transmission of Plant Diseases." McGraw-Hill, New York. 615 pp.

Leach, L. D. 1938. Determining the sclerotial population of *Sclerotium rolfsii* by soil analysis and predicting losses of sugar beets on the basis of these analyses. *J. Agr. Research* **56:** 619–631.

Limasset, P. 1939. Recherches sur le *Phytophthora infestans* (Mont.) de Bary. *Ann. épiphyt.* **5:** 21–39.

Liming, O. N., E. G. Rex, and K. Layton. 1951. Effects of a source of heavy infection on the development of Dutch elm disease in a community. *Phytopathology* **41:** 146–151.

Linford, M. B. 1943. Influence of plant populations upon the incidence of pineapple yellow spot. *Phytopathology* **33:** 408–410.

McCallan, S. E. A. 1946. Outstanding diseases of agricultural crops and uses of fungicides in the United States *Contribs. Boyce Thompson Inst.* **14:** 105–115.

McClean, A. P. D., and J. E. van der Plank. 1955. The role of seedling yellows and stem pitting in tristeza disease of citrus. *Phytopathology* **45:** 222–224.

McClintock, J. A., L. O. Kunkel, and H. H. Thornberry. 1951. Peach rosette. *In* Virus diseases and other disorders with virus-like symptoms of stone fruits in North America. *U. S. Dept. Agr. Agr. Handbook* **10:** 7–10.

Mills, W. R. 1940. *Phytophthora infestans* on tomato. *Phytopathology* **30:** 830–839.

Moore, P. W., E. Nauer, and W. Yendol. 1957. California scaly bark disease of citrus. *Calif. Agr.* **11:** 8–9.

Moore, W. C. 1943. The measurement of plant diseases in the field. *Brit. Mycol. Soc. Trans.* **26:** 28–35.

Newhall, A. G. 1938. The spread of onion mildew by wind-borne conidia of *Peronospora destructor*. *Phytopathology* **28:** 257–269.

Norman, G. G. 1956. Where do we stand on budwood certification? *Citrus Ind.* **37:** 16–17.

Peace, T. R. 1957. Approach and perspective in forest pathology. *Forestry* **30:** 47–56.

Posnette, A. F. 1947. Virus diseases of cacao in West Africa. *Ann. Appl. Biol.* **34:** 388–402.

Posnette, A. F. 1951. Virus research at the West African Cacao Research Institute, Tafo, Gold Coast. *Tropical Agr. London* **28:** 133–142.

Posnette, A. F. 1953. Virus diseases of cacao in West Africa: the present position. *Rept. 13th Intern. Hort. Congr., London, 1952* pp. 1224–1230.

Riker, A. J. 1951. The spread of oak wilt in local areas. *Phytopathology* **41:** 30.

Rowell, J. B. 1957. Oil inoculation of wheat with spores of *Puccinia graminis* var. *tritici. Phytopathology* **47:** 689–690.

Sprague, R. 1953. Powdery mildew on apples. Plant Diseases, *U. S. Dept. Agr., Yearbook Agr.* pp. 667–670.

Stevens, N. E. 1939. Disease damage and pollination types in "grains." *Science* **89**: 339–340.

Stevens, N. E. 1948. Disease damage in clonal and self-pollinated crops. *J. Am. Soc. Agron.* **40**: 841–844.

Storey, I. F., and A. E. Godwin. 1953. Cauliflower mosaic in Yorkshire 1950–51. *Plant Pathol.* **2**: 98–101.

Thomas, H. E., C. E. Scott, E. E. Wilson and J. H. Freitag. 1944. Dissemination of a peach mosaic. *Phytopathology* **34**: 658–661.

Todd, H. 1940. A note on random associations in a square point lattice. *J. Roy. Statist. Soc.* **7**: 78–82.

van der Plank, J. E. 1946. A method for estimating the number of random groups of adjacent diseased plants in a homogeneous field. *Trans. Roy. Soc. S. Africa* **31**: 269–278.

van der Plank, J. E. 1947. The relation between the size of plant and the spread of systemic diseases. *Ann. Appl. Biol.* **34**: 376–387.

van der Plank, J. E. 1948. The relation between the size of fields and the spread of plant disease into them. I. Crowd diseases. *Empire J. Exptl. Agr.* **16**: 134–142.

van der Plank, J. E. 1949a. Some suggestions on the history of potato virus X. *J. Linnean Soc. London, Botany* **53**: 251–262.

van der Plank, J. E. 1949b. The relation between the size of fields and the spread of plant diseases into them. *Empire J. Exptl. Agr.* **12**: 18–22.

van der Plank, J. E. 1958. Some epidemiological consequences of systemic infection. *Plant Pathol.*: Problems and Progress 1908–1958.

van der Plank, J. E., and E. E. Anderssen, 1945. Kromnek disease of tobacco: a mathematical solution to a problem of disease. *Union S. Africa Dept. Agr. and Forestry Sci. Bull.* **240**: 6 pp.

van der Zaag, D. E. 1956. Overwintering en epidemiologie van *Phytophthora infestans*, tevens enige nieuwe bestrijdingsmogelijkheden. *Tijdschr. Plantenziekten* **62**: 89–156.

Waggoner, P. E. 1952. Distribution of potato late blight around inoculum sources. *Phytopathology* **42**: 323–328.

Wellman, F. L. 1937. Control of southern celery mosaic in Florida by removing weeds that serve as sources of mosaic infection. *U. S. Dept. Agr. Tech. Bull.* **548**: 16 pp.

Wolf, F. A. 1935. "Tobacco Diseases and Decays." Duke Univ. Press, 454 pp.

Zentmyer, G. A., P. P. Wallace, and J. G. Horsfall. 1944. Distance as a dosage factor in the spread of Dutch elm disease. *Phytopathology* **34**: 1025–1033.

CHAPTER 8

Forecasting Epidemics

PAUL E. WAGGONER

Department of Soils & Climatology, The Connecticut Agricultural Experiment Station, New Haven, Connecticut

I. INTRODUCTION

Man found his crops destroyed by rusts and smuts, mildews and blights long before he recognized the microscopic pathogens. Some men correlated disease with sinfulness; others, finding only a slight variation in the amount of sin and a large variation in the weather, obtained a better correlation—that between weather and disease. Consequently, they called the weather the cause of plant disease. In this imperfect state of knowledge they were able to forecast disease outbreaks before they were able to name the pathogenic fungi. Now, in our still imperfect state of knowledge, we too can forecast disease outbreaks from our science of the interaction of host, pathogen, and weather.

The forecasting of epidemics is a contribution to the forecasting of crop yields. Yield forecasts are useful if they arrive sufficiently early to permit adjustments in acreage or transportation or if remedies can be applied to prevent the prophesied disaster. An empirical relation between weather and yields can assist in adjustments. The relation becomes more logical and satisfying and is productive of remedies if it also includes a

291

knowledge of the contributions of soil fertility and of varieties to yield. Of primary interest here, the relation is more logical and fruitful if it includes a knowledge of the interaction of pathogens with weather, soil, and host; this is most fruitful if a remedy can be applied after the forecast is made.

Reviews of the forecasting of epidemics of plant disease have appeared in the past. Because the weather relations of diseases are often obvious, the practice is a venerable one, and the many examples over the world have been examined by Foister (1929) and by Miller and O'Brien (1952, 1957). These reviews provide complete coverage. Therefore, the subject will not be neglected if the present examination takes a different path: the etiology of plant diseases has been examined for opportunities for prognostication of disease and subsequent loss. Illustrative examples will be cited where possible.

The forecasting of epidemics is quantitative epidemiology applied with courage. The better to make it quantitative, a formal framework is proposed and employed as follows:

The number of spores reaching a host will double as the production is doubled or arrivals are proportional to Q, the number of propagules released. The arrivals also increase as the trapping efficiency p increases; however, the relation is not linear because the disseminating "cloud" of pathogens is depleted by this trapping. Thus, arrivals are proportional to $pe^{-\text{constant } pf(X)}$ where $f(X)$ is a function of distance X. The number of spores per volume of air or other medium decreases rapidly with distance X or arrivals are proportional to $1/X^n$; since dissemination is generally three-dimensional, n is about 2. Finally, the number of infections D is related to arrivals or $D = $ constant $[(Q/K)p/X^n]e^{-\text{constant } pf(X)}$. The K is the proportionality constant between arrivals and infection. For the important case of aerial dissemination, estimates of the parameters have been made: p can be about $\frac{1}{20}$, n about 2, the $f(X) = X^{1/8}$ (Gregory, 1945; Waggoner, 1952).

As the etiology is examined for possibilities for prognosis, these possibilities are evaluated in terms of the above model.

II. The Primary Inoculum

Many factors will affect the magnitude of the explosion called an epidemic, but the spark that ignites, i.e., the primary inoculum, must be present. And, as the model shows, the greater the quantity Q, the greater the epidemic likely. Thus, the quantity of primary inoculum can be a criterion for forecasting, a criterion particularly useful because of its early appearance.

The diseases of crops grown in the temperate zone have been the objects of most forecasting schemes. Here the pathogen often must assume a resistant form, take shelter, become dormant, or be eliminated and renewed from the tropics. The forecaster can examine these survival mechanisms for his first hint of the new season's prospects.

An early indication of the amount of overwintering primary inoculum is the severity of disease in the previous season. Although many factors can modify the amount, a persistence in amount is seen from year to year in certain diseases due in part to the greater primary inoculum carried over after an epidemic year. For example, the persistence of the catastrophic severity of potato late blight from year to year increased the disastrous consequences of the appearance of *Phytophthora infestans* in Ireland in the "hungry forties." The appearance of the new *Helminthosporium victoriae* (Meehan and Murphy, 1946) led to the persistent decimation of the varieties derived from Victoria oats and necessitated the introduction of new varieties. Thus, the "grand cycle" of disease, the steady increase and decrease of severity from year to year, caused partially by the overwintering of inoculum, is an early straw in the wind indicating the prospects in a new season.

If an overwintering, resistant—often perfect—stage of the pathogen is known, the procedure is more satisfying than complete dependence upon the "grand cycle." Here the forecaster can search for the overwintering form itself and see the spark that may ignite the coming explosion. Many classic schemes for forecasting apple scab proceed by this means. The pathogen *Venturia inaequalis* overwinters in the perfect stage in fallen leaves where its maturity is dependent upon the winter and early spring weather (Wilson, 1928). Microscopic examination of the perithecia (Young and May, 1928), ripening in the warmth of the laboratory (Holz, 1939a), and considerations of winter weather (Holz, 1939b; Louw, 1947) have formed the bases for prediction of the first discharges of ascospores in the spring. Forecasts of infection then can be made from a knowledge of the stage of tree development, the response of growers to the spray warnings, and subsequent discharge and infection periods.

Brown rot of peaches, caused by *Monilinia fructicola*, is another ascomycetous pathogen that overwinters in the perfect stage although the imperfect stage is also functional. A search of orchards for the cankers and mummified fruit that harbor the pathogen reveals primary inoculum for the succeeding season, and could form the basis of a forecast.

Ergot of cereals, especially rye, is another classic disease that overwinters as an easily visible, perfect stage. The discovery of a multitude of the sclerotia of *Claviceps purpurea* in seed or even in a field can be a warning of an epidemic in the field to be planted or in the field where sclerotia may have fallen.

A pathogen may take shelter during the cold season, and a forecasting scheme can be founded upon the amount sheltered. For example, *Bacterium stewartii*, the pathogen of bacterial wilt of sweet corn, survives the winter in the bodies of adult flea beetles. The survival of the sheltering beetles is encouraged by warm winters. Stevens (1934) found that severe epidemics of wilt followed warm winters, and, hence, founded a forecasting scheme employed successfully by him and Boewe in Illinois and by other workers in New Jersey and New York.

A pathogen can invade seed and be sheltered for the winter with the crop. *Phytophthora infestans* infects tubers in the autumn and overwinters in the storage bin. Here the inspector can estimate the amount of primary inoculum available for the following season. Wallin (1956) has done this with some success. Of equal importance when blighted tubers are culled from the storage and dumped, the sprouts on the cull piles are a fruitful source of inoculum (Bonde and Schultz, 1943) and an opportunity for the forecaster to take a census of primary inoculum (Hyre and Bonde, 1956).

The extent of virus infection can be accurately predicted by indexing potato seed, a practice generally followed.

Loose smut of wheat or barley derives from seed infected by *Ustilago tritici* or *Ustilago nuda* during the previous season. Thus the census of the infection in the seed can lead to a forecast of epidemics; the detection of infection can be made by germinating or by examining microscopically a sample of seed (Simmonds, 1946). A forecast can also be based upon an even earlier event, the weather at blossoming time in the preceding season, because this is the time of susceptibility (Dickson, 1947).

Some pathogens lie dormant awaiting the arrival of warm weather and a host. Their numbers are an index of epidemics to come. This is the case of many soil-borne pathogens—pathogens that spread relatively slowly. The extent of *Phymatotrichum omnivorum* and its depradations can be predicted almost to the foot from its extent in the previous year (Taubenhaus and Killough, 1923). Nematode infestation can be forecast because of the persistence of the worms or cysts. Whether or not a crop will be infected by *Verticillium albo-atrum* has been predicted from the response of an index plant, the tomato, grown in soil samples from the intended field (Wilhelm, 1950). If rotation decreases the population of a pathogen, severity of infection can be predicted from the intensity of management.

Pathogens can lie dormant in an overwintering crop. If the crop, like winter wheat, is harvested in midsummer, the pathogen must race against time if an epidemic is to occur. Hence, the overwintering fungus and its early multiplication are critical. Thus, Chester (1946) found that *Puccinia rubigo-vera* overwinters in Oklahoma in pustules of wheat leaf rust; the level of infection on April 1 is determined by the weather in the late winter; and this level of infection determines the extent of any epidemic, because weather after that date is rarely limiting. Forecasts by this method have been eminently successful, the only failure being caused by the rare event of later weather limiting infection (Young and Wadsworth, 1953).

A pathogen may be largely eradicated from a region by the winter, and primary inoculum may be borne in on southerly winds. Following the frequent observation of fungal spores in the upper atmosphere, much attention has been devoted to this concept. For example, the annual renewal of *Puccinia graminis* var. *tritici* and the production of epidemics of stem rust of wheat has been attributed after extensive studies by Stakman and co-workers to spores borne aloft in Mexico and showered down upon the Great Plains (Christensen, 1942). Epidemics of tobacco blue mold in Quebec have been associated with the production of *Peronospora tabacina* in Kentucky and a forecasting scheme devised accordingly (Stover and Koch, 1951). Two considerations should be kept in mind in evaluating the foregoing. First, as spring progresses northward, even diseases of local origin will appear to move northward. Second, the rapid dilution by distance of spore clouds, as evidenced by the steep gradients of infection about isolated sources (Gregory, 1945), makes the probability extremely small that spores from continental distances will alight on a given field. The second consideration renders spore traps of little use in forecasting; Rusakov found no spores upon traps until 1% of the plants in the neighborhood had been infected, and he suggested a local field inspection instead of dependence upon traps (Chester, 1946).

The characteristics of stem rust make it more susceptible than many diseases to a forecast based upon spore movement from the South. The astronomical numbers of spores produced in the large acreages of wheat in the South and the large acreages of hosts to the North somewhat counteract the dilution by distance. The sturdiness of the *Puccinia* spores assures that they will be viable when they arrive. The broad and nearly continuous belt of wheat extending from Texas to Saskatchewan permits *Puccinia* to leap, frog-like from county to county, never requiring it to move continental distances at a single jump. Thus, a forecasting scheme for stem rust can logically be based upon the systematic movement of primary inoculum from the South. The sensitive spores of the downy mildews, produced on limited acreages and seeking out limited acreages separated by miles deserted of hosts, presents a contrasting picture.

Thus, a survey of the inoculum available at the beginning of a new season provides a rational point of departure for a disease forecast. It has the advantage of earliness, with the consequent opportunities for remedial measures, such as selecting an alternate crop, roguing, or chemical control. It has the disadvantage of occurring so early that many factors can subsequently modify the outcome. Nevertheless, the forecaster courts disaster if he does not issue a word of warning when the inoculum potential is obviously high, or, on the other hand, if he forecasts an epidemic solely from weather data when the pathogen is absent.

III. The Dispersal of Inoculum

When a given amount of primary infection is present, the successful pathogen must next produce units such as cells or spores, and have them detached. Garrett (in Chapter 2 of this volume) calls these units propagules. The product of the primary infection times the output of propagules per lesion comprises the source strength of Q and the subsequent epidemic is proportional to Q. Hence, another opportunity for forecasting is presented.

Here, in considering the production and detachment of propagules such as spores, weather is met in all of its effectiveness. Many diseases, especially mildews, have long been associated with damp weather; the late blight forecasts of Martin (1923) and Cook (1949) were based upon average or accumulated rainfall and average temperatures. This is, however, an oversimplification. Crosier (1934), interpreting his own and Melhus's studies of the biology of *Phytophthora infestans*, wrote, "It is not the total rainfall nor the average temperature, but the coexistence of moisture and low temperature (from 10 to 15° C.) for one-half hour or longer, that makes possible the formation of swarmspores, and . . . infection follows promptly if the moisture persists." Further, he emphasized, "No swarmspores can be formed, irrespective of the temperature and moisture, unless viable sporangia are present." The present discussion, following the life cycles of pathogens, attempts to recognize these fundamentals.

Crosier, in the above study, found sporulation was most abundant in an atmosphere saturated with water and at a temperature of 18 to 22°; sporangia were abundant within 8 hours. Production was slower at lower temperatures, and sterile at temperatures 3 to 5° higher. Here is the necessary information for a description of an environment suitable for the multiplication of *Phytophthora* and the forecast of late blight epidemics.

Quantitative estimates of sporulation of this important pathogen have been made, permitting a more exact weighting of the forecast according to the production (Wallin, 1957). At 21° sporangia appeared in 6 hours, while 8 hours were required at 18°. If more time was permitted, most isolates produced more sporangia at 18 than at 21°. For example, a typical isolate produced about equal numbers of spores, N, in 6 hours at 21° and 8 hours at 18°; in 12 hours at 18° it had produced about 20 N while at 21° it had produced only 3 N. The forecaster should beware of environmental races, however: one isolate was able to produce between 1 and 2 N sporangia in 12 hours at the high temperature of 27°. Employing data of this type and a survey of primary infection one can estimate the production of spores from hygrothermograph records, and a forecast can be begun.

The final step in the estimation of Q, the number of propagules dispersed, is an examination of the discharge of the units into the air. The units have been attached to the host for nutrition; now they must break this attachment, pass through the enveloping 100 microns of the laminar flow layer of air, and reach the turbulent air above. Many viruses are borne by insects, and their numbers at critical times in the host's life can form the basis of a forecast of epidemics (Doncaster and Gregory, 1948). Some bacteria are borne in splattering raindrops; the arrival of rain might be employed in forecasting a bacterial epidemic.

Fungi have developed many clever devices for dispersing their spores—devices that have been studied by deBary, Buller, and Ingold. Among these are some that depend upon the weather and, hence, can be limiting and of interest to the forecaster. Tobacco blue mold is a case in point. DeBary observed how the sporangia of some Oomycetes are discharged as the sporangiophores dry and twirl; Pinckard (1942) found this phenomenon specifically in *Peronospora tabacina*. The disease tobacco blue mold does not increase during prolonged rains (Dixon *et al.*, 1936); spores are found in the air as dew or rain dry, not while the lesions are wet (Waggoner and Taylor, 1958). From these observations the forecaster of blue mold can learn to look beyond rains and dews and consider the critical hours after the leaves have dried and the spores have flown (Waggoner and Taylor, 1958).

This completes the estimation of the number of spores released, the source strength Q to which the subsequent epidemic will be proportional if other things are equal. This early omen depends upon the quantity of primary inoculum and infection and upon conditions favorable for the production and release of the propagules. The omen appears to the forecaster early enough for chemical control to be initiated, probably not early enough for the selection of an alternate crop or for roguing. Many hurdles must yet be taken by the pathogen before an epidemic occurs, but the presence or absence of spore production is a valuable, early clue.

IV. THE TRANSFER OF INOCULUM

The propagule, once separated from its parent, can be carried to an infection court on some object, in the soil or in water, or through the air. This transfer is generally not under the control of the pathogen, can be limiting, and, hence, is an opportunity for forecasting.

Many contaminated objects such as seed, soil, and machinery are borne by man. The speed and volume of commerce, the wide distribution of hosts—particularly economic species—and the prolific nature of pathogens causes the probability of permanent nonintroduction of new pests into a region to approach zero. A knowledge of sanitation and of quarantine measures, as well as the foregoing factors, permits the forecaster to estimate how soon the inevitable introduction and subsequent epidemic will come.

The annual reintroduction of pests can be forecast in the same way. For example, the coming incidence of potato ring rot, caused by *Corynebacterium sepedonicum,* can be anticipated from the liveliness of its transfer. Is seed inspected? Is contaminated equipment sterilized? Is whole seed used? If not, then an epidemic can be safely forecast whenever the inoculum was introduced into the seed-growing regions during the previous season.

Many viruses are transferred in insects, particularly aphids. As the number of aphids is decreased, transfer—as is dispersal—is decreased. This may be due to a northern climate, e.g., that of Maine or Scotland; the time of the year (Doncaster and Gregory, 1948); an exposed site (Waggoner and Kring, 1956); or sometimes an insecticide (Broadbent, 1957). Whatever drastically reduces the population of insect vectors reduces Q, and a lower incidence of infection can be forecast.

In many cases a sharp decrease in infection is observed at increasing distances from the source of aphid-borne viruses (e.g., Gregory and Read, 1949). In another case the sharp decrease observed by Waggoner and Kring (1956) became a broad distribution when the susceptible Green Mountain variety and extremely high insect populations were encountered (unpublished work). Nevertheless, under the usual field conditions of moderate populations of insects and some host resistance, the decrease with distance will be sharp, disease being proportional to $1/X^n$ where n is about 2 (Gregory and Read, 1949). This is not surprising; Wolfenbarger (1946) has catalogued many insect dispersal patterns and found them similar. From this the forecaster can derive two useful conclusions: disease severity will be slight at considerable distances from sources, especially in a single generation of the pathogen; and numerous widely scattered sources are necessary for an epidemic.

The spread of insect-borne fungi behaves in a manner similar to the spread of the viruses, providing similar bases for forecasting. For example, infection by *Ceratostomella ulmi*, the cause of Dutch elm disease, increases with the population of bark beetles (which can be limited by insecticides) and with propinquity to diseased trees (Zentmyer *et al.*, 1944). Therefore, a forecast could be based upon a knowledge of the number of beetles and diseased elms in the neighborhood.

In undisturbed soil the spread of pathogens can take place through the contact or grafting of roots. The spread of *Phymatotrichum omnivorum* in cotton fields (Taubenhaus and Killough, 1923) and of *Endoconidiophora fagacearum* in oak forests (Beckman and Kuntz, 1951) can occur in this fashion. Because the span of root systems is relatively small, the forecaster should be able to draw an orderly prognostic map for these diseases and see it verified.

Plant pathogens can be carried by water: rain, irrigation, or spray. If these are the channels by which a pathogen travels, its distribution can be predicted to be localized. Faulwetter's (1917) classic study of the dissemination of bacteria by splashing rain demonstrated the short range of this type of distribution. Spores suspended in some fungicide or insecticide mixtures can infect plants (Dimock, 1951); unpublished experiments with *Phytophthora infestans* demonstrated that spray blasts do not increase its spread consequentially. Pathogens that spread in water evidently spread slowly.

Air-borne fungi have been classic subjects for studies in epidemiology as well as forecasting. Basing his analysis upon the statistical theory of the turbulent transfer of matter through air, Gregory (1945) has proposed a hypothesis for the transfer of inoculum; with slight modification this is the relation introduced in an early paragraph of this review. Gregory demonstrated the wide applicability of the hypothesis, infection generally being proportional to $1/X^n$, where X is the distance from the source of inoculum and n is about 2. Thus, one of the strongest clues available to the forecaster of these diseases is the nearness of inoculum: at half the distance, the probability of infection is fourfold. A concrete example can be seen in the map of an epidemic of tobacco blue mold: a few yards from the source of inoculum in an infected seedbed more than 100 lesions were present on each plant; at the far end of the 3-acre crop less than 5 lesions were present per plant; on a neighboring farm only 1 plant in 4 was infected (Waggoner and Taylor, 1955). With the location of the source of inoculum in this neighborhood known, the course of the epidemic could be predicted for given weather and control practices.

A significant modification can be made in the average decrease with distance predicted by the inverse square relation. The spread of the pathogen downwind from the source is more rapid (Wilson and Baker, 1946; Waggoner and Taylor, 1955). Naturally, downwind refers to the direction of the wind during dissemination. Thus, the highest rate of infection would be forecast to the west of a pathogen that spread during rains.

The distribution of insect-, soil-, and air-borne pathogens all being commonly characterized by sharp decreases with distance from the source, van der Plank's (1949) analysis of the relative danger from field size is generally applicable. Thus, small fields and evenly distributed sources call for a forecast of a greater epidemic than do large and widely separated fields.

Two clues for forecasting have been pre-eminent in the discussion of transfer: the increased danger due to more vectors and that due to greater proximity to a source. These factors would have slight importance if the disease were permitted to run its course, but this it is rarely permitted among annual crops. Rather, the host and the pathogen race to the end of the season, and a winner is declared without a steady or equilibrium state ever becoming established. Thus, the number of vectors and the proximity of inoculum are important bases for the prediction of the damage sustained when the crop is harvested.

V. The Trapping of Propagules

As the peripatetic plant pathogens pass over a unit area of the field, a proportion p becomes attached to the soil and to plants. An increase in this attached proportion leads to an increase in the number of infections D. Increased trapping exerts another influence: it depletes the cloud of pathogens at a more rapid rate. Thus, D is proportional to $pe^{-constant\ pf(X)}$, and a knowledge of the rate of trapping p should assist in forecasting the subsequent distribution of infection.

Unfortunately, little is known about the contribution of this factor. Logical conclusions can be drawn from the above hypothesis to supplement our meager knowledge. Contrast the case of a potato infected with Y virus situated among other potatoes attractive to *Myzuz persicae* with the case of a source situated among plants unattractive to the aphid. In the first case, the danger to the adjacent plants is great, but the probability that this nonpersistent virus will be carried afar is slight;

in the second case, the danger to adjacent plants is decreased at the expense of more distant ones.

Now let us consider the spores of fungi—objects carried at the mercy of the winds. They vary in density, volume, and consequent settling velocity in the viscous air; presumably this might alter the proportion attached, but experience has shown the effect is inconsequential (Gregory, 1945). The ability of the spores to attach themselves to objects does, however, increase as spore size increases, leaf width decreases, or velocity increases; the small or slow-moving spores drift around a broad leaf (Gregory, 1951). From these considerations more infection nearby, less at a distance, has been forecast for large-spored pathogens in tall grass; and more infection afar, less nearby, for small-spored pathogens in low, broad-leaved plants (Waggoner, 1956). Verification is lacking, but the logic is compelling.

More than a forecast of distribution can be assisted by the foregoing. We have seen in preceding sections the necessity of a nearby source of propagules if infection and losses are to be consequential at harvest. From this it follows that widespread sources and subsequent epidemics should be frequent with the small spores pathogenic on broad leaves. This conclusion, too, is worth testing with a view to its eventual use in forecasting.

Rain is a well-known cleanser of the atmosphere, washing spores out of the air and onto foliage and soil. This effectively increases p, the trapping efficiency. Rain has thus been an important factor in the consideration of long distance dissemination of spores: spores of, say, *Puccinia graminis* are carried aloft and then northward in a maritime tropical air mass, eventually being washed to earth by precipitation (Stakman, 1942). The forecaster must bear in mind the dilution of the spore cloud with distance, but conceivably synoptic charts of the air currents at several levels could be useful in predicting the transfer of prolific fungi that infect large acreages.

VI. Infection

The pathogen has avoided many pitfalls before alighting, but it now has another crucial step to accomplish: it must infect a plant. In our hypothesis the number of spores deposited per successful infection is K; infection increases as K decreases.

The first prerequisite is that the propagule be alive. The forecaster will have investigated the hardiness of the pathogen and entered this into his "rules." For example, he will be confident that the hardy rust spores or apple scab ascospores or the virus safe within an aphid are alive, and that this step provides no opportunity for a forecast criterion. On the other hand, he knows that the spores of the downy mildews are susceptible to drought and that sunlight is a signal for a forecast of "no epidemic."

Germination is the second prerequisite for the success of a spore. This step is frequently susceptible to weather and has been a most fruitful source of forecasting methods. Satisfactory conditions for germination must arrive while the spore is viable. The requirement for moisture is common and has been widely applied in forecasting, e.g., the downy mildews. In contrast to this are the powdery mildews with their requirement for high humidity but not water (e.g., Delp, 1954); presumably, this could be employed in forecasting.

The temperature is also critical during germination. Not only can the temperature itself be limiting, but it determines the speed of germination, and hence, the number of hours of satisfactory moisture conditions required (e.g., Crosier, 1934). Thus, varying critical lengths of moist periods can be set for varying temperatures.

Next, the landing and germination must occur on a host. This success is improbable if few of the host species grow near the source or if the plants are small and cover little of the soil. In this case few of the spores will alight on a host, and many will fall on strange species or barren soil. Here, K is large, since many spores fall and few infect; the forecaster may be conservative in his warnings.

Finally, the host that receives the pathogen must be susceptible. In the case of a heteroecious fungus, epidemics are most likely if the repeating stage is on the economic crop. Stakman (1942) has provided us with examples: *Gymnosporangium juniperi-virginianae* sporidia alone can infect apple, and no epidemic of rust would be forecast far from red cedars; *Puccinia graminis* var. *tritici* uredospores can infect wheat, and the pathogen can spread through a wheat belt by repeated, relatively short jumps with scattered sources appearing near many hosts.

In any case the strain of the pathogen must be capable of infecting the variety of the host. One of the forecaster's most important indicators is a survey of the various races present and the varieties being grown. Thus, the appearance of Race 56 of *Puccinia graminis* var. *tritici* and the large acreages of Ceres wheat foretold the elimination in the mid-thirites of that hitherto resistant variety.

The damage wrought by an infection could be the D of our hypothesis. If this were our thinking, then the proportionality constant K would be the number of propagules deposited per unit value destroyed. Then K would fall, and the probability of damage would rise if we were concerned with a systemic disease, particularly of a large host (van der

Plank, 1947). The effect is increased further if the individual plant is valuable. Consider how the probability of damage rises as we turn from the spots of apple scab to the systemic infection of Dutch elm disease or oak wilt of a prized shade tree.

In the preceding sections we have dealt with the several steps in the multiplication of an air- or insect-borne pathogen. The life of a soil-borne fungus may be less complicated, but an infection must be accomplished and the pathogen flourish within the host if an epidemic is to ensue. The separation of infection and incubation is incomplete in our knowledge but largely unimportant for this discussion. Seedling diseases are frequently associated with slow emergence and retarded early growth. Thus, the occurrence of damping-off of corn by *Pythmin* spp. can be forecast for cold, wet springs (Johann *et al.*, 1928). The more specific, soil-borne wilt fungi also prosper best in certain environments: *Verticillium* wilt of tomatoes can be forecast for cool and *Fusarium* wilt for warm climates (Bewley, 1922; Clayton, 1923).

Infection phenomena are often susceptible to the weather and provide a wealth of opportunities for forecast criteria. Can the pathogen survive, germinate, and infect in the environment of the host? If the forecaster answers these in the affirmative, he knows that a frequent barrier to epidemics has been removed and that he had best beware.

VII. The Incubation Period

The rapidity of increase of a pathogen has already been mentioned as critical to the development of epidemics and consequential losses. This is so in large part because the pathogen and host rarely reach equilibrium during the life of an annual crop. Rather the pathogen is racing against the time when unfavorable weather will arrive. Therefore, what Chester (1950) has called "tempo" is critical.

The length of the cycles as well as the successful infections per cycle determine the tempo. The discharge, transfer, and trapping of inoculum and the infection of the host can, and often do, occur within a few hours. Incubation is generally a more extended process and considerable variation in its duration is frequent. Here, then, is an opportunity for alterations in the tempo, alterations critical to forecasting, alterations in the rapidity of reappearance of new sources and in their size Q.

With the fungus safely within the moist host tissues during incubation, temperature—not humidity—becomes the important factor. An example of the importance of temperature in the length of the incubation period is provided by *Phytophthora infestans* (Crosier, 1934). Decreasing the maximum and minimum temperatures from 23 and 15° C. to 20 and 10° C. increased the length of the period by one-fourth. This would result in only 5 instead of 6 multiplications of the pathogen per month. Of course, raising the maximum and minimum temperatures to 35 and 25° C. destroyed the pathogen within the host.

A similar example of altered length of period is provided by *Uncinula necator* (Delp, 1954): the incubation period was halved by raising the temperature from 15 to 26° C.

Peronospora tabacina illustrates the disastrous effect upon the pathogen's prosperity of high temperature during incubation: hot weather causes "dry weather" blue mold lesions which are devoid of spores, and hence, ends the multiplication of the pathogen (Jenkins, 1952). Unquestionably many examples of accelerated multiplication by warm temperatures and truncated epidemics due to hot temperatures can be found among bacterial and viral as well as fungal incubations. If the forecaster is aware of these relations for his charges, he can estimate whether the tempo of multiplication is sufficiently rapid for an epidemic to develop within the season.

A second use for a knowledge of the length of incubation is in detecting synchrony of the cycles of weather and pathogen. Imagine that a period of weather unfavorable for sporulation and infection is followed by a day when infection does occur. If a second day of weather suitable for multiplication occurs before the end of the incubation, new infections will be added. If, instead, the second suitable day occurs at the end of the incubation, infections will be multiplied, not just added. Thus, favorable conditions alone are not enough; they must be meshed with the cycle of the pathogen, a cycle timed in large part by the temperature during incubation.

One large class of pathogens need not race with the host to a deadline at the end of the season. These are the pathogens of perennial plants, such as trees. Here ample time is allowed for an equilibrium to be established, and eradication and exclusion are relatively harmless to the pathogen over the long pull. The forecast will, therefore, be in terms of "when," not "if." The forecaster must guess the equilibrium rate from the best knowledge of the susceptibility of the host, the multiplication of both host and pathogen, and any deterrents to spread applied over the entire region concerned. As an example, among the American elms in the climate of Connecticut one can forecast with some confidence that in the neighborhood of 20% of the elms will become infected annually with Dutch elm disease if an insecticide is not applied, 3%, if it is (Dimond *et al.*, 1949).

The incubation period is lengthy, relative to the other periods of the pathogen's multiplication, and hence, provides a wealth of opportunities for the forecaster, who must estimate how the race between an annual crop and its pest will end or at what level the equilibrium between a perennial host and its pest will be reached.

VIII. INTEGRATIONS

The large number of possible prediction criteria enumerated above are not only opportunities for improving forecasts, but are also opportunities for hopeless confusion because of their number. How can such complexity be resolved?

Fortunately a study of the biology of a particular pathogen will generally reveal a critical step to which attention can be directed. Chester's (1946) description of the forecasting of wheat leaf rust provides an excellent example. In Oklahoma, March is the critical month. If the weather during this period permits the first cycles of rust renewal, there is enough time during the ensuing season for the pathogen to reach epidemic proportions. After this month, the weather is rarely limiting. Therefore, the weather and rust behavior during this month can form the basis of a forecast of rust intensity 2 to 3 months later.

The well-known Dutch (van Everdingen, 1933; Beaumont, 1947) and Irish (Bourke, 1953) rules for forecasting potato late blight also are a simplification based upon the existence of a critical stage in the pathogen's life. In the maritime climates of northeastern Europe the weather during incubation is rarely limiting, and adequate primary inoculum is apparently common. Therefore, the multiplication of the pathogen is limited only by the conditions for dispersal, transfer, and infection. Satisfactory conditions for these three steps are defined by simple rules, and hence, late blight forecasting is straightforward in Europe.

In the central United States, drought or hot weather frequently persists long enough to destroy *Phytophthora infestans* in the host. Therefore, Wallin (1958) deletes from his forecasts of blight the effects of earlier favorable periods if unfavorable weather persists for 21 days or more.

The length of the incubation period can be the critical factor in epidemics. Shatsky's modification of Müller's incubation calendar for vine mildew illustrates this point (Miller and O'Brien, 1952). The incubation period is related quantitatively to the mean temperature, and fungicide spraying is indicated at the end of the periods thus estimated.

An integration with a strong family resemblance to the above devices has been employed in Connecticut for several years for the prediction of tobacco blue mold epidemics. The biology of the parasite has been reviewed by Stover and Koch (1951), and the spores are known to be air-borne in the morning (Waggoner and Taylor, 1958). Bearing this information in mind, the forecaster examines the hygrothermograph, sky cover, and rainfall records, together with a census of primary inoculum from the tobacco region and decides whether the pathogen could or could not have completed dispersal, transfer, and infection. If an infection period is thought to have occurred a "2" is entered on the calendar. If two more periods occur before incubation of the first is complete, 2's are added each time and the numbers entered on the calendar are "4" and "6." If instead the second infection period occurs near the end of the incubation period of the first infection, the number is doubled and a "4" is entered on the calendar. When a drought or heat wave intervenes and sterile lesions appear, the number on the calendar is reduced to "1," and the multiplication process must begin anew. Thus, the forecasting scheme is an estimate of the population of *Peronospora tabacina* derived from a knowledge of its biology, its primary population in seedbeds, and the weather. We have found in Connecticut that damage of consequence will appear in the field when the estimate on our calendar reaches "64." The arrival of this level can be anticipated from the tempo of the disease and the weather outlook.

The preceding examples illustrate how the complexities of the pathogen's biology can be digested into rational forecasting criteria. Therefore, the prospective forecaster need not become lost in a maze on the one hand or rely upon empirical criteria upon the other hand.

IX. The Usefulness of Forecasting

When one speculates about the value of weather, yield, or disease forecasts, no difficulty is encountered in convincing oneself that forecasts are useful, even necessary. The desire to foretell the future is strong. Nevertheless an enumeration of the characteristics that determine the practical usefulness of predictions is healthy, especially if it is made before a forecasting system is initiated.

The first requirement of a forecast is that it be correct. Perfection is rarely possible in forecasting, and the natural tendency is to be conservative, to "overforecast." In disease forecasting this leads to the warning "epidemic" whenever a chance of such exists. At the same time that the forecaster is being "conservative," the growers' other advisors are naturally enough behaving in the same manner: they urge the grower to exercise control measures at all times. Therefore, the usefulness of the forecaster's warning of "epidemic" may be limited because his is but one more voice added to the chorus of voices urging him to repent and spray.

On the opposite side, the forecaster may be more helpful. He may lead the grower to omit costly control measures by forecasting "no epidemic." Before he can persuade the grower to make such a savings he must have established the accuracy of his predictions in the minds of the grower and his advisors and have overcome the natural tendency to be conservative. In France this happy state has apparently arrived: the warning service for vine mildew has led to the omission of two sprays in most years at an annual savings of two and one-half billion francs (Darpoux, 1949). Thus, if the forecaster can bring about the elimination of unnecessary and costly measures through accurate forecasting, he can be truly helpful.

The distance that the forecaster can see into the future, as well as his accuracy, affects the usefulness of his methods. If the prediction arrives in time for remedial action to be taken, it is helpful. If it arrives too late for action, it only lengthens the time over which the grower must bear his sorrow. The predictions of epidemics of seed-borne smuts and virus from the conditions during the flowering of the wheat or from an index of potato tubers has already been mentioned. Here the prognostication can be made for many months in advance, and the grower has ample time to remedy the matter.

The predictions of wheat leaf rust (Chester, 1946) and of bacterial wilt of sweet corn (Stevens, 1934) extend for several months into the future. Hence, the farmer has time in which to benefit from the forecast by planting an alternate crop or variety. The French warnings concerning vine mildew are of much shorter period; nevertheless, they arrive in sufficient time to be helpful because fungicidal control can be applied or omitted on short notice.

Long-range or climatological predictions of plant diseases have been made informally. Men have recognized that certain climates are conducive to a disease, others are not. Seed production has been located in regions where the climate makes important seed-borne diseases unlikely. In addition to this a formal study of long-range or climatological prediction would be interesting. The epidemics of certain diseases can be traced to critical weather events. The probability of these events can frequently be estimated from the series of weather observations that have now reached great lengths in many localities. The knowledge of biology and weather could be combined to produce estimates of the probabilities of disease at various localities and seasons. These "forecasts" should prove useful because of their long, almost infinite, extension into the future.

The discussion of the period of the forecast has brought out the importance of the control method. If the forecast is to provide more than intellectual satisfaction, there must be a control method that can be exercised and the impending epidemic forestalled. The usefulness of the above predictions of smut and virus epidemics depends upon the existence of alternate, clean seed. The usefulness of the predictions of wheat leaf rust and bacterial wilt of corn depends upon the existence of profitable alternate crops or resistant varieties. The benefit from the warning systems for downy mildews is dependent upon the efficacy of fungicides.

Two diseases stand in contrast to the ones we have just examined. Apple scab infection can be eradicated by suitable chemicals. Hence, a census of infection can be used and the need for a forecast is consequently less. Wheat stem rust control at the present depends practically upon the choice of a resistant variety. Consequently, the forecast of a stem rust epidemic issued in the middle of the growing season is nearly useless to the individual farmer because there is as yet no remedy he can apply to forestall the impending calamity.

The use of a forecast necessitates changes in operations. Flexibility is a prerequisite to the employment of prediction. At least two things affect this flexibility. The first is the quantity of labor and equipment available for control measures relative to the acreage that must be treated. If the entire area can be treated in a day or two, treatment can be delayed safely until a forecast is issued. If the entire area requires many days for treatment, however, the machines must be kept in operation continuously; otherwise, a large proportion of the area might be damaged before treatment in response to a warning could reach it. The second thing that affects flexibility is the complexity of the farming organization. If the man who applies the treatment is also the man who decides when to treat and if supplies are readily available, a treatment can quickly follow warning. Alternatively, if a large organization is involved, planning must precede action. Here the confusion that would follow a change in plans following a warning might well cost more than the application of an occasional unnecessary treatment. Consequently, a short-range forecast is not highly useful; perhaps climatological "forecasts" would prove to be.

An important—perhaps the most critical—factor in the usefulness and in the adoption of forecasting is the ratio of benefit to cost. How great is the benefit from disease control relative to the cost of the control measure? If this ratio is large, the rational grower will apply controls whether the disease is forecast or not. If this ratio is small, no amount of urging will induce the rational grower to act.

In the northeastern United States apple and potato growers know that the yield, appearance, and keeping quality of their produce are profoundly affected by apple scab and potato late blight. They also know that including an effective fungicide among the pest sprays they are already applying is inexpensive. Thus, the ratio of benefit to cost is high, and the growers tend to apply fungicides routinely with little regard for the likelihood of an epidemic.

At the opposite pole stands the owner of a large wood lot populated in part by elms. The death of the elms would not be disastrous to the production of the lot. The cost of an annual application of an insecticide to kill the vectors of the pathogen of Dutch elm disease would be large relative to the annual production of the lot. Therefore, the ratio of benefit to cost is small, and the owner is unlikely to apply a control measure, even when he is assured of the imminence of an epidemic of Dutch elm disease.

Between these two extremes lies a region where the benefit : cost ratio is favorable to the employment of forecasts. The example of the vine mildew warning system in France cited above lies in this region of a favorable ratio. The losses from mildew are disastrous. On the other hand, considerable savings can be made by eliminating unnecessary sprays. Hence, the warning system is employed by the growers (Darpoux, 1949).

The benefit : cost ratio also depends upon the annual variation in the amount of disease. If the amount is nearly constant from year to year, experience has taught the farmer how to make his own forecast: next year will be just like this year and will have the same benefit : cost ratio and demand the same measures. This leaves little for the forecaster to do that is useful. When the amount of disease is variable from year to year, the forecaster can be useful, for he will predict when the benefit of treatment will be great or small relative to the cost of treatment.

X. SUMMARY

The forecasting of disease is a contribution to the prediction of yields. It logically proceeds from a knowledge of the interaction of host, pathogen, and environment. In this review the etiology of disease has been examined for opportunities for prognostication of disease and subsequent loss.

The magnitude of the primary inoculum affects the subsequent epidemic. As a clue to the size of the epidemic it has the advantage of earliness, the disadvantage of being subject to many influences before harvest time.

The production of inoculum and its dispersal into the medium about the plant is one of the processes upon which weather can exert its influence and is, therefore, a rich source of forecast criteria.

The transfer of inoculum by air and soil, and as a contaminant is for the pathogen a risky business, because it is dependent upon fortune.

The forecaster profits from a knowledge of the proximity of the source of inoculum and of the number of vectors during this random process.

Propagules are trapped and their numbers depleted more rapidly by some types of foliage and weather than by others. This is probably important in predicting the distribution of infection about a source of inoculum.

Infection is a late step in the pathogen's multiplication, but its requirements are sufficiently critical to provide a wealth of criteria for prediction. The general requirement for liquid water at this stage provides the basis for several classic forecasting schemes.

The incubation period is generally much longer than the preceding steps, and therefore is subject to changes of length. Thus, it can influence the rapidity of development of the disease and the level attained before unfavorable weather or harvest ends the annual race between host and pathogen.

The myriad influences can frequently be digested into simple forecasting rules because of the limitation placed upon epidemics by a few critical stages.

The usefulness of the prediction of epidemics depends upon the accuracy and range of the forecast, upon the existence of remedies and the ease with which they can be applied, and upon the benefits from disease control relative to the cost of remedies.

REFERENCES

Beaumont, A. 1947. The dependence on the weather of the dates of outbreak of potato late blight epidemics. *Brit. Mycol. Soc. Trans.* **31**: 45–53.

Beckman, C. H., and J. E. Kuntz. 1951. Translocation of poisons, dyes, and radioiodine, and its relation to oak wilt. (Abstr.) *Phytopathology* **41**: 2–3.

Bewley, W. F. 1922. "Sleepy disease" of the tomato. *Ann. Appl. Biol.* **9**: 116–134.

Bonde, R., and E. S. Schultz. 1943. Potato refuse piles as a factor in the dissemination of late blight. *Maine Agr. Expt. Sta. Bull.* **416**: 229–246.

Bourke, P. M. A. 1953. Potato blight and the weather in Ireland in 1953. *Irish Meteorol. Service Tech. Note* **15**: 4.

Broadbent, L. 1957. Insecticidal control of the spread of plant viruses. *Ann. Rev. Entomol.* **2**: 339–354.

Chester, K. S. 1946. "The Cereal Rusts." Chronica Botanica, Waltham, Massachusetts. 269 pp.

Chester, K. S. 1950. Plant disease losses: their appraisal and interpretation. *Plant Disease Reptr. Suppl.* **193**: 233.

Christensen, J. J. 1942. Long distance dissemination of plant pathogens. *In* "Aerobiology" (F. R. Moulton, ed.). Am. Assoc. Adv. Sci., Washington, D. C. pp. 78–87.

Clayton, E. E. 1923. The relation of temperature to the *Fusarium* wilt of the tomato. *Am. J. Botany* **10**: 71–88.

Cook, H. T. 1949. Forecasting late blight epiphytotics of potatoes and tomatoes. *J. Agr. Research* **78**: 545–563.

Crosier, W. 1934. Studies in the biology of *Phytophthora infestans* (Mont.) deBary. *Cornell Univ. Agr. Expt. Sta. Mem.* **155:** 40 pp.

Darpoux, H. 1949. Les avertissements agricoles. *Ing. Serv. Agr. Bull. Tech. Inform.* **41:** 403–411.

Delp, C. J. 1954. Effect of temperature and humidity on the grape powdery mildew fungus. *Phytopathology* **44:** 615–626.

Dickson, J. G. 1947. "Diseases of Field Crops." McGraw-Hill, New York. p. 49.

Dimock, A. W. 1951. The dispersal of viable fungus spores by insecticides. *Phytopathology* **41:** 152–156.

Dimond, A. E., G. H. Plumb, E. M. Stoddard, and J. G. Horsfall. 1949. An evaluation of chemotherapy and vector control by insecticides for combating Dutch elm disease. *Conn. Agr. Expt. Sta. Bull.* **531:** 49–58.

Dixon, L. F., R. A. McLean, and F. A. Wolf. 1936. Relationship of climatological conditions to the tobacco downy mildew. *Phytopathology* **26:** 735–759.

Doncaster, J. P., and P. H. Gregory. 1948. The spread of virus diseases in the potato crop. *Agr. Research Council (London) Rept. Ser.* **7:** 189 pp.

Faulwetter, R. C. 1917. Wind-blown rain, a factor in disease dissemination. *J. Agr. Research* **10:** 639–648.

Foister, C. E. 1929. Relation of weather to plant diseases. *Conf. Empire Meteorol. Agr. Sec. H. M. S. O.,* London. 50 pp.

Gregory, P. H. 1945. The dispersion of air-borne spores. *Brit. Mycol. Soc. Trans.* **28:** 26–72.

Gregory, P. H. 1951. Deposition of air-borne Lycopodium spores on cylinders. *Ann. Appl. Biol.* **38:** 357–376.

Gregory, P. H., and D. R. Read. 1949. The spatial distribution of insect-borne plant-virus diseases. *Ann. Appl. Biol.* **36:** 475–482.

Holz, W. 1939a. Eine Methode zur Prognose des Askosporenfluges von *Fusicladium dendriticum* (Wallr.) Fckl. *Nachrbl. deut. Pflanzenschutzdienst, Berlin* **19:** 12–13.

Holz, W. 1939b. Der Einfluss der März-Temperaturen auf die GeschwindigKeit des Reifungsvorganges von *Venturia inaequalis*-Perithezien. *Angew. Botan.* **21:** 209–214.

Hyre, R. A., and R. Bonde. 1956. Forecasting late blight of potatoes in Aroostook County, Maine, in 1956. *Plant Disease Reptr.* **40:** 1087–1090.

Jenkins, W. A. 1952. Notes on early season pathology of flue cured tobacco in southside Virginia and portions of the old belt in North Carolina. *Plant Disease Reptr.* **36:** 278.

Johann, H., J. R. Holbert, and J. G. Dickson. 1928. A *Pythium* seedling blight and root rot of dent corn. *J. Agr. Research* **37:** 443–464.

Louw, A. J. 1947. *Fusicladium* of apples. III. A few factors affecting the incidence of the disease. *Farming in S. Africa* **22:** 833–836.

Martin, W. H. 1923. Late blight of potatoes and the weather. *New Jersey Agr. Expt. Sta. Bull.* **384.** 23 pp.

Meehan, F. C., and H. C. Murphy. 1946. A new *Helminthosporium* blight of oats. *Science* **104:** 413–414.

Miller, P. R., and M. J. O'Brien. 1952. Plant disease forecasting. *Botan. Rev.* **18:** 547–601.

Miller, P. R., and M. J. O'Brien. 1957. Prediction of plant disease epidemics. *Ann. Rev. Microbiol.* **11:** 77–110.

Pinckard, J. A. 1942. The mechanism of spore dispersal in *Peronospora tabacina* and certain other downy mildew fungi. *Phytopathology* **32:** 505–511.

Simmonds, P. M. 1946. Detection of the loose smut fungi in embryos of barley and wheat. *Sci. Agr.* **26:** 51–58.

Stakman, E. C. 1942. The field of extramural aerobiology. *In* "Aerobiology" (F. R. Moulton, ed.). Am. Assoc. Adv. Sci., Washington, D. C. pp. 1–7.

Stevens, N. E. 1934. Stewart's disease in relation to winter temperatures. *Plant Disease Reptr.* **18:** 141–149.

Stover, R. H., and L. W. Koch. 1951. The epidemiology of blue mold of tobacco and its relation to the incidence of the disease in Ontario. *Sci. Agr.* **31:** 225–252.

Taubenhaus, J. J., and D. T. Killough. 1923. Texas root rot of cotton and methods of its control. *Texas Agr. Expt. Sta. Bull.* **307:** 1–98.

van Everdingen, E. 1933. The Dutch Warning Service for outbreaks of potato blight. *Proc. Pacific Sci. Cong.* **3:** 1757–1759.

van der Plank, J. E. 1947. The relation between the size of plant and spread of systemic diseases. *Ann. Appl. Biol.* **34:** 376–387.

van der Plank, J. E. 1949. The relation between the size of fields and the spread of plant diseases into them. II. Diseases caused by fungi with air-borne spores, with a note on horizons of infections. *Empire J. Exptl. Agr.* **17:** 18–22.

Waggoner, P. E. 1952. Distribution of potato late blight around inoculum sources. *Phytopathology* **42:** 323–328.

Waggoner, P. E. 1956. Weather and plant diseases. *Can. Phytopathol. Soc. Proc.* **23:** 15–17.

Waggoner, P. E., and J. B. Kring. 1956. Use of shade tent and insecticides in studies of virus spread. *Phytopathology* **46:** 562–563.

Waggoner, P. E., and G. S. Taylor. 1955. Tobacco blue mold epiphytotics in the field. *Plant Disease Reptr.* **39:** 79–85.

Waggoner, P. E., and G. S. Taylor. 1958. Dissemination by atmospheric turbulence: spores of *Peronospora tabacina. Phytopathology* **48:** 46–51.

Wallin, J. R. 1956. Prediction of potato late blight incidence from samples of blighted seed tubers. *Am. Potato J.* **33:** 220–222.

Wallin, J. R. 1957. Crop disease forecasting project, North Central States. Unpublished Rept.

Wallin, J. R. 1958. Forecasting potato and tomato late blight from temperature and relative humidity data obtained in plant cover. (Abstr.) *Am. Meteorol. Soc. Bull.* **39:** 57.

Wilhelm, S. 1950. Vertical distribution of *Verticillium albo-atrum* in soils. *Phytopathology.* **50:** 368–376.

Wilson, E. E. 1928. Studies of the ascigerous stage of *Venturia inaequalis* (Cke.) Wint. in relation to certain factors of the environment. *Phytopathology* **18:** 375–418.

Wilson, E. E., and G. A. Baker. 1946. Some aspects of the aerial dissemination of spores with special reference to conidia of *Sclerotinia laxa. J. Agr. Research* **72:** 301–327.

Wolfenbarger, D. O. 1946. Dispersion of small organisms. *Am. Midland Naturalist* **35:** 1–152.

Young, H. C., and C. May. 1928. The timing of apple scab sprays. *Ohio Agr. Expt. Sta. Bull.* **403:** 3–28.

Young, H. C., Jr., and D. F. Wadsworth. 1953. Experimental forecast of wheat leaf rust in Oklahoma for 1953. *Plant Disease Reptr.* **37:** 311.

Zentmyer, G. A., P. P. Wallace, and J. G. Horsfall. 1944. Distance as a dosage factor in the spread of Dutch elm disease. *Phytopathology* **34:** 1025–1033.

CHAPTER 9

Quarantines*

ERNST GRAM

Statens Plantepatologische Forsog, Lyngby, Denmark

The walls built for the purpose of interdicting dispersal of dangerous diseases and pests that are unknown within the walls are founded on rock.

One has had recourse to such rocks as biology and taxonomy, geography and climatology, agronomy and economy for the necessary foundation material. If the desired information is not to be found, research must be promoted, at home and also abroad, with the direct purpose of providing the solid basis of regulatory measures. A study of the accumulated facts will show an amazing variability: one parasite may have a territory distinctly narrower than that of the host, while another will have some race accompanying a rare host plant in every one of its hiding places. "Unknown within the country," therefore, must sometimes be modified to "restricted to a certain area or to a special type of locality."

A selection of regulatory measures is presented here as an example. The digests published by FAO (Ling, 1952, 1954; Dumbleton, 1956),

* Editors' footnote: Another approach to the principles underlying the application of plant disease quarantines is discussed in the Prologue (Chapter 1) of this volume.

followed up by abstracts in FAO's "Plant Protection Bulletin," will direct the reader to a more complete survey than that attempted here.

I. Natural Spread and Man-Provoked Dispersal

The resources of pathogens in relation to natural spread (see Volume III, Chapter 3) vary extremely, even in different stages of the same fungus. Observations from isolated vegetation in Alaska seem to prove that spores of *Cronartium ribicola* from pines may find *Ribes* bushes 500–600 km. away, while the spores formed on *Ribes* hardly spread more than 300 meters.

Even the classic barriers, oceans, deserts, and mountains, are not 100% efficient. Colorado beetles may be found on glaciers; mycologists find polar fungi inside bits of stems drifting hundreds of miles over the ice— until the scanty vegetation of a remote coast stops them and is one day machine-gunned with spores from the pycnidia or perithecia. Moreover, oceans are crossed by ships, deserts quickly traversed by jeeps, and mountains penetrated by railroad tunnels. Any confidence based on distance is destroyed by the airplane, which carrys pests and diseases in passengers' luggage, the cargo, inside the cabin, and even on the fusilage.

When man and nature thus join forces, catastrophes are likely to arise. *Phytophthora infestans* undoubtedly was carried from South America by ship to other continents where potato late blight spread to all potato fields, causing enormous losses. The Colorado beetle traveled by train and ship, and, although it was frequently discovered in harbors and incipient infestations energetically put down, one introduction (namely, that to the district of Bordeaux) was missed, and this permitted the pest to spread over most of Europe.

The Roman citizen knew that it was his concern when his neighbor's house was on fire. We have been forced to accept a wider vision of neighborliness and have been taught the possibilities of international aid through teamwork across the borders and through preparedness.

A. Important Cases of Introduction

1. Clubroot, Caused by Plasmodiophora brassicae

This disease, which is found in most plants belonging to the Cruciferae, was known as far back as the 16th century, when in Spain it was called "the devil." In 1736 it was reported from England, from Scotland in 1780, and in 1870 it was ruining cabbage fields around St. Petersburg, where Woronin described it in such a splendid way that attacks found here and there in Europe in the following years were seen more as an interesting mycological event than as a cause of local quarantine—an idea which had not at that time been conceived.

One attack in a single year may produce billions of spores, capable of surviving in the soil for 5–6 years. Spores are easily spread through the soil, by drifting on wind or water, in manure containing remains of diseased plants, in soil clinging to plant roots, or from nurseries where cabbage is sold for planting out.

Clubroot is so universally spread (Colhoun, 1958) that quarantine measures for the most part would be useless. Nevertheless, local measures may be useful, as, e.g., when Norway prohibits the sale of cabbage plants from nurseries not free from clubroot.

2. White-Pine Blister Rust, Caused by Cronartium ribicola

A rust fungus (producing uredo and teleuto on black currant and other species of Ribes, and bark blisters on Pinus cembra) has been known in many places in Central Europe and Russia, at least from 1860, but damage was considered slight. However, from 1865 attempts were made to acclimatize the North American Weymouth pine (Pinus strobus) in Europe, where it proved so susceptible to blister rust that foresters gave it up. But nurserymen still propagated this beautiful pine, and about the year 1900 many nursery plants were exported to the United States. Only later on was it found that these plants carried infection hidden in their twigs. In 1906 the rust was discovered in the United States, where it wrought havoc in the valuable forests of Weymouth pine and white pine (Pinus monticola); besides 4 cultivated species of Ribes, 9 species grow wild in the North American forests. Thus, there are plenty of intermediate hosts! An enormous effort has been necessary in order to eradicate Ribes: first, man power was used; later, this was followed up with hormone weed killers. Resistant pines are on the way as a result of breeding in New York, Wisconsin, Canada, Denmark, etc.; they will be useful in difficult terrain, and they may mean that, in spite of everything, Europe will have forests of Weymouth pine.

California had the blister rust introduced directly in 1910 with nursery plants from France, but the rust was not discovered until 1921. In order to save the threatened Pinus lambertiana, an intensive Ribes eradication campaign was started.

A few countries have placed embargoes on the susceptible pines. White-pine blister rust is a striking instance of the unpredictable results of carrying a healthy host plant to the locality of an apparently innocuous pathogen.

3. *Citrus Canker, Caused by Xanthomonas citri*

The home of this bacterial canker, harbored in several Rutaceae, is southeast Asia, including Japan and the Philippines. It was found in Florida, in Texas, and in Mississippi in 1913–1914—probably introduced with plant material from Japan—and an intensive eradication campaign (see Volume III, Chapter 10) was carried through so successfully that during surveys (the last one in 1947–1949) the seven southeastern states were found free from the canker. South Africa also suffered from an introduction, but later reported a complete eradication.

Immune varieties, on which breeding may be based, occur. Although eradication has proved possible (but extremely expensive), it is natural that countries with any interest in the production of citrus fruits maintain strict quarantine regulations against fruits and against propagation material. New varieties are introduced with all measures of caution, with extended post-entry quarantine, and with repeated graftings.

4. *Chestnut Blight, Caused by Endothia parasitica*

The home of chestnut blight is eastern Asia, where it is quite innocuous because of resistance in the local forms of *Castanea*. The first sign of its escape came from a report of blight in a tree in the New York Botanical Gardens, but it is probable that the fungus was introduced a few years earlier, for, in 1906, the blight was already quite widespread in New York state. During the course of three to four decades *Castanea dentata*, the dominating tree in eastern American forests, was practically eradicated by the blight; it was found that some oaks and a few other trees had been attacked, although not with such disastrous results.

Long-distance spread of chestnut blight is, in the first instance, brought about by transport of infected nursery trees; furthermore, wood and bark will carry infections, frequently permitting production of innumerable spores. It seems likely that woodpeckers and other birds are capable of spreading the inoculum over great distances.

In Europe swift action has put an immediate stop to a few solitary introductions (Belgium–1923; France–1936). Attacks found in northern Italy in 1938 spread very quickly, and the blight was reported as far south as Naples; oaks were infested here also, although not so seriously. In Switzerland chestnut blight was reported in 1947 in Tessin, a canton bordering on Italy, and here, too, infection has spread in many localities. Attacks in Spain (from 1948) have been so limited that there is reason to hope for complete eradication. Yugoslavia has fought the blight since its discovery in that country in 1949. From Russia, blight in oak and elm has been reported. France has been on the alert, and in 1956 surveys disclosed a number of cases in two districts.

Eradication has been attempted, and with success in limited localities. From Washington and Oregon complete success has been reported; in California the disease has, at least, been brought to a standstill.

Far-reaching measures in the eastern American forests may seem to be a failure, but they have, in fact, delayed the destruction. Resistance is common in Asiatic chestnuts, and *Castanea mollissima*, especially, seems useful in breeding work.

It is only natural for countries with an economic interest in the chestnut to place embargoes on the import of living trees. Wood and bark usually come under the same ruling, although trunks and barrel staves may be admitted after a process of scorching and steaming, respectively. In the case of nuts: (1) origin from uninfested districts has been insisted upon, and (2) formaldehyde disinfection has been practiced. Whether this can be maintained for severely infected nuts is a point to be discussed. An embargo directed against plants and fruits of the resistant *C. mollissima* may seem absurd, but it is directed against oak wilt (*Chalara quercina*), and import necessary for breeding work can be secured by means of post-entry quarantine.

5. Elm Disease, Caused by Ceratostomella ulmi

Since 1918 or thereabouts thousands of elm trees have died in northwestern Europe. In 1930 elm disease was found in Ohio, probably introduced from Europe in trunks of knobby elm (burrknots, Maserholz) imported for use as veneer; it spread widely in the eastern United States, and in 1948 elm disease had spread westward to Colorado. Canadian outbreaks, found in 1950, probably have their origin in the States.

The Scandinavian countries long remained free from elm disease, but in the Swedish capital, Stockholm, a good many park trees were killed in 1950 and during the following years; in Denmark, where sickly elm trees had been examined several times, the fungus was found in 1955, but the disease does not seem to spread.

In North America, where the elm is a very popular shade tree, public control has been seriously attempted, some $25,000,000 having been spent on felling diseased trees—but in vain. This measure has now practically been given up. In some European countries, where elm is considered a nuisance because of its greediness and its abundant seed production, no serious control has been tried. Many Asiatic elms are resistant, and several resistant varieties have been found in breeding work, particularly in the Netherlands.

California has embargoed elm trees (and wood with bark on) from states not free from the elm disease and phloem necrosis of elm. The last named American disease probably provides the motivation for the maintaining of embargoes in several countries outside of North America. Canada permits import of logs with bark only when kiln dried.

6. *Potato Root Eelworm, Heterodera rostochiensis*

This cyst-forming eelworm is called "the golden nematode" because of the orange color of the mature cysts. Potato is the most prominent host plant, but tomatoes may also suffer severely, while eggplant, *Solanum nigrum,* and *S. dulcamara* are less liable to infection. One potato plant may leave many thousands of cysts in the soil, each cyst containing hundreds of eggs from which larvae emerge for the next 8–10 years.

Spread is possible in many ways: through cysts attached to seed potatoes, by potato peel being thrown on the compost heap and reaching the garden, and by old potato stalks. Loose cysts in infested soil may spread with potatoes, on plant roots, or on dirty sacks and crates. The role of muddy boots in local distribution should not be underestimated; tractor wheels and other machinery are also very efficient carriers. Water and sedimented soil from potato starch and sugar factories may carry cysts and spread the pest if discharged into agricultural land.

A list of dates, stating when the pest was first observed in the various countries is given below, but such a list should not be regarded as a reliable guide to the course of distribution. Intensity of potato growing and thoroughness of surveys determine to a much higher degree the moment of first observation.

1881	Germany: cysts on potato roots mentioned by Kühn	1941	The Netherlands; Long Island, New York State (probably 20 yr. old)
1913	Scotland, Germany (Rostock, whence the name)	1946	Finland
1917	England (or even earlier) Considerable increase during World War I	1948	France
		1949	Belgium
		1951	Austria (1949 ?)
1922	Sweden, Ireland	1952	Spain
1928	Denmark	1953	Greece, Algeria, Iceland
1938	Guernsey Severe increase during World War II	1955	Israel, Norway
		1956	Portugal
		1958	Switzerland

Reports of occurrence also exist from Luxembourg, Jersey, Peru, Egypt, Libya, Morocco, and Malta. On the whole, this pest does not seem to thrive in the dry soils common in the Mediterranean region.

Sins against the "law of rotation" are the worst factor in releasing visible attacks: potato-rye-potato or potato-cauliflower-potato are striking instances. Town gardens with no rotation at all are ideal for the nematode. In rational agriculture the attack is rarely seen, until production of fancy potatoes once (or even twice) a year goes beyond the bound of all reason; in such cases exchange of crates returned from market may well speed up the disaster.

Soil analyses for cysts give reliable information if samples are taken conscientiously in the field. Following the Long Island case, all important potato districts of the United States were searched—fortunately, with negative results. That the golden nematode has not spread to the American continent is a marvel; only one case (from New Jersey in 1952) was reported.

Nurseries are strongly advised not to grow potatoes; in several countries potato growing in nurseries is strictly forbidden, and sampling is a prerequisite to export and issuing of health certificates. The same is true in potato seed certification and export. For table potatoes, screening of surface-borne soil for cysts may perhaps be sufficient. Since nurseries, potato fields, and bulb-producing areas may be infested from nearby gardens, protective zones may be established in which potato growing can be forbidden or long-term rotation be enforced. Old sacks, crates, and tools and machinery can be efficiently fumigated.

Washing of potato tubers is not 100% efficient; disinfection of tubers is not possible in practice. How difficult washing really is may be seen in the case of pips of lily-of-the-valley first washed before export from Europe, next washed in New York, but still containing cysts. A hot water treatment or growing in a quarantine greenhouse, the soil of which could be steamed, has been found necessary in such cases.

There is a marked tendency to replace the obsolete "years-and-kilometers" restrictions with the request that the locality of origin shall be proved free from golden nematode.

The EPPO (1955a), after repeated discussions in a working group, recommends to member governments the following policy:

There is no scientific justification for prohibiting the entry of potatoes or other planting material into countries where potato root eelworm is already known to be widely established. If there are countries where the nematode has been shown not to exist, it may be reasonable to prohibit the entry of potatoes and tomato plants, but not of other planting material. The only practicable method of detecting the presence and degree of soil infestation is by the systematic sampling of fields. . . . Therefore exporting countries should be required to have in operation an effective sampling system.

We strongly urge the adaption of a uniform sampling system in all countries. . . . From the biological standpoint, a certificate of freedom from eelworm will remain valid for as long as potatoes are not grown in the field sampled.

Countries which are partly or entirely free from eelworm may reasonably require that any planting material should be admitted only from land which, as a result of sampling tests, had been declared "free" from eelworm; and further that such planting material should as far as practicable be free from soil.

7. Discussion

It is only human for people who are plagued by restrictive measures, and who cannot—or will not—see the other side of the problem to feel a certain satisfaction if the sign "failure" can be hung on the plant inspection offices. Analogies of the platitude "my pocket was picked, therefore the police are no good" are not unknown to the quarantine authorities. The cases described in Sections I, A, 1–6 above may appear as so many failures in attempts to forbid introduction. A thorough study will, however, show a striking difference from the epoch of clubroot dispersal to citrus canker introduction—and its eradication.

Colorado beetle invasions are surveyed and eradicated at low cost, compared with a country's expenses for spraying all potato fields. Potato wart was said to be introduced into the United States after the crucial year of 1912, but actually it seems to have arrived with European table potatoes in 1911. Dispersal inside the United States has been prevented, and in Europe the time gained for breeding of valuable immune potato varieties has been important. Pathologists should not promise to keep a disease or pest out forever, but they should stick firmly to the fact that every year's delay means that money for control is saved, that export difficulties are avoided, that breeders and chemists have time to work, and that officers can prepare for local quarantines and other measures of retardation or even eradication.

It is a time-worn dogma that diseases spread by the wind fall outside the quarantine officers' bailiwicks. Rust spores and wind-borne insects are not stopped by political frontiers. The hordes of rust spores carried by the wind from Mexico to the prairie states are greatly reduced when, as a result of co-operation between the two countries, rust resistant cereals are bred and grown in Mexico. In India, where the rust is exterminated by the summer heat of the valleys, but reestablished from grainfields in the mountains, the growing of the grain has even been forbidden in certain mountain districts, a measure to be replaced by the introduction of resistant varieties. In organized campaigns it has, under some conditions, been practical to compensate for eradicated trees or other crops, not with money, but with plants—in order to seize the opportunity to introduce immune varieties.

It is the experience of advisory departments that a "new attack" is rarely discovered immediately, but within one particular week or fortnight several cases turn up. One cause is stressed by Smith (1957) writing on cereal yellow dwarf: "In New Zealand the disease has apparently been present for many years and the slowness with which trained plant pathologists are able to recognize even common diseases makes one question the value of quarantine regulations (carried out by less highly skilled technicians) under our present state of knowledge of disease distribution."

Plant species or varieties valuable in one region succumb to attacks of hitherto innocuous diseases or pests when brought into another. The results of bringing the potato to the home of the Colorado beetle were unpredictable. *Berberis vulgaris* (recommended by learned societies for hedges), spiny and with useful berries, made the density of *Puccinia graminis* spores soar sky-high, and enabled the fungus to form new races. Introduction of "innocuous" pests or diseases has sometimes proved equally fatal. The yellows virus is not found in aster in China, but in wild plants in North America; in order to establish aster yellows the flower had to be imported from the East and a leaf hopper (European ?), from the West!

To establish a certain balance with these tragic events we must admit that in untold cases the introduction of a pest has not caught on (McCubbin, 1946). It may happen that the fungus or insect finds no suitable host; because of climate or edaphon, it develops too slowly, is knocked out by competitors, and disappears unnoticed. It is agreeable to know that a pathogen frequently imported with seeds or tubers will not thrive; but it is rather risky, with no experience at hand, to investigate whether it will or not.

Not all "new" attacks are introduced. New physiologic races may turn up, as is too well known from the rust fungi. Alarming cases of race formation have appeared in potato wart, which in many countries is still found to be due to one race of the fungus—and in potato root nematode, too. In Wageningen, new races of *Melampsora* in poplar have been studied *in nascendi*; they were due to crossing while growing in the intermediate host, larch (Van Vloten, 1944).

B. *Potential Dangers of Introduction*

Much stubborn rear-guard action has been necessary because of lack of foresight and also because of the limited funds available for thorough surveys. Both above (Section A, 1–7) and in the following pages instances are mentioned of unknown or unheeded diseases which have developed into catastrophes. Citrus canker was not serious in Japan; neither was the Japanese beetle. Many fungus attacks are inconspicuous, at least to the untrained eye, their spores being for the most part invisible, and the same is true of many other groups of pathogens.

For tourists it is often difficult to secure an outport inspection; however, pests dangerous to tropical crops have been introduced by tropical ornamentals brought home by interested collectors.

1. *Potato Viroses*

In reading through import ordinances of some particular country in order to ascertain obligations to be fulfilled before a certificate is issued, one may wonder at the strange diseases which must be mentioned in "additional declarations." The explanation is usually that the country in question is importing from widely separated regions and wishes to safeguard itself on all sides.

The virus disease potato spindle tuber (*Solanum* virus *12*) has its home in North America, where affected plants are rogued out in connection with potato seed certification. The disease is reported from Russia and Poland, where it is thought to have been introduced from North America, and passed on to Rhodesia. Potato yellow dwarf (*Solanum* virus *16*) seems to be limited to the United States and Canada; several host plants are described, among which are red clover and other species of *Trifolium*. A cicada (*Aceratagallia sanguinolenta*) is the vector of the virus, not only between potato plants, but rather frequently from red clover to potato.

A group of viruses, causing big bud in tomato and stolbur disease in potato, and attacking several plants of widely separated families, still needs much research, but the stolbur phenomena in potato are alarming. From Russia and from a region including Czechoslovakia, central Germany, Switzerland, and Italy attacks are reported. Potato purple-top wilt, mentioned from Maine and New Mexico, may belong in this group of viroses too. Stolbur is transmitted by potato tubers, and their sprouting is badly affected.

Concerning spindle tuber and other potato viroses, EPPO (1955b) advises inspection of seed in the fields of the exporting country and post-entry quarantine.

Potato virus X is the subject of increasing interest, since it has been possible, by means of serological reactions, to test plants, produce X-free clones, and demonstrate a considerable decrease in yield due to the virus infection. Like virus X, the more or less related viruses S—first found by Dutch pathologists, but apparently common in Europe—and virus M, found in the United States, frequently show weak symptoms or none at all. Since sera are available, it should be natural first to investigate the representation of such viruses in the national varieties and then to take the measures to have virus-free seed potatoes produced or introduced.

Countries with a well-developed certification of potatoes (and other plants intended for propagation) based on field inspection and laboratory testing and which publish their tolerances are justified in requesting that imported plants should be certified on the basis of tolerances at least equal to their own.

2. *Stone Fruit Viroses*

Of botanical families the stone fruit trees have proved to be among those plants which suffer most frequently from virus attack, and investigations of the geography of these viroses is bound to give an abundant and deplorable harvest.

Phony peach is a classic disease, recognized as a virosis in the late twenties. It seems transmissible only by means of root grafts and, as has recently been discovered, by one or more species of leaf hoppers; moreover, the incubation is usually more than 1 year. Peach yellows has even 2–3 years of incubation, but it is transmitted by the grafting of twigs and buds; cicada are responsible for local spread. These diseases, like several viroses of the various stone fruits are, as yet, only noted from North America; others are so similar to viroses found on other continents that attempts at identification will probably give positive results. A dangerous trait is that they are somewhat inclined to be "omnivorous"; many of them attack a number of species, a few of them are even harbored by plants outside the stone fruit family.

Internal quarantines in connection with eradication measures have given positive results in the case of phony peach, aided by a special color reaction. Thermotherapy has given results which may be valuable in practice. Most important is a thorough certification of nursery trees based on tested, healthy mother trees.

Embargo is a natural first reaction to fruit tree viroses, especially since post-entry quarantine is difficult in cases of long incubation. However, a next step must be taken: the admitting of products passed by a reliable nursery certification, possibly combined with post-entry quarantine (Cochran *et al.*, 1953). For *Prunus americana* and *P. virginiana*, which are symptomless carriers, embargo is necessary. When the occurrence of the different viroses is better known, a group action (see Section III, C, 2) of neighboring states will, in all probability, simplify and alleviate international requirements.

Virus transmission through seed is known for at least four viroses in stone fruits, a matter that inspires a conservative view toward importation of such seeds.

3. Coffee Rust

Discovered in Ceylon in 1869–1870, coffee rust forced coffee farmers (because of immense losses in the following decades) to give up this profitable culture and to change over to the growing of tea. Both in Ceylon and in East Africa local study and old herbarium material suggest that the rust existed as an innocuous parasite on wild coffee, turned loose by the monoculture. Toward the East it has been carried and spread as far as Samoa; in Africa it was noted in Natal in 1878 and has, by its spread, frustrated coffee growing in many low-lying districts of East Africa. West Africa, South America, Mexico, and the West Indies are uninfested. Reports exist that the rust was seen and eradicated in Puerto Rico.

Where the climate is more favorable to the coffee bush than to the rust—mostly at altitudes over 5000 ft.—protective spraying is profitable. Crossbreeding for resistance is practiced in several places but decisive results have not been obtained; as an aid to safe exchange of plant material, F.A.O. is maintaining a quarantine station in Portugal.

The uninfested coffee-growing countries are of course highly interested in keeping this danger at a maximum distance. Regarding a commission appointed in Ceylon in order to promote the study of the disease Large (1940) writes: "The action was taken 10 years too late."

4. Cereal Smuts

A few species of smuts are so commonly associated with grain culture (although reduced in intensity by seed disinfection) that they might well be termed standard smuts. Apart from these, a couple of varieties have been discussed as objects of exclusion measures.

Bunt of rye (Tilletia secalis) is reported from a belt beginning in the French Alps and stretching over Czechoslovakia and Bulgaria to Russia; it has been found 2 or 3 times in Great Britain but never outside Europe. Seed disinfection is reported to be efficient. Flag smut of wheat (Urocystis tritici) has a rather widely spread range (Commonwealth Mycological Institute, 1953); the United States forbids import of wheat grain and straw from certain countries, while Canada in general forbids import of wheat, including straw, bran, etc., but exempts states which can certify that wheat flag smut does not occur in the localities of origin. EPPO (1955b) has pointed out that in spite of enormous quantities of wheat imported to Europe, introduction of these two smuts seems minimal; furthermore, the knowledge of races is scanty. For these reasons special measures would seem unnecessary at present.

Dwarf bunt of wheat (*Tilletia brevifaciens*) seems mainly to spread by soil, and the Indian carnal bunt of wheat (*Neovossia indica*), by the wind only, circumstances which make quarantine measures concerning grain uncalled for.

5. *Discussion*

Several deserving authors have published lists of diseases and pests occurring outside their own country (Stevenson, 1926; Hunt, 1946; Pierce, 1917). Such lists are of lasting value for reference, but they should not be used as the only basis in compiling lists of plants or products to be embargoed or admitted conditionally. The most important factor is communication between pathologists of the countries which exchange plants and products. Foreign diseases and pests may be items of minimal danger, as, for example, when the host plant is rarely cultivated. However, we have experienced painful surprises (see Section I, A, 2). All grades exist—from "no danger" to "immediate danger"—because of the everyday possibilities of quick transport and the economic importance of susceptible cultures. In such cases the Services may be prepared by having regulatory measures authorized for immediate printing, by means of control, by sprayers and remedies, by having posters and press material ready, and, last but not least, by having men and money available for quick transfer to the scene of an emergency.

It is particularly aggravating to find, when the danger of a certain import has been assessed, that the plants or plant parts have been designed for propagation. As pointed out by Stevens (1949) those ornamentals most hit by disease are vegetatively propagated.

It may seem absurd to enforce severe restrictions against attacks which have already gained a certain foothold in a country; the explanation may be that the item is very dangerous and that "we have enough of it," but another good reason is that the invasion until now has been limited to a certain district or to a special type of locality (e.g., town gardens) and that much money and energy is being spent in pushing back the invader. In fact the Netherlands have practically eradicated the Narcissus eelworm (*Ditylenchus dipsaci*) in the bulb fields, as Denmark has practically eliminated black currant reversion in its nurseries.

Increased attention may be advisable where pathogens split up into races of varying infectivity. Races of rust fungi or smuts could very well be spread over long distances with straw and hay. Regulations vary somewhat, called forth sometimes by veterinarians' fear of foot-and-mouth disease; in other cases, by phytosanitary considerations; in this case, regulations are often lacking for straw used for packing of material other than plants. Australia, however, requires that all imported straw be burned or disinfected with formaldehyde, and Cyprus prohibits the import of straw if not accompanied by a veterinary certificate (order, 1957). Similar precautions are taken in Rumania, where not only straw from packing, but also remains of straw and feed from cattle import may be landed only when accompanied by a veterinary health certificate.

Waste and discarded material are sometimes more dangerous than the product itself; regulations against pests and diseases carried with fruit or potatoes, for example, are often characterized by these possibilities. When a ship arrives in a Rumanian port, the captain must sign a declaration promising not to import waste or throw it into the harbor.

Manure is embargoed in many plant regulations, and now and then veterinary inspectors have had to use this embargo for their own purposes. A cooperation of plant pathologists and veterinarians might well contribute to uniform and simple rules.

Soil is excluded as an import by several countries; others limit the rules to soil found on roots, tubers, bulbs, etc. There seems to be a quite understandable tendency to fix more rigorous rules in regard to dirt in potato sacks, Cyprus having set the limit at ½%. Brazil permits import of soil with plants or independently if free from pests; disinfecting soil on arrival or providing imported plants with new soil is recommended, however (order, 1934).

Wood, in general, is a question not quite satisfactorily settled from a sanitary viewpoint. There are not only elm disease, oak wilt, and the devastating chestnut blight, but also several insects which may persist even longer in dry wood than the fungi. Much wood is carried around the world in the form of boxes and crates, at temporary bulkheads in ships' holds, etc. If a California quarantine station finds crates with bark on the wood, the staff will look for bark beetles and eventually order the goods to be fumigated; similarly, willow withes from Europe and Canada are not admitted to the United States.

From a legal point of view advisory information has no place in an ordinance; it may be smuggled in, nevertheless, by plant pathologists eager to make the paths easy for exporters and importers. Thus the United States specifies "permitted packing materials" (when free from sand, soil, and earth) such as: buckwheat hulls, charcoal, coral sand (from Bermuda), excelsior, exfoliated vermiculite, ground cork or peat, sawdust, shavings, and sphagnum moss.

Grain, oil seed, etc., for food and cattle feed (subjects of an enormous world trade) have to a large extent been left alone, although important pests and troublesome weed seeds are constantly depreciating values. A few countries actually require phytosanitary certificates; Canada, for example, has very appropriate regulations for export grain. Seeds may be imported unknowingly. Purebred merino sheep were selected with all possible care in California and sent to Australia; their health proved excellent, but in the fine wool they carried seeds of species of *Bromus, Erodium, Festuca,* and *Trifolium.* It is well known that legume seeds may harbor both viruses and wasps (Trumble, 1946). On the other hand seed may be quite severely infested, and the plants still escape any infection (Section II, B, 6).

Oak seeds are embargoed by some European countries because it is uncertain whether or not oak wilt (*Charlara quercina*) is transmitted by seed; if further investigations show that the wilt is not seed-borne or that seed disinfection is efficient and simple, no embargo will be necessary.

Uncertainty may cause varying reactions. Assuming that the virus causing Pierce's disease is transmitted by lucerne seed, Greece forbids import of lucerne seed from Argentina, California, Florida, and Texas. Birch decline, which has been disastrous in New England and Canada, has been tentatively ascribed to several fungi and insects, to climatic influence, and even to virus attack; quarantine measures have been discussed in Europe but postponed.

The risk of quite fortuitous transport is ever present. A Colorado beetle may well find concealment in the cuff of a man's trousers if, for example, when passing an infested district, he has walked through a potato field in order to behold the ravages.

A frontier inspector's imagination cannot cover all cases; cooperation between countries that "have" and "have not" may be stimulating, but probably a public alert to suspicious phenomena is the best safeguard. Thus, according to Canadian law, the owner, occupier, or lessee of any place or premises where any pest or disease is found which is not widely prevalent or distributed within or throughout Canada shall immediately notify the Chief, Plant Protection Division, thereof, and shall send to him specimens of such pest or disease (Destructive Insect and Pest Act, 1954). Most countries include an obligatory notification in orders concerning the control of a special pest; both ways may be valuable— if the public is induced to be cooperative.

C. Evaluation of Transport Interference

1. Economic Motives and Effects

Many attempts are being made to determine the losses caused by plant diseases and pests. The International Commission on Plant Disease Losses (under The International Union of Biological Sciences) is gathering material and methods for a computation with a known degree of exactitude. A concise review is given by Ordish (1953).

The losses of crops caused by an introduced pest or the cost of control in order to prevent spread of a disease must be calculated with due regard to the scarcity or abundance of crops influencing the market price. A simple instance may be given. During the period from 1949 to 1958 Denmark spent about $75,000 on survey and eradication of the Colorado beetle, which threatens the country's southern districts. It has proved possible to eradicate each year's quota and to prevent the beetle from establishing itself. One single spraying of the Danish potato area would cost about $500,000—thus 70 times more than 1 year's prevention.

Much larger undertakings, promoted by EPPO or its forerunners, have been carried through in Europe, but the economy is less easy to grasp. Help in kind or money between countries has had excellent results, both in direct control and in mutual response.

In the Danish case the state has defrayed all expenses, and a hearty cooperation by the public has resulted. McCubbin (1954) asks: Who shall pay? and gives the answer: The man who profits! However, quarantine measures are not always appreciated by those whom they are intended to benefit. Most states seem to cover at least a part of the over-all costs, while the importer or exporter must reimburse the special expenses in each particular case. This may be enough to call forth complaints from the trade when a prospective profit may disappear or an expected business is eliminated by a quarantine.

Quarantine measures have frequently been accused of concealing protectionism. In fact persons have on certain occasions sought in some pest the fine-sounding reason for stopping an inconvenient import.

In most countries new quarantine measures must, in some way, be discussed with the organizations of the trade and the growers before being implemented. New proposals may be delayed, perhaps *ad calendas graecas*, because funds have not been granted; the brakes may be applied because interests are too conflicting, by sheer apathy, or because it is found that quarantine officers have gone too far (in actual fact, as specialists, they have been more foresighted). They are then accused of painting the devil on the wall, because the evil is still so far away that the costs seem excessive in relation to the danger. The pathologists may now and then have been too zealous, but in most cases the positive results, exclusion or delay (see Section I, B, 5), have been well worth some inconvenience.

It is even worse if a measure cannot be realized because of pressure from outside, risk of trade retaliations, etc. Shelve the proposal for a better day and try again!

2. Biological and Administrative Limitations

The quarantine officer's need of information is insatiable. One pathogen may have only one host plant or hundreds; there may be unsuspected symptomless carriers; we never dare think that we know the host range completely. How will foreign fungi or pests, perhaps split up into races of the most varying infectiousness, react in a new habitat? What may be hidden in indeterminable incubation stages in imported plant material? We must trust the field inspection and pedigree work of the exporting country. Because of lack of information, control work was started too late or too sparingly, but great improvements have been made. EPPO distributes news from its member countries; FAO's "Plant Protection Bulletin" spreads information from and to the entire world, and American publications such as "Plant Disease Reporter" and others are studied eagerly—and not only in North America. Other countries issue monthly or annual reports on the occurrence of diseases or pests.

The state of California is protected by mountains, deserts, and the sea, and has built on that natural basis a system protecting its intensive plant production. Other states may lie open to invasion from all sides, the situation further aggravated by a lively transit trade. Modern traffic, with its enormous volume and speed, has created huge problems; but it is evident from the lists of intercepted pathogens that quarantine officers have by no means given up. The cost of inspecting a box of carnations, arriving by air freight at 3 A.M. is prohibitive—and the market cannot wait; it opens at 5 A.M. Therefore, agreements are being developed, placing the main responsibility on continual greenhouse inspection and outport checking. On continents like Europe, long-distance truck transport is a hard problem; the routes of the trucks are ever changing, the arrival at highway customs houses is most irregular, and as trucks run, for example, directly from a nursery in one country to a distributor in another, the consignor feels it to be absurd that the plants cannot be jammed into the truck—completely inaccessible to a frontier plant inspector. A *modus vivendi* can be arranged, letting the truck run in customs bound directly to the consignee, where a customs officer and a plant inspector supervise the unloading. But a cooperation among groups of neighboring countries, placing an increased weight on inspection in field and packing shed, might improve the situation.

The world trade in grain and in wood, forms a problem largely unsolved because the volume is so enormous, the trade mostly reluctant (to state it mildly), and the conditions on unloading adverse to inspection. When a ship collects its cargo in many small lots from several harbors, inspection is not only very difficult, but mutual infestation between lots likely. For grain, at least, a reliable outport inspection would solve the main problems. The argument that "it cannot be done" is frequently heard; nevertheless, it is done; e.g., in Canada. Quite the opposite side of the spectrum is represented by passenger luggage; many countries admit, e.g., 5 kg. of fruit, vegetables, etc., for a passenger, although not always without misgivings. It is the wormy fruit that is thrown out of the compartment window—to end where? Gift packages sold to tourists are, deplorably enough, not always fancy in quality. Moreover, there is a general tendency to minimize customs inspection; a botanist may travel unhindered from Stockholm to Rome with living potato wart placed in a flask openly in his suitcase! Certain countries take a rather liberal view, allowing passengers to import 10 or more kg. or plant material on modified conditions when it is not for planting or propagation.

Illegal trade and carelessness in private traffic involve considerable danger. It is supposed that the potato root eelworm was introduced to America by way of a ship's ballast, illegally consisting of soil instead of gravel, and subsequently dumped on Long Island. A serious first infestation with San José scale was smuggled into Germany with fruit trees imported in violation of customs and sanitary regulations. Physiologists import the largest cockroaches for their experiments; geneticists smuggle scions and small plants containing dangerous viruses; gene hunters bring potatoes home from South America, disregarding one or more potato smuts hidden in the tubers. "Professors are among the worst quarantine breakers," says an experienced European official.

The sport of finding loopholes has an irresistible attraction for some people. The undesirable result is that in order to stop loopholes, acts and regulations are made more severe and intricate than would otherwise be necessary.

It is desirable to create—perhaps best by repeated small doses—a public opinion agreeable to the needful regulations. Leaders of farmers' and nurserymens' organizations and farsighted tradesmen should be kept informed—and thrilling news will always have the interest of the press. "Acts and ordinances remain more or less powerless when an honest will does not place them in man's heart" (Gustav V, King of Sweden).

II. Quarantine Measures

A. *Embargo*

Embargo may seem an easy way to keep out a newly reported attack from abroad, but several difficulties and objections have been registered; in many cases an embargo ought to be only temporary until better measures can be outlined as the result of a more intensive study of the attack and its limitations.

A perfect embargo, built like a Chinese wall around a country, would stop all development—but breeders and scientists, nevertheless, must have new material. On the other hand, a country with less exacting requirements than most others is apt to be a dumping ground for low grade products.

1. *Local Regulations*

In order to stop a local but menacing attack, delimitation of a district from which host plants or other plants must not be taken away has proved useful; sometimes a protective zone with less severe restrictions is placed around the district. The Norwegian regulation against spread of clubroot has been mentioned (Section I, A, 1). In certain cases, both in Europe and in North America, such a local quarantine includes several states or districts within states. In other cases states, on their own account, declare an embargo in order to protect themselves, e.g., against the potato root eelworm on Long Island (see Section I, A, 6). Such an embargo has been followed up in California by the establishment of inspection stations in all places where highways lead into the state with the result that forbidden material is frequently discovered and retained. A demarcation line has been drawn between Colorado east of the Rockies and west of them in order to protect Utah from invasion by the Colorado beetle. In the United States internal quarantines can quickly be established by the individual states, while quarantine ordered by the federal government must inevitably take longer; the trade, however, prefers federal quarantines because of their more uniform character.

2. *National Prohibitions*

Most embargoes are directed against special plants (barberries, hops, tobacco, *Hevea*, and many others) or seeds; in some cases, against special plants of particular origin. New Zealand (order, 1957) bars all fruits and vegetables from countries infested by the Oriental fruit fly, as well as oaks from North America and Japan; England excludes *Prunus* plants from outside Europe and *Rosa* spp. from Australia, New Zealand, and

Italy; in principle the United States forbids nursery trees and shrubs generally, and potatoes from most countries; however, certain exemptions are provided for.

EPPO has from the beginning maintained an attitude of reserve concerning embargoes. An early report (EPPO, 1951) suggests a minimum of complete embargo on imports and then only after careful study. For example, potato ring rot, caused by *Corynebacterium sepedonicum* is considered as follows (EPPO, 1955b). Nothing short of a complete embargo on the import of main crop potatoes from infested countries can guarantee against the introduction of the disease. On the other hand, before considering such drastic measures, governments should bear in mind that if potatoes intended for seed are not cut before planting, there seems to be little risk of the disease becoming serious.

When an import of corn borer larvae for bird feed is started, it is natural to intervene; in fact many countries have a paragraph forbidding the import of living insects (except honeybees, for which special rules exist) and of cultures of pathogenic bacteria and fungi. It may be difficult enough to make such a paragraph logical as well as making it "hold water," but the intention is clear enough; perhaps a sentence from Sweden's law could be added: Whosoever acts against the aim of the law breaks the law.

Countries with no phytosanitary service might expect to see embargoes rising up against them everywhere; as a matter of fact it is these very countries that are the happy hunting grounds of botanists and geneticists. The limited material brought home is usually inspected thoroughly and guarded under a prolonged, post-entry quarantine.

For small countries densely surrounded by others, quarantine walls are likely to be only paper walls, if neighboring countries cannot agree to establish group action.

B. *Conditional Import*

1. *Inspection at Place of Origin*

Among the early recommendations from EPPO is field inspection during the growing season in the exporting country; this is especially necessary for virus diseases. The wording of the Rome certificate (FAO, 1951) ". . . were found to the best of his knowledge to be substantially free from injurious diseases and pests" is understood to refer mainly to the final outport inspection. Since field inspection is practiced in several countries for potato certification and in some countries for nursery sanitation, very precise tolerances are listed for first, second, and third field inspections, and for foundation and elite material, as well as for the stock to be offered for sale. Often these tolerances are included in the inspectors' instructions in order to make it easier to revise them annually, and to tighten up rules, using the thumb-screw method, when conditions allow for it. The tolerances may, to some degree, be influenced by the individual requirements of importing countries, but in most countries the certification is just as important for the national market.

Inspection of seed fields is carried out by seed firms and is mostly concerned with purity and quality. Very few countries have arranged for sanitary inspection of seed fields, but it will be necessary to take the matter up. EPPO (1955b) indicates some diseases for which a request for field inspection (or production in a territory where the disease is unknown) is justified: barley stripe mosaic, bean bacterial wilt, tomato bacterial canker, common bean blight, pea bacterial blight, and bacterial spot of tomato and pepper.

The selection of individual mother plants, clones, etc., is, in some countries, entrusted to special semiofficial committees, or the entire certification instrument is assigned to one or several committees in connection with the official service which takes over responsibility for outport inspection and certificates.

This system has proved useful in temperate zones for nursery stock and seed potato certification; it may be equally practical where healthy stock must be selected from sugar cane or other tropical crops propagated vegetatively.

When the rules for field inspection are published, foreign services and prospective buyers estimate which grades they can approve. No country need accept stock inferior to its own.

Pedigree work is especially important when the crops harbor diseases with long incubation (see Section I, B, 2). A gradation may be desirable according to symptoms and to the economic importance of the crop. Some countries embargo roses from Australia, New Zealand, and Italy because of rose wilt; or elm from North America because of phloem necrosis. EPPO (1955b) finds post-entry quarantine sufficient; a reliable nursery inspection would strongly support this viewpoint. What should be done with a consignment of *Daphne* full of mosaic? Presuming that the mosaic is due to the omnipresent *Cucumis* virus 1, leniency has been argued for; "but to send infested produce from one country to another is one of the surest ways of hindering international trade . . ." is one of the conclusions of a conference convened by EPPO (1958b) in order to discuss two important fruit pests.

Field inspection will always in practice supply growers with advice concerning control. This advisory work may well be worth the extra cost of field inspection. Moreover, intensive control in an exporting country is the first line of defense of importing countries. For countries with an important plant export, embargoes and other hindrances may mean that no margin is left to pay for rational control of diseases and pests.

2. Outport Inspections

The standards set for inspection of plants and plant parts leaving the country and the tolerances admitted are to a large extent determined by the requirements of importing countries. When requirements differ essentially, it is seen that a service may be authorized to use varying tolerances. It should be added at once, however, that several countries aim at standardized products and at a reputation for high standards, not only of health but also of quality grading. Canada (1954) gives elaborate rules for health of apples, potatoes, etc.; Denmark has special acts concerning quality grading of export fruit, vegetables, and potatoes, but the inspection is referred to the phytosanitary service. Some countries have the supervision of, e.g., fruit export allotted to two or three ministries, a method inclined to create overlapping and some confusion among both buyers and sellers.

It is a matter for discussion whether depreciation of the commercial value, such as bruises in fruits or *Penicillium* in bulbs, is not entirely the concern of the trade. The tendency, however, is apparently shifting from the old "it will just scrape through" to "how will the consignment look on arrival?" Slow or fast transport is also a decisive factor: if *Exobasidium japonicum* and other fungi attacking *Azalea* are not thoroughly controlled at the place of production, they may well become visible during transport.

It is prescribed, in some ordinances, that consignments should be inspected and sealed on the premises where produced. Experience, however, has shown, as, e.g., in the case of the Colorado beetle, that it is safer to take the goods to special riddling yards or packing houses where the inspectors have every possibility of getting an over-all picture and can pounce upon lots needing more than a mere inspection of samples. Riddling and packing, moreover, can be much more efficient in large establishments; the grower, on the other hand, has not always the heart to be too severe when grading his own product. Even when the inspection in the riddling yard is thorough, the existence of an inspection immediately before loading has, in actual fact, improved quality and prevented "mistakes."

Where export of orchids or carnations becomes a regular industry— with a very fast shipment as a prerequisite, arrangements are made to inspect the greenhouses weekly, thus considerably expediting outport inspection.

It is natural to inspect the whole of small consignments. Of large shipments samples must of necessity be selected, usually a definite proportion being prescribed in the inspectors' instructions. However, variations are natural; lots from regions exposed to infection will be scrutinized carefully; and the same applies to concerns which are felt to take a carefree view of grading or to practice window dressing. The outport inspection of grain, oil seed, etc., is bound to be an important question in the coming years (see Section II, B, 6).

Soil, teeming as it is with both useful and harmful organisms, must always be suspect (Section II, B, 5). When a country absolutely prohibits the import of mold (top soil), compost, and manure, it will not always be the plant inspector who must intervene. When it is a question of "soil, sand, and dirt" accompanying plants, the outport inspector must clarify the strict meaning of "free from," which is so foreign to the professional nurseryman's ideas. Neighboring countries suffering to the same degree from the same soil-borne pest may agree on a tolerance regarding soil on roots. EPPO (1951) recommends the term "reasonably free from soil," a good formulation—when the services concerned are on good speaking terms.

A plant inspector from the importing country cooperating with his colleagues of the exporting country—from the packing house to loading —will save a lot of inport inspection. When a cargo of potatoes is loaded for export, the critical representative of the buyer will be on the quay. Why not the phytosanitary inspector of the importing country? This practice has been initiated and found equally profitable to both seller and buyer—not to mention its soundness for the inspectors.

The influence of proper packing on quality is important. The incongruity of healthy plants packed in infested straw, dirty sacks, or unstripped wood cannot be tolerated.

At long last the phytosanitary certificate has been issued (see Section III, C, 1). Exporting countries should take note that some countries may not require a certificate, e.g., at import of fruit, but they may still reserve to themselves the right of inspection; if then San José scale is listed among dangerous pests and the scales are found, the consignment may be rejected.

3. Transport Measures

Transport lasting for weeks in ordinary ships may aggravate attacks invisible or hardly visible at outport inspection. Slight frost injury just before loading may develop into serious nests of rot; "heating during transit" may cause retarded germination of potatoes and special bulbs. Cases are known where powdery scab, caused by *Spongospora subter-*

ranea, has developed from tiny blisters on loading into typical lesions during a 4-week journey.

Ships with cold storage installations have proved useful in the control of fruit flies (*Ceratitis* spp.). Early experiments have been carried out in connection with transport from the Hawaiian Islands (Back and Pemberton, 1916). The U. S. Department of Agriculture prescribes 34° F. for a period of 20 days for the Mexican fruit fly. For citrus fruits and grapes New Zealand permits a combination of cold storage before loading with cold storage during transit. The treatments, which may be slightly varied according to the species of flies and origin, are also accepted as efficient against scale insects (FAO, 1957a). Documentation of temperature and duration of treatments may be obtained from self-recording instruments.

4. Inport Inspection

The majority of countries, by means of acts and ordinances, have reserved to themselves the right to a phytosanitary inspection of most kinds of incoming plants and plant parts. The Service should have the right to take samples for closer inspection.

Efficiency depends on the knowledge and skill of the inspectors, but also on a very close cooperation with customs authorities in airports, prominent ports, railroad stations at frontiers, and market halls. Sometimes it may also be necessary to call for the assistance of the public appraiser.

That inport inspection can be efficient is evident from the published lists of intercepted pests and diseases. The increasing knowledge of virus attacks and other diseases invisible at the moment of import may seem to reduce the value of the customary inspection, but it would be more correct to state that it is being extended by referring a good proportion of plants to post-entry quarantine—and some to disinfection.

The routine trade with large shipments, according to many experienced quarantine officers, is not the most dangerous; there will usually be the best contact between services as far as staple products are concerned. The tourist and other passenger traffic, with its manifold and unpredictable luggage, is raising questions which call for a practical solution. Sherman (1957) points to the more than 100,000 aircraft coming from abroad to the United States in the course of a year, which are inspected, together with the luggage of perhaps 4,000,000 to 5,000,000 passengers; he points to one case where an aircraft arriving at Honolulu from Japan brought, as stowaways, 48 living Japanese beetles—certainly enough for development of a prolific clan—and this happened in spite of the usual public health dose of aerosol. Sherman's proposals are mainly aimed at arrivals in the United States; continents divided into many countries or territories are much worse off. And if the countries merge into smaller or larger economic units with the intention *inter alia* of lowering customs walls—and since customs inspection of passengers goods is more or less made a sheer formality—it is not too soon for quarantine officers to look out for other possibilities of inspection.

It is known that the Mediterranean fruit fly was introduced into Florida in 1929 and soon eradicated; when it was discovered again, in 1956, tourist traffic was blamed for the transfer. Since the fly had been intercepted 1217 times between the two periods named, this is a justifiable assumption (Shepherd, 1957).

To prohibit all plant material in passengers' luggage would be a drastic measure. There might be more time available at outport than at inport inspection, and apprehension of prized plant material would, perhaps, be less irritating before departure than on arrival. However, with outport customs inspection dwindling, there seems little hope of making this change. For some countries, at least, it might be practical to print an attractive and concise folder, telling what not to import and why, and to request simultaneously that it be delivered with each ticket sold to such and such a country. It is illogical to cater to tourists and then on arrival to deprive them of corsages and treasured cuttings brought along for friends!

It is more practical to examine passenger vehicles than the passengers. The surroundings of aerodromes should be searched for possible escapees; traps can be very useful, and the interest of collectors could perhaps be aroused. Goods carried by trains may be well inspected, yet casual remains in freight cars be overlooked, as well as fruits and vegetables in the pantry of dining cars. Not a few pests and diseased plant parts have been intercepted in ships' stores.

The expenses of comprehensive inspection are high; for a large country like the United States, with a relatively short frontier, the nation can bear it. For small countries the burden usually is too great, and some parts of the frontier are neglected. Here again group action of neighboring states must be the way out. Europe could not afford to keep the Colorado beetle out, but must now afford the control of it.

In the majority of cases the inspector gives the customs the notice permitting the goods to be imported. Some are directed to a more or less extended post-entry quarantine, and a few must be disinfected or rejected—all according to the instructions the inspector has received. He is justified in expecting these to be clear, consistent, and that due regard be given to experience.

5. Disinfection

Fumigation against insects and other invertebrates is treated in Section III, B, 3 and disinfection of seed is considered below (Section II, B, 6). In a few cases, when bulbs, tubers, etc., are exported from countries where the Colorado beetle is established to countries free from this pest, agreements are made regarding treatment with DDT, naphthalene, etc.

The possibility of utilizing thermotherapy against viruses may become useful in international trade with budsticks, cuttings, etc. Methods have been sought for disinfecting nursery tree roots against dangerous company such as potato wart and nematodes, for an additional protection of roots against the hardships of severe washing, and against damage en route, but as yet with no practical results.

For the control of grubs in earth balls U. S. Department of Agriculture advises the simple and quick method of injecting ethylene dibromide into the balls.

6. Seeds in Tons and Grams

According to the International Plant Protection Convention (see Section III, C) the contracting governments decide to what extent seeds should be included under "plants" or under "plant products." Seeds are so diversified in type and use that it is difficult to bring them all under common rules.

Studies of seed transmission have been carried out in several centers, resulting in lists such as those of Orton (1931) and LeClerg (1953). From Egypt a list of diseases not found is published; from Indonesia a list of seeds admitted. EPPO (1954) has, in cooperation with the International Seed Testing Organization, appointed a working party on seedborne diseases; in the first report it indicates 15 diseases worth attention in international trade, and for 8 of these advises that the locality of origin should be free from the disease in question.

One great difficulty is that a certain fungus may be disastrous in one country but innocuous in another; even within one district growth conditions may be decisive. Fortunately all seed-borne infestations are not seed transmitted, as is found in comprehensive experiments (Neergaard, 1949). Notices on fungi found in a sample of seed, therefore, should not be framed in such a way as to give the buyer a pretext for refusing it. On the other hand, of some hundreds of viroses described, about 50 are seed-borne, and sometimes in unexpected ways, as, for instance, when *Cineraria* seed is 50% infected with tomato spotted wilt. Even a slight seed infection may, through secondary spread, be injurious. In these cases field inspection (see Section II, B, 1) is called for if the country cannot be declared altogether free from that particular virosis.

Freedom from seeds of parasitic plants and even from noxious weeds or weeds rare in the importing country may be included in the demands for imported seed. This stresses the necessity for coordination of seed testing with sanitary inspection. Several countries prohibit the importation of coniferous seeds from a genetic standpoint, mostly leaving open the question as to who in the exporting country should shoulder the responsibility.

About thirty countries require that all seed imported should be accompanied by a phytosanitary certificate—an almost too easy way of solving the problem. "An official declaration that a seed consignment has been examined and found reasonably free from injurious pests and diseases has unavoidably profound limitations, which should be realized by the importing country in accepting such a statement . . . we trust that Governments will not demand a general health certificate for all seed-borne diseases, but will specify the particular diseases which they consider injurious and against which they would desire to be protected" (EPPO, 1954).

Fourteen countries consider only a few kinds or groups of seed, declare embargo in general or for certain regions, or require a certificate based on field inspection or laboratory analysis. Three countries request freedom from only one disease, e.g., tomato bacterial canker.

Laboratory methods are standardized, and further methods are worked out by seed-testing experts in cooperation with plant pathologists. Since the seed trade has its rush season, samples for analysis can be taken as soon as seed lots arrive at the stores, a method which gives valuable information on the individual grower's product.

Field inspection (see Section II, B, 1) may be necessary for diseases not detectable in the laboratory; the country which leads the way here will be in a strong position.

Disinfection of imported seed is prescribed by a few countries. As modern seed disinfectants develop, disinfection may become more reliable than inspection in the laboratory, especially where a very low percentage of seeds is infected. Disinfection of foundation seed may become advisable, since there is a possibility of new races of smut being introduced. New Zealand thus requests disinfection of maize seed, against *Ustilago zeae* and *Physoderma zea-maydis*. The possibility of importing nematodes and other animal pests should not be overlooked.

Consignments of vegetable and flower seeds frequently consist of numerous but very small quantities, perhaps produced in several countries; a strict documentation of origin, with transit certificates, health certificates, etc., would form a stack of paper needing yards of red tape to keep it together. FAO (1955) therefore recommends that in general certificates should not be requested for small packets unless there is some specific reason for doing so.

According to the Southeast Asia and Pacific Agreement all seeds of annual or biennial field crops or vegetables and all seeds or cut flowers of annual, biennial, or perennial ornamental plants which are essentially herbaceous in character are in principle excepted from the rules.

World trade in grain for food and feed, oil seeds for milling, and barley malted or for malting runs into many thousands of tons annually. Phytosanitary restrictions have been slow to develop; mention may be made of Canada's outport inspection and of the requirements of the Federal Republic of Germany (see Section III, A, 4). If grain, infested even slightly with pests, is loaded into a clean (fumigated) ship, the insects will develop abundantly during transport, the value of the cargo will depreciate, and remnants of it remaining in cavities and crevices after unloading will render the expensive fumigation worthless.

The sanitation of export grain, oil seed and oilcake, etc., must be made the responsibility of exporting countries; the care of accidental infestations and of re-export supervision is the responsibility of inport inspection.

7. Postentry Quarantine

Quarantine in its strictest sense, i.e., to keep the arriving man, beast, or goods isolated until all fear of disease transmission was thought to be excluded, has occasionally been practiced against early intruders before plant quarantine was put on a systematic basis. The first organized step seems to have been U. S. Department of Agriculture's quarantine nursery, established chiefly to safeguard the import of plants from little known regions and mainly implemented by the Department itself.

It is, indeed, risky to import interesting but little known plants from undeveloped areas without the services of such nurseries, where plants can be kept under observation for months or even years. In Europe such nurseries are under development on isolated islands or other localities where the chance of spread is minimal. In some cases the importers themselves—geneticists, breeders, seed potato committees, botanical gardens—are able to provide suitable localities where the plants must be kept until the service decides that they can be released or that they must be destroyed. Botanical gardens outside the danger zones have acted as quarantine nurseries for breeding material or for new varieties to be transferred from one continent to another.

Post-entry quarantine undoubtedly will be highly developed during the coming years. It is worthy of note that as an interesting addition to its services the U. S. Department of Agriculture has arranged to have imported primulas tested for tobacco necrosis virus by means of test plants, in this way establishing a brief detention.

III. Legal Aspects

A certain tension is frequently felt between the jurist, who wishes acts and ordinances drafted in such a way that they will always "stand up in court," and the quarantine officers, who know how difficult it is for businessmen—and to an even greater extent for private persons—to understand the scope of such rules. It has even been proposed to issue one edition for use in court, which might be drafted "in the most difficult Chinese," and another for the public; one solution is to accompany the order with an explanation of the changes intended; another, to print such an explanation as an appendix to the order. Our legislators should keep in mind the preamble of a Danish law more than 700 years old: The land shall be built on law. . . . The law shall be worthy of respect, righteous, bearable, serviceable and useful, following the custom of the country, and plain so that every man can know and understand what is written in the law.

A. *Acts and Regulations*

No doubt McCubbin (1954) is right when, in his harsh but extremely readable section on human nature, he concludes that in order to curb violations many regulatory measures have to be drawn up and enforced with far greater severity than should be necessary (even so he seems to have forgotten the scientific nonconformists).

1. *The Act and the Ordinances*

Ideally, an act on plant protection should be as general and brief as use and custom of the country permit. It should be drafted so as to be valid for decades and should give the minister of agriculture sufficient authority concerning the following items:

(a) *Purpose.* What diseases and pests are deemed dangerous to cultivation, the storing and selling of plants and plant parts, and what measures shall be taken? This includes prevention by prohibiting or regulating import, transit, and export (of plants, etc., cultures of pathogens, and living invertebrates) in relation to certain or all countries, to fixed seasons, to certain methods of transport, to packing materials, and to soil, manure, straw, etc., imported with plants or independently.

(b) *Definitions.* Define authority of inspectors allowing the minister to decide in cases of doubt and to mitigate requirements. The definitions listed in current Canadian and English regulations save many repetitions.

(c) *Inspection.* Rules are needed for inspection of consignments at import and also later (e.g., in 1 or 2 years' time), for inspection desirable to meet local needs or foreign requests, for issuing of certificates and permits, for inspection of stores reserving the inviolability of the dwelling to a court decision.

(d) *Responsibility.* State the services' freedom from economic responsibility; the importer's duty to see that imported plants, etc., are inspected; the duty of importers, dealers, occupiers, customs and quarantine officers, and police to give information concerning plants, etc. falling under the act—such information to be used only according to law and custom; the manner of the serving of notices to occupiers and others—personally, by mail, or by advertising.

(e) *Funds.* Ensure authority for the disposition of money for administration, inspection, and public control measures; to pay indemnities to persons suffering *bona fide* unreasonable losses due to control measures; to secure payment for special expenses of inspection.

(f) *Prosecution.* State procedure for violations, limits of fines or other sanctions, recovery of cost of public control from negligent occupiers.

Many countries have provisions obliging the minister to call a public hearing or to ask for the advice of the organizations concerned before a new ordinance is issued. Changing conditions will, however, necessitate amendments to the most carefully prepared order; for this reason it is practical to have separate orders concerning export (voluntary or compulsory inspection in field and at dispatch), import, eradication of sources of infection (see Volume III, Chapter 10), and control of "new" attacks.

Grading of products may be supervised by the Phytosanitary Service but should be decided on by separate acts.

If it is found that a danger has been exaggerated, it is time to consider a revocation of safety-first orders. Obsolete prescriptions have a stultifying effect. The dead should not govern the living!

Ordinances must as a rule contain lists, preferably in the form of appendices. Lists of plants which it is forbidden to grow and import cause but few discussions. A standard list of host plants most likely to carry San José scale is published by EPPO and accepted by several countries, and lists of pathogens and pests considered dangerous—and therefore embargoed—are necessary for the guidance of exporting countries. It is common to use the reservation "in particular those listed

. . . ," but the addition "and other pathogens known as dangerous" seems too comprehensive. Short lists make a deeper impression on trade than long ones, which apparently aim at forbidding everything not found in one's own country.

Lists of forbidden packing materials are now a matter of course; a list of suggested material is good service. Lists of goods more or less free from certificates, etc., are a valuable service, but they vary immensely; there is hardly an item listed free in one country which is not restricted in some other. Lists of countries or continents which are excluded in some respects may be necessary, but it will promote control work if regard is taken to a country which quickly eradicates a newly introduced pest or safeguards itself and others by efficient local quarantines and danger zones.

Definitions. The International Plant Convention (FAO, 1951) lays down in Article II that ". . . the term 'plants' shall comprise living plants and parts thereof, including seeds in so far as their supervision . . . may be deemed necessary by contracting Governments, and the term 'plant product' shall comprise unmanufactured and milled material of plant origin, including seeds in so far as they are not included in the term 'plants.' " A rationale (FAO, 1955) recommends that manufactured material of plant origin be considered as coming within the purview of the convention as long as the process of manufacture has not eliminated or substantially reduced the likelihood of its transmitting insect pests or plant diseases. It is to be expected that definitions in regional agreements or national ordinances may be more explicit, as in the Southeast Asia Agreement (FAO, 1956): " 'plant' or 'plants' means all the species of plants or parts thereof, whether living or dead (including stems, branches, tubers, bulbs, corms, stocks, budwood, cuttings, layers, slips, suckers, roots, leaves, flowers, fruits, seeds, and any other parts of plants."

2. Survey and Control

Most countries run more or less intensive surveys, but too few publish the results regularly; special surveys are a necessity when an eradication campaign is planned and when the results will be checked. They are valuable when the extent of forecasting (see Chapter 8) or of public control measures is stipulated; they are a natural intelligence department for immunity breeders (see Chapter 14). Special and frequent surveys around ports and airports are recommended by EPPO (1951), which emphasizes the fundamental importance of early reports on new and dangerous pests or diseases. "It is a necessary corollary that the reporting country should have adequate safeguards that its honesty will not be rewarded by the imposition by neighbouring or distant countries of regulations having the effect of permanently restricting its trade."

3. Inspection

The different aspects of inspection are treated above (Section II, B, 1–7) as well as the necessity for adequate legal authority (Section III, A, 1). At least three countries—Egypt, Sweden and the United States— have on invitation sent inspectors to work in other countries, together with the local Service, a practice preventing the dispatch of undesirable products and securing closer cooperation of Services. The training of inspectors is discussed below (Section III, B, 1).

4. A Modern Ordinance

An ordinance published by the Ministry of Agriculture of the Federal Republic of Germany on August 23, 1953, gives full consideration both to the International Plant Protection Convention and to the recommendations of EPPO; from a legal viewpoint it is very clear and well arranged. A complete English translation has been distributed by EPPO; the following abstract is published by FAO (1957b)·

Diseases and Pests Prohibited

I. Importation of any plants infested or infected with any of the following plant pests or pathogenes is prohibited, even if only part of the consignment is found infested.

1. Virus diseases of strawberry
2. Virus diseases of fruit trees of the genera *Cydonia, Malus, Prunus, Pyrus, Ribes* and *Rubus*
3. Virus diseases of roses
4. *Endoconidiophora fagacearum*
5. *Endothia parasitica*
6. *Synchytrium endobioticum*
7. *Ceratitis capitata* (living stages)
8. *Hyphantria cunea* (living stages)
9. *Laspeyresia molesta* (living stages)
10. *Phthorimaea operculella* (living stages)
11. *Popillia japonica* (living stages)
12. *Rhagoletis pomonella* (living stages)
13. *Tortrix pronubana* (living stages)
14. *Viteus vitifolii* (living stages)
15. *Heterodera rostochiensis* (living or dead)

16. *Quadraspidiotus perniciosus* (living or dead; slight infestation of fruit may be permitted from 1 December to 31 March if the fruit is to be immediately processed)

II. Importation of the following plants is prohibited if found infected or infested with the specific pests or diseases indicated (the nematode and insects refer to living stages). In case of slight infestation, the entry of consignments may be permitted.

1. Vines—virus diseases of *Vitis*
2. Rooted cotoneaster, roses and fruit trees (*Cydonia, Malus, Prunus, Pyrus, Ribes, Rubus*)—*Agrobacterium tumefaciens*
3. Potato tubers—*Corynebacterium sepedonicum*
4. Gladiolus and freesia corms—*Pseudomonas marginata; Fusarium oxysporum* f. *gladioli; Sclerotinia gladioli*
5. Gladiolus corms—*Septoria gladioli; Taeniothrips simplex*
6. Begonias (excluding fruit and seed)—*Xanthomonas begoniae*
7. Hyacinth bulbs—*Xanthomonas hyacinthi; Sclerotinia bulborum*
8. Flower bulbs and tubers—*Botrytis* spp.; *Sclerotium tuliparum; Ditylenchus dipsaci; Eumerus strigatus; E. tuberculatus; E. narcissi; Lampetia equestris*
9. Iris rhizomes—*Botrytis* spp.
10. Rooted azalea—*Exobasidium japonicum; Ovulinia azaleae; Septoria azaleae; Acalla schalleriana; Gracilaria azaleella*
11. Narcissus bulbs—*Fusarium bulbigenum*
12. Chrysanthemum—*Diarthronomyia chrysanthemi*
13. Cherries—*Rhagoletis cerasi*

Plants Prohibited

Importation of following plants and parts of plants is prohibited.
1. Living red oaks (*Quercus borealis maxima; Q. coccinea; Q. falcata; Q. ilicifolia; Q. palustris; Q. velutina*) grown outside Europe (except fruit and seed).
2. Rooted vines (*Vitis*), their living perennial aerial parts, leaves, and dry wood.
3. Living chestnut trees (*Castanea*) (except fruit and seed).
4. Living woody dicotyledonous plants and chrysanthemums prohibited from 16 April to 30 September, except fruit and seed, cut flowers and binding material, cactus and plants grown in and imported from Belgium, Denmark, Finland, Great Britain and North Ireland, Ireland, Iceland, Luxembourg, the Netherlands, Norway, Poland and Sweden.
5. Living plants with soil from Japan, Canada, and U.S.A.
6. Used vine poles.
7. Soil containing plant material or humus, except peat.

Imports Requiring Disinfection

1. Living rooted woody dicotyledonous plants (except cactus and plants grown in and imported from the European countries mentioned above) imported from 1 October to 15 April must be disinfected at the place of entry under supervision of the Plant Protection Service.

2. Living woody dicotyledonous plants without roots (except fruit and seed, cut flowers and binding plants imported from 1 October to 15 April, cactus, and plants from the European countries mentioned above) must be disinfected at the place of entry during the period when importation is permitted.

Imports Subject to Special Requirements

1. Rooted plants except vegetables and medicinal plants may be imported only if originated in an area where vines were not grown during the preceding five years and where freedom from potato root eelworm (*Heterodera rostochiensis*) was ascertained by official soil tests. They must also originate in a field where potato wart (*Synchytrium endobioticum*) does not occur.

2. Fresh potato tubers are subject to the same requirements as rooted plants. In addition, they must not contain soil in excess of 2 percent of the net weight, and they must be packed in new containers whenever containers are used.

3. Fruit trees (*Cydonia, Malus, Prunus, Pyrus, Ribes, Rubus*), strawberry plants and roses (except cut flowers and fruit and seed) may be imported only if grown under official supervision during the growing season and found free from virus diseases.

4. Fresh grapes must be free from other parts of vine.

5. Living vine plants must be air dry and free from soil.

Requirements for Cereals and Dry Pulses

1. Cereals (*Avena, Hordeum, Panicum, Secale, Setaria, Sorghum, Triticum, Zea*) for milling or processing for human consumption shall be disinfested, processed or re-exported within a time limit under the supervision of the Plant Protection Service, if found infested with: *Calandra granaria, C. oryzae, C. zea-mais, Laemophloeus* spp., *Oryzaephilus surinamensis, Rhizopertha dominica, Sitotroga cerealella, Tenebroides mauritanicus, Trogoderma granarium.*

Cereals not mentioned above and oil cakes if infested with the pests enumerated, will be disinfested before storing, or re-exported or processed immediately after leaving the first granary or storage (see also requirement under *Certification*).

2. Dry pulses (*Cicer, Lathyrus, Lens, Lupinus, Phaseolus, Pisum, Soja, Vicia*), except seed for sowing, if infested by any species of Bruchidae, will be disinfested before storing, or re-exported or processed after leaving the first granary or storage (see also requirement under *Certification*).

The above provisions with regard to cereals and dry pulses will come into effect on 1 July 1958.

Certification and Inspection

The following plant materials may be imported from the countries indicated only if accompanied by a phytosanitary certificate issued by the country of origin within 20 days before shipment in the form annexed to the International Plant Protection Convention, in German, or with a certified German translation and in the language of the country of origin. Whenever disinfection or disinfestation has been carried out, particulars of the treatment should be indicated.

In case of cereals, dry pulses and oil cakes, the certificate should be issued by the country from which the materials are directly imported, instead of the country of origin. This provision will come into force on 1 July 1958.

Where a consignment has been split up outside the country of origin, each splitted consignment should be accompanied by a certified certificate and also a certificate in the prescribed form issued by the country in which the splitting took place.

All the following plant materials, including packings and conveyance, will be inspected upon arrival.

1. Timber and saw wood of oaks from Canada and U.S.A.
2. Living angiospermous plants from Japan, Canada and U.S.A.
3. Living angiospermous plants imported between 1 November and 15 April (except subterranean parts, seed, monocotyledonous plants and tomato fruit), potato tubers, flower bulbs and tubers, and iris rhizomes from Greece, Yugoslavia, Austria, Romania, Czechoslovakia, Hungary and U.S.S.R.
4. Living plants (except fruit and seed) enumerated below from countries not mentioned under 2 and 3:

   a) living woody dicotyledonous plants
   b) chrysanthemums
   c) strawberries
   d) carnations
   e) begonias
   f) potato tubers
   g) flower bulbs and tubers in dormant stage

h) iris rhizomes

5. Fresh fruits enumerated below from countries not mentioned under 2 and 3:

a) deciduous fruits and berries (*Cydonia, Malus, Prunus, Pyrus, Ribes, Rubus*)

b) citrus fruit

c) hard-shelled fruit with green skin or green cupule (particularly almonds, hazelnuts, walnuts, chestnuts, pistachio nuts)

d) ripened fruit of rose

e) grapes

6. Cereals and dry pulses (referring to the genera specified under Requirements for cereals and dry pulses)

7. Oil cakes of plant origin

Personal properties removing from certain European countries, individual plants and parts of plants in bouquets and wreaths not for commercial use, food provisions, and consignments less than 5 kilograms for consumption are exempt from certification requirement.

Points of Entry

Plants and plant products which require to be accompanied by phytosanitary certificates may be imported only through the customhouses listed in the Ordinance; some of the customhouses are reserved for mail, air consignments, or for specific commodities.

Consignments in Transit

Transit shipments via free ports or via mail are not subject to restrictions, certification and inspection.

Exemptions

Exemptions from prohibition or restrictions may be granted if imports are for scientific purposes, and in some other cases.

5. Economic Liability of Services

Most governments have found it wise to disclaim economic responsibility for any loss or damage in connection with inspection, certification, and other duties of their Phytosanitary Services. An act of negligence may be so gross that the Service finds it right to propose that the Ministry should pay an equitable compensation. The moral responsibility of the Service and its inspectors should not be lessened.

If nursery plants are sold which ought not to have been approved, the liability, if any, remains with the seller; the decision will depend on use and custom, which presume that the seller has acted as a reasonable and conscientious man. A Service will, of course, see to it that the consignment is not larger than indicated on the certificate. A moral responsibility for botanical names can hardly be disclaimed by any Service insofar as embargoed plant species are concerned.

B. Inspectors and Their Instructions

The power of an inspector is formulated in the regulations of Canada (1954/5), Sections 108–115. The inspector may carry out his work as directed by the ordinance(s), but in many cases the Service will have issued detailed regulations which state exactly what is meant and which he is bound—and able—to follow consistently and with the conviction that his service will back him up. If he finds points of the instruction too rigid or too lax, he should direct the attention of the service to it; if on his own initiative he mitigates the rules, he will repent it, for the public will become confused, and the trade will take advantage.

There are splendid inspectors who have started from scratch in a Service, but usually the best inspectors will be college graduates who, in addition, have had special training in course work and as assistants to senior officers. The United States has special textbooks for study within the Service, England (England Ministry of Agriculture, 1953) an illustrated book, and Germany (1958), an illustrated guide which includes hints for laboratory equipment, instructions for fumigation, and the text of the ordinance.

The question of inspection of tourists' luggage is treated above (see Section II, B, 4). False alarms may be frequent, especially if some new pest is the object of much publicity; such alarms should be received with all the consideration due a public eager to cooperate. It is praiseworthy for the ground personnel of an airport to phone about a Colorado beetle, black with yellow stripes—even if the stripes do run crosswise.

A good many inspectors will have the task of supervising fumigation and heat treatments, for which they should have as exact prescriptions as possible. They may be based on foreign requirements or agreements with Services of importing countries. Much may be said for outport fumigation; in the large-scale trade it can be done with great efficiency. The fumigation may be entrusted to contractors or undertaken by the Service itself. Fumigation equipment in which small parcels, items from passengers luggage, etc., can quickly be treated by the inspectors may contribute a good deal to good public relations. Fumigation prescriptions ought to have their place in instructions which can be easily revised.

C. International Coordination

1. Quarantine Procedures under the Convention

The 1951 Convention refers particularly to pests and diseases of importance to international trade (Article II, 3). It aims at improved control, requires the contracting governments to set up a satisfactory plant protection organization, and lays special emphasis on the undesirability of quarantine measures not based on phytosanitary considerations. A model certificate is annexed to the Convention which, on the whole, has uniformity as its aim. In connection with the anticipated regional organizations, instruments for the settling of disputes and for a world reporting service are provided; the service already has completed the sixth volume of the FAO "Plant Protection Bulletin," which is as much valued for news of changes in quarantine measures as for general information on the occurrence of diseases and pests.

Although the use of the model certificates has not yet become global, so many countries have accepted it that the improvement is evident. EPPO advocates that only one certificate be issued per consignment; if copies are needed for official use or banking operations, they should be marked "Duplicate." Generally, the consignment is to be exported shortly after inspection and issue of certificate, but some exceptions must be made for inspection of seeds and flower bulbs. The space left for additional declarations should be used only in cases of exceptional danger, not for a general repetition of well-known requirements. The botanical names and quantity of consignment are conveniently stated by means of an invoice duplicate, signed by the Service and affixed to the certificate. If the certificate or invoice is lacking or incorrect, the consignment should be rejected or, in exceptional cases, be inspected in detail and possibly disinfected, all at the expense of the owner. If a certificate is not rquired (as, e.g., in the case of agricultural products for industry, or fruits and flowers), the Service will usually have the right to inspect the goods, but not to be directly informed about arrival. Several countries are liberal concerning gift packages. This is understandable from the point of view of avoiding petty business, but dangerous if generosity becomes professional.

"Permit" is a term used in at least two senses: (1) permission given in advance to submit certain goods for inspection by the importing country's Service and (2) a note from the service to customs that the goods may be imported. For the benefit of highway traffic, arrangements are known by which travelers may apply for a permit for certain goods and have it issued by the inspector on the spot. Certain modifications are also granted to the "small frontier traffic."

The FAO will publish in its "Plant Protection Bulletin" new or amended regulations from all over the world as they are received. EPPO distributes the original regulations and translations thereof among its member countries. The tempo in which governments inform the two organizations might be accelerated. In an emergency an immediate and direct notification to all Services concerned would be appropriate. Whether a new ordinance should be published well in advance of coming into force is a matter for discussion. For long-distance transports it is only fair, but the waiting period may be exploited.

2. Regional Groups

In 1951 the cooperation of countries in northwestern Europe in controlling the Colorado beetle was consolidated, and the scope greatly extended by the establishment of the European and Mediterranean Plant Protection Organization (EPPO). Corresponding groups have come into existence—in 1954 through the Phytosanitary Convention for Africa South of Sahara (H.M. Stationery Office, Treaty Series No. 31, 1956) and the Plant Protection Agreement for the Southeast Asia and Pacific Region (FAO, 1956). Furthermore an Inter-African Phytosanitary Commission, an organization concerning the countries from Mexico to Panama, and organizations from eastern Europe to China have been established.

These organizations are not working only on legal matters. Direct assistance in the form of contact meetings, of visiting specialists, of sprayers and chemicals, and of financial support has been rendered to member countries when dangerous situations have arisen.

Countries in a group may have no natural barriers between them. For one small country an embargo against some agile pest would most likely result in disappointment, while an embargo common to several neighbors might be efficient and might simplify matters between such a group of countries. "Rationalize" is, perhaps, a happier term than "simplify." The postulated "simplicity" of an embargo is our last resort —or the first and temporary resort in cases of little known perils.

If growth conditions are similar and also import restrictions, the mutual relations are simpler. (Norway and Denmark run about even in the matter of soil-borne pests and have, therefore, agreed to dispense with the strict freedom-from-soil rules.) Other local agreements on disinfection of plants with earth balls are a result of neighborliness. On the whole, an exchange of views is a good basis for exchange of plants.

3. Origin of Plant Consignments

In the "Description of the Consignment" of the Rome Certificate the heading "origin" gives only a slight impression of the complications arising when both trade and quarantine administration are to be satisfied.

First, the identity of the goods presented for outport inspection with those inspected infield must be considered. It is easy enough when a Service can insert "as declared by sender," but this will not satisfy all importing countries; the decisive factor is the degree of responsibility assumed by the Service.

It has been customary to require that plants must not be imported unless grown at a prescribed distance from localities infested with, e.g., Colorado beetle (varying from 5 to 200 km.) or potato wart (0.5 to 20 km.); this is a handicap to the well-surveyed country compared to one which only files the casual notifications received. As methods of supporting field surveys with laboratory analyses develop, it will be found safer to lean on a direct investigation of the premises of production rather than on uncertain information of the surroundings.

The extreme diversity of plants and plant products bought and sold has, in fact, created what might be called a grading of indication of origin.

(1) The individual containers of seed potatoes (and of some fruits) are marked with a number indicating the premises, a custom favoring an improvement in quality.

(2) Flower bulbs, some seeds, and fruits are collected from several growers and graded according to quality forming uniform lots for sale; provided all areas concerned are inspected in due season (rejected products being properly disposed of) and again before shipping, it seems sufficient to indicate the grading center as origin.

(3) Table potatoes, most seeds, and fruits are not inspected in the field; as all containers are marked with the name of firm responsible for grading, the province (state, country) might be a sufficient description of origin.

(4) For nursery plants and propagation material, with its frequent virus infections, field inspection and testing is, in some countries, highly developed; when, moreover, all nurseries are thoroughly inspected, all rejected plants destroyed, and the areas found free from golden nematode, etc., nurserymen ought to be allowed to pool and grade their products. The original nursery can always be traced by means of a key number on the trees.

(5) The origin of seed lots is discussed above (Section II, B, 6).

Direct transit should normally be watched by the customs. If goods arrive in bulk and are broken up into several carloads or consignments (indirect transit), each one must be provided with a photocopy of the original certificate, signed by the Customs of the transit country, attesting that the quantity of goods and certificates correspond. In special cases the Phytosanitary Service may take over this function; in warm climates an eye must, perhaps, also be kept on the possibility of fruit flies escaping from wagons in transit.

In the case of re-export, when goods are stored (possibly divided or treated) and exported later, perhaps together with products of another origin, the Service may authorize original certificates or photocopies of these; a condition is, however, that the Service shall be in a position to keep track of the identity of the imported product and, if required, state that this has been kept in conditions which maintained its original freedom from diseases and pests (EPPO, 1957). The Netherlands forbid re-export of plants unless grown in the country for two full seasons, well separated from other plants in the nursery.

4. Owners' Interests

If a consignment is approved at outport inspection but rejected at the following inport inspection, the cause may be negligence, misunderstanding of the foreign requirements, fraudulent intercalation of low-grade material, or development en route (frost damage, powdery scab). Investigation may clear up the cause for rejection, but the important question then arises: Which of the two owners, the seller or the buyer, is to assume the responsibility of defraying the costs and bearing the loss. Does the consignment change owners on certification, on loading, or perhaps even on approval in the importing country?

It may be permitted to disinfect or regrade defective goods or to have them directed to industrial processing, but in many cases they must be destroyed on the owner's account or re-exported. A more tolerant land may be found, but if the certificate is retained or provided with a remark on rejection, new losses loom up. If dangerous parasites are in question, the passing on of information between Services should be a natural consequence of existing cooperation (EPPO, 1957).

On inspection, bulbs may be halved or potatoes cut into pieces, losses which must be reckoned with in trade costs; compensation may be given for losses of larger samples, e.g., for control fields.

Good packing is important for the condition in which the buyer receives plants and also for the inport inspectors. Waxing of plants impedes inspection and should be restricted to colorless wax for protection of budsticks, etc. The sale of plants in attractive plastic packings may also hinder inspection or fumigation and in some cases lead to condensation favorable to mold and rot; a way out is to export the plants in bulk, accompanied by the plastic bags, and to pack the individual plants after approval at inport inspection. Interference of this sort will cause irritation in business circles. When exporting plants, the seller may not wish to have his customer informed about his suppliers;

the solution is to use key numbers, known to the exporting service, on a small label tied to the trees. This may, incidentally, save some invoice documentation of eking out and pooling. One country has gone so far as to forbid peddling of nursery products in order to simplify matters for the regular trade.

Consulate visas accompanying phytosanitary certificates are required by some countries; since all national services know each other quite well, such visas are of no use in a phytosanitary respect; they are also a delay and an expense to the trade. Through good relations the trade and the Phytosanitary Service will find several common interests, both aiming at "few papers and true papers."

IV. Evaluation of the Quarantine System

If one of two countries, identical in all respects, adopted a strict quarantine system, while the other took things easy, it would be interesting to see—after a decade or two—how many foreign pests and diseases would have established themselves in both. The United States may be considered one of the best guarded countries, and the number of pests and diseased plants intercepted is amazing; on the other hand, lists of the hundreds of pests and diseases which actually have been introduced (McCubbin, 1954, p. 39) supply the skeptic with strong arguments.

When the aim is to keep out foreign pests, etc., it is natural for large, more or less self-supporting countries to ask: "What is the minimum of plants and plant products necessary for us to import?" But it is just as natural for countries of limited area and relatively long frontiers to ask: "How little interference with trade will be sufficient?" In fact, it is not only a question of area and isolation; both viewpoints are heard in both types of country.

When specialists meet, therefore, discussion is animated; it might seem as if plants were more important than man, when plant quarantine and human quarantine are compared. *Non curat minima praetor* is stressed against regulations appearing too trifling; again, San José scale and chestnut blight undeniably started as minima.

Common sense is frequently appealed to and applied; in fact it is soon worn out if not constantly reinforced by means of scientific research; biological investigations at home and abroad are necessary. Is the North American birch decline a climatic phenomenon or a virus disease against which to apply quarantine? Specialists in taxonomy of pests and fungi are indispensable to quarantine authorities, even if they try to hide their results from outsiders by means of constant changes of Latin names!

The regulations in force must always be a result of weighing pros and cons as advanced by the producers, the trade, and the quarantine authorities. Regulations and prohibitions should, without undue strain, be able to blend with the universal conception of justice.

REFERENCES

Appel, O., and H. Blunck. 1952. *In* "Handbuch der Pflanzenkrankheiten" (P. Sorauer, ed.), 2nd ed., Vol. 6. Paul Parey, Berlin and Hamburg.

Back, E. A., and C. E. Pemberton. 1916. Effect of cold-storage temperatures upon the mediterranean fruit-fly. *J. Agr. Research* **5:** 657–666.

Camp, A. F. 1956. Modern quarantine problems. *Ann. Rev. Entomol.* **1:** 367.

Canada. 1954/5. Destructive Insect and Pest Act. Destructive Insect and Pest Regulations. Ottawa.

Cochran, L. C., E. C. Blodgett, J. D. Moore, and K. G. Parler. 1953. How nurseries get virus-free stock. *Yearbook Agr. U. S. Dept. Agr.* **1953:** 152–158.

Christensen, J. J. 1942. Long distance dissemination of plant pathogens. *Publ. Am. Assoc. Advance Sci. No.* **17:** 78–87.

Colhoun, J. 1958. Club-root disease of crucifers caused by Plasmodiophora brassicae. Woron. *Commonwealth Mycol. Inst. Phytopathol. Papers* **3:** 1–108.

Commonwealth Mycological Institute. 1953. Distribution Maps of Plant Diseases. No. 80, 2nd ed. London.

Dumbleton, L. J. 1956. Digest of plant quarantine regulations. Suppl. II. FAO, Rome. pp. 1–20.

England Ministry of Agriculture. 1953. Diseases and pests on horticultural planting material. pp. 1–38.

England. 1955. The importation of plants order 1955. Statutory instruments 1955, No. 81. London.

European and Meriterranean Plant Protection Organization (EPPO). 1951. Report of the working party appointed to consider the danger to European countries of pests and diseases which might be introduced. pp. 1–15. Paris.

European and Mediterranean Plant Protection Organization (EPPO). 1954. Danger from seed-borne diseases. Paris. pp. 1–31.

European and Mediterranean Plant Protection Organization (EPPO). 1955a. Heterodera Rostochiensis Woll. Rept. Intern. Conf. Wageningen July 1955. Paris.

European and Mediterranean Plant Protection Organization (EPPO). 1955b. Report of the working party on phytosanitary regulations. Paris. pp. 1–48.

European and Mediterranean Plant Protection Organization (EPPO). 1957. Second report of the working party on phytosanitary regulation. Paris.

European and Mediterranean Plant Protection Organization (EPPO). 1958a. Pests and diseases of foodstuffs in store. pp. I-XXVII, 1–17. Paris.

European and Mediterranean Plant Protection Organization (EPPO). 1958b. Report of the international conference on oriental fruit moth and San José scale. Paris. pp. 1–15.

FAO. 1951. International plant protection convention. Rome. pp. 1–10.

FAO. 1955. Report of the advisory committee on international plant protection convention. Rome. pp. 1–23.

FAO. 1956. Plant protection agreement for the south-east Asia and Pacific region. Rome. pp. 1–16.

FAO. 1957a. Plant quarantine announcements. New Zealand. *Plant Protect. Bull.* **6:** 60–63.

FAO. 1957b. Plant quarantine announcements. Federal republic of Germany. *Plant Protect. Bull.* **6**: 27–29.

Germany. 1958. Biologische Bundesanstalt. Anleitung fur die Pflanzenbeschau, 3rd ed. Berlin. pp. 1–160.

Gram, E. 1957. Ursprungsfragen im internationalen Pflanzenverkehr. *Z. Pflanzenkrankh. u. Pflanzenschutz* **64**: 396–401.

Hunt, N. R. 1946. Destructive plant diseases not yet established in North America. *Botan. Rev.* **12**: 593–627.

Large, E. C. 1940. "The Advance of the Fungi." Jonathan Cape, London.

LeClerg, E. L. 1953. Seed-borne plant pathogens. *Plant Disease Reptr.* **37**: 485–492.

Ling, L. 1952. Digest of plant quarantine regulations. FAO. *Development Paper No.* **23**: 1–164.

Ling, L. 1954. Digest of plant quarantine regulations. Suppl. I. FAO, Rome. pp. 1–100.

McCubbin, W. A. 1946. Preventing plant disease introduction. *Botan. Rev.* **12**: 101–139.

McCubbin, W. A. 1954. "The Plant Quarantine Problem." Copenhagen, pp. 1–255.

Neergaard, P. 1949. Orienterende undersøgelser vedr. frøsmittens betydning for angreb of ærtesyge (*Ascochyta pisi* Lib.) i marken. 13. aarsber. fra I. E. Ohlsens Enkes plantepatologiske laboratorium. Copenhagen. pp. 13–19.

Ordish, G. 1953. "Untaken Harvest." London. pp. i–xi. 1–171.

Orton, C. R. 1931. Seed-borne parasites. *West. Va. Univ. Agr. Expt. Sta. Bull.* **245**.

Pierce, W. D. 1917. "A Manual of Dangerous Insects Likely to be Introduced in the United States through Importations" U. S. Dept. Agr., Washington, D. C.

Shepherd, D. R. 1957. Eradication of mediterranean fruit fly in Florida. *FAO Plant Protect. Bull.* **5**: 101–103.

Sherman, R. W. 1957. Co-operation of world tourists sought in plant quarantine enforcement. *FAO Plant Protect. Bull.* **5**: 89–90.

Smith, H. C. 1957. New Zealand notes. *Commonwealth Phytopathol. News* **3**: 10.

Stakman, E. C., and J. G. Harrar. 1957. "Principles of Plant Pathology." Ronald Press, New York.

Stevens, N. E. 1949. Characteristics of some disease-free ornamental plants. *Science* **110**: 218.

Stevenson, J. A. 1926. "Foreign Plant Diseases." U. S. Dept. Agr., Washington, D. C.

Trumble, H. C. 1946. "Blades of Grass," p. 35. Georgian House, Melbourne.

Van Vloten, H. 1944. Is verrijking van de mycoflora mogelijk. *Tijdschr. Plantenziekten* **50**: 49–62.

CHAPTER 10

Cultural Practices in Disease Control

RUSSELL B. STEVENS

Department of Botany, The George Washington University, Washington, D. C.

I. INTRODUCTION

If we are to be completely honest with ourselves, and at the same time willing to depart from the rules of orthodox journalism, the boundaries of this chapter must be defined in the negative. Inevitably, one must include all those means of disease control not clearly reserved to other, more specifically delimited, categories. "Cultural" must then be inter-

357

preted in the broadest possible terms, to include measures involving
agricultural cropping practices, harvesting and storage methods, tillage,
crop rotation, soil management, resistant varieties, land-use planning and
all of like nature. One must seek to bring order within a miscellany—and
we are encouraged to think that this can be accomplished.

Plant disease, that is, pathogenic plant disease, is three- perhaps
four-dimensional. One dimension is represented by the pathogen—virus,
bacterium, fungus, nematode—and forms the subject matter of Volume
II of the present treatise. A second dimension, the host plant, is treated
in Volume I. The complex of diverse factors comprising the environment
represents the third dimension—and it can be argued effectively that by
introducing a time factor (disease development or epidemiology) it
achieves a fourth.

Disease control, it may now be perceived, interestingly parallels the
above concept. Traditionally, the popular means of combating pathogenic diseases have been: (1) application of agricultural chemicals to
foliage, seeds, and soil, and (2) adoption of resistant crop varieties. The
one aims almost entirely at the pathogen; the other concerns itself as
exclusively with the host. Cultural control, our immediate consideration
in this chapter, has these same facets, but centers chiefly about the
environment—the environment as it affects crop and pathogen, the interaction of crop and pathogen, and their interactions through time.
Chemical control and disease resistance thus tend to become essentially
one-dimensional, monolithic problems; cultural control often becomes
three- and four-dimensional. Small wonder that the issues are less clearly
drawn and that, as a general rule, it enjoys less popular understanding
and support.

Having these considerations in mind we should be willing to accept
the fact that cultural measures cannot be dissected with the conceptual
cleanliness of other approaches. Indeed, too rigorous an attempt to do
this may lead to unsought and unwanted difficulties. We deal with a
sort of network, and just as a net is distorted when a single cord is
arbitrarily drawn into a straight line, yet forms a pleasing symmetry in
its undisturbed whole, so the consideration of cultural control measures
cannot be on a strictly one-at-a-time basis. Rather, in the discussion to
follow, it is primarily the viewpoint, not the basic maneuver itself, which
changes as the outline unfolds.

II. GENERAL CONSIDERATIONS

Cultural control is not without its rationale, its useful generalizations,
its problems, and its promise. Recognition and understanding of these
form a foundation upon which a consideration of specific measures can
most surely rest.

A. *Nonpathogenic Diseases*

Cultural measures directed against pathogenic diseases operate indirectly through effects on host or pathogen; against nonpathogenic, abiotic, or physiologic diseases they directly alter the environment. And the over-all importance of the nonpathogenic diseases must not be underestimated. Deficiencies or excesses of soluble materials, irregularities and extremes in such factors as temperature, moisture, and light, and toxic gases in soil and atmosphere decrease by a very large factor the health and productivity of crops, forests, and ornamental plants. Considering disease to be "any impairment of structure or process of sufficient intensity or duration noticeably or permanently to affect the normal development of the plant (Stevens and Stevens, 1952)," we cannot easily establish just what proportion of plant disease is attributable to nonpathogenic causes, but it can scarcely be less than half. Stakman and Harrar (1957, pp. 49–64) present a useful summary of what they term "inanimate" causes, to which the interested reader is referred, although they make no attempt to establish the relative importance of these several factors or their total effect.

More often than not, once the cause or causes of nonpathogenic diseases are established, the sort of measures needed to alleviate them are self-evident. The relationship is direct, even in those cases where other considerations—technical or economic—preclude their implementation. In short, the problem is how to modify the environment so as to minimize the damage done to the plant species in question. Final action is almost always predicated on assessments of cost, feasibility, secondary effects on other species, and related management problems.

All too often the causes of diseases thought to be of inanimate nature are imperfectly known. Some, such as the brown root rot of tobacco, later prove to be pathogenic (in this case one of the root-invading "meadow" nematodes). Others, such as "frenching" in tobacco, prove to be the immediate result of inanimate, nutritional imbalance, but linked in turn to the activities of the soil microflora. Still others, such as a form of "soil sickness" common in greenhouses, are controllable through measures worked out by strictly empirical means, while the cause continues to elude the pathologists concerned (Mader, 1947). It has been found that the gradual decline of greenhouse-grown plants may be halted if the "sick" soil is thoroughly drenched with dilute sulfuric acid and that—provided the plants are protected by asphalt-coated collars—it is not even necessary to remove them from the bench during treatment. Yet every indication to date has failed to show that cultural practices, pathogenic organisms, or nutrient supply are responsible for the situation, and sterilization of the affected soil is to no avail.

B. Basis of Cultural Control

1. Environment and Disease

Environment, the third dimension in the complex biological phenomenon we call pathogenic disease, is now recognized as critically important. This has not always been so, for its full realization awaited the investigations of the late 18th and early 19th centuries, which clearly established the pathogenic nature of many plant maladies. The pendulum thereafter swung, as is so often the case, overly far in emphasizing the causal organism. By the mid-30's the importance of environment in disease development was coming into its own, as attested by Foister's early review article and later supplement (1946), Wilson's bibliography of nearly four thousand titles (1932), and similar publications. Interest continues unabated to the present, and environment is now a fully established element of all serious studies of epidemiology and disease development, be it microorganism (Allen, 1954) or virus (Bawden and Pirie, 1952), and extends through the entire spectrum of extrinsic and intrinsic cultural control measures (see Sections IV and V).

Because environment is demonstrably the most powerful controlling factor in pathogenic disease, alteration of the environment is equally the most potent weapon available to man in his efforts to obtain for himself the maximum productivity from his crops. And attention to the environment is but another term for cultural control. His problem is to identify the environmental factors which most profoundly affect the disease in question and to develop techniques which can be employed to ameliorate these factors. That this is often not easy, and at times unattainable, does not lessen the cogency of the argument.

2. Direct and Indirect Effects

As noted earlier, cultural practices aimed at alleviating nonpathogenic diseases are characteristically direct. Many of those employed against pathogenic diseases are equally so, particularly as they pertain primarily to the diseased host plant—roguing, sanitation, eradication, storage management, heat therapy, and shifts to resistant varieties; or primarily to the inoculum—disease-free seed, certification of propagating material, indexing, soil sterilization, flooding, eradicant sprays, and disinfectants. But others are more or less indirect—vector control, nutritional and other soil amendments, dispersal, isolation, crop rotation, elimination of alternate and reservoir hosts, and establishment of trap and buffer crops. In these last instances, the grower seeks, by manipulating one or more factors in the chain of events and circumstances, to retard the development of disease and lessen its eventual impact. By destroying the vector of bacterium, virus, or fungus, he seeks to intercept the movement of inoculum. By soil amendment he seeks sometimes to abet host resistance, sometimes to inhibit pathogen growth. By dispersal, isolation, or barrier crops he seeks to prevent the juxtaposition in time and space of susceptible crop and virulent pathogen. Measures such as these are often effective, sometimes dramatically so, but they are indirect, and thus inherently more difficult to identify, develop, and administer.

Disease control by cultural measures is not only frequently indirect, even obscure, but it is very likely to involve more than one operation, to require the joint application of two or more practices. Thus attention not to seeding rates alone, but to seeding rates, timing, and depth of sowing are required for results to be satisfactory. Care in storage avails but little unless preceded by care in harvest. Vector control must often be supplemented by destruction of weed hosts and sanitation within the crop. In our discussion of specific measures later in this chapter we attempt to focus on each of many possible approaches one by one, but with the full realization that, in practice, they do not operate in a vacuum and that crop production, by whatever combination of means proves practicable, is the ultimate goal.

It is perhaps not an unwarranted oversimplification to say that the basic approach in cultural control is to invoke every aspect of cropping practice which will promote crop growth; inhibit or otherwise obstruct the pathogen; avoid, delay, or lessen the impact of disease, should it ensue—and rigorously to discover and eliminate any and all practices which operate in the opposite direction. To the extent that these steps can be knowingly instituted, so much the better, but it is a rare individual indeed who does not, wittingly or unwittingly, employ certain practices calculated to control disease.

3. Cultural vis a vis Other Methods

In public and private favor, two methods of disease control stand out head and shoulders above all others (see N. E. Stevens, 1940). First rank must clearly go to application of fungicidal (and bactericidal) chemicals to foliage, seeds, and soil; next most popular is the development and introduction, through plant breeding and selection programs, of disease-resistant varieties. These two approaches have little in common, it is true, being directed at different facets of the crop-pathogen-environment complex, and finding their greatest popularity in different sectors of the agricultural structure. But in the aggregate they dominate the time, attention, resources, and enthusiasm of growers, professional plant pathologists, and the lay public. What, then, is the status of cultural measures as contrasted to the "big two"?

It is instructive here to turn to the experience of entomologists concerned with forest insects (Graham, 1951). Some, at least, recognize that to accomplish "preventive control" it is always necessary to manipulate factors of "environmental resistance," and that the interrelations between forces of production and resistance are more often than not highly complex. Graham insists that even with DDT available in large quantities and application methods both cheap and efficient, prevention is still less expensive in the long run and more effective than direct control. He warns us lest in our enthusiasm for chemicals we blind ourselves to the fact that although the current crop of organisms can be poisoned, conditions favoring outbreaks cannot be thus directly changed to our advantage, that never will all the individuals of a species be killed nor can harm to other species be always avoided. After all, we must agree that whether it be a population of insects or of plant pathogens, it can be held in check only when destructive forces at least equal reproductive capacity and when the situation is stabilized at a relatively low population level, such that damage is not unduly severe. With but slight modification these strictures apply directly to our use of fungicidal sprays or dusts.

It is, likewise, no disservice to the recognized contribution of the plant breeder and to the importance of disease resistant varieties to remind ourselves that each new achievement in this direction wins but a temporary skirmish in the never-ending war with plant pathogens. Ceres wheat, Victoria oats, and a host of less publicized varieties stand as monuments to the ability of the pathogenic species to mutate, multiply, and survive. We are needlessly risking our welfare if we rely solely on chemicals and resistant varieties, alone or in concert, and ignore the third and fourth dimensions—environment and disease development—and the cultural practices by which matters in these dimensions can be turned to our advantage.

Chemical treatments to control disease are furthered or hindered by cultural practices, and resistant varieties vary in success, depending on how they are managed in the field. There is no necessary conflict between cultural and other measures, and the wisest course lies in a well-informed, objective welding together of all possible offensive and defensive aspects into a coordinated, integrated whole.

No association is more inextricably close than that between cultural measures and biological control (see Chapter 13). In many instances we are not yet even certain whether the ultimate effectiveness of a given practice is the one or the other, particularly when available evidence suggests that the immediate result is so to alter the environment that growth of nonpathogenic organisms is accelerated at the expense of pathogenic forms.

Finally, when other, more orthodox methods fail, grower and pathologist turn, if only for interim relief, to the diverse measures of cultural and environmental nature.

C. Economic Considerations

In every aspect of disease control economic considerations come to bear importantly, none more so than in the application of cultural measures. As N. E. Stevens (1938b) pointed out some years ago, outside the field of ornamentals, control should cost demonstrably less than losses from the disease are likely to be. "However much we may enjoy experimenting with seemingly impracticable problems and solutions, we owe it to our profession not to urge the use of any control method unless it meets this economic test." He suggests that to make this possible we need much more accurate information on the actual cost of disease and insect losses. He regards some of the dollar estimates of losses from plant diseases and insects published earlier as "little short of fantastic," which did plant pathologists very little good with the public or with their colleagues in other fields of biology. "In their zeal for demonstrating their ability to solve difficult problems of disease control, plant pathologists seem a little like the old time volunteer firemen who were more interested in beating the other outfit to the fire and putting on a good show there than in saving the building. Pathologists seem sometimes to forget that the real purpose of agriculture is not to control plant diseases but to grow profitable crops. For growing profitable crops, disease prevention is often better than disease treatment."

Informative discussions of the economic aspects of plant disease losses are to be found in a recent monograph by Chester (1950) in the classic bulletin published some years ago by a committee of the California State Agricultural Experiment Station on plant quarantine problems (Smith et al., 1933) and Brooks' (1935) sound treatment of botanical aspects of food storage and marketing.

1. Criteria

Because the relationship between outgo and income, as it pertains to cultural control, is more obvious than in the case of better-known alternative measures, it is far more likely to be taken directly into consideration. Not only does this prove true, but one suspects that rather more stringent criteria of economic feasibility are applied to cultural practices than to chemical control measures or the use of resistant varieties. It is not uncommon to find sprays and dusts recommended, and applied, in situations where the economic soundness of the program is not clearly demonstrated—if, indeed, considered at all. But only rarely do we see cultural procedures undertaken until there has first been serious thought given to whether it will "pay off" in increased crop value.

Naturally, those cultural measures which are synonymous with, or only a slight modification of, practices and programs already being carried out in the routine planting, tillage, and management of crops will cost little, if anything, and can be instituted without undue concern for their economic outcome. In a word, there are instances when, as the saying goes, "it doesn't cost anything to try." Our chief point is that, when it does cost something to try, the probable gain must be rather clearly shown before the grower can be persuaded to take the suggested steps. We will have more to say on this point shortly.

2. Crop Value

Granted that cultural control is forced, to a degree not encountered elsewhere, to meet the criterion of economic feasibility, we find a number of factors influencing the final decision. Not the least of these is the consideration of crop value. Understandably, the higher the basic worth of the crop, the greater expenditure of time, effort, and money becomes justifiable in its defense. Other things being equal, one can wisely expend more upon a perennial than upon an annual crop, more upon ornamentals than other commercial crops, more upon horticultural than agronomic varieties. Forest stands, traditionally, are not subjected to measures having a high per acre cost. When they have been converted into processed materials, they (like all market produce) attain minimum volume and maximum value, and can be protected by the more expensive measures characteristic of storage and market pathology. Each case must be judged and decided upon its own merits—weighing crop value, control expense, and predicted benefits. Sometimes the answer will be a clear affirmative, sometimes negative—and too often in the uncertain intermediate gray zone. The obligation to make an honest assessment is inescapable.

3. Cost, Liability and Responsibility

Who, then, bears the cost of cultural control, once it has been undertaken? We can agree that it is the producer who must nearly always make the effort and foot the bill, however surely the costs will eventually be passed along to the consumer.

This is in sharp contrast to the situation as regards fungicidal control and adoption of resistant varieties. In the case of fungicides and other agricultural chemicals the cost of development (variously estimated at between $1,000,000 and $2,000,000 for each new spray, dust, or insecticide) has already been borne by society before the grower makes his initial purchase, in the form of research and development establishments, experiment station facilities, and professional manpower. Even more strikingly, virtually the whole cost of developing disease-resistant varieties is underwritten by public and private funds before the seed or propagating stock is ever made generally available for sale.

While it might be argued that costs are in the last analysis the liability of the producer, the point to remember is that the grower is aware of paying only a tiny fraction of the full cost of resistant varieties, a somewhat larger proportion of the costs of chemical control, and is likely to feel the full burden of cultural practices. To him, then, the last may well seem disproportionately expensive and correspondingly unattractive. Thus, while in actuality they are often the cheapest available control, cultural measures may and often are judged the most dear— even in those cases where total costs are reduced by combining one or more practices with each other or with agricultural programs unrelated to disease control.

Responsibility for instituting cultural controls is often, but by no means always, to be laid at the feet of the producer. In those instances where the immediate cropped area is affected, the grower may come to a decision with only his personal interests in mind. Vector control, on the contrary, almost always depends ultimately upon the attitude of a group of growers, and the individual has an obligation to cooperate which goes beyond his immediate prejudices. When weeds act as sources of inoculum, it may be necessary for governmental agencies to take action (Broadbent, 1957). Fixing responsibility, in the special instance where eradication of incipient infections is carried out as an adjunct to plant quarantine, becomes an interesting and difficult question of property rights. Smith *et al.* (1933) provide a particularly penetrating analysis of this situation in pointing out the important difference between requiring a grower to control a pest or disease which otherwise continually threatens his neighbor and requiring him to eradicate it. They argue that if a reasonably effective control is available at moderate cost, it can be assumed to be to the mutual advantage of all to adopt these measures and that the individual can be held liable if incidence on his property reaches a state which menaces others. He is not, however, fairly held responsible for the occurrence of disease or pest organisms on his property above and beyond ordinary methods of control, and ought to be compensated for any considerable cost in excess of this or for any destruction of property involved in eradication. In their opinion, compulsory control is a proper function of the police power, but compulsory eradication, since it deprives the grower of valuable property for the benefit of society, is an altogether different matter, and should be fairly compensated.

In countries whose resources are less than adequate or where industry and scientific agriculture are as yet underdeveloped, economic considerations operate to stress cultural control practices. In primitive agricultures throughout the world, what little disease control effort is made is entirely based on cultural measures; they are the first and the last resort of the producer who is unaided by public or private support and who farms without benefit of modern experimental research. Even in large nations such as the USSR, a survey of published literature clearly indicates above-average interest in cultural control, although this undoubtedly stems from lack of information and general unavailability of more orthodox materials and procedures rather than a special appreciation of the full potential of cultural methods.

D. *Obstacles to the Adoption of Cultural Measures*

A number of obstacles to the more widespread adoption of cultural control measures are implicit in the foregoing discussion. Two deserve further emphasis.

1. *Problems in Research*

All too frequently our research methods must be empirical, and progress is seriously hampered by the multiplicity of variables encountered—more, by far, than beset those who work with more generally recognized approaches. The latter research, too, is largely empirical, but demonstrable results are more easily come by, and much of the collected data less complex. In case after case the investigator of cultural techniques finds himself hampered in trying to see his way to a clear analysis, and is distressingly unable to duplicate his experimental results. This is not an inherent weakness of the research man, but a measure of the sheer complexity of the material circumstances with which he deals.

2. *Problems in Application*

Several problems arising in the application of cultural control measures further hinder their more widespread adoption. The impact of popular fashion is certainly paramount among these. Control by chemicals or by the use of resistant varieties has become so firmly fixed in the minds of pathologist, producer, and public that any alternative method is handicapped from the start. A thread of oppressive conservatism runs conspicuously through the whole fabric of agricultural research and practice, and militates against departure from orthodox and long-established procedures.

Application—demonstrably successful application, that is—very often requires cooperative action, and the achievement of this ranges from the difficult to the impossible. The grower who chooses to apply chemical substances to his crops, seed, or soil may—provided he exercises the most rudimentary safety precautions—do so with impunity and on his sole initiative, encouraged by the assurance that at least some direct benefits will accrue whether his neighbor on either side chooses to act accordingly or not. He may plant seed of resistant varieties or employ disease-resistant propagating material and confidently hope for some improvement in his situation whether or not his colleagues follow suit. But very often, as will be shown later, the whole success of an unorthodox measure rests upon its simultaneous, conscientious application by a group of individuals. This cooperation must often be initiated by law and bolstered by public opinion, for, as Racicot (see Stevens and Stevens, 1952, p. 176) has phrased it in referring to eradication programs, "without adequate legislation, a goodly number of people believe that in this free country of ours it is their duty to do as they please and others put it off until it is too late. The result is frequently failure."

Basic to the normal application (not necessarily the experimental study) of disease control procedures, but most conspicuously in the case of cultural methods, is the absence of rigid controls. It is very like taking medicine or not taking medicine, going to bed or refraining from it when afflicted with the common cold virus. For any particular instance or individual it is impossible to do both—and impossible to show, therefore, what would have occurred had the rejected alternative been adopted. The same is true of cultural control of plant diseases as applied to the farm, backyard, or forest. There is just no possible way, in most instances, of assessing how different the eventual outcome may be because of cultural measures undertaken. This inherent indecisiveness is highly prejudicial to the popularity of unorthodox practices among men who very humanly wish to see, or to think that they see, tangible gain for their efforts.

The far greater complexity of cultural control situations stands as an obstacle to adoption of these techniques because there is the ever present danger of worsening the existing damage. Spraying and dusting may not be the sinecure they are commonly held to be, but rarely are matters made worse (except perhaps by insecticides, where instances of unfavorable side effects are well publicized). The maximum loss is customarily no more than of money and labor. In the same sense, adoption of resistant varieties is, by and large, a thoroughly "safe" procedure, despite such dramatic failures as of the Victoria oat lines, which fell before a hitherto unknown *Helminthosporium* pathogen. But, in the web of interacting variables within which cultural measures must operate, it is not at all uncommon to encounter practices which have led to a harmful, rather than helpful, outcome. Adjusting the environment, which is in the last analysis the basis of cultural control, is at best a risky business. The wise and able producer, the one best able to understand and apply these special measures, is well aware of the hazards just pointed out and rightly reluctant heedlessly to risk them. The implications of this state of affairs for the professional research pathologist and extension worker are obvious.

Finally, many cultural control measures are by their very nature necessarily instituted well in advance of the appearance of disease. They do not, therefore, lend themselves as readily to use against diseases of the sporadic type as does chemical control, which can often be delayed until forecasting systems detect a specific threat. Economies in time and labor made possible by disease forecasting are not possible in relation to cultural control.

E. *Desiderata*

We have painted, thus far, a somewhat dismal picture of disease control by cultural methods, stressing the overwhelming complexities involved, the general reluctance of those concerned to think and act in this area, and the obstacles standing in the way of more widespread adoption. This pessimism has been wholly intentional, of course. At the same time we have tried to give some indications of future promise and have hinted at some of those aspects wherein cultural methods can and do compete very favorably with orthodox programs. If these promises are to be realized, what further work needs doing and what further information is essential?

1. *Biological Information*

Graham (1951) has given us, with specific reference to forest insects, to be sure, convincing evidence of the absolute indispensability of sound and thorough knowledge of the biological basis of disease as a prelude to cultural control and an indication as to the frame of mind in which this information must be sought. He points out, for example, that the white-pine weevil was for many years studied only where it was abundant, until it eventually dawned on someone to look in those areas where it was normally scarce. This new lead soon showed that where the trees grew from infancy in dense stands a good crop was invariably produced, whereas scattered plantings were always severely injured or worthless, and that pines growing intermixed with hardwoods were practically never attacked. This all pointed to obvious ways by which forest management could materially reduce damage.

A second major insect menace, the spruce budworm, is estimated to have destroyed, in a 10-year period, enough timber to have operated the then existing pulp mills for 40 years—a volume sufficient, piled as cordwood, to have encircled the globe at the equator 10 times. This problem also proved solvable through the same basic approach when it was shown that spruce-fir stands having, in the upper crown, less than 50% balsam were seldom killed because the newly hatched young, contrary to popular opinion, enter almost immediately into a period of hibernation. The balsam appears to serve as an ideal site for their survival. It was shown, further, that the pine form of the insect led to outbreaks only when the proportion of twigs bearing staminate cones was in excess of 20% of the total twigs on the tree. This proportion, in turn, depends on the root-to-crown ratio and is based on the relatively greater amounts of carbon than of minerals in large-crowned individuals. Once the complex interdependencies were established, control needed to be no more involved than the cutting out of scattered, large-crowned trees.

Satisfactory progress in the identification, development, and application of cultural control measures will be achieved only through similarly meticulous and persistent researches on the biology of disease in plants, coupled with close observation of the effects of empirical field tests and a genuine willingness to evaluate objectively the long-established, tradition-based practices of the commercial producer. Along with these studies it will be necessary to make major improvements in our ability to recognize and evaluate disease losses and, in pushing toward this goal, to accept every new technique which presents itself—such as, for example, aerial color photography (Colwell, 1956).

2. Historical Information

History, long neglected, might provide us with priceless keys to disease control, particularly by cultural measures, if we were to seek them diligently enough—history not of disease control; or of the identification, nomenclatural vicissitudes, or laboratory studies of the pathogen; but history of diseases *per se*. Plant pathology does not have, to its great detriment, any such monographic study of disease development, epidemic spread in prior times, geographic origins, and the like, as is to be found in the magnificent volumes on human medicine brought out by the Geomedical Research Station at Heidelberg (Rodenwaldt, 1952–1955). Plant pathology faces the same challenges as does public health, but plant pathologists neglect to use some of the tools in the hands of the

public health specialists. Contemporary experimentation plus observation
of current field incidence cannot always discover the circumstances in the
host-pathogen-environment complex which can lead to disease development. If we were to make careful studies of the origin, spread, and
fluctuations of diseases as entities—much as one would chronicle the
rise and fall of human civilizations and societies—against a background
of weather, crop varieties, farming methods, etc., we might find new and
highly promising leads toward effective control. After all, in looking at
past outbreaks we would at least know that the peculiar set of circumstances necessary to produce them had existed at that particular time
and place. Our problem would be to find out what factor was common to
many epidemics and thus of proved importance. Large (1940) has done
something of this nature for potato late blight, but the whole approach is
virtually unexplored and we shall be handicapped until it is attended to.

3. Cooperative Action

Cultural control in many situations is best carried out as a joint
venture—if large geographic areas are involved it must always be so
handled. Valleau (1953) has given us a good example of this in reference
to the blue mold of tobacco (*Peronospora tabacina*) in the eastern
United States. As he says, any informed tobacco grower can with comparatively little labor, be certain that his farm does not originate an
epidemic. The joint efforts of a majority of tobacco growers in the
region could reduce losses to the vanishing point. In the over-all picture, by eliminating the pathogen from Georgia, where it survives the
winter on living plants and as oospores could prevent the spore
showers to which tobacco in the Carolinas and Virginia are subject and,
hopefully, engineer the gradual disappearance of the disease in those
more northerly regions. Here is the extreme case of joint action, wherein
success in disease control in one area would be totally dependent on the
efforts—and joint efforts at that—of growers in a far distant sector.

A somewhat similar suggestion has been made with a view to reducing cereal rusts in the Indian plains by arbitrarily limiting plantings
in the nearby highlands (see Section V, C, 1). Neither of these plans has
been tried, and either might be challenged on biologic, economic, or
political grounds, but the principle of cooperative action is still valid.

III. ELEMENTS OF CULTURAL CONTROL

The diseased plant, the pathogen, and the diseased population form
the framework of this treatise and the point of view emphasized, in turn,
by each of its three volumes. Save in the exceptional case of individual

ornamental plants, disease control measures are directed toward the diseased population, but they may operate primarily in relation to the host plant, the pathogen, or the environment. Pathogenic disease is not an entity in itself—it is the sum of innumerable specific interactions between individuals of the pathogen population and individuals of the host population. Control of pathogenic disease is the net effect of the particular measures involved upon these specific interactions, a generalization which holds as true for the cultural approaches to disease control as for the more orthodox endeavors. The effect is general, the mechanism specific.

A. *The Diseased Plant*

N. E. Stevens (1949) has tabulated certain data in an effort to establish, with respect to ornamentals, the characteristics which lead to freedom from, or propensity for, disease damage. Disease-free forms are found to be predominantly of foreign origin, to have no near relatives within the native flora, and to be of no more than minor commercial importance, at times even decidedly rare. Disease-prone forms, by contrast, are characteristically native to the area, vegetatively propagated, and found in great abundance. Similar generalizations could be established for crops species, and forest plantings.

1. *Epidemiological Aspects of Host Defense Devices*

Chapters 11, 12, and 13, Volume I are especially pertinent to a consideration of cultural control. The reader is directed particularly to such matters as disease escape, the influence of environment on histological mechanisms of defense, hypersensitivity, the acquisition of apparent immunity to invasion by virus proteins, and the development in the host of tolerance to the presence of the pathogen (Hart, 1949). In the laboratory, greenhouse, and experimental plot these are problems in the physiology of host-parasite relations; in the field they become attributes of population dynamics and of disease control by cultural measures. As noted earlier in this chapter (see Section II, E, 1), it is of this basic stuff of biology that effective control must be compounded.

Cultural control, when it is specifically directed to the plants of the host population (see Section IV) works through the agency of host defense—be it histological (cuticle, work formation, lignification, hypersensitivity, etc.), avoidance, degree of receptivity, habit of growth, rate of maturation, or sheer fortuitous escape—and seeks so to alter the environment as to maximize the net effectiveness of these host defenses from the standpoint of the entire population.

2. *Host Predisposition in the Diseased Population* (see also Volume I, Chapter 14)

Mineral nutrition, temperature, moisture, light, soil reaction—these and related factors of the environment prior to inoculation act to predispose the host to invasion by pathogen or to minimize the likelihood of its becoming established, although Gäumann (1950, p. 362) insists that in general "disease proneness" is less markedly affected by external influences in plants than in man and that the pathogen therefore dominates plant pathological thought. In any event, whatever effect there is, is upon individual and specific plants, not upon the population. Only when attention is fixed on practical application does the emphasis shift from the biology of the individual plant and pathogen to the over-all effect of management practices upon that relationship. For example, water congestion and the role of guttation droplets in facilitating the entry and establishment of pathogens (Eide, 1955) is a problem, and a very stimulating one, in plant physiology; transferred to disease control, it becomes a problem in soil and air temperature, rainfall, humidity, wind, selection of varieties, cropping practices and, often, manipulation of irrigation water.

3. *Therapeutic Measures in Disease Control* (see also Volume I, Chapter 15)

The concept of therapy assumes that the pathogen has become established and that disease exists; therapy seeks to remove the affected portion or to exorcise the invader in such a way and in such good time that the host plant will resume essentially normal growth. Excision, pruning, chemotherapy, heat treatment, are representative measures directed to this end.

The distinction here between the biology of the individual plant and the control of disease in a population is one only of degree. The research investigator applies his techniques to one or to a small number of host plants; the grower attempts to find means whereby these same measures can, perhaps by simplification and mechanization, be imposed on large numbers of plants within a diseased population. For once he does not operate primarily through the environment, but, like his professional colleague, directly upon the individuals of the host population.

B. *The Pathogen*

Volume II examines plant disease from the standpoint of the pathogen. Control by cultural methods has its parallel aspects wherein the chief target is the inoculum (see Section VI) and where techniques are designed to take advantage of any vulnerable spots in the biological role of the disease-producing organisms: their reproduction, pathogenicity, or dispersal.

1. Reproduction (see also Volume II, Chapters 3–5)

Virus multiplication, the reproduction of bacteria, fungi, and nematodes, and seed formation by parasitic flowering plants contribute ceaselessly to the fund of inocula threatening host populations. Reproduction potential is reflected in the epidemic pattern of disease. Inoculum production is, in turn, much conditioned by environmental factors, especially of the microclimate and of the soil, and is, therefore, subject to alteration by cultural measures.

Individual cases differ. Some foliage diseases, serious when hosts are crowded and humidity in the immediate vicinity of the leaf surfaces is high, can be favorably altered by reducing the seeding rate. Others, such as the aphid-transmitted peanut rosette virus, are made worse by dry weather and can be partially controlled by sowing more thickly. In any event, plants requiring much moisture, if it be supplied by irrigation, do not normally suffer from pathogens requiring high humidity (Hunt, 1946).

Spore germination, viability, survival and longevity, resistance or sensitivity to extremes of light, temperature, drought—all these elements of the pathogen are in the last analysis influenced by the environment and hence affected by cultural practices.

2. Pathogenicity

Volume II of the treatise, particularly Chapters 6–8, treats of the mechanical and chemical means whereby pathogens invade their host species and of the interactions of pathogen, soil, and other microorganisms. Here, too, environmental factors play a part, and cultural control measures have a rightful place.

3. Production and Dispersal of Inoculum

Pathogen reproduction is a manisfestation of the biology of an individual organism—virus, bacterium, fungus, nematode, or flowering plant. Inoculum production is the cumulative result of reproduction of a given population of a pathogenic species and as such is reserved to Volume III (see Chapter 2). Data on spore discharge and movement is part of the biology of the fungus pathogen and properly belongs in Volume II; inoculum dispersal is a problem in epidemiology and its consideration as rightly appears in Volume III (see Chapters 3–6). Reference to those chapters will show the impact of the physical environment upon the amount of inoculum produced; on dispersal by insects, air, and water; and the importance of the biotic environment, as exemplified by alternate hosts, symptomless carriers, reservoir hosts, vector species, and the like.

4. Inoculum Control

Efforts to control the inoculum may be directed at the source (biological control, Chapter 13; or chemical soil treatment, Chapter 11), during the process of dispersal (through quarantines, Chapter 9), or at the site of the newly contacted host plant (chemical protection of foliage and seeds, Chapter 12). Cultural and related special measures, insofar as they operate against inoculum, lie mostly in a transitional zone not yet sharply delimited. Sometimes they aim primarily at the site of production, sometimes at the site of invasion, sometimes at both. In the detailed enumeration to follow, this variability will be clearly evident. Strategy and efficiency differ, and must be separately evaluated for each host-pathogen situation.

C. The Diseased Population

While it is entirely proper to consider a single plant as diseased, it is only when a population of plants is damaged to an appreciable extent by some agent or circumstance that disease, as the word is customarily thought of, exists. When this damage results from the interaction of two populations (host and pathogen), the study of their interaction is epidemiology, which van der Plank has treated in Chapter 7. Epidemiology, in its best established and most reliable form, leads to prediction and the benefits of forecasting (see Chapter 8).

The epidemic characteristics of a disease complex, whether swift moving or slow, whether of sporadic or regular occurrence, whether of relatively uniform or sharply fluctuating severity, influence greatly the extent to which cultural control measures prove practicable or (better said) whether a particular cultural control measure will prove practicable.

IV. Intrinsic Measures Directly Affecting the Individuals Comprising the Host Population

Of the cultural measures employed for disease control, some act primarily by direct action on the individuals of the host population. They are applied, in almost every case, to the diseased crop as a whole, but the effect is to alter in some physical, genetic, or physiologic way, the plants themselves.

Intrinsic measures are not always devoted exclusively to disease control—often this is an ancillary aspect. The following discussion can be extended to include, however, only the plant pathological implications of the subjects covered irrespective of whether they are primarily or incidentally devoted to that end.

A. *Cultural and Related Practices*

"Cultural" as used in the title, and thus far throughout this chapter, has been accorded the broadest possible meaning. As noted earlier, it incorporates all control measures other than imposition of quarantines, application of chemicals to soil, seed and foliage, disease-resistant varieties, and biological interference. In the present section, however, the word is employed in a much more restricted sense to refer to those management, tillage, and handling practices which relate to disease and disease control. We are attempting thus to see, in a few examples, how the often routine practices of the grower—what he does or doesn't do— are of importance in the eventual pathology of the crop in question. Oftentimes, disease control is only incidentally related to the procedure discussed; oftentimes it is not yet clearly understood why the observed results are obtained. That there can be a consistent, significant effect is pretty well established.

Growth habit, for instance, natural or as altered by pruning, influences the disease propensities of the host plant. Gäumann (1950, p. 258) reminds us that, in general, erect bean plants are less subject to anthracnose than squat, drooping varieties; what he refers to as "standard" roses are less troubled by black spot than bush roses; and potato varieties with open habit are less damaged by late blight.

Avoidance of heart rots of orchard, shade, and ornamental trees is largely a matter of preventing wounding, treating promptly such wounds as do occur, and stimulating growth to promote rapid healing (Wagener and Davidson, 1954). In the important area of market pathology of perishable fruits and vegetables, care in handling, all the way from harvest to eventual sale, is of first-rank importance (see Section 4, below).

Soil characteristics and tillage practices are among the factors involved in crop culture in the restricted sense used here. Gäumann (1950, p. 423) mentions the influence of heavy- and light-textured soils on potato tuber infection with late blight, and comments on the widely recognized importance of soil reaction and humus content. Fischer and Holton (1957), discussing wheat bunt, underscore the advantage of fall plowing of summer fallow, which has the effect of turning the smut spores to a depth below the usual placement of seed.

Soil, soil management, and cropping procedures have been convincingly implicated in the matter of root rots, a category of disease which has been long recognized as of major importance, but one only recently subjected to carefully controlled experimental research. Results have been disappointingly hard to come by, largely because a multiplicity of variables is inevitably encountered, but some very useful leads have been struck and the outlook for the future is encouraging. "Take-all" of cereals, particularly of wheat, is made worse by continuous cropping, by weed competition, and by low soil moisture (resulting in low fertility) primarily because diseased roots cannot be replaced rapidly enough. A dry topsoil seems particularly unfavorable (Simmonds, 1953). Irrigation can, of course, profoundly alter the entire pathology of a crop (Chester, 1947, p. 477).

Silvicultural methods can be enlisted in campaigns for pest and disease control. Graham (1956) discusses the regulation of insect populations through planned forest management, aimed chiefly at reducing the amount of land occupied by what he terms "hazardous" forest types, but with due regard for economic considerations and in harmony with efforts to control pests by chemicals. Much study has gone into the matter of dwarf mistletoe infestations as encountered in conifer stands of the southwestern United States. As noted earlier, the economy of standing timber largely precludes control measures other than those which can be instituted as an integral part of the over-all silvicultural program. Except in a relatively few cases, chemical control of forest diseases is prohibitively expensive and technically difficult, and the peculiar problems of forest tree breeding have seriously postponed the development of resistant varieties, even assuming that the bulk of our forest lands will eventually be occupied by set trees rather than naturally reseeded. According to Kuijt (1955) mistletoe infestation is most favored by selective cutting and least by clear cutting. He recommends: (1) cutting infested blocks first, where the block system of cutting is in vogue; (2) selection of seed trees free of the parasite; (3) removal of infested trees first in thinning operations; and (4) where possible, cessation of logging and pruning operations during the parasite fruiting season.

Burning has proved valuable in scattered situations as a means of reducing disease damage, wholly aside from its routine use in seedbed soil sterilization. As N. E. Stevens (1938a) pointed out in a review some years ago, destruction of diseased plant parts by burning in order to reduce inoculum has been very often recommended, although perhaps less generally practiced. A 5-year study of the brown spot needle blight of longleaf pine seedlings by Paul Siggers has shown that a single fire greatly reduces the disease for a season or two, and that, once the seedlings are established, controlled winter burnings at three-season intervals is effective as a control in areas devoted to timber.

More recently, Hardison (1948) has recorded control of blind-seed disease of perennial rye grass (caused by *Phialea temulenta*) in Oregon for at least 1 year by burning straw and stubble. He does not recommend this as the only action. Indeed, a complex of measures is indicated: (1) elimination of badly diseased fields through inspection of seed samples; (2) where possible, ageing of seed for 2 years; and (3) planting seed to a depth of ½ inch or more, completely covered, to prevent emergence of the apothecia.

Tobacco blue mold or downy mildew furnishes another good example of control, largely cultural, achieved by joint employment of a considerable number of individually unrelated measures (McGrath and Miller, 1958). Current recommendations include: (1) selection each year of a new seedbed site, with a view toward adequate air drainage, ventilation, and surface water runoff; (2) sterilization by steam, burning, or chemicals of seedbed sites when new ones are not available; (3) destruction of holdover plants; (4) watering, when necessary, in forenoon only; and (5) field sanitation, i.e., removal and destruction of diseased plants and plowing under or cutting down of all plants remaining after harvest.

Seldom, if ever, are cultural control measures encountered which are entirely independent of other practices; often they are part of a whole fabric of activities which, in the aggregate, suffice to produce a dependable crop. We cite the above examples not as special instances but as illustrative of the normal state of affairs; similar relationships hold, even though unspecified, in most that is to follow.

1. Removal of Plants

Roguing, so-called, or the systematic removal of diseased individuals from a host population is an obvious and often practiced control procedure. Because it is characteristically a hand operation, it involves, on any extensive scale, undeniably high labor costs. While frequently recommended, roguing has fallen rather out of favor with the advent of control measures which are more specific and supported by more experimental evidence. Of itself, it is doubtful whether roguing ever achieves a degree of control which would be fully satisfactory. This is in part because by the time disease symptoms are so conspicuous as to indicate removal of the plant, inoculum will have spread to nearby healthy individuals. By far the most appropriate use of this device is as an adjunct to other practices, as in the production of virus-free propagation stock, as a preliminary to chemical disease control in small plantings, and in combating diseases of forest and shade trees.

Akin to roguing is the removal of volunteer plants, usually holdovers from the crop of the preceding season. These serve not infrequently as a source of inoculum threatening the new host population, importantly as a means whereby pathogenic organisms survive the unfavorable environment of the winter season, as a bridge for nutritionally fastidious organisms between successive cropping periods, and as a site for the development of viruliferous vector populations. In many—but not all— ways, volunteer plants play the same role as do weeds and other reservoir hosts (see Section VI, B, 1), and their consideration overlaps somewhat the discussion of sanitation and eradication (see below, subsection A, part 5).

2. Physical Alteration of Host Individuals

At times a physical alteration of the host plant, rather than its removal, is indicated as a means to disease reduction or control. Among these treatments are girdling, poisoning, root severing, desiccation, and defoliation.

Root rots of woody species furnish interesting examples. Berkeley, in a 1944 review which covers control by varietal resistance, crop rotation, biological interference, fertilization, soil disinfection, green manuring, etc., recounts how the *Armillaria* root rot of tea in Nyasaland is reduced by ring-barking trees before they are felled in the process of land clearing. This prevents passage of carbohydrate from leaves to roots and—to be most effective—should be carried out just before trees break into leaf, thus accelerating the rate at which roots die. Trees which die slowly should be felled 1 year after ringing. Similar advantages have been gained in Ceylon as a protection for tea against *Poria* in jungle clearings, and in Nyasaland for tung plantations. The efficacy of these steps can be further enhanced by injecting stumps with sodium arsenite, which hastens decay and invasion by saprophytic fungi at the expense of pathogenic fungi—in some sense, therefore, a biological control measure.

Wagener and Davidson (1954) argue that methods of control of decay feasible for forests must usually be applied to stands of trees rather than to individual trees. This follows from the fact that forests are not sufficiently valuable to justify the kind of care usually given other woody perennials. At first glance, this would seem to rule out physical alteration in forest stands, but selective thinning and related silvicultural measures can prove effective, and rot can be much reduced by thinning hardwood sprouts before a bridge of heartwood forms at the base. Low-origin sprouts and those from small stumps should be retained rather than those of high origin and from large stumps. Wagener and David-son advise pruning of crop trees while the branches are still small, which —aside from improving timber quality—reduces decay in young conifer stands by fungi such as Polyporus anceps, which enter through dead side branches.

Colonization of stumps by butt rot fungi entering through roots (which may then lead to invasion of adjacent living roots) may be prevented by girdling and exhausting food supplies. Experiments on artificial colonization of stumps by saprophytic-decay fungi holds promise, and early infection of conifers may be reduced by setting the roots at planting time in such a way that taproot formation is hindered. But these workers conclude that, for some conditions, "conversion to mixed stands is probably still the most practical means" and that the reasons for the natural arrestment of decay and the natural dying out of infections need to be better understood.

Forest tree diseases have frequently aroused much public interest in the United States, none more so than oak wilt. For some years it has been observed to progress slowly through local groves of oaks and to spread over greater distances in a most erratic fashion. The cumulative efforts of workers at a number of experiment stations have established that tree-to-tree spread is accomplished in large measure by vascular transport of inoculum across root grafts and that overland spread is due to the activities of certain beetles and is associated with formation by the fungus of what are called "mats" beneath the bark. The former has been controlled in experimental areas by poisoning a strip of trees immediately surrounding the infected individuals and (more interestingly perhaps) by passing a large, subterranean, tractor-drawn knife between diseased and adjoining healthy trees in an effort to sever the root connections (Kuntz and Riker, 1950). Mat formation by the oak wilt fungus—and consequent overland spread—is substantially reduced by early felling of the wilted trees, by deep girdling (preferably in the first part of the summer), or by application of sodium arsenite to a band of exposed heartwood (Gillespie et al., 1957; Morris 1955).

Resort to destruction, defoliation, and desiccation as adjuncts to disease control has in the main awaited the development of special-action chemicals and of means for their cheap and effective application. Thus, as N. E. Stevens and Nienow point out (1947), under certain conditions a major portion of infection of tubers with potato late blight occurs at the time the potatoes are dug, chiefly, if not solely, if the tops of the plants are green at that time. It has been long recognized that little or no rot occurs in storage when the potato plants are completely killed by blight prior to digging. With this in mind, and particularly since better control of both disease and insects have in recent years materially prolonged the period during which the foliage remains actively growing, methods have been worked out whereby the above-ground parts are killed by an herbicide and allowed to dry out thoroughly before the crop is harvested. One has only to visit the potato-growing sections of Long Island, New York, or Aroostook County, Maine, to observe the widespread adoption of this highly successful procedure in the spectacle of field after field of dead brown plants in an otherwise green and luxuriant landscape. As presently carried out, destruction of potato vines is thought not only to prevent infection of tubers by the late blight fungus but to reduce spread of virus diseases. It is not routinely done, however, in the Far West, where the vines are allowed to remain alive in order to shade the soil and reduce losses from heat injury (Addicott and Lynch, 1957).

Defoliation is of demonstrated value in reducing disease and pest damage. In cotton culture, defoliation by calcium cyanide seems to induce lodged plants to return to an erect position, and to reduce boll rot and the injuries of leaf-feeding insects. When the leaves of nursery stock being dug preparatory to storage or shipment are defoliated, diseases normally associated with foliage are reduced. Several means are available: (1) hand beating; (2) application of ethylene gas to stored stock, either from tanks or by including a bushel of apples for every 400–500 cubic ft. of the chamber; or (3) in the case of California roses, by allowing sheep to graze prior to lifting (Addicott and Lynch, 1957).

Field defoliation has been advocated as an aid in bacterial canker of stone fruits, which invades the host through freshly exposed, incompletely healed leaf scars. The procedure of choice is to defoliate the trees in mid-autumn and then protect them with a single spray application until leaf scars are completely healed.

3. Sanitation and Eradication

Sanitation has been advocated repeatedly as a means of reducing the amount of inoculum to which the host population is exposed. In this sense its consideration might be postponed to Section VI, but, while the final aim is inoculum reduction, the sought-after result is achieved through actions immediately involving the host plant proper. Sanitation as a direct means of disease control and as an adjunct to use of chemicals can be summarized in the following terms (Stevens and Stevens, 1952, pp. 166–167):

"One of the simplest of all these means is, of course, removal and destruction of diseased plants or plant parts. In the home garden, especially the ornamental garden, and in the greenhouse, this is of far greater utility than is generally realized. In fact, the very obviousness of the method is one of its greatest weaknesses—it is not exciting; it is not expensive; and makes no appeal to the imagination. Sanitation is also of utility in the orchard, primarily for such diseases as black rot of apple, and some stone fruit viruses.

"The effectiveness of this type of sanitation in the home garden is due to the fact that infection is almost always heaviest in the immediate vicinity of a source of infection [see also Wilson and Baker, 1946]. Falling off in concentration of spores or other inoculum is at first very rapid. At greater distances the rate of falling off is much slower, but the concentrations are so much lower that this is of less practical importance.

"As sanitation is the simplest of all methods of attempting disease control it may well have been one of the first attempted.

"In many cases sanitation is of unquestioned utility as an aid to disease control by spraying. If the amount of inoculum can be markedly reduced by relatively inexpensive sanitation procedures the likelihood of achieving commercially adequate control by spraying is vastly enhanced. There are many instances of this well known to growers and to plant pathologists. Perhaps there is no better example than black rot of grapes. Given reasonably favorable conditions this disease is readily controlled by standard spray schedules. As a matter of fact it serves as an unusually satisfactory subject for demonstrating the efficacy of spraying. However, if the disease has been severe in the previous season such control is usually possible only if, when the grapes are pruned, adequate precautions are taken to remove and destroy dead portions of the vines which bear fruiting bodies of the black rot fungus. This involves destruction of all mummies and dead branches. Tendrils, even, must be removed from the wires; a step most easily accomplished by burning.

"The same general principles apply to apple blotch and black rot, and to brown rot of stone fruits. Keitt's work on eradicant sprays (see also VI, A, 3) for the control of apple scab is essentially an attempt to cut down the amount of inoculum present during the period of rapid growth of the host plant."

Sanitation takes many forms; sometimes the removal of infected plant parts and sometimes the removal of the body or reproductive parts of the pathogen, as the apple rust galls from cedar, conks of wood rot fungi, leafy mistletoe, and corn smut galls (Chester, 1947, p. 480). It may be cleanliness in the literal sense, as the avoidance of dissemination of tobacco mosaic virus on the hands of workers through use of disinfectants (Chester, 1947, p. 477); or "housekeeping" care, as when leaf mold and surface litter, in wet seasons, are removed from tea plantations to prevent the spread of the *Rosellinia* pathogen (Berkeley, 1944). It may be employed directly in the control of smut diseases, as by the burning of diseased stubble against flag smut in Australia, reduction of corn and sugar cane smuts, excision of infected buds in combating anther smut of carnations, or mechanical removal of bunt spores from seed grain by special machines (Fischer and Holton, 1957); or indirectly as an adjunct to other cultural control measures for the production of virus-free cabbage seed in western Washington (Pound, 1946). It may be achieved by routine, self-evident techniques, or by such unique procedures as that cited by Stevens and Nienow (1947) in connection with *Sclerotinia* on lettuce. In this last instance, lettuce harvesting methods in the Salt River Valley of Arizona leave obviously diseased heads, bearing their abundant sclerotia, in the field. At least part of the time sheep are allowed to pasture on these fields—with the result that the vast majority of the inoculum is consumed and digested.

Eradication differs from sanitation only in the matter of degree; it aims at the *complete* removal of diseased plants or infective material. Summarizing the situation several years ago, Stevens and Stevens (1952) said: "The earliest successful eradication campaign of which the writers have found record is that against the Colorado potato beetle in Germany in 1875. . . . A very limited area was given such a drastic clean-up that the pest never reappeared. A second introduction was reported in 1934 and the insect again eradicated at a cost which appeared trifling when compared with the value of the German potato crop.

"The first apparently entirely successful eradication campaign conducted on a large scale in the U. S. A. was that against citrus canker. Of this work Fawcett says, 'the eradication of this disease in Florida and other Gulf states and in South Africa, after it had become well established on susceptible varieties and in spite of great difficulties, is perhaps one of the most remarkable achievements in the history of plant disease control. In Florida citrus canker was found at various times on 515 properties scattered through 26 counties . . . it was necessary to destroy 242,502 grove trees and 2,740,850 nursery trees.

"Complete eradication of at least two other tree diseases has also been achieved in the U. S. A. These are larch canker which was recently introduced into New England and eradicated by destruction of all infected trees, and witches' broom on Japanese cherry eradicated from the District of Columbia and adjacent Maryland.

"On the other hand there have been three major attempts at eradication of tree diseases in the U. S. A. which were abandoned as impracticable. Accounts of the campaigns against the chestnut bark disease, and the Dutch elm disease will be found in a recent edition of texts in plant pathology published in the United States of America. Less emphasis was placed on eradication of white pine blister rust by this means, and attention soon concentrated instead on removal of the currant species."

Eradication of incipient infections as a means to increase the importance of plant quarantine is considered by Smith *et al.* (1933), who in so doing emphasize that quarantine is only a part of the machinery required for the prevention of permanent disease establishment and that it may often be unnecessary to discover the last individual pathogen and destroy it.

Yarwood, in a recent review of the powdery mildews (1957), cites several instances where a sort of eradication has been invoked as a control measure: of the lower leaves of tobacco in Southern Rhodesia; removal of apple shoots in Switzerland; elimination of *Rosa banksia* in control of apricot mildew; and the "clean-digging" of raspberries. In the last instance (Peterson and Johnson, 1928) powdery mildew is controlled in wide-row propagative plantings by digging all canes in the row each fall and permitting new rows to come up from the underground parts in the inter-row space. In this way rows are alternated each year and there are no above-ground plants in which the pathogen can overwinter. Fruit plantings, on the other hand, can be benefited by pruning tips and by removing stunted and late-season growth.

4. Harvest Practices

As harvest time nears, whether it be the approaching end of the annual growing season or the last few years of a maturing forest stand, it becomes increasingly important to be vigilantly attentive to the welfare of the produce. Not only is it too late to make adequate substitution in the event of disaster, but the investment represented is second only to that of the harvested item. After all, "of all losses caused by plant diseases those which occur after harvest are the most costly, whether measured in monetary terms or in man hours. Even a crop like corn or potatoes which is harvested on a large scale by machinery has cost society measurably more in storage than in the field. By the time a crop, particularly a highly perishable crop, has reached a city consumer its cost has multiplied. The consumer's apple, for example, is the producer's apple plus the cost of picking, packing, shipping, storing and handling, as well as sales cost, allowance for spoilage, and profits" (Stevens and Stevens, 1952, p. 191).

Preharvest inspection can provide information on the pathology of a given crop as it completes its growth and maturation and enters into the harvest phase. Particularly when coupled with experimental tests, reliable forecasts of postharvest conditions are attainable; this has been conclusively demonstrated by N. E. Stevens in relation to fruit rots of the cultivated cranberry.

Handling procedures and the care with which they are executed have a great deal to do with the ultimate welfare of agricultural commodities, particularly as they relate to the more perishable fruits and vegetables. "This is one of the simplest methods to explain and to understand. It is also one of the most difficult of all to maintain at a really effective level. So in everyday plant disease control it is easier to sell patented processes, machinery and appliances than to convince each of ten thousand (or even ten) strawberry pickers that he should keep his fingernails trimmed" (Stevens and Stevens, 1952). Studies in a number of regions and for a number of commercial fruits and vegetables leave no doubt that decay can be very substantially reduced by exercising care during harvesting. Some well-organized industries seem better aware of this situation than others, taking every precaution to insure minimum injury and introducing special methods for the express purpose of cutting down on loss of produce during shipping and storage.

Care in harvesting is of proved benefit in a number of situations. Strawberries picked early are less subject to fruit rots because the tissues, when cool, offer more resistance to mechanical injury (N. E. Stevens, 1938a), whereas vacuum cooling, presumably because it results in minor injuries, leads to high percentages of loss (DiMarco and Davis, 1957b). In Britain dry rot of potatoes (*Fusarium*) has been found to be worse following mechanical grading, which necessitates agitation on bare wire screens, and in the United States the better insect control achieved with DDT is partly offset in late-maturing varieties by an increased tendency to harvest immature tubers and consequently greater damage from bruising. Threshing of dry flax is considered injurious to seed coats, producing cracks so small as frequently to be invisible to the unaided eye, but leading to poor quality seed (Eide, 1955). Gaskill (1950) emphasizes the value of prompt removal of harvested sugar beets from the field, showing that if they wilt in the field before storage not only are respiratory losses increased but also, very sharply, loss from rotting. All of this strengthens the argument in favor of mechanical harvesting—with either direct loading from the harvester or immediate pickup from the windrows.

A number of food articles are subjected to immediate postharvest treatments prior to storage or shipment. Black rot of sweet potatoes, for example, is effectively controlled by a momentary dip in 1% borax solution (Martin et al., 1949). Bratley and Wiant (1950) list a considerable number of preshipping treatments, most of them chemical in nature: (1) borax; (2) addition of hypochlorite and free chlorine to the wash water; (3) painting stems of watermelons with copper sulfate and of pineapples with benzoic acid; and (4) application of sulfur dust for control of brown rot in defuzzed peaches. DiMarco and Davis (1957a) have demonstrated substantial reduction in *Botrytis* and *Rhizopus* rot of strawberry by adding mycostatin to the cooling water and of brown rot and *Rhizopus* rot of peaches with mycostatin and Dowcide as a postharvest dip (DiMarco and Davis, 1957b).

Citrus, a crop on which much research time and effort has been expended, furnishes instructive information on prestorage treatment (Miller, 1946; Hopkins and Loucks, 1948). Benefits of "curing" or exposure to CO_2 may be due to an accelerating effect on certain processes before the fruits enter low temperature storage. It has been discovered that in the early part of the season, when fruit is being held 60–70 hours for coloring, stem end rot (caused by *Diplodia natalensis*) is high, but that when coloring is discontinued later, there is a sharp drop in end rot and a marked increase in *Penicillium* mold. The latter can be avoided by inserting a curing period in place of the degreening, at a cost far overbalanced by the advantages gained.

Reports by Graham (1951), Wagener and Davidson (1954), and Verrall (1945) are representative of a very extensive literature on the relation of harvest and prestorage handling on quality of timber and forest products, and provide convincing evidence of the critical importance of this phase of operations. In general, heart rots are reduced by a preliminary light sanitation cut, which permits a rapid removal of defective trees, it having been shown that even when sporophores are formed on felled trees, they are less dangerous than when the hosts remain standing. Adjustment of cutting age, special salvage cuts in fire or storm-damaged stands, protection against fire and wounding, clear cutting where otherwise practicable, and, in species with an age-decay relationship, logging practices designed to minimize risk and to harvest the crop before heavy losses occur—each of these contributes to the eventual quality and quantity of the final product. Handling methods that permit treatment before infections become deep-seated are a useful adjunct to chemical control of fungi in air-seasoned lumber. Storage in water proves effective, provided the entire log is kept wet, although prolonged immersion may remove certain water soluble toxic extractives and increase susceptibility to fungus pathogens. Contributory measures are: quick utilization of logs, minimum delay between milling and chemical treatment, reduction of bulk-piling periods to a minimum, and good air-drying conditions—all of which become more important as the proportion of sapwood in the timber increases.

5. Storage Management and Market Pathology

Fully adequate coverage of postharvest pathology is not possible within the space limitations of this discussion. It has always been (more's the pity) a study apart from the body of plant pathology, but is particularly pertinent to a treatment of cultural control methods. Shippers and dealers are understandably reluctant to apply chemicals in appreciable quantities to a commodity that will soon be consumed—the very produce whose perishability poses troublesome market pathology problems. Thus deprived of one convenient approach to control, the pathologist, shipper, middleman, and retail merchant turn to cultural techniques.

General summaries of market pathology are available in varying detail in Stevens and Stevens (1952, Chapter 19), Stakman and Harrar (1957), Bratley and Wiant (1950), and Pentzer and Heinze (1954). Discussing transit losses, Stevens and Stevens (1952, p. 190) summarize Bratley and Wiant as follows: "In this paper is presented for the first time a summary of the losses as they occurred in a true random sample of all rail shipments of various commodities unloaded in a great terminal market. This was made possible by an agreement between a group of produce dealers in New York City and the U.S.D.A. whereby all car lots of produce received by members were inspected on arrival by a federal inspector. Of those commodities that were included in the study, 14 were fruits, and 31 were vegetables.

"The average decay per carload ranges from 0.6% in a few cars of nectarines to 2.9% in over 3,000 carloads of apples. Among the vegetables, the lowest average per cent of decay is for green corn, 0.1% of the relatively few cars inspected to well over 11% average decay in endives and lettuce. Perhaps only those who have actually worked in terminal markets will appreciate either the high accuracy of the certificates used in the study or the very large amount of work involved in this preparation. The writer's conclusion that on the basis of the figures given, 'decay of these forty-five commodities during rail transit to New York City totalled nearly 3,000 carloads annually' cannot fail to arrest the attention of anyone who is seriously interested in the national food supply."

This same report (Bratley and Wiant, 1950) lists blue mold, gray mold, Rhizopus, and bacterial soft rots as leading the transit and marketing phase; brown rot and apple scab as representative of pathogenic troubles originating prior to harvest but continuing into postharvest situations; blossom end rot of tomatoes, bitter rot of apples, and scald as major nonpathogenic problems; and bruising, freezing, and heating as the most common environmental injuries. Stakman and Harrar (1957) reduce nonpathogenic diseases to three classes: (1) suboxidation—black heart of potatoes, brown heart of apples, internal browning of citrus; (2) accumulation of aromatic esters; and (3) unfavorable temperature and humidity. They consider two categories of pathogenic storage diseases: (1) those attacking dry, bulk materials (chiefly stored grains); and (2) those affecting succulent fruits and vegetables.

Pentzer and Heinze (1954) in their review of postharvest physiology of fruits and vegetables first remind us that some maladies, such as water core and cork spot of apples, are really not true postharvest troubles, and then set up three categories: (1) functional diseases related to volatile emanations, lack of oxygen, etc.—the most publicized of these, apple scald, once thought to be caused by ethylene, can be prevented or minimized by allowing fruit to become riper or by accelerating removal of volatile substances with oiled wraps, air movement, intermittent warming, etc.; (2) chilling injury; and (3) problems arising out of the use of growth substances. These last-named materials are used in a rapidly increasing variety of ways: to maintain the "buttons" of pineapples longer in a green condition, thus reducing *Alternaria* rot; to control fruit drop or hasten maturity of orchard fruits which may affect storage; to prevent abscission and conserve color and moisture in snap beans; and to increase rate of ripening in banana, with subsequent accelerated spoilage. In a related situation, increased use of sprout inhibitors in storage bins, which delays suberization of cut surfaces and formation of wound cork, seems to aggravate dry rot of potatoes.

Control of market and storage diseases involves a large and diverse list of measures. Modified atmospheres of several types are used: sulfur dioxide, nitrogen trichloride, ozone, ethylene oxide, and methyl bromide, in a variety of techniques. Nonvolatile substances, oiled wraps, copper-impregnated materials, etc., prove useful in certain instances. Probably the most widely adopted of all preventive measures is temperature control, ranging from precooling to transit refrigeration and cold storage. Optimum temperatures for different commodities vary, and it is necessary to establish specific conditions for each group of fruits and vegetables. In the special area of stored grains, damage is minimized by the use of fungicides, by storage under toxic or inert gases such as CO_2, and—most of all—by drying to the point where no portion of the mass is moist enough to support the growth of fungi (Christensen, 1957).

Special methods are introduced from time to time with limited success. Radiations of various types—ultraviolet, high energy electrons, gamma radiations, ultrasound—have been tried (Morgan, 1948; Imshenetskii and Nazarova, 1937; Metlitskii and Soboleva, 1936). In the case of perishable foods, the major objective is the economy of storing and transport without refrigeration. As yet these techniques have not been approved by federal agencies for treatment of edible items.

The expedient but otherwise unfortunate schism between plant pathology and economic entomology extends into commerce and the market place. But the problems are much the same, as evidenced by Parkin's review (1956) of several years ago, and the gap between knowledge and practice is just as great. He bemoans the fact that application of knowledge lags sadly behind the scientific advances of "stored product entomology" in all but the most highly developed countries, and in plant pathology we find instances where the crudest sort of conditions lead to postharvest damage. In Greece, for example, because apples are simply piled in the orchards for some time after picking, sunburn becomes a significant problem (Krochmal, 1956).

Market pathology introduces basic problems in the physiology of mature tissues (Smock, 1944). Studies of respiration in deciduous fruits show marked fluctuations which can be related to maturity at time of picking, temperature, size, presence of mechanical injuries, and composition of the atmosphere in the storage chamber. Intentional adjustment of the gas content of the atmosphere, by introducing CO_2, oxygen, ozone, or nitrogen, is undertaken with the avowed purpose of favorably affecting the rate of respiration and other metabolic activities in stored produce (Miller, 1946; Bratley and Wiant, 1950; Schomer and McColloch, 1948). Transpiration rate, also, significantly affects the quality of produce, and depends on maturity at picking, size, vapor pressure deficit, air movement, and wax coatings—if any (Smock, 1944).

B. Genetic Resistance

Without exception, practices included in the immediately preceding discussion of "cultural" control, in the restricted sense, result in no fundamental change in the host plant nor are they effective for succeeding generations. As we have indicated, they are mainly physical alterations—sometimes complete removal or destruction—of the individuals of the host population or, not infrequently, measures subsidiary to routine agricultural practices.

The use of disease- and pest-resistant (Snelling, 1941) crop varieties on the contrary, takes advantage of genetically based, permanent changes in the host individuals. Chapter 14 of this volume is devoted to the problems of the plant breeder and the genetics of disease resistance. It would be inappropriate to dwell further on this subject here.

It will be recalled, further, that in the first three sections of this chapter considerable emphasis was put upon the relative popularity and advantages of cultural control on the one hand as opposed to use of chemicals and resistant varieties on the other. We seem now, by including resistant varieties as but one of a host of cultural control measures, to be contradicting ourselves. As a matter of fact, the selection and use of disease-resistant crop varieties is just another weapon available to the grower from a very large and diverse arsenal. But because it is so exceedingly popular, because it is so nearly independent of other measures and so often employed alone—without the support of any other cultural control, and because research and development in this direction require considerable special information and training, genetic resistance has come to deserve consideration as a topic in itself.

Exploitation of disease resistance in the great majority of instances involves little more than a choice of established resistant varieties, either as seed or propagating material. It need not always be thus simple and direct, and some interesting complications arise from time to time.

"In the past greater attention has been given to breeding for disease resistance among field crops than among those usually considered horticultural. This difference is concretely shown by the publications of comparable societies in the U. S. A. There are several fairly obvious reasons for this difference. Cereal crops are almost entirely annuals; many of the fruits are perennial. Moreover, among cereals the per acre returns are usually not sufficient to permit any known form of disease control other than modified culture, seed treatment, or breeding. On the other hand it is among the fruits that disease control by spraying has been most generally economically practicable. Vegetable crops occupy an intermediate position" (Stevens and Stevens, 1952, p. 180).

The basis for resistance, whether mechanical or chemical, may have in any particular instance been identified, but is often obscure. It may be direct, in the sense that the host resists in some way or ways the establishment or spread of the pathogen; it may be indirect, as when the host is repellent to an insect vector (Walker, 1941). It may be highly specific, as in the hypersensitive reaction so welcome to the plant breeder; it may be relatively nonspecific, resulting in an ill-defined but often very desirable "field" resistance. Field resistance of potatoes to late blight in Mexico, for example, limits blight in years when weather is only moderately favorable, and makes for easier fungicidal control (Eide, 1955). These less specific types of resistance are effective against a broader range of pathogenic races than is resistance based on hypersensitivity.

In the special case of woody perennials we find situations wherein useful resistance need not involve the entire individual. To nematode-resistant peach understocks, for example, any number of named varieties may safely be budded (Groves, 1958). A more complex situation involves "double-working" or multiple grafts, a technique which has been adopted in several cases, most spectacularly in combating the South American leaf blight of *Hevea* rubber, which was earlier responsible for the destruction of the industry on that continent. As finally developed, a high latex-yielding variety is first grafted to a selected rootstock, and, to it, somewhat later, a blight resistant clone which develops into the leafy crown. The resulting tree has roots of one genetic make-up, a trunk selected for productivity, and a top having genetic resistance to the blight pathogen.

There is considerable literature dealing, directly or indirectly, with the complications arising from the introduction of disease-resistant varieties, among these a brief treatment by N. E. Stevens (1942). Stakman and Harrar (1957, p. 30) point to an instance of the often contradictory results of attempts to use resistant varieties wherein tristeza or quick decline of citrus has wrought havoc on trees budded to sour orange stocks, but is relatively harmless to those on sweet orange stocks. This has reversed the shift from sweet orange to sour orange stocks which had stemmed from the susceptibility of the former to fungi. "The choice had to be made between two evils, and these evils have been very disruptive of an important agricultural industry and have been a heavy tax on producer and consumer alike."

C. Physiologic Changes

A third and final category of intrinsic measures includes those where the conspicuous effect on the host is not anatomical, does not include removal or destruction, and has no relation to the genetic make-up of the plant, but is chiefly a temporary alteration in some functional or physiological property of the host. Other than this general resemblance there is no convenient uniformity about the measures included here, and all too often their mechanism of action is unknown. Generally, they involve an alteration in the environment with a view to increasing the disease resistance of the host, reducing its vulnerability to disease establishment, or ridding it of associated pathogens.

1. Nutritional and Related Soil Amendments

Conventional soil treatment, wherein the primary objective is to reduce inoculum, is discussed in Section VI; at this point we are concerned with those measures whose most significant effects are, or seem to be, upon the host plant.

The January, 1946, issue of "Soil Science" was entirely devoted to soil-plant disease relationships, a series of eleven commendable papers which, although now more than a decade old, are very well worth careful study. Those by Sanford on soil-borne diseases in relation to the microflora associated with various crops and soil amendments, by Walker on soil management and plant nutrition in relation to disease development, and by Daines on control of plant diseases by use of inorganic soil amendments are especially germane. Additional thoughtful comment has been contributed by Hart (1949), who reminds us that, exceptionally, nutrients exert their effect directly on the pathogen and influence its growth and multiplication within the host plant—witness the relation of nitrogen in tracheal sap to the growth of the corn wilt bacterium, *Phytomonas stewarti*.

A few generalizations may be hazarded: (1) that the influence of nutrients and other soil amendments is usually through their effect on the host plant; (2) that secondary soil factors governing availability of nutrient elements are at times as important as total nutrient content; (3) that imbalance, as well as the absolute amounts of each element, must be taken into consideration; (4) that the form in which a substance is applied (e.g., as ammonia nitrogen versus nitrate nitrogen) affects the final outcome; (5) that the type of disease under consideration, the weather, and other environmental factors are importantly significant; and (6) last but not least, that the results of laboratory research can by no means always be transferred to field conditions.

Most writers (for example, Wingard, 1941; Stakman and Harrar, 1957; Coons, 1953) agree that, by and large, high levels of nitrogen predispose toward disease, whereas increases in potassium and phosphorus, particularly the former, render plants more resistant. They are equally in agreement that there are many exceptions to the rule. *Sclerotium rolfsii* rot of sugar beet, for example, has been markedly reduced by applications of nitrogenous fertilizers (Cooley, 1946; Berkeley, 1944). Stakman and Harrar deal effectively with the whole problem and distinguish between the situation as it affects diseases caused by facultative saprophytes, which show the relationship just noted, and those caused by obligate parasites, where vegetative vigor of the host is generally favorable for disease development. However, extensive experiments with cereal rusts lead to the cautious conclusions that "fertilizers had relatively little effect on stem rust except as they affected density of stand and consequent moisture retention; lodging and its direct and indirect effects; and rapidity of ripening, either premature or delayed, depending on temperature and moisture conditions. There are other data that indicate strongly that environmental factors such as moisture and temperature affect rust development in the field far more than any direct predisposing or protective effects of nutrients. . . . The percentages of leaf rust, *Puccinia rubigo-vera* var. *tritici*, were affected somewhat more by fertilizers than was stem rust, but the differences were mostly in degree rather than in kind."

Fertilizers in relation to smut control are discussed by Tapke in a review put out in 1948. Bunt is increased by potassium and phosphoric acid, reduced by nitrogen, increased by potassium chloride in two very different soils, reduced by calcium cyanamide. Stalk smut of rye is decreased by solutions high in potassium and phosphorus and low in calcium nitrate and magnesium sulfate; the reverse situation tends to increase damage.

The influence of soil reaction on plant disease is widely recognized. In some instances its effect is known to be primarily upon the pathogen and inoculum; at other times it may act indirectly as it affects nutrient availability; in still other cases the mechanism is a combination of effects or is unknown. Berkeley's review (1944) of root rots in noncereal crops recognizes not only that soil reaction is important in disease incidence, but that it is related to the temperature range at which infection takes place. According to him, soil reaction is related to the accumulation of certain toxic substances that may be absorbed by the plant. As a result of this, it becomes more susceptible to attack, a correlation which has been demonstrated between absorption of aluminum and root rot of corn and sugar cane.

In all likelihood, the benefits derived from incorporation of organic manures far more often results from a biological interference with the pathogen (see Chapter 13) than from any physiological effect on the host population.

It is only fair to include, in a consideration of nutritional relations and fertilizer applications, a reminder that there are not only formulations newly available for soil amendment (e.g., liquid ammonia) but new techniques, particularly foliar feeding, the disease control implications of which have not yet been fully investigated.

2. Heat Therapy

N. E. Stevens, two decades ago (1938a), summarized a number of instances of heat treatments of seeds and other plant parts for control of fungi, nematodes, and virus diseases. In this review he pointed out that heat (usually hot water or steam) has been used for many years against pathogens in seeds and bulbs. An ingenious modification of this has been employed in India, where seed grain is exposed either to the sun in a blackened iron vessel filled with water or, after being moistened, directly to the sun. Similar results were obtained in Nigeria in attempts to free cotton seed from the bacterial wilt organism. Hot water has been used successfully against nematodes infesting strawberry, chrysanthemum, violet, and begonia, and against the mycelium of mint rust and brown rot of tomato fruits. Finally, great interest has been developed over the possibilities of inactivating the viruses of potato, sugar cane, stone fruits, and the like.

More recently, Fischer and Holton (1957) on the subject of heat treatment of seeds for smuts insist that increases of 65–70% in the water content of the embryo are essential to effective action against dormant smut. When soaked seed is held under anaerobic conditions (see Section VI, A, 1), smut is eliminated. On the amount of water absorbed may depend the temperature necessary to destroy the smut mycelium.

Virus diseases, of course, still occupy the forefront among those diseases against which heat therapy is regularly employed. Kassanis (1957) has furnished us with a recent summary of the effects of changing temperature on plant virus diseases, on susceptibility to infection, incubation period, symptoms, and virus multiplication. He contends that heat is the only therapeutic treatment known which has proved consistently effective in freeing plants from many different viruses—an attribute particularly essential when the entire stock of some valuable clonal line is virus-infected. Among the better established uses of heat therapy is the preparation of planting stock of sugar cane threatened with such diseases as sereh, chlorotic streak, or Ratoon stunt. In Queensland, Australia, a steam-heating apparatus has been developed employing tanks capable of handling 3 tons at a time, or 12 tons in an 8-hour shift. Using these, one establishment can prepare enough healthy stock to plant an area yielding 10,000 tons of clean "seed" for the ensuing season (King, 1953). Wire baskets, which cool more rapidly than bags, seem to enhance germination and to be generally preferable.

In special situations normal atmospheric temperatures have been sufficient to inactivate viruses within host tissues. Peach yellows in the southern United States and potato leaf roll in India (until such time as the crop came to be raised from tubers in cold storage) apparently belong in this category (Kassanis, 1957). It will be apparent, too, that foliage pathogens are subjected to leaf temperatures which reach maxima well above that of the surrounding air.

Much of the importance of heat therapy, it will have become obvious, derives from its contribution to production of disease-free seed and propagation stock. Rather than divorce this from other means of achieving the same end, it is treated in Section VI, A, 1, to which the reader is referred.

3. Other Physiologic Measures

Vernalization has been shown to affect smut incidence, although not always in the same direction. Gäumann (1950, p. 383) points to disease reduction following vernalization, possibly because the growth of the seedlings is accelerated and outdistances the infection. Aberg (1945) in experiments with barley stripe found that vernalization for 38 days favored development of the disease.

There has been some difference of opinion, too, over Chester's suggestion that disease can be reduced if acid-delinted cotton seeds are separated into light and heavy fractions on the basis of their specific gravity in water. Arndt (1945) feels that the improvement observed depends upon the characteristics of each lot of seeds and that the general applicability of the procedure is questionable.

In the highly specialized area of medical mycology, where man is the host, dermatophytes are commonly treated with a fungicide plus a keratolytic agent to induce peeling of the infected skin layers. Deeper mycoses require surgical drainage, X-ray therapy, medication with potassium iodide, desensitization, and improvement of the general condition of the patient (Emmons, 1940).

Careful consideration of the various current uses of chemicals in the control of plant growth will uncover several possible and probable applications to disease control. Avery and Thompson (1947) list the following: rooting of cuttings; blossom thinning of fruits; control of preharvest drop, manipulation of fruit set, and production of seedless fruits; an antidote to the effect of fungicides in seed treatment; regulation of time of flowering and of fruit ripening; in weed control; and in breaking or prolongation of dormancy.

Whether or not practical advantage can be taken of cross-protection reactions in plant viruses in much the same way as immunization in human pathology is debatable. The phenomenon of cross protection itself is well established, even in viruses of the insect-transmitted group (Kunkel, 1955). Suggestions along this line appear from time to time in the literature. Gäumann (1950, p. 350) notes that in potato an apathogenic form of the X-virus will be transmitted to progeny and will exclude more virulent forms, but that resistance to frost may be lowered and that the virus may mutate to a more severe form or that another group of viruses, e.g., Y and leaf roll, may be worse. Stout (1950) suggests that a mild form of the peach mosaic virus from normal-appearing shoots protects against the severe form of the virus found in the remainder of the tree. Stakman and Harrar (1957, p. 367) feel that the most effective control of tristeza will be obtained by using virus-free scions on tolerant rootstocks, although they recognize the suggestion that susceptible hosts might be inoculated with mild strains of the pathogen.

On the basis of preliminary experiments a few years ago, in which TMV virus was subjected to ultrasound, Newton (1951) makes the interesting suggestion that we thus have available an exclusively physical method for reducing the virulence of plant viruses without affecting their antigenic properties, with obvious implications for the preparation of virus vaccines.

Finally, N. E. Stevens (1938a) and Stevens and Nienow (1947) cite several unique methods of disease control that might fairly be termed physiologic.

1. Freeing of tomato seed from the organism causing bacterial canker by submitting the fruit pulp to fermentation for from 3 to 6 days at approximately room temperature.

2. Prevention of heat injury to forest tree seedlings by inclining the trees slightly toward the south at time of transplanting; reduction in smothering by sowing black soil on the snow over seedling plots to hasten snow melting in the spring.

3. Prevention of leaf drop in cranberries, resulting from lack of oxygen, by withdrawing the water from the frozen bogs in winter and allowing the sheet of ice to rest directly on the vines or by freezing the vines into the ice itself.

4. Restoration of trees girdled by *Phytophthora* rot by banking soil about the base and stimulating the formation of new roots.

5. Injection of chemicals into host plants—chemotherapy.

V. EXTRINSIC MEASURES INDIRECTLY AFFECTING THE INDIVIDUALS COMPRISING THE HOST POPULATION

Primary attention in the foregoing section (Section IV) centered upon those measures wherein some actual change in the host plant was achieved, ranging from its complete removal or destruction, through physical, physiological, and genetic alteration. In the discussion to follow, so far as possible, emphasis will be placed upon practices which elicit their effect without producing any immediate change in the individuals of the host population. These are instances in which the host population continues to occupy the center of interest, but without there being any attempt, either permanently or temporarily, to alter it.

A. *Practices Involving Number of Host Plants*

Stevens and Nienow (1947) contend that although overplanting as a means of obtaining a crop despite seedling diseases is probably of common occurrence, it seems only rarely to be spelled out in technical literature. It was resorted to in an effort to obtain satisfactory stands of sweet corn in New York and New England during the outbreaks of bacterial wilt in 1932 and 1933. Pool, somewhat earlier, had called attention to a similar means of reducing losses from *Fusarium* stem rot of sweet potatoes in New Jersey; and in the Carolinas it has been the custom, ever since the first outbreak of blue mold, to increase the size of seedling beds to double the size formerly used.

Recommendations on seeding rates are often made with reference to cereal diseases, usually as part of general instructions including rate, timing, and depth. Severity of root rots in wheat seems often to increase with increases in seeding rate (Greaney, 1946), as does bunt or stinking smut (Tapke, 1948), whereas both very wide or very close plantings, particularly the former, should be avoided if leaf rust is to be kept at a minimum (Chester, 1946).

Gäumann (1950, p. 256) demonstrates that dense stands of rye, with consequent limited tillering, tend to flower simultaneously and thus suffer less secondary infection from "honeydew" conidia of the ergot fungus, while more widely spaced plants lead to increased infection. Chester (1947, p. 477) comments in regard to rate of seeding that fungus diseases favored by high humidity are most destructive under excessive rates of seeding (cereal rusts, powdery mildew, damping-off) but that heavy seedling loss from disease of crops such as cotton may be compensated for by increased seeding rates.

B. Practices Involving Position of Host Plants

1. Placement

Important effects upon disease may result from the proximity of host plants to each other. The microclimate, rather than the over-all meteorological conditions, most influences the rapidity with which many kinds of diseases develop. By microclimate is meant the conditions of moisture, temperature, and air movement of the atmosphere in the immediate vicinity of the host plants. Close spacing, however arrived at, tends to raise the atmospheric humidity, encourage sporulation of pathogenic fungi, and reduce air circulation (Gäumann, 1950, p. 482). Growth habit, whether luxurious and dense or sparse, contributes to or reduces the effect of spacing on microclimate. Thus, in France, the Early Rose variety of potatoes is as susceptible to late blight as Saucisse, but less receptive, since its aerial parts are not luxurious enough to provide favorable microclimate (Foister, 1946). And the so-called pink disease of rubber, caused by *Corticium salmonicolor*, which may be serious in wet seasons, can be reduced by providing for air circulation, drainage, and access of sunlight, and by proper location and spacing of trees (Hubert, 1957).

Placement as related to disease includes the selection of planting site. Always, albeit sometimes without conscious effort, the grower chooses a planting site with attention to the general welfare of the projected crop. Usually this concern includes matters of disease hazard. In Chester's (1946) monograph on cereal rusts we find these recommendations given on choice of planting site: well-drained, somewhat exposed upland; elimination of volunteer grain by tillage; separation of fields of winter and spring varieties or location of spring wheats to windward.

In its extreme form, "placement" control need be no more elaborate than a very local adjustment in farming practice. Good results in control of sugar beet damping-off have been obtained by growing the plants on ridges with furrows on either side, thus facilitating soil drainage in the immediate vicinity (Berkeley, 1944). According to Dobromyslov (1932) nonridged plantings are more favorable to bunt in the early stages than are ridged furrows.

2. Dispersal

It is unquestionably true that as man developed an agriculture and as that agriculture became more and more specialized, there has been an increasing tendency to concentrate large numbers of host individuals in contiguous plantings. It is likewise unquestionably true that disease hazards are thereby increased.

"The greatest need for plant disease control is in connection with those crops that are artificially cultivated. When several hundred human beings dwell within a single square mile, the area is said to be crowded, and great care is taken to prevent the development of serious public health problems. In comparison, one acre of wheat may contain approximately a million individual plants, all more nearly identical than individuals in any group of human beings; and the plant pathologist is concerned with the fact that the crowding together offers optimum conditions for the development of epidemic diseases. This crowding is a deliberate modern agronomic technique designed to promote maximum agricultural production through the use of improved varieties and soil management, but it provides highly favorable conditions for the devastating attacks of plant pathogens. Thus, agriculture takes the form of plant urbanization in which tremendous populations are abnormally concentrated in a relatively small area, and in a sense each cultivated field becomes a gigantic culture medium for pathogens. Every successful effort to improve yield by adding to the carrying capacity of the soil intensifies disease problems which must be met if agriculture is to progress" (Stakman and Harrar, 1957, pp. 3–4).

In view of these trends in modern agriculture, one finds very little if any material in the literature recommending dispersal as a means of disease control. Yet within the very severe practical and economic limitation imposed, it is an obviously desirable move, to be taken advantage of whenever possible, and stands as one of the few compensating features of primitive agriculture.

3. Physical Barriers

Quite naturally, Smith *et al.* (1933) in their outstanding examination of the basis for quarantines deal with the role of physical barriers to the spread of disease. True, barriers act primarily to interrupt the movement of inoculum, but because they often directly affect the choice of planting site or otherwise impinge on the host plant, they will be dealt with here. Barriers, according to the committee, may be topographic (high mountains, large bodies of water, deserts), biological (absence of host plants or vectors, territory occupied by competitors), or climatic (meteorologically unsuitable areas). Absolute barriers can be traversed only through the agency of man. As evidence of the effectiveness of natural barriers, they cite only one disease of importance to California, asparagus rust, which appears to have entered the state by natural means.

On a much smaller scale, trenching has been used to stop the advance of soil fungi. It is apparently the only known method for controlling the fairy ring caused by *Psilocybe agrariella vaccinnii* in cranberry bogs (N. E. Stevens, 1938a). Trenching was also recommended for control of *Armillaria* and *Rosellinia* (Berkeley, 1944). Cotton root rot has been confined not only with trenches but with artificial barriers such as galvanized iron and by mixing into the soil various substances such as oil, sulfur, acid, copper sulfate, etc. At least one effect of the addition of sulfur is to lower the pH very sharply in the 4–6 inch barrier of treated soil. Kuijt (1955) refers to a 60 ft. mistletoe-free zone surrounding stands infested with this parasite; and Hunt (1946) cites marked reduction in incidence of pupation disease of oats in Russia by providing barriers 2 meters high between sown fields and weed-grown fence rows.

4. Geographic Location

Many important cultivated plants have a more extensive geographic range than their pathogens. Stakman and Harrar (1957, p. 431) suggest several instances wherein it is possible to grow crops in areas free of their principal pathogens: e.g., the production of coffee in the Western Hemisphere, where coffee rust does not occur; and of rubber in Southeast Asia, which is free of the South American leaf blight. They add that, occasionally, disease can be avoided by planting out of season; in Mexico, both potatoes and wheat are commonly grown during the dry season under irrigation to avoid destructive attacks from late blight and rust, respectively.

These same authors summarize (Stakman and Harrar, 1957, pp. 304–305 and 313–314) the effects of temperature and moisture on the geographic incidence of disease, pointing out that temperature is often the limiting factor in seasonal and regional incidence and that latitude and elevation can be very important in determining temperature extremes. Diseases commonly associated with cooler northern climates will thus be found during the winter season in more southerly latitudes or at higher altitudes during the high temperatures of the tropical summer. Pathogens vary with regard to their optimum temperature ranges, and this must be taken into account in developing effective cultural control measures.

Seasonal and geographic distribution of disease is alike conditioned by moisture—particularly distribution of rainfall during the year—and the frequency and intensity of fogs and dews. The practice of producing disease-free seed in arid regions (see also Section VI, A, 1) takes advantage of the moisture dependency of the pathogen.

Baker and Snyder (1950) list a number of diseases which normally cause serious loss in regions of high rainfall but are generally absent from California: bean anthracnose, bean bacterial blight, black rot of cabbage and cauliflower, *Septoria* leaf spot of tomato, anthracnose of watermelon, angular leaf spot, and scab of cucumber. Tapke (1948) believes that the floral infection smuts are usually scarce in sections of the country where humidity of the air is low at flowering time; in California, for example, damage is too slight to be of economic importance because the dry season is near at hand when cereals are heading. Yarwood (1957), discussing powdery mildews, on the other hand, attributes the absence of *Sphaerotheca* from hops on the west coast of the United States and Canada, as compared to the eastern United States and Europe, and of *Oidium* from rubber in the Americas, as compared to Malaya and Central Africa, to the fact that they have not been introduced rather than to any basic incompatibility of environment and pathogen.

To be informed about the geographic range of host and pathogen does not constitute *per se* a control measure. The foregoing discussion is intended, of course, to focus attention on the possibility of employing this kind of data in trying to select, most wisely, optimum areas for a given crop or the most promising crops for a given area, as the case may be. N. E. Stevens (1938b) has made specific recommendation to this end in suggesting the preparation of "disease hazard" maps based on information some of which is already in the hands of the professional pathologist and entomologist. He bolsters this argument by pointing to a number of instances where agricultural enterprises have been undertaken in ignorance of disease and pest threats, only to fail entirely or to provide only very meager returns for the investment of time and energy.

He argues that the preparation, or at least an effort to begin the preparation, of maps of regions considered extra hazardous because of unusual risks from crop pests is well within our scientific capabilities, provided we are willing to attempt it. Wood and Miller (1949) add strength to the argument favoring some such effort in reporting a questionnaire which they sent out several years ago (as a follow-up of a much earlier one distributed by N. E. Stevens) to collect data on the effects of disease losses on crop industries and farm life. Of greatest interest are those cases where disease has forced the abandonment of what otherwise appeared to be promising enterprises.

Geographic location, in a very much more limited sense, is employed whenever plantings are isolated for the express purpose of disease control. Such a technique as this is most promising for diseases caused by pathogens that do not give off aerial spores, and is not often employed in connection with seedling production and seed-increase plots. Because the total area thus isolated is relatively modest, it becomes possible to utilize fungicides on crops where economic considerations preclude their use under ordinary field conditions. Thus small quantities of seed from wheat and barley affected with loose smut are first treated with hot water or by some similar technique, and this supply then increased in plots isolated by a few hundred yards from any commercial grain fields which might be a source of contamination, often under the supervision of selected growers.

Crops to be set out in the field as seedlings are first sown in isolated beds, particularly when one or more of the common diseases is primarily a seedling problem. The widespread practice of isolating tobacco seed beds as an anti-blue mold measure is a case in point. Pound (1946) provides us with a less widely known example in his discussion of control for virus diseases of cabbage in the Pacific northwest. Because cabbage is a biennial, no crop-free period is possible, and strict sanitation becomes imperative. The vector, a cabbage aphid, has proved difficult to control and is best avoided by isolation of the plant beds, since wild cruciferous hosts and other weeds do not appear to be, as a general rule, responsible for more than scattered appearances.

C. Practices Involving Timing

1. Noncoincidence of Host Population and Inoculum

The precision with which host and pathogen must synchronize and the span of time over which successful infection and establishment are possible vary greatly from one disease to another. More often than not, pathogen spores germinate only during a limited period or under given environmental conditions. If, in addition, the possibility of host infection is limited to a particular phase of development or to certain, often transient, plant organs or parts, the chances of disease are greatly reduced. The principle of disease control involved here remains the same; it is an effort to upset this timing and to produce a crop in spite of the presence of pathogenic organisms and of host varieties susceptible to them. A considerable variety of such instances are of record, some few of which will suffice in illustration.

It was some time ago recognized that early-maturing varieties of crop plants will complete their growth before the threat from disease has materialized. Varieties of cowpeas are known, for instance, which mature before the season for wilt and root-knot development arrives; certain varieties of potatoes commonly mature before the appearance of late blight, although they succumb quickly enough if planted later in the season (Wingard, 1941).

Noncoincidence stems also from topographic and climatic factors. In India, for example, some 2,000,000 acres of grain at lower elevations is annually threatened by leaf rust coming from less than 4,000 acres in the nearby highlands (Chester, 1946). It has been suggested that sowing in April and June be suspended and that it be delayed in areas of secondary foci of infection or, more drastically, that culture be entirely stopped for a period of 2 or 3 years at altitudes of 3,000 ft. and above where the pathogen survives the hot season. Because of differing governmental jurisdictions and other practical considerations, this has not yet been tested as an actual control step. In parts of Russia small patches of winter wheat serve as sources of infection for very much greater acreages of spring wheat. Noncoincidence could, in this instance, be very readily achieved.

Without resort to earlier maturing varieties, or relying upon peculiarities of terrain and climate, the grower still may benefit by selecting the most favorable seeding time. Most reports in this area refer to cereal grains although Gäumann (1950, p. 482) speaks of the possibility of accelerating potato crops by sprouting the tubers prior to planting, and Hunt (1946) indicates that the beet leaf hopper, key to curly top incidence, does not thrive if beets are large enough to cast considerable shade and produce increased humidity before the time when insects abandon native weeds and migrate to beet fields.

Fischer and Holton (1957) recommend that winter wheat be seeded early when temperature and moisture are unfavorable for germination of bunt spores and infection of the seedlings—with the result that the seedlings get beyond the susceptible stage before smut is active. Incidence of infection in the Pacific northwest is high for fields sown in the

4-week period from mid-September to mid-October, low for fields sown before and after that time. In Pakistan early seeding at temperatures above 28° C. reduces flag smut. Similar relationships between sowing time and disease incidence are noted by Tapke (1948) for bunt of wheat in Kansas, Missouri, Australia, Siberia, and Italy, and for stalk smut of rye. Simmonds (1953), discussing root rots of cereals, advises seeding spring wheat early, when soil temperatures are low, to avoid common root rot; his testimony is corroborated by Greaney (1946). Chester (1947, p. 477) says that time of seeding, usually directly related to the influence of temperature, has an important bearing on disease control, dry-land foot rot of wheat being practically controlled by selecting a proper date for sowing. Early spring seeding may be effective in dealing with diseases such as root knot or Texas root rot, which are common only in the hot summer months.

Hunt (1946) lists three diseases which may be substantially reduced by seeing to it that seedlings are not in a susceptible stage at the time environmental conditions are favorable for infection: flag smut of wheat, pupation disease of oats, and flax rust. He contends that if corn is planted early enough to be nearly mature before vectors become prevalent after mid-summer, it will suffer very much less damage from the virus of wallaby ear.

The advantages sought in choosing a planting time may be antithetic. Bunt and scab (*Gibberella*) on wheat, for example, are favored by, respectively, slow and rapid growth (Gäumann, 1950, p. 482). Perhaps the best-known research in explanation of apparently contradictory results is that by Dickson on *Gibberella* (see Brown, 1936), which showed that wheat is attacked at high temperatures, corn at low. When soil temperatures are low, rapid hydrolysis of wheat starch produces seedlings rich in sugar, having thick cell walls, and consequently reduced susceptibility; protein formation and tissue growth are accelerated at higher temperatures—with consequent increase in susceptibility. In corn, on the other hand, walls of unmodified pectic materials are formed at low temperatures, and more resistant, suberized walls at higher temperatures; hence the greater damage to seedlings of this crop at low readings.

Rarely, drastic measures are recommended in order to achieve non-coincidence of host and pathogen, such as the crop-free period recounted by Chester (1946) in connection with leaf rust in India. Just such a crop-free period has been put to the test in California and has proved an effective control of Western celery mosaic (Stevens and Nienow, 1947; Milbrath, 1948). This plan was voluntarily established by growers in 1943 to break the continuous culture of celery and adopted by the state legislature the following year. Within a very short time yields returned to the levels commonly reached before virus inroads had become serious.

Depth of sowing, in the literal sense, refers to position, not timing, but the net effect is primarily to determine the interval required for the seed to germinate and the resulting seedling to emerge and begin maturing. The usual result of deep sowing is to prolong the seedling stage; it thus bears the same relation to disease incidence as late sowing. Rye, therefore, sown deeply, takes longer to appear and is in direct contact with the soil for an added period, materially increasing *Fusarium* invasion (Gäumann, 1950, p. 256), whereas in favorable weather shallow sowing encourages germination and shortens the susceptible phase. Increased depth of seeding is directly correlated with increase in bunt of wheat (Tapke, 1948), and shallow planting of potatoes is known to reduce *Rhizoctonia* (Stakman and Harrar, 1957, p. 433). Small seed size, when it is correlated with slow emergence and increased exposure to infection, leads to high incidence of barley stripe, *Helminthosporium gramineum* (Gäumann, 1950, p. 255).

Comparison of grain-sowing methods in Egypt affords convincing evidence of the importance of seeding depth to disease losses (Fischer and Holton, 1957; Tapke, 1948; Stevens and Nienow, 1947). Several systems are in common usage, but evidence indicates that seed sown on moist land and then plowed in (germinating at an average depth of 8 cm.) shows the highest incidence of smut; seed sown on dry land, then harrowed and immediately irrigated (average depth 4 cm.), consistently less damage; and broadcast sowing 1 hour after flooding (surface planted), the least. Wheat bunt, covered smut of barley, and millet and sorghum smuts respond in similar patterns.

2. Age, Life Span

Cultural practices involving timing include those situations where the grower takes advantage of age or life span of the host in avoiding serious disease damage. A number of instances are of record which demonstrate that the age of the host materially affects the likelihood that it will become diseased. To every generalization there are exceptions, but seedlings are often more susceptible than mature plants—as mature or moribund leaves are more likely to be invaded than those less aged. Perennial plants have, with respect to flowers, fruit, and foliage, a cycle of growth from youth to senescense each year while the remainder of the plant tissues gradually age. It is reasonable, therefore, to speak of "old" trees in describing the greater root rot damage in long-established orchards or in stands of mature trees (Cooley, 1946).

Gäumann (1950) discusses at some length the problem of susceptibility as it relates to the stage of development of the host plant in three classes of cases: (1) where the pathogen has a store of inoculum available only after a given time (e.g., late blight); (2) where the host has a susceptible growth period for only a limited time (e.g., *Rhizoctonia* on potato); and (3) most commonly, in which the availability of pathogen inoculum and susceptibility of host are both limited (e.g., stem rust). He examines also, with special emphasis, the ontogenetic or developmental changes in the host as they affect susceptibility and resistance, and spread of disease within the host plant, citing a number of specific examples in documentation of the thesis.

Papers dealing with the relationship between host age and disease damage are much more readily located than are specific recommendations for cultural control based on these established facts—much less records of measures actually employed in commercial agriculture. The application of these principles is, however, a direct one and is probably, for all practical purposes, frequently in operation.

Life span refers to the length of time necessary, here restricted to annuals or biennials, for a crop plant to develop from seed to harvest. Both age and life span are special aspects of noncoincidence, a topic dealt with more extensively in the preceding section. Life span could signify the length of time required to get safely past a particularly susceptible stage, but is more usefully thought of as the total time needed to "make a crop." From the viewpoint of its importance to disease control, consideration of life span leads, usually, to the adoption of early-maturing varieties (Walker, 1941) which, in one way or another, avoid the severest inoculum threat. Sometimes the advantage can be compounded by coincidentally slowing down the pathogen, as by deep plowing the stubble of foot-rotted cereals (Gäumann, 1950, p. 254). Care must be exercised whenever varieties developed and adapted for one geographic region are introduced into another lest differences in photoperiod or other factors unfavorably alter the time of maturity and harvest.

If life span can, in effect, be arbitrarily shortened by early harvest, without at the same time introducing new and equally troublesome pathogenic and agronomic problems, disease will be reduced. This maneuver has been instituted in the case of seed potatoes, in an attempt to avoid tuber invasion by viruses which have been introduced into the foliage during the current growing season. Cooperative, simultaneous early harvesting by all growers in a contiguous area could materially reduce bacterial ring rot and several virus problems (Schultz *et al.*, 1944). Chester has suggested early harvesting as a means of salvaging severely rusted grain fields.

3. Longevity of Inoculum

Just as the age and life span of the host are special aspects of non-coincidence of host and pathogen, focusing attention on attributes of the host, so longevity of inoculum is a special aspect of noncoincidence which focuses attention on an attribute of the pathogen. Persistence of inoculum is so directly pertinent to a consideration of crop rotation and nonchemical soil treatments that it will be referred to later from those points of view (see Sections V, D, 2 and VI, A, 2). For the moment we are concerned with the special situation wherein host material may be freed from associated pathogens simply by allowing sufficient time to elapse.

When seed of crop plants is held beyond the customary length of time in order that inoculum borne therein may be eliminated or reduced, the grower takes advantage of the greater longevity of the host species. Several cases of this are on record; perhaps the best-known instance relates to cotton seed invaded by the anthracnose organism (N. E. Stevens, 1938a). Arndt (1946) has studied the effect of storage conditions on survival of *Colletotrichum gossypii* on cotton seed, and finds that at moisture levels from 8 to 16% there is a reduction in the number of seedlings infected with each successive increase in seed moisture. Hardison (1948) cites blind seed disease of perennial ryegrass as one that can be eliminated by aging seed 2 years. Benefits from routine chemical treatment are apparently in no way reduced when seed are held in storage for an additional season (Miles, 1939).

D. Practices Affecting Sequential Relationships

As we have seen, number, position, and timing can be turned to advantage by the grower who seeks to hold disease to a minimum. Lastly, certain practices can be identified which emphasize the particular sequence in which different crops occupy a given plot of ground.

1. Specific Crop Sequences and Associations

By all odds the best-known and most widely adopted cultural control based on host sequence is crop rotation. This will be taken up presently. Rotation deals in generalities and seeks primarily to avoid crops with peculiar susceptibilities by substituting any of a wide selection of other types; the key to the problem immediately before us is the specificity of the relationship. The mechanism by which the effect is achieved may be toxic, nutritional, biological, or as yet unknown, but to be fairly included here it must be a demonstrated crop-to-crop influence.

Coons and Kotila (1935), Coons (1953), and Buchholtz (1944)

have published extensively on crop sequences affecting sugar beets, and demonstrate that damping-off is increased when the crop follows legumes, decreased when it follows corn, soybeans, or small grains. This effect seems to be tied in with the higher nitrogen levels reached in the former situation and may be avoided by careful timing of the several agronomic steps involved. Tip rot in Iowa, which is very widely distributed in those soils and which is built up to damaging proportions through successive cropping to sugar beets, can be substantially reduced by a prior crop of alfalfa. Other diseases and other primary crops might be cited in support of the basic thesis. Chester (1947, p. 458) lists scab, wilt, and *Rhizoctonia*, troublesome to Nebraska potatoes on virgin soils and in some rotations, as diseases which can be reduced to a minimum when alfalfa immediately precedes the principal crop. And the pathogen so controlled need not be a bacterium or fungus—the brown root rot of tobacco, now known to be primarily due to the invasion of meadow nematodes, seems generally to be favored by previous crops of timothy and corn (Berkeley, 1944).

Plant residues cannot always be assumed to be the cause of the reaction observed in succeeding crops, but there is convincing evidence that this is often the basis of the relationship. Cochrane (1949) feels that, at least part of the time, residues exert a direct toxic effect on the roots of susceptible plants, probably aggravated by the action of secondary rot-producing microorganisms. Actively growing roots of walnut and other species are known to secrete toxic materials—with the result that surrounding plants are visibly harmed; other root interactions are traceable to nutrient relations, pH, alterations in soil texture, and so on (Loehwing, 1937).

Woody perennials, like field crops, can be affected by species which occupied the land immediately before planting, a fact which can be put to good use in choosing an orchard site. Cases are known where all ornamental shrubs planted on stumpy land, in the immediate vicinity of the stumps themselves, have been killed by white rot; presumably they were invaded by pathogens remaining in the roots of the original trees (Cooley, 1946). Replanting of peach after peach often intensifies survival problems even where no disease seems prominently present, whereas peach after other prunus rootstocks or fruit varieties do not suffer appreciably. The explanation seems to lie in a toxic microbial degradation and decomposition of amygdalin, which cannot be alleviated by soil fumigation (Groves, 1958).

Reduction in disease following specific crops does not result solely from the absence of a susceptible variety, as noted. *Ophiobolus graminis*, for example, disappears more rapidly from soil under a nonsusceptible crop than in fallow because of the depletion of nitrogen reserves (Simmonds, 1953). Similar gains derive from coincident plantings of two varieties. According to Simmonds, there is very little take-all of barley when undersown with trefoil, which makes luxuriant growth after the barley is cut. On the other side of the ledger, Groves (1958) points to the greatly increased probability of *Verticillium* troubles in stone fruits when a susceptible species is used as an intercrop. The same holds for nematode injury to peach when aggravated by the presence of a susceptible cover crop. Destructiveness of *Sclerotium rolfsii* on apple is influenced by the nature of the cover crop, susceptible legumes such as lespedeza tending to intensify the hazard to nurseries and young orchards (Cooley, 1946).

Admixtures of rye with wheat result in increased damage from wheat bunt in proportion as the content of rye increases; damage is greater following peas than following wheat and highest on soil newly broken from grass and alfalfa (Tapke, 1948). Hunt (1946) explains the interrelations of sugar cane and corn in respect to downy mildew under Australian conditions by pointing out that the pathogen forms large numbers of short-lived conidia on corn but not on sugar cane and that, therefore, corn plantings are necessary if disease is to spread rapidly during the growing season.

An interesting suggestion of admittedly limited applicability comes from Chitwood and Oteifa (1952). Based on the fact that a particular level of invasion of the proper species of nematode is sometimes stimulatory to certain host varieties, they propose that this effect might be stabilized by growing perennials in conjunction with a moderately resistant plant serving to maintain a proper inoculum balance.

2. Crop Rotation

Diseases caused by soil-borne pathogens are usually the targets against which crop rotation is brought into play. Stakman and Harrar (1957, p. 439) point to a few nonsoil pathogens—certain cereal rusts, late blight, banana leaf spot, and virus diseases—which are usually more destructive where continuous cropping is practiced, due in most instances to increased amounts of overwintered inoculum or to increased vector populations. They admit, of course, that "monoculture" is at times dictated by economic or other considerations—bananas in Central America; sugar cane in Cuba; pineapple in Hawaii; rice in Japan—but insist that where done it is despite heightened disease hazard, and then only on the basis of high cash value, cheap hand labor, mechanization, or especially effective chemical control measures.

"The efficacy of rotation as a disease control measure lies in the fact that, in the absence of susceptible crops (i.e., in the presence of non-susceptible crops), the population of a given pathogen materially decreases. Other pathogens, those to which the alternate crop or crops are susceptible, must as surely increase; but by rotating crops subject to widely different pathogens, effective control is often achieved" (R. B. Stevens, 1949).

Literature on crop rotation is extensive; only a tiny sample is included in the bibliography to this chapter (for example, Stakman and Harrar, 1957; Hunt, 1946; Berkeley, 1944; Leighty, 1938). It is a very old and very widely adopted cultural measure. Leighty, for example, lists twenty-four diseases of seventeen crops controlled solely or mostly by crop rotation and the list could be much increased. Throughout, one finds general agreement on the two factors which, when encountered, constitute the chief obstacles to success in disease control through crop rotation: (1) pronounced longevity of the inoculum; and (2) wide host range. Longevity may stem from the existence of resistant resting spores or sclerotia, or from the ability of the pathogen to exist as a saprophyte. However explained, if it requires a decade or more to disappear from agricultural soils (e.g., flax wilt, cabbage yellows), then crop rotation loses its point. If, on the other hand, a very large number of possible hosts are vulnerable (e.g., *Agrobacterium tumefaciens; Phythium debaryanum; Rhizoctonia solani;* or *Phymatotrichum omnivorum*), it becomes very nearly impossible to establish a favorable rotational pattern.

Economic considerations loom large in weighing the advantages and disadvantages of rotations. It is not feasible, whatever the gain in disease control, to set up a rotation with too few and too infrequent cash crops. Neither can soil fertility, erosion problems, and maintenance of desirable soil structure be ignored. At best, disease relations are but one of several factors to be kept in mind in establishing agricultural crop series.

R. B. Stevens (1949) has suggested a means whereby, in his opinion, the principles and advantages of crop rotation and resistant varieties (see also Section IV, B, 1) can be simultaneously achieved and, at the same time, some of the continuing problems of plant breeding minimized. His argument, which relates most specifically to nonsoil diseases of cereal crops, runs as follows: "Why not practice a rotation of host varieties, rather than of distinct, often widely divergent, crop species? While focusing our attention on the striking and often disturbingly rapid increase in 'new' races or species of pathogens in the presence of newly emphasized host varieties, we should not forget that some, at least, of the 'old' races are correspondingly decreasing. There is likely as significant a decrease in the inoculum of hitherto prevalent pathogens as there is increase in hitherto rare ones! This, coupled with the very possible fact that the old host varieties well may be resistant to the new pathogens, leads to our main thesis: that varietal rotation should be studied as a means of disease control.

"The simple fact that a pathogen is new stands as direct evidence that the older varieties were highly resistant to it, and that it was therefore formerly rare. After five or ten years of widespread plantings of a new host type, it may well be that formerly well-known species or races of pathogens will have become scarce, and that older host varieties can be replanted with profit. By selecting for a given crop, such as wheat or oats, several commercially desirable varieties of widely differing susceptibility, it should be possible to work out a type of rotation which would hold disease losses at a low level."

To our knowledge this suggestion has not yet been proved in actual practice; neither has it been shown invalid.

VI. MEASURES AFFECTING ELEMENTS OTHER THAN THE HOST POPULATION

Repeatedly, throughout this chapter, we have pointed out that the ramifications of cultural control are such that no one item can be clearly dissected from all others. The outline upon which we have based our discussion does not pretend to be either completely logical or entirely free of inconsistencies. Each successive section or subsection represents primarily a new point of view, but we are entirely conscious that facts and instances are partially duplicated from time to time. In Sections IV and V the center of interest was upon actions taken with reference to the host plant. Whatever the particular aim of the control measure discussed, and whatever the specific medium through which that aim was achieved, it was the host plant that was manipulated. Often it was desired to affect the inoculum as well, but the host plant itself was the factor principally involved.

In this, the final section, a full turn about is contemplated. We are concerned now with measures which involve elements in the disease complex other than the host—pathogen or other hosts, as the case may be. Objectives often parallel those recounted in earlier sections; the point of view and emphasis are new.

A. Affecting Inoculum

Chapters 11, 12, and 13 present the case for chemical and biological control of inoculum. It remains here to see what cultural measures there are which have this same objective.

1. Disease-Free Seed and Propagating Material

Chester (1947, p. 466) distinguishes two categories of "noninfested" seed: (1) uninfested (from uninfested areas, from protected seed blocks, indexed material, cleaned or selected seed, certified seed and registered propagating material); and (2) disinfested (by chemicals or heat). This seems an acceptable organization and suggests some of the diversity of ways in which the objectives are sought.

Stevens and Nienow (1947), among others, recount instances of the production of disease-free seed, particularly that of legumes (beans and peas) in semi-arid areas of the western United States. This device is effective against such pathogens as those of anthracnose, bacterial blight, and *Ascochyta*, which are seed-borne and which cannot be destroyed by any currently practicable seed treatment. Because the spread of these diseases in any particular growing season is strictly dependent upon atmospheric moisture, the pathogen does not develop under arid conditions, even when the original seed used is contaminated. The net result is, of course, that seed certified free of the pathogen in question can be made generally available for planting in commercial producing areas.

In an earlier section (IV, C, 2) we referred to heat therapy as one way of ridding seed and propagating material of pathogenic inoculum; chemical seed treatment is discussed in Chapter 12. A few related and miscellaneous techniques deserve mention at this point, most importantly perhaps some recent developments in seed treatment for the blossom-infection loose smuts of wheat and barley. For many years the accepted practice has been a modified hot water treatment, designed to kill the contained mycelium without undue damage to seed and reduction in germination. It now appears (Tyner, 1953; Arny and Leben, 1955; Leben *et al.*, 1956; Tandon and Hansing, 1957) that the same result can be achieved, with much less trouble, by simply soaking the seed in water, a technique which is enhanced if the seed be held in an air-tight container, after soaking, for, say, 48 hours at 80° F. This method has come to be known as the "anaerobic" method, and is both simple and effective. Laboratory studies point to the presence of certain volatile acids (formic, acetic, butyric) produced by the moist seeds as responsible for the disinfecting action and show that spores of several of the pathogens involved do not germinate well under anaerobic conditions and at the pH levels reached (Leben *et al.*, 1956). Addition of various chemicals to the water in which the seeds are placed is thought by some to be an advantage (Tyner, 1953). Others recommend germination tests as a precaution against possible sharp reductions in viability (Arny and Leben, 1955).

Pathogen-free propagative material of ornamentals and orchard crops is much sought after, for reasons that will be self-evident. A number of examples come to mind, some few of which can be cited here. In a recent paper, Baker and a committee (1956) summarize efforts to prepare disease-free items for a number of plants: chrysanthemums, carnations, gladioli, roses, foliage and succulent plants, geraniums, stocks, zinnias, nasturtium. Soaking plum budwood in solutions of streptomycin has been reported successful as a means of ridding it of the bacterium *Phytomonas pruni* (Brown and Heep, 1946).

Sooner or later, if the crop or disease in question has appreciable economic importance, represents a significant portion of the agriculture of a given political unit, or extends over a relatively large area, some kind of governmental regulatory machinery usually comes into operation. This machinery varies greatly in its complexity, and in most cases develops gradually over a period of time, becoming more exacting and effective as the advantages of clean stock become increasingly apparent, and, with this, picks up added public support. In its simplest form, provision for producing disease-free budding and propagating stock consists in an inspection of source trees or nurseries and the selection of only those individuals that seem free of viruses or other undesirable pathogens (Stout, 1950; Boyer, undated; Hildebrand, 1953). Inspection need not be a once-only affair nor cursory; bramble fruit nursery stock in Michigan has been the subject of a careful inspection program for some years (Boyer, undated), involving two inspections so timed as to minimize aphid transmission and to avoid the hotter months when symptoms are masked. Low tolerances are in force, roguing is carried out at time of inspection, and all systemic pathogens are included in the survey.

Regulations governing production and sale of plants and propagating material usually involve a certification system of some kind—the word can be extended, of course, to cover seeds as well and to refer to properties other than freedom from disease, but our usage here is in the more limited sense.

Levy (1948) outlines the development of fruit plant certification in England under the Ministry of Agriculture. Black currant material must be produced under a compulsory system. Strawberry plants, on which great emphasis has been placed since World War I (Demaree, 1948), come either under an "A" or ordinary certificate, which is compulsory, or under a "special stock" certificate introduced in 1945, which is voluntary. The latter is ordinarily only for growers specializing in production of "runners" and hence likely to qualify. Presently, four varieties are included in this certification system, which sets very high standards for care in propagation and allows only very low disease incidence. Raspberry certification is voluntary and confined to certain varieties; while the fruit tree scheme is mostly aimed at accurate naming.

Strawberry certification in California (Mather, 1952) covers yellows, crinkle, nematodes, and red stele. It was first officially sanctioned in 1941 and the present program adopted in 1949 at the request of the growers. Fees adequate to make the program self-supporting have been set. Features of the system include: low tolerances on the pests and diseases named; intensive pest control, roguing, isolation, and plant indexing. There are four field inspections during the first year, before plants can be set in an increase field; three inspections are made in the second year. Provision was made in 1951 for a registry of foundation stock actually indexed and found to be virus-free. Otherwise, this newer program parallels the certification system except for the additional requirement that the source plants first be proved virus-free by 1 year in an index bed. Indexing is to *Fragaria bractata*, a suitable indicator plant.

In the eastern United States (Demaree, 1948) strawberry yellows and related viruses can be avoided, on a stop-gap basis, by using only vigorous plants, but more certainly by indexing the more desirable varieties to Marshall or other good indicator. Demaree suggests that each state experiment station undertake to handle the comparatively few varieties grown commercially within its geographic region. Maintaining virus-free stocks in the West has been very difficult, due to the wide distribution and common occurrence of principal insect vectors.

The technique of indexing, just mentioned, is often employed in programs to develop certified stock when the pathogen is a virus. It involves grafting material from the plant to be tested to a selected host, known to produce consistent and recognizable symptoms, and makes possible confirmation of the presence or absence of virus even when systemic symptoms on the original host are masked or uncertain. A large number of indexing procedures are now available and many suitable test plants identified. As a general rule, each virus of stone fruits (Hildebrand, 1953), strawberries, etc., must be indexed separately, although at times more than one virus can be checked in a single operation. A very common technique is to index a systemic virus on a host which produces local lesion reactions.

Propagating methods in several ways influence for better or worse the spread of disease in vegetatively increased crops and ornamentals. Dimock (1951b) tells how when nurserymen abandoned the practice of grafting roses to imported stocks (*Rosa manetti*) in favor of buying plants already budded to understocks grown on the Pacific Coast,

Verticillium difficulties were augmented; the pathogen in the majority of cases is introduced with the plant and not acquired from infested soil in the area where planted. Christie (1942) points out that in vegetative propagation of chrysanthemums, foliar nematode injury can be held to a minimum if cuttings are taken from the tips of new growth on old crowns rather than by breaking off lateral shoots. Only this simple change is needed to avoid hot-water treatment. Dissemination of nematodes in deciduous fruit trees seems to be favored by the layering propagation method commonly used in multiplying clonal apple rootstocks (Groves, 1958).

Elimination of red stele from valuable strawberry stock by a curious cultural technique has been effected by Vaughan (1956). His procedure takes advantage of the fact that the fungus does not invade the crowns and stolons, even in susceptible varieties, that it grows poorly at temperatures above 65° C., and that it does not thrive in adequately drained soil. Special sterilized flats with wire bottoms were prepared, sterilized, and the whole apparatus set at a level above the soil of potted plants. New runners forming on these plants were kept physically free from the soil in which the mother plant grew, glass wool was employed to prevent splashing, and, when long enough, the new runners pegged down to the surface of the clean flats. As soon as possible after rooting, the new plant was cut free and later checked for freedom from disease by growing under conditions favorable for development of red stele symptoms.

Finally, a special instance of propagation which reflects unusual ingenuity is called to our attention by Stout (1950). In this case certain citrus viruses are avoided by the propagation of "nucellar" seedlings, which technique permits vegetative propagation (and thus retention of varietal characteristics) without danger of virus transmission, since virus does not enter the seed itself.

2. Soil Treatment Other than Chemical

In Chapter 11 are recounted all those techniques whereby inoculum resident in the soil is got rid of or at least where attempts are made to reduce it by the action of chemical agents. Possible alternatives open to the commercial grower or other practicing agriculturist are by no means limited to a choice among chemicals and methods for the application thereof. At several points in our discussion we have alluded more or less specifically to the soil as a source of inoculum and to cultural methods whereby this threat can be lessened; we have reached the point now where these matters are of central interest.

Chester (1947, p. 457) makes the same distinction relative to non-

infested soil as he had made in connection with noninfested seed, i.e.:
(1) uninfested soil (new land, save in those instances where the native
flora harbors pathogens which will invade the first crop; land freed of
pathogens through crop rotation; and land "sanitized" through avoidance
of undesirable crop residues, infested manure, and contaminated tools,
or by the erection of trenches and other physical barriers); and (2)
disinfested soil (by heat, or by fumigation). Other breakdowns could be
made, but this one is useful and the distinctions might profitably be kept
in mind when examining cultural measures.

Except for chemicals, heat is probably the most commonly employed
means for achieving complete or partial sterilization of the soil. There
are several important ways of doing this: with steam, hot water, dry heat,
and so on. The effect of soil heating, regardless of how it is accomplished,
is often to destroy the beneficial nitrifying bacteria, which are nonspore
forming species, but to allow ammonifiers to escape (Newhall, 1955).
Soluble salts are frequently liberated as a result of heat treatments and
colloids destroyed, which latter event can lead to deterioration in soil
structure and to loss in capillarity and water-holding capacity.

Steam heat, a method of long standing, has been employed against
nematodes chiefly, but can render other kinds of inoculum impotent as
well. As a technique, it has the advantage of being very easily learned
and understood. Furthermore, live steam is dissipated almost immediately
after application ceases, leaving no undesirable residues, although reinvasion by fungi is often rapid. Newhall (1955) lists several means
whereby steam may be introduced into the soil under field conditions:
inverted pans, buried perforated pipe or tile, steam harrow or rake. For
very limited volumes of soil, autoclaving is an effective procedure.

Less widely applicable means of heat treatment of soil include: (1)
hot water, which is less effective than steam; (2) firing, as when sites for
seed beds are prepared by first burning quantities of wood on the area,
when natural and other existing vegetation is deliberately set afire or, in
limited situations (control of *Sclerotium rolfsii* in India), when flame
throwers are utilized; or (3) electrical sterilization, relying either upon
the resistance set up by the soil itself or upon some form of heating
apparatus containing resistance units (Newhall, 1955).

Rarely, soil temperatures in warm latitudes rise to levels that inactivate contained pathogens. In Texas, at times, larvae of the root knot
nematode are unable to survive in the top 3 inches or so of the soil, and
it is therefore feasible to destroy high percentages of the population by
the simple device of plowing 3 times at 7–10 day intervals during hot
weather. In some instances, greenhouses can be successfully rid of pests
and soil borne diseases if they be tightly closed in mid-summer sunlight

and the heating systems turned on. Needless to say, this can be done only if the plants therein are either removed or sacrificed .

In the review above cited, Newhall includes a summary of disease control by flooding, and notes its use in the last century against the *Phylloxera* threat to French vineyards. Other pests have been attacked in this manner: wireworms in California, root knot nematode, garden centipede, etc., but the two most publicized examples at present are in connection with the Panama wilt of cultivated banana in Central America and *Sclerotinia sclerotiorum,* affecting truck crops in Florida (Moore, 1949; Stoner and Moore, 1953; Stevens and Nienow, 1947; Stevens and Stevens, 1952). It has been demonstrated that soil inoculum of the *Fusarium* responsible for banana wilt can be materially reduced by several months' inundation of the soil and that it will not again reach troublesome levels for perhaps 6 years. Subsequent experience soon showed that second cycles were not nearly so effective as the first and that considerable inoculum persisted in the upper few inches of soil. This was got rid of by one or both of two means: (1) by plowing and reflooding; and (2) by chemical treatment. Flooding for control of banana wilt was an outgrowth of earlier experience with silting of diseased areas.

From 3 to 6 weeks' flooding suffices to kill the sclerotia of *Sclerotinia sclerotiorum* in Florida soils, and it does not seem to matter much whether it be marl, muck, or sand nor whether the water be held continuously or flooded and drained at 3-day intervals—sclerotia do not, however, deteriorate at all rapidly if subject only to prevailing rainfall in nonflooded fields (Moore, 1949). Stoner and Moore (1953), more recently, have pointed to an economically attractive possibility for cultural control of *S. sclerotiorum* through summer plantings of lowland rice. Not only are the sclerotia rotted under the conditions normally maintained for lowland rice growing, but destruction is completed in a period as short as 20 days, some 2 weeks sooner than in "static" flooding. By fitting rice into an acceptable crop rotation, valuable winter-vegetable land can be profitably occupied in summer.

It must be perfectly clear that flooding associated with rice growing is in this instance directed against diseases of crops (mostly vegetables) in the rotation other than rice itself. The general approach is also practicable as a pest and disease control measure even when the primary crop is flooded in the course of its normal agronomic or horticultural management. Cranberries, bog-grown plants, are often flooded for the express purpose of reducing diseases and pest damage. Perhaps the greatest drawbacks to wider use of flooding are: (1) the sheer physical impossibility, in the majority of places, of getting adequate water supplies and establishing the necessary grading and ditching; and (2) the danger of spreading some unsuspected pathogen other than the one against which the measure is invoked.

One or more forms of tillage is almost invariably involved in agricultural crop production; certain sod-grown orchard crops, forage crops, and forest trees are the only obvious exceptions. The literature of plant pathology contains occasional reference to tillage as related to reduction in soil-borne inoculum, consisting usually of recommendations that surface inoculum be plowed under to such depth that fruiting is prevented or reinvasion of the upper layers delayed (Simmonds, 1953; Hardison, 1948). Such difficulties as result are largely in doing a sufficiently thorough job, without which much inoculum remains on or in the surface layers.

Darpoux and Vuittenez (1949) discovered, experimentally, that pear scab (*Venturia pirina*) could be reduced sharply by "digging in" the fallen, ascospore-producing leaves. It is questionable whether this would be a practicable measure in commercial orchards or whether it would prove superior to eradicant sprays for the same purpose.

Chinn and associates (1953) report a curious means for reducing common root rot of wheat which does not fall clearly into the class of soil amendments (Section IV, C, 1) or of antibiotics (Chapter 13). They indicate a drop in infection following the addition of soybean meal to soil, but insist that this is not related to any increased activity of soil microflora. Instead, it appears that whereas conidia of the fungus (*Helminthosporium sativum*) remain dormant in natural soils, the soymean meal stimulates germination, whereupon lysis ensues and the organism is destroyed.

Soil-borne pathogens differ from each other widely in respect to the pH levels which they find optimum. This fact has long been recognized and taken advantage of by pathologists and others interested in disease control. One can find in the literature lists of organisms favored by relatively acid soils and others favored by alkaline soils. Adjustments of soil pH are regularly made within the tolerances of the host itself. N. E. Stevens (1938a) points to a special instance of pH manipulation worked out by Eddins in Florida against a bacterial pathogen causing brown rot of white potato. Both extremes in pH were combined into a regular yearly alteration wherein soil was rendered acid for an interval sufficient to reduce the population of the organism and then returned to alkaline conditions during the period necessary to grow the crop.

For additional useful, readily available summaries of cultural soil treatments, the interested reader is referred again to the January, 1946, symposium issue of the journal "Social Science."

3. Antisporulants, Eradicant Sprays

By all odds the greater portion of the chemicals used against plant disease, more specifically against inoculum, are used in the form of fungicides and related materials applied to the soil, seed, and foliage (see Chapters 11 and 12). There are special situations, however, where fungicidal substances are employed in a somewhat different manner or where materials not commonly classed as fungicides are used in disease control.

First and foremost are eradicant sprays, at one time treated experimentally for control of overwintering ascospores of the apple scab fungus, 90% of which were eliminated by spraying the orchard floor with Elgetol (sodium salt of dinitro ortho cresol). The remaining inoculum was sufficient to produce scab abundantly however. More recently 5% Puratized (phenyl mercury triethanol ammonium lactate) has been applied to young leaves, flowers, and fruits with greater effectiveness (Goldsworthy et al., 1949). Eradication can, at times, extend to the elimination of pathogens already established in the living host. The striking eradicative action of actidione (cycloheximide) on cherry foliage invaded by the leaf spot fungus (*Coccomyces hiemalis*) is coming to be regarded a classic example (Stout, 1950). Yarwood (1945) gives us a much less well known instance wherein copper sulfate or other soluble coppers, plus a spreader, almost completely eradicated the powdery mildew of beans. At the other extreme, Dimock warns us that phyto-pathogenic spores in viable condition may be disseminated by fungicides as sprays, thus aggravating rather than improving the situation (Dimock, 1951a), although unpublished studies by Waggoner indicate that this occurs but rarely under field conditions.

Several miscellaneous citations, summarized below, will serve to indicate the very considerable diversity of cultural disease control employing fungicides and fungicide-like substances:

1. Lear and Mai (1952) describe the use of methyl bromide for disinfecting burlap bags, tools, and equipment against spread of the golden nematode. The material is effective between 50–80° F., and, by employing vinyl resin coated covers, can be used to fumigate trucks and other comparable farm vehicles.

2. Ayers and Lambert (1955) report that bacterial blotch, soft rot of "pinheads," *Verticillium* spot, and mycogone disease of mushrooms can be controlled by chlorinating the water used for wetting the beds at approximately 50–200 p.p.m., applied when mushrooms begin to appear in the beds. It had apparently been mistakenly thought for some years that this treatment could be used only locally, not as an over-all drench.

Chlorination is, of course, a common way of preventing fungus growth in pulp circulation systems and in other industrial processes.

3. Stevens and Nienow (1947) make reference to a paper by Yarwood to the effect that a spray of water under pressure will check growth of a considerable number of powdery mildews, apparently because, once dislodged, the mycelia cannot regenerate from haustoria.

4. If we can judge from Katznelson's review (1937), control of plant disease by bacteriophage is as yet largely in the experimental stage.

5. Bawden (1954), considering inhibitors of plant viruses, makes the interesting suggestion that such materials as ribonuclease and glycoprotein from *Phytolacca*, if used with a sticker, might prove an effective protectant and a far less irritating substance with which to disinfect the hands of workers in tobacco and tomato growing than those now in fashion.

4. Vector Control

The many ramifications of inoculum dispersal by insects have been thoroughly covered by Broadbent in Chapter 4, and in a recent review of insecticidal control of the spread of plant viruses (Broadbent, 1957). Additional comment comes from Smith and Brierley (1956) and in a number of texts, summary articles, and research reports. A related topic, the resistance of plants to insects, with obvious implications for vector relationships, is covered by Painter (1958).

Vector control illustrates, as does no other phase of the subject, the diverse nature of cultural control. There seems to be almost no detail of transmission of pathogens by insects which, when scrutinized, cannot be shown to have some relationship to possible control measures. In a sense, one could rest content with an admonition to learn all that can possibly be known of the biology of the host-pathogen-vector relationship—and then to so manage affairs that the effectiveness of transmission is held to a minimum. But this would be to beg the question, and a few selected examples will very likely prove helpful—bearing always in mind that the summary is in no way complete.

Vectors are not always insects. Some few vertebrates, notably birds, are responsible for inoculum spread, and various soil microfauna have been implicated from time to time. By all odds, however, insect- or arthropod-transmission is the most frequent association of pathogen and vector and is satisfactorily illustrative of the basic viewpoints and problems encountered.

Provided the ecology of the insect population and the biology of its vector role are adequately known, worthwhile results can be expected. Depending upon individual circumstances, removal of diseased plants may be useful if diagnostic symptoms are such as to be apparent before transmission to new hosts has occurred or where the diseased host serves as a site for increase in vector populations (elms, killed by Dutch elm disease, harbor the beetle vector and furnish conditions ideal for its multiplication). Physical barriers and removal of native reservoir hosts (see Section VI, B, 1–2) can, without directly affecting the insect vector, contribute to the desired end of reducing disease incidence in cultivated crops, just as silvicultural methods (Graham, 1951, 1956) directed against insect populations may, in special instances, be invoked against vectors. Occasionally (Galakhov, 1946) readjustments in crop rotation and re-scheduling of sowing dates can be instituted to upset the pattern of reproduction, hibernation, and dispersal of the vector. Finally, there is always the possibility of utilizing biological control of arthropod vectors, where appropriate predator species are known.

The greater emphasis in arthropod vector control has always been upon insecticides, a very natural outgrowth of the extensive use of chemicals against insects causing direct damage by feeding and oviposition. Principles are not entirely the same, for the effectiveness of vector insects is not necessarily proportional to the degree or duration of the infestation, and the level of insect kill must be very high as well as quickly accomplished.

In writing of virus transmission, Broadbent (1957) shows that insecticides more often than not are ineffective in stopping the spread of disease even when inspection seems to indicate that the vector has been largely eliminated. This is especially true of those viruses which are quickly inoculated into the plant—the nonpersistent group—and which allow, therefore, very little time for the toxic substance to take effect. It thus proves better strategy either to spray contact insecticides on the source plants with a view to killing the largest possible number of insects before they depart for new hosts or to apply persistent chemicals, i.e., those which remain active for some period, such as DDT or Parathion, to the surface of plants to be protected in the hope of killing viruliferous insects as they arrive. Slower-acting materials can be used against vectors carrying viruses of the persistent group, which require an appreciable incubation period in the insect. Systemic insecticides are much like the long-lasting surface materials, with the added advantage that they better protect new foliage as it appears and act more selectively against only the harmful insect species. There is a genuine need for development of new insecticides especially suited for the problems posed by vector control as distinct from general insect control.

B. *Affecting Hosts Other than the Primary Crop*

At times cultural measures center about other host plants, their destruction, removal, or manipulation. Naturally, these control practices are often employed in league with efforts with inoculum or principal host, and depend for their effectiveness upon how closely and importantly the secondary host species is tied in with the survival, reproduction, and spread of the pathogen.

1. *Alternate and Reservoir Hosts*

As a rule, cultural control measures receive little recognition either publicly or privately. To this generalization, the control of heteroecious rusts by the removal of their alternate host species is a conspicuous exception. The fact is that such success as has been attained has in each case required sympathetic response from an informed public. Removal of the economically less important host species has been widely advocated and vigorously prosecuted in North America in three instances: (1) barberry (stem rust of wheat); (2) currant and gooseberry (white pine blister rust); (3) cedar (apple rust). The story of these campaigns need not be retold here, although each is a fascinating study encompassing the biology of the organisms, the economics of crop production and cost of eradication procedures, the strategy of mobilizing public opinion, and the traditions and technicalities of legal codes. Suffice it only to remind ourselves that the success of any eradication and the strategy of its program depend upon the role played by the alternate host in the life of the pathogen. In the case of apple rust, all of the infection of that host comes from spores produced by the cedar phase of the pathogen; alternation is, then, absolutely critical to the continuation of the pathogen. Because leaves and fruit are shed each fall, the apple host commences each spring season free of the pathogen, and will be invaded only if cedar has been allowed to remain nearby.

New infections of white pine rust, likewise, come only from currant and gooseberry, but, since pine cankers form in tissues which persist from year to year, an individual once diseased will be progressively damaged as time goes on, even if the native alternate host be completely eliminated.

Cereals, the economically more desirable member of the pair of alternate hosts of black stem rust, carry not only spores which infect barberry, but, unfortunately, also spores capable of reinvading wheat. Thus disease incidence is not entirely dependent upon barberry once the pathogen is established on wheat. The once very vigorous and extensive eradication program has been continued, but on a new and somewhat reduced basis—primarily to limit the number of new genetic races evolving out of sexual reproduction on barberry.

By "reservoir" hosts are meant those species, frequently indigenous, which are not demonstrably involved in any exact or exclusive way with the life cycle of the pathogen, as are alternate hosts, but which provide an additional site of persistence or multiplication of the pathogen. There are a large number of these recognized, and probably many more not yet incriminated. The concept of reservoir hosts includes not only species serving as sources of air-borne inoculum of vector-borne diseases and as sites of vector survival and multiplication (Steinbauer and Steinmetz, 1945). It involves instances wherein weeds: (1) provide means of pathogen survival when cultivated hosts are inaccessible; (2) are the site where new pathogenic races arise; (3) act as accessory hosts of pathogens. Finally, it should be extended to include what might be called "carrier" varieties—varieties of crop plants in which viruses known to be responsible for destructive diseases do not produce visible effects, but from which they can be transmitted to other varieties of the same crop.

There is a considerable literature on weed control by mechanical, biological, or chemical methods—it would be impossible to include even a representative sample at this point. Probably the most striking trend in recent years is the almost explosive development of herbicidal chemicals, many of them highly selective in their action. Adoption of these means has in no wise changed the rationale for cultural control of diseases by this approach but has favorably altered the economic aspects of the situation. Some interesting viewpoints on the over-all biology of weeds are to be found in a paper by Weiss (1949), including speculations on their striking freedom from disease.

Piemeisel (1954) describes a somewhat different form of weed control associated with disease reduction as "replacement control," or "changes in vegetation in relation to control of pests and diseases." By and large this is a special case of applied ecology or of range management whereby pest populations and pathogen load are reduced through changes in the vegetation from weeds and other ephemerals toward grasses and native perennials. As alteration from the original becomes progressively greater, the problem of replacement control is made more difficult, and the length of time required for its realization longer. With special reference to curly top of sugar beet and other crops in the semi-arid west, the usual story has been the loss of natural cover, occupation of the denuded lands by weeds, enormous increases in the beetle leaf hopper populations, and subsequent increase in disease incidence and damage. By returning all lands not continuously farmed to good desert range—not necessarily either climax or even of what was originally there—the threat can be substantially reduced.

2. Trap and Buffer Crops

A final category in the area of cultural control as it pertains to host species other than the primary crop concerns trap crops and buffers.

Plantings used as buffers are in reality a special instance of the general category of physical barriers introduced under Section V, B, 3; strictly speaking, the species utilized are not even hosts to the pathogens or vectors. One might go so far as to consider isolated plots, seed beds, etc., as extreme examples of protection by barriers, wherein the areas occupied by the buffer species far exceed that occupied by the host. A more useful concept would confine the term to situations where the preponderance of area is occupied by the principal crop and the buffer is truly marginal. Forest windbreaks have been employed in part for disease control (Beilin, 1951) and presumably reduce the overland movement of air-borne inoculum. Their effect on microclimate, especially as they increase temperature and retard drying up of surface moisture, is often to increase disease hazard.

Barriers are reported effective in some instances against spread of insects to seedbeds and cropped areas. Stakman and Harrar (1957, p. 442) find some evidence that legumes sown with *Hevea brasiliensis* form root barriers which retard the growth of subterranean mycelium of fungi causing root rot of the rubber tree, and they suggest that similar relations might pertain to citrus, grapes, and orchard fruits. Sideris (1955) recounts the occurrence of a leaf tip necrosis of pineapple appearing within 1.5 miles of the sea in plantings exposed to wind-blown sea water; partial control can be achieved by establishing multiple rows of *Casuarina equisetifolia* on the seaward side in order to trap wind-blown sea water. The effects on pineapple can also be partly overcome by ample applications of nitrogen and potassium. Chester (1946) mentions the possibility of a rust barrier zone in the south central plains of the United States.

Use of trap or catch crops is based on the notion of providing a host species other than the primary crop, which is particularly susceptible to the pathogen, and, at an appropriate later time, destroying both host and pathogen in a single operation. By so doing it is hoped that the more valuable host will be left relatively free of the inroads of the pathogen.

In field and greenhouse trials with pineapple root knot nematode in Hawaii, Godfrey and others (Godfrey and Hagan, 1934; Godfrey and Hoshino, 1934) found that the population could be very greatly reduced by one or more plantings of a crop such as tomato if the latter were killed at the most favorable time either by mechanical means or by poisons. Decay or destruction must come before eggs are produced or the net result will be to worsen rather than to reduce the population problem. These studies seemed to indicate that the best that can be hoped for is a quick reduction of heavy infections, not complete eradication, and that to plant the trap crop beside the pineapple row was ineffective. Weed killers appear to be a satisfactory means of destroying the catch crop.

Berkeley (1944) includes a somewhat different type of catch or trap crop in pointing to the use of indicator plants of three different varieties in areas of Ceylon about to be replanted to *Hevea* rubber. The chief purpose here is not to destroy the soil pathogen but quickly to establish its presence and extent of infestation in order that diseased material may be identified, removed, and burned.

VII. SUMMARY AND PROGNOSIS

Several points emerge conspicuously from our consideration of cultural control. In the first place, cultural measures are a miscellany. A few are well recognized and widely adopted; many are obscure or so intricately tied in with other steps in the agricultural program that they are not accorded full credit for their contributions to crop production. Curious anachronisms show up as one studies disease control by cultural means. It has, on the one hand, been characteristic of primitive agricultures, poverty of scientific information, and inadequate supplies of agricultural chemicals and equipment; on the other hand, it requires the most exacting, critical, and detailed knowledge of the biology of disease—far beyond that needed for more orthodox operations. In one sense these can be the least expensive and most rewarding of disease control efforts; in another, because the full cost is often immediately apparent and chargeable to the individual producer, cultural control is avoided as being too expensive and troublesome. Reduction of disease damage by cultural means involves more variables, is more difficult to evaluate by controlled experimentation, requires more extensive cooperative action, and impinges on the complex structure of agricultural and forest practice at more points than any alternative pathway open to the pathologist and producer.

No one can possibly say with certainty what the future will bring. It is more than likely that there will be no sudden shift in the popularity of cultural control measures as a whole, although we can expect continuing change and improvement in individual techniques. As time goes on and the knowledge of disease as a pathologic phenomenon accumulates, there is every likelihood that new and provocative cultural control devices will be developed and that more and more producers will take advantage of what this sector of plant pathology has to offer. More particularly, cultural control will continue to be important in situations where other methods prove inadequate, in cases where the biology of pathogenic disease is particularly well known, in the preservation of harvested materials and produce, in forest pathology, as an adjunct to chemical control, and, of course, in alleviating many nonpathogenic troubles. We can also hope that the economy of cultural practices will in time be more realistically evaluated and this obstacle to their wider adoption removed.

It will be immediately apparent that no complete review of the literature of disease control by cultural methods has been attempted. In selecting the few titles to be cited in the bibliography, at least four points were emphasized: (1) where possible, reference is made to survey and review articles, thus affording access to the often very complete and far-ranging literature compilations included there and materially reducing the number of bibliographic entries in the present paper; (2) recent papers were given priority over older publications, particularly from the works of a single author; (3) emphasis was upon readily obtainable material from established sources; and (4) an effort was made to strike some sort of balance among the multiplicity of subtopics comprising the very diverse subject of cultural control.

We are greatly indebted to recent texts and monographs by Chester (1946, 1947), Stakman and Harrar (1957), and Stevens and Stevens (1952), to which a number of page references are made; and to reviews by N. E. Stevens (1938a) and N. E. Stevens and Nienow (1947).

References

Aberg, E. 1945. Effect of vernalization on the development of stripe in barley. *Phytopathology* **35**: 367–368.

Addicott, F. T., and R. S. Lynch. 1957. Defoliation and desiccation: harvest-aid practices. *Advances in Agron.* **9**: 67–93.

Allen, P. J. 1954. Physiological aspects of fungus diseases of plants. *Ann. Rev. Plant Physiol.* **5**: 225–248.

Arndt, C. H. 1945. Viability and infection of light and heavy cotton seeds. *Phytopathology* **35**: 747–753.

Arndt, C. H. 1946. Effect of storage conditions on survival of Colletotrichum gossypii. *Phytopathology* **36**: 24–29.

Arny, D. C., and C. Leben. 1955. The effect of the water-soak seed treatment on the germination of certain barley varieties grown at different locations. *Phytopathology* **45**: 518–519.

Avery, G. S., Jr., and B. F. Thompson. 1947. Chemical control of plant growth. *Econ. Botany* **1**: 176–187.

Ayers, T. T., and E. B. Lambert. 1955. Controlling mushroom diseases with chlorinated water. *Plant Disease Reptr.* **39**: 829–836.

Baker, K. F., and committee. 1956. Development and production of pathogen-free propagative material of ornamental plants. *Plant Disease Reptr. Suppl.* **238**: 57–95.

Baker, K. F., and W. C. Snyder. 1950. Plant diseases; restrictive effect of California climate on vegetables, grains and flowers. *Calif. Agr.* **4:** 3, 15–16.

Bawden, F. C. 1954. Inhibitors and plant viruses. *Advances in Virus Research* **2:** 31–57.

Bawden, F. C., and N. W. Pirie. 1952. Physiology of virus diseases. *Ann. Rev. Plant Physiol.* **3:** 171–188.

Beilin, I. G. 1951. In regard to the effectiveness of forest plantings in protecting young crops from fungus diseases. *Nauch. Voprosy Polezashchitnogo Leso-Razvedeniia Inst. Lesa, Akad. Nauk S. S. S. R.* **1:** 252–264.

Berkeley, G. H. 1944. Root-rots of certain non-cereal crops. *Botan. Rev.* **10:** 67–123.

Boyer, C. A. (undated) Bramble fruit plant inspection in Michigan. 3 pp. mimeo.

Bratley, C. O., and J. S. Wiant. 1950. Diseases of fruits and vegetables found on the market, and means of controlling them. *Econ. Botany* **4:** 177–191.

Broadbent, L. 1957. Insecticidal control of the spread of plant viruses. *Ann. Rev. Entomol.* **2:** 339–354.

Brooks, C. 1935. Some botanical aspects of perishable food products. *Sci. Monthly* **40:** 122–137.

Brown, J. G., and D. M. Heep. 1946. Effect of streptomycin on budwood infected with Phytomonas pruni. *Science* **104:** 208.

Brown, W. 1936. The physiology of host-parasite relations. *Botan. Rev.* **2:** 236–281.

Buchholtz, W. F. 1944. Crop rotation and soil drainage effects on sugar beet tip rot and susceptibility of other crops to Aphanomyces cochlioides. *Phytopathology* **34:** 805–812.

Chester, K. S. 1946. "The Nature and Prevention of the Cereal Rusts." Chronica Botanica, Waltham, Massachusetts. 269 pp.

Chester, K. S. 1947. "Nature and Prevention of Plant Diseases." 2nd ed. Blakiston Div., McGraw Hill, New York. 525 pp.

Chester, K. S. 1950. Plant disease losses: their appraisal and interpretation. *Plant Disease Reptr. Suppl.* **193:** 191–362.

Chinn, S. H. F., R. J. Ledingham, B. J. Sallans, and P. M. Simmonds. 1953. A mechanism for the control of common rootrot of wheat. *Phytopathology* **43:** 701.

Chitwood, B. G., and B. A. Oteifa. 1952. Nematodes parasitic on plants. *Ann. Rev. Microbiol.* **6:** 151–184.

Christensen, C. M. 1957. Deterioration of stored grains by fungi. *Botan. Rev.* **23:** 108–134.

Christie, J. R. 1942. The influence of chrysanthemum propagation methods on dissemination of the foliar nematode. *Proc. Helminthol. Soc. Wash. D. C.* **9:** 1–4.

Cochrane, V. W. 1949. Crop residues as causative agents of root rots of vegetables. *Conn. Agr. Expt. Sta. Bull.* **526:** 34 pp.

Colwell, R. N. 1956. Determining the prevalence of certain cereal crop diseases by means of aerial photography. *Hilgardia* **26:** 223–286.

Cooley, J. S. 1946. Root diseases of deciduous fruit trees. *Botan. Rev.* **12:** 83–100.

Coons, G. H. 1953. Some problems in growing sugar beets. *Yearbook Agr. U. S. Dept. Agr.* **1953:** 509–524.

Coons, G. H., and J. E. Kotila. 1935. Influence of preceding crops on damping off of sugar beets. *Phytopathology* **25:** 13.

Darpoux, H., and A. Vuittenez. 1949. Role des peritheces de Venturia pirina dans la region parisienne. Influence de l'elimination des fuilles mortes par le bechange sur l'intensite des premieres contaminations et sur l'evolution ulterieure de la tavelure du Poirier. *Compt. rend. acad. agr. France* **36:** 592–594; 1950. *Rev. Appl. Mycol.* **29:** 217.

Demaree, J. B. 1948. Yellows or xanthosis in strawberries in eastern United States. *Plant Disease Reptr.* **32:** 428–432.

DiMarco, G. R., and B. H. Davis. 1957a. Prevention of decay of peaches with post-harvest treatments. *Plant Disease Reptr.* **41:** 284–288.

DiMarco, G. R., and B. H. Davis. 1957b. Prevention of decay of strawberries with post-harvest treatments. *Plant Disease Reptr.* **41:** 460–464.

Dimock, A. W. 1951a. The dispersal of viable spores of phytopathogenic fungi by fungicidal sprays. *Phytopathology* **41:** 157–163.

Dimock, A. W. 1951b. Bud transmission of Verticillium in roses. *Phytopathology* **41:** 781–784.

Dobromyslov, P. N. 1932. Degree of infection with bunt of spring wheat grown in ridges as against flat rows. *In* "Diseases of Grain Crops." Siberian Scientific-Research Institute of Cereal Economy." Omsk. pp. 72–79; 1933. *Rev. Appl. Mycol.* **12:** 155.

Eide, C. J. 1955. Fungus infection of plants. *Ann. Rev. Microbiol.* **9:** 297–318.

Emmons, C .W. 1940. Medical mycology. *Botan. Rev.* **6:** 474–514.

Fischer, G. W., and C. S. Holton. 1957. "Biology and Control of the Smut Fungi." Ronald Press, New York. 622 pp.

Foister, C. E. 1946. The relation of weather to fungus diseases of plants. II. *Botan. Rev.* **12:** 548–591.

Galakhov, P. N. 1946. Measures for control of "zakuklivanie" virus disease on oats in the Subtaiga Zone of East Siberia. *Doklady Vsesoyuz. Akad. Sel'skokhoz. Nauk im. V. I. Lenina* **9–10:** 16–18; 1948. *Field Crops Abstr.* **1:** 34.

Gäumann, E. 1950. "Principles of Plant Infection." Hafner, New York. 543 pp. (Engl. ed.).

Gaskill, J. O. 1950. Drying after harvesting increases storage decay of sugar-beet roots. *Phytopathology* **40:** 483–486.

Gillespie, W. H., A. L. Shigo, and R. P. True. 1957. The degree of mat-production control obtained by girdling oak wilt trees in West Virginia and some factors influencing mat formation in girdled trees. *Plant Disease Reptr.* **41:** 362–367.

Godfrey, G. H., and H. R. Hagan. 1934. A study of the root-knot-nematode trap crop under field soil conditions. *Phytopathology* **24:** 648–658.

Godfrey, G. H., and H. M. Hoshino. 1934. The trap crop as a means of reducing root-knot-nematode infestation. *Phytopathology* **24:** 635–647.

Goldsworthy, M. C., J. C. Dunegan, and R. A. Wilson. 1949. Control of apple scab by ground and tree applications. *Plant Disease Reptr.* **33:** 312–318.

Graham, S. A. 1951. Developing forests resistant to insect injury. *Sci. Monthly* **73:** 235–244.

Graham, S. A. 1956. Ecology of forest insects. *Ann. Rev. Entomol.* **1:** 261–280.

Greaney, F. J. 1946. Influence of time, rate, and depth of seeding on the incidence of root rot in wheat. *Phytopathology* **36:** 252–263.

Groves, A. B. 1958. Root diseases of deciduous fruit trees. *Botan. Rev.* **24:** 25–42.

Hardison, J. R. 1948. Field control of blind seed disease of perennial ryegrass in Oregon. *Phytopathology* **38:** 404–419.

Hart, H. 1949. Nature and variability of disease resistance in plants. *Ann. Rev. Microbiol.* **3:** 289–316.

Hildebrand, E. M. 1953. Fruit virus diseases in New York in retrospect. *Plant Disease Reptr. Suppl.* **222:** 185–223.

Hopkins, E. F., and K. W. Loucks. 1948. A curing procedure for the reduction of mold decay in citrus fruits. *Florida Agr. Expt. Sta. Bull.* **450:** 26 pp.

Hubert, F. P. 1957. Diseases of some export crops in Indonesia. *Plant Disease Reptr.* **41:** 55–63.

Hunt, N. R. 1946. Destructive plant diseases not yet established in North America. *Botan. Rev.* **12:** 593–627.

Imshenetskii, A. A., and E. S. Nazarova. 1937. The action of ultrashort waves on wood-destroying fungi (Merulius lacrymans Schum. and Poria vaporaria Pers.). *Izvest. Akad. Nauk S. S. S. R. Ser. Biol.* **1:** 221–230; 1937. *Rev. Appl. Mycol.* **16:** 721.

Kassanis, B. 1957. Effects of changing temperature on plant virus diseases. *Advances in Virus Research* **4:** 221–241.

Katznelson, H. 1937. Bacteriophage in relation to plant diseases. *Botan. Rev.* **3:** 499–521.

King, N. J. 1953. Progress in control of ratoon stunting disease. *Australian Sugar J.* **45:** 484, 486; 1954. *Rev. Appl. Mycol.* **33:** 503.

Krochmal, A. 1956. Apple storage in Northern Greece. *Econ. Botany* **10:** 174–175.

Kuijt, J. 1955. Dwarf mistletoes. *Botan. Rev.* **21:** 569–627.

Kunkel, L. O. 1955. Cross protection between strains of yellows-type virus. *Advances in Virus Research* **3:** 251–273.

Kuntz, J. E., and A. J. Riker. 1950. Oak wilt in Wisconsin. *Wisconsin Agr. Expt. Sta. Stencil Bull.* **9:** 9 pp.

Large, E. C. 1940. "The Advance of the Fungi." Holt, New York. 488 pp.

Lear, B., and W. F. Mai. 1952. Methyl bromide for disinfesting burlap bags and machinery to help prevent spread of golden nematode of potatoes. *Phytopathology* **42:** 489–492.

Leben, C., R. W. Scott, and D. C. Arny. 1956. On the nature of the mechanism of the water-soak method for controlling diseases incited by certain seed-borne pathogens. *Phytopathology* **46:** 273–276.

Leighty, C. E. 1938. Crop rotation. *Yearbook Agr. U. S. Dept. Agr.* **1938:** 406–430.

Levy, B. G. 1948. Certification schemes for fruit plants. *Ann. Rept. East Malling Research Sta. Kent* **1947:** 178–181; 1949. *Rev. Appl. Mycol.* **28:** 340–341.

Loehwing, W. F. 1937. Root interactions of plants. *Botan. Rev.* **3:** 195–239.

McGrath, H. and P. R. Miller. 1958. Blue mold of tobacco. *Plant Disease Reptr. Suppl.* **250:** 1–35.

Mader, E. O. 1947. A corrective measure for "soil sickness" occurring in sand media. *Phytopathology* **37:** 682–683.

Martin, W. J., J. M. Lutz, and G. B. Ramsey. 1949. Control of black rot in washed, uncured sweet potatoes. *Phytopathology* **39:** 580–582.

Mather, S. M. 1952. Strawberry plant certification and registration in California. *Calif. Dept. Agr. Bull.* **41:** 3–8.

Metlitskii, L., and V. Soboleva. 1936. The lethal action of high frequency field on Sclerotinia Libertiana and Botrytis cinerea. *Zashchita Rastenii* **10:** 32–36.

Milbrath, D. G. 1948. Control of Western celery mosaic. *Calif. Dept. Agr. Bull.* **37:** 3–7.

Miles, L. E. 1939. Effect of type and period of storage on cotton seed after treatment with organic mercury dust. *Phytopathology* **29:** 986–991.

Miller, E. V. 1946. Physiology of citrus fruits in storage. *Botan. Rev.* **12:** 393–423.

Moore, W. D. 1949. Flooding as a means of destroying the sclerotia of Sclerotinia sclerotiorum. *Phytopathology* **39:** 920–927.

Morgan, E. P. 1948. Food's paradise. *Colliers* **121**:(18) 18–19, 40–42.

Morris, C. L. 1955. Control of mat formation by the oak wilt fungus by early felling of diseased trees. *Plant Disease Reptr.* **39**: 258–260.

Newhall, A. G. 1955. Disinfestation of soil by heat, flooding and fumigation. *Botan. Rev.* **21**: 189–250.

Newton, N. 1951. Some effects of high-intensity ultrasound on tobacco mosaic virus. *Science* **114**: 185–186.

Painter, R. H. 1958. Resistance of plants to insects. *Ann. Rev. Entomol.* **3**: 267–290.

Parkin, E. A. 1956. Stored product entomology (the assessment and reduction of losses caused by insects to stored foodstuffs). *Ann. Rev. Entomol.* **1**: 223–235.

Pentzer, W. T., and P. H. Heinze. 1954. Postharvest physiology of fruits and vegetables. *Ann. Rev. Plant Physiol.* **5**: 205–224.

Peterson, P. D., and H. W. Johnson. 1928. Powdery mildew of raspberry. *Phytopathology* **18**: 787–796.

Piemeisel, R. L. 1954. Replacement control; changes in vegetation in relation to control of pests and diseases. *Botan. Rev.* **20**: 1–32.

Pound, G. S. 1946. Control of virus diseases of cabbage seed plants in Western Washington by plant bed isolation. *Phytopathology* **36**: 1035–1039.

Rodenwaldt, E. (ed.) 1952–1955. "World Atlas of Epidemic Diseases," Vols. 1, 2, 3. Falk, Hamburg.

Schomer, H. A., and L. P. McColloch. 1948. Ozone in relation to storage of apples. *U. S. Dept. Agr. Circ.* **765**: 24 pp.

Schultz, E. S., R. Bonde, and W. P. Raleigh. 1944. Early harvesting of healthy seed potatoes for the control of potato diseases in Maine. *Maine Agr. Expt. Sta. Bull.* **427**: 19 pp.

Sideris, C. P. 1955. Effects of sea water sprays on pineapple plants. *Phytopathology* **45**: 590–595.

Simmonds, P. M. 1953. Rootrots of cereals. II. *Botan. Rev.* **19**: 131–146.

Smith, F. F., and P. Brierley. 1956. Insect transmission of plant viruses. *Ann. Rev. Entomol.* **1**: 299–322.

Smith, H. S., E. O. Essig, H. S. Fawcett, G. M. Peterson, H. J. Quayle, R. E. Smith, and H. R. Tolley. 1933. The efficacy and economic effects of plant quarantine in California. *Calif. Agr. Expt. Sta. Bull.* **533**: 276 pp.

Smock, R. M. 1944. The physiology of deciduous fruits in storage. *Botan. Rev.* **10**: 560–598.

Snelling, R. O. 1941. Resistance of plants to insect attack. *Botan. Rev.* **7**: 543–586.

Stakman, E. C., and J. G. Harrar. 1957. "Principles of Plant Pathology." Ronald Press, New York. 581 pp.

Steinbauer, G. P., and F. H. Steinmetz. 1945. Eradication of certain Maine weeds, an important step in control of potato diseases spread by aphids. *Maine Agr. Expt. Sta. Misc. Publ.* **602**: 21 pp.

Stevens, N. E. 1938a. Departures from ordinary methods in controlling plant diseases. *Botan. Rev.* **4**: 429–445, 677–678.

Stevens, N. E. 1938b. Problems involved in control of plant diseases and insects. *J. Econ. Entomol.* **31**: 39–44.

Stevens, N. E. 1940. Recent trends in plant disease control. *Trans. Illinois State Acad. Sci.* **33**: 66–67.

Stevens, N. E. 1942. How plant breeding programs complicate plant disease problems. *Science* **95**: 313–316.

Stevens, N. E. 1949. Characteristics of some disease-free ornamental plants. *Science* **110**: 218–219.

Stevens, N. E., and I. Nienow. 1947. Plant disease control by unusual methods. *Botan. Rev.* **13:** 116–124.

Stevens, N. E., and R. B. Stevens. 1952. "Disease in Plants." Chronica Botanica, Waltham, Massachusetts. 219 pp.

Stevens, R. B. 1949. Replanting "discarded" varieties as a means of disease control. *Science* **110:** 49.

Stoner, W. N., and W. D. Moore. 1953. Lowland rice farming, a possible cultural control for Sclerotinia sclerotiorum in the Everglades. *Plant Disease Reptr.* **37:** 181–186.

Stout, G. L. 1950. New methods of plant disease control. *Calif. Dept. Agr. Bull.* **39:** 129–136.

Tandon, I. N., and E. D. Hansing. 1957. Control of loose smut of barley by water-soak and anaerobic treatments. *Plant Disease Reptr.* **41:** 202–204.

Tapke, V. F. 1948. Environment and the cereal smuts. *Botan. Rev.* **14:** 359–412.

Tyner, L. E. 1953. The control of loose smut of barley and wheat by Spergon and by soaking in water at room temperature. *Phytopathology* **43:** 313–316.

Valleau, W. D. 1953. Suggestions for more complete control of downy mildew or blue mold of tobacco. *Phytopathology* **43:** 616–618.

Vaughan, E. K. 1956. A method for eliminating the red-stele fungus from valuable strawberry stocks. *Phytopathology* **46:** 235–236.

Verrall, A. F. 1945. The control of fungi in lumber during air-seasoning. *Botan. Rev.* **11:** 398–415.

Wagener, W. W., and R. W. Davidson. 1954. Heart rots in living trees. *Botan. Rev.* **20:** 61–134.

Waggoner, P. E. 1958. Private communication.

Walker, J. C. 1941. Disease resistance in the vegetable crops. *Botan. Rev.* **7:** 458–506.

Weiss, F. 1949. Weeds, fungi, and the education of botanists. *Sci. Monthly* **68:** 257–261.

Wilson, E. E., and G. A. Baker. 1946. Some features of the spread of plant diseases by air-borne and insect-borne inoculum. *Phytopathology* **36:** 418–432.

Wilson, J. D. 1932. Environmental factors in relation to plant disease and injury: a bibliography. *Ohio Agr. Expt. Sta. Tech. Ser. Bull.* **9:** 203 pp.

Wingard, S. A. 1941. The nature of disease resistance in plants. I. *Botan. Rev.* **7:** 59–109.

Wood, J. I., and P. R. Miller. 1949. Losses from plant diseases: effects on crop industries and on farm life. *Plant Disease Reptr. Suppl.* **186:** 254–282.

Yarwood, C. E. 1945. Copper sulphate as an eradicant spray for powdery mildew. *Phytopathology* **35:** 895–909.

Yarwood, C. E. 1957. Powdery mildews. *Botan. Rev.* **23:** 235–301.

CHAPTER 11

Soil Treatment

W. A. KREUTZER

Agricultural Research Division, Shell Development Company, Modesto, California

"At the present time, there is insufficient food production to provide adequate nourishment for the people of the world, and the population is rising rapidly." Harrison Brown (1954).

I. INTRODUCTION

Plants are vulnerable to attack in two general areas: the leaves and stems above the ground, and the stems and roots below the ground. It is easy to see blight or leaf spots on the aerial portions of plants; it is considerably more difficult to detect root rot or the onset of vascular attack in the equally important underground tissues. It has been said that plant pathogens are a shifty lot; if so, the pathogens of roots and basal stems are the shiftiest of the lot.

Wherever there is soil, there is soil-borne disease. Whether plants grow in the soils of arctic tundras, the black chernozems of the plains,

431

the podzols of northern forests, or the latosols of the tropics makes little difference; soil-borne pathogens exact their unceasing toll. The losses to man can be counted in millions of tons of food, clothing, and building materials.

No one knows the true extent of this waste. It has been estimated that over a third of the losses from plant diseases in the United States is due to soil-borne disease, undoubtedly caused by the more spectacular pathogens (Clark *et al.*, 1957). How much damage is induced by low-grade and, doubtlessly, universal root pathogens is open to speculation.

At present we do not do a very good job of controlling soil-borne plant diseases. Resistant crop varieties have given relief, especially in the fight against vascular diseases. Crop rotation has proved beneficial primarily in the control of the more specialized pathogens, but is un-popular with agriculturists for economic reasons. Improved cultural practices, the use of proper cover crops, and soil amendments have helped. Soil treatments with heat and chemicals have been useful. Cooking the soil to destroy the plant killers is very effective. This ancient method is excellent in greenhouse carnation culture, but is quite impractical for field-grown beans and tomatoes. Seed treatments to date have been the sole and generally effective chemical method of control. Unfortunately, seed treatments work well against only the earliest phases of seedling attack by pathogens such as *Pythium* and *Rhizoctonia*.

It boils down to this: we are at least holding our own. This is not good enough. We cannot substantially increase the 350-odd million acres of crop land in the United States. Realtors are chopping away at the best of this land to provide housing for the ever-increasing population. There are more people to feed from the production of less land. There is only one answer: more food must be produced on less land.

It is the purpose of this chapter to discuss the treatment of soil for the control of soil pathogens. Heat treatment which has played an im-portant role in the past will be considered but briefly; major emphasis will be placed on the newer phases of chemical control. This will not include the use of chemicals as seed treatments or soil amendments, since these uses are not considered pertinent to the present subject. Soil treatment with chemicals is the newest tactic in the never-ending battle against soil pathogens. The approach is crude today. Tomorrow this will not be so.

II. Basic Concepts

The present method in the chemical control of soil pathogens is to introduce fungicides and nematocides into soil for the purpose of killing or preventing the growth of these organisms. There are two ways of doing this. The first is by seed treatment, in which a small amount of chemical on the seed is introduced into soil to protect the seed and seedling against pathogens in the immediate vicinity. The second is to increase the zone of protection by introducing larger quantities of the chemical into soil either before planting or at the time of planting.

The practical and beneficial effects of seed treatment are well-known. The introduction of larger amounts of chemical into soil ("soil treatment") to control pests and pathogens, although not a new idea, is not as well-known or understood. It began with Thenard in 1869, almost 80 years ago, when he recommended soil injections of carbon disulfide for the control of the grape parasite *Phylloxera* (Fleming and Baker, 1935). This was followed by Thaxter's soil treatments with sulfur in 1891 and Selby's use of formaldehyde in 1900 to control onion smut. The initial modern impetus in soil treatment came from Godfrey's field trials with chloropicrin in 1935 and Carter's discovery of dichloropropene-dichloropropane mixture in 1943.

Fungicides and nematocides, following their introduction into soil, most frequently bring about beneficial crop responses. This has been especially true where pathogenic nematodes are present in soils (Godfrey, 1935). Pathogenic soil fungi have been controlled directly (Young, 1940) or indirectly by activating an antagonist of the pathogen (Bliss, 1948). There have been instances of plant stimulation in the absence of known pathogens (Kreutzer and Montagne, 1950; Koch, 1955). These examples adequately indicate that there is much to learn about the etiology of soil-borne diseases.

There have also been unfavorable results from soil treatment. Cases have been observed where a major pathogen is controlled, but the treatment has brought about the development, to a damaging degree, of a pathogen that previously was considered to be of minor importance (Haasis, 1952; Wilhelm, 1957). Sometimes the application of a biocide to the soil aggravates a disease condition (Gibson, 1956).Obviously soil treatment affects organisms other than those which we wish to control. A biocide may kill indiscriminately both the detrimental and favorable organisms of the soil population. Some soil organisms are susceptible to chemical poisoning; others are resistant. Some die; some live. The soil population changes, and these changes are reflected in the developing crop plant.

We need more fundamental knowledge to enable us to predict crop response to chemical treatment. Some of this information already exists, scattered throughout the literature. Collation and integration are needed. There are small gaps requiring extrapolation. There are wide crevasses justifying guesses. This brings us to the fundamental phase of our subject.

A. *The Soil Biophase and Disease*

The environment affects all things that live in the soil. Every organism is acted upon directly or indirectly by single environmental factors or by combinations of them. Any organism or combination of organisms influences directly or indirectly all or any of the parts of the environment. Each living entity reflects the impact of every other living form or combination of forms.

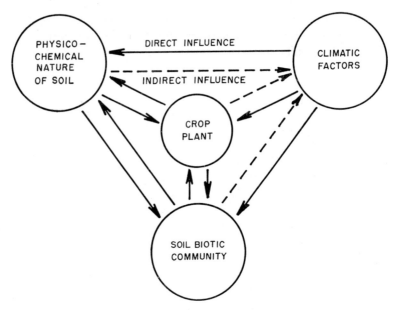

FIG. 1. Fundamental interrelationships between the crop plant and its environment.

There is, then, a complex interrelationship between (1) the physicochemical nature of the soil; (2) the basic environmental factors of light, temperature, and moisture; (3) the microorganisms living in the soil; and (4) the crop plant growing in the soil. These relationships are shown in Fig. 1.

An endless series of changes and complex interactions begin when a plant grows in soil. As the roots penetrate into the soil, excess water is lost through the transpiring leaves. Soil aeration increases. Fungi, streptomycetes, and aerobic bacteria multiply; anaerobic bacteria wane. The permeability of the soil increases, the pH shifts, and the chemistry of the soil changes. The quality and quantity of the soil population is altered. Root secretions determine the character of the rhizosphere. Minor elements are fixed or made available, and levels of nitrate and phosphate fluctuate. The plant responds, producing leaves which reduce light on the surface of the soil, and the surface soil temperature falls. The microclimate is created. The character of the soil surface population changes. The end result is a better or poorer plant to harvest.

This is the framework within which soil-borne disease develops and soil treatment exerts its effect.

1. *The Microbiological Balance*

In 1932 Weindling noted that *Trichoderma viride* prevented the development of *Rhizoctonia solani* in soil. Introduce *Trichoderma* into steamed or acidified soil containing *Rhizoctonia*, and the pathogen is controlled. Introduce *Trichoderma* into nonsteamed neutral soil, and *Rhizoctonia* flourishes (Weindling and Fawcett, 1936). The soil has its own system of checks and balances. If green rye manure is plowed into field soil, *Streptomyces scabies* can be controlled (Millard and Taylor, 1927). If the soil organisms are given something new to work on, they may take care of the problem in their own way.

In any agricultural soil for any given set of conditions in time and space an equilibrium tends to exist between the members of the biotic community (biophase). This equilibrium state is constantly altered by changes in the soil environment (Waksman, 1952; Martin and Aldrich, 1954; Martin *et al.*, 1957.) These changes are usually the results of cultural practices and the normal growth and death of crop plants.

Sometimes cataclysmic changes occur in the soil. Heavy prolonged flooding or soil treatments with biocides or steam are examples of treatments that cause such changes. Under these conditions, new and sometimes radically different equilibria succeed one another.

A microbiological balance can be favorable or unfavorable to the crop plant (Zagallo and Katznelson, 1957). This balance may supply the proper nutrients or make them unavailable. It may sustain plant pathogens or depress and inhibit them. It can prevent an increase in the quantity of indigenous organisms or the establishment of exotic organisms (Weindling and Fawcett, 1936; Park, 1955). This brings us to a consideration of the concept of plant sustainers and plant inhibitors.

2. *Plant Sustainers and Inhibitors*

The soil biophase is a vast microcosm: an endless array of genera, species, varieties, and races of microorganisms. These organisms live in a dark jungle in which all kinds of gaseous, liquid, and solid inorganic and organic chemicals intermingle and interact. Each and every one of these living entities have an important direct or indirect end effect on the developing crop plant. This is the biotic community which we treat with a nematocide or a fungicide.

There are two zones of importance in the soil biophase: the more critical rhizosphere (near the root) and the less critical "outside" zone. The organisms of the rhizosphere, principally bacteria and mycorrhizal fungi, differ in numbers and kinds from those of the outside zone (Katznelson and Richardson, 1943).

The activities of many soil organisms are well-known. The nutrient producers *Azotobacter, Nitrosomonas,* and *Rhizobium* fix nitrogen in a form available for use by plants; other bacteria increase the availability of sulfur, phosphorus, molybdenum, and iron (Waksman, 1952).

Then, there are the important soil-forming organisms: the great hosts of bacteria and fungi that decompose carbohydrates, proteins, and fats. There are the cellulose and lignin-splitting fungi and bacteria, and those organisms which degrade hemicelluloses, pentosans, and lignocelluloses (Waksman, 1952; Bracken, 1955). The soil aggregators, the producers of mucin and polyuronides, are also present (Cornfield, 1955).

We must not forget the plant pathogens: the parasites, the toxin formers, and the nutrient competitors. Pathogens of seedlings are here, such as *Rhizoctonia* and *Pythium;* the stem rotters, *Phytophthora* and *Fusarium;* the root invaders, *Meloidogyne* and *Verticillium.* There is the plant poisoner, *Periconia,* and the tobacco distorter, *Bacillus cereus* (Steinberg, 1956). There are also those microorganisms that war against plants by attrition. These are the competitors for plant nutrients, such as the denitrifying *Thiobacillus* (Waksman, 1952) and the phosphorus, molybdenum, zinc, manganese, iron, and copper-locking organisms (Thornton, 1956).

So much for the direct effects, either beneficial or detrimental to the crop plant. There are those organisms which exert their effects on the plant in indirect fashion. Here we find the great group of antagonists and parasites of phytopathogens: fungi such as species of *Trichoderma, Cephalothecium,* and hosts of others; the fungal parasites of nematodes, *Arthrobotrys,* and *Dactylella* (Duddington, 1957). Antagonists of nutrient formers and antagonists of antagonists are here. *Streptomyces lavendulae* inhibits the nitrogen-fixing *Azotobacter,* and *Bacillus subtilis* poisons *Cephalothecium,* which in turn antagonizes the plant parasite *Helminthosporium* (Waksman, 1947).

Finally, there are even such organisms as *Aerobacter,* the thiamine former, which stimulate and sustain other organisms, and thus in an indirect fashion benefit or inhibit the crop plant (Morton and Stroube, 1955).

A soil organism then, at a given moment in space and time either acts directly or indirectly to inhibit a crop plant or to sustain it. In other words, it is either good or bad for the crop plant. It is never neutral. We can consider any inhabitant of the soil, therefore, to be either a plant sustainer or a plant inhibitor. This concept is shown in Fig. 2. This is a simplification, since complex chain reactions and interrelationships are not indicated.

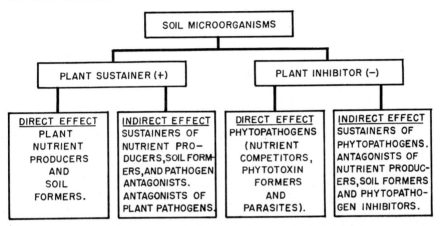

FIG. 2. The concept of plant sustainers and plant inhibitors.

Unfavorable and favorable microbiological balances are determined by the dominance of either the inhibitors or sustainers present primarily in the rhizosphere.

Finally, the role of any one organism is not necessarily fixed. Borderline types can shift their nature with a change of soil or crop conditions, becoming inhibitors instead of sustainers or sustainers instead of inhibitors. Plow straw into soil, and *Chaetomium* may build up. Under certain conditions *Chaetomium* is a good antagonist of phytopathogens. Too much *Chaetomium* may shift its dominant role from sustainer to inhibitor, since it can create a nitrogen deficiency by directly competing with the crop plant for this element.

We are beginning to see why soil treatment with nematocides or fungicides can give unexpected responses. We need to know more about sustainers and inhibitors and the effects of soil biocides on the microbiological balance. Our goal in soil treatment is not only the direct control of plant pathogens, but also the changing of the microbiological equilibrium from the plant inhibitor to the plant sustainer side.

3. *The Norm and Disease*

When plants that are considered normal for a given population show an unexpected growth response as a result of soil treatment with a

chemical, we find ourselves in a dilemma. Either the chemical is killing
or inhibiting soil pathogens or it is acting chemically to stimulate the
plant in some unknown fashion. It is difficult to consider the plants of the
"normal" untreated population as diseased, since our concept of a
disease dictates that it should be a significant decline from the norm.
To avoid the disrupting implications of our finding, we speak of "stimulation" or "increased growth response."

This situation is not new. Oberlin in 1894, using carbon disulfide
soil treatments to control *Phylloxera* in grape vineyards, noted unexpected plant responses in fumigated soils (Loew, 1909). Oberlin,
according to Loew, "recommended carbon bisulphid . . . in cases where
the soil ceased to produce in spite of rich manuring and the absence of
parasites." Loew also noted increased growth of plants in CS_2-treated
plots over that of control manured plots in the "absence of parasites."

In the years following Loew's observation many new fungus parasites
of stems and roots were described. The field work of Godfrey (1935),
Young (1940), and Carter (1943) showed that favorable responses to
soil treatment with such materials as carbon disulfide, chloropicrin, and
dichloropropene-dichloropropane mixture were due largely to control of
pathogenic soil nematodes and fungi.

Increased plant vigor in the apparent absence of pathogens has been
noted in the control of "replant diseases" by soil fumigation (Martin
et al., 1953; Koch, 1955). From such results as these, Garrett (1956)
concluded that "the normal crop is one that suffers an appreciable and
regular degree of root damage by parasites."

We can conclude that "increased growth response" means control of
unknown plant inhibitors in the rhizosphere. They may be ectoparasitic
or endoparasitic forms, weakly pathogenic facultative saprophytes
(Wensley, 1956), obscure obligate parasites, plant toxin formers, or
nutrient competitors. They may even be supposedly benign endotrophic
mycorrhizal fungi (Reed and Frémont, 1935). Knock the fleas off a dog,
and its appetite will improve.

It is probable that crop losses from such low-grade plant inhibitors
may be many times greater than those recorded for the more spectacular
plant pathogens. Soil treatment may eventually change our concept of
plant health and disease. Perhaps some day we will know just what a
really healthy plant looks like.

4. *Soil Zones of Attack*

All soil-borne disease is either the result of root or basal stem attack.
If we wish to control a soil pathogen by chemical treatment, it is obvious that the chemical should be placed in the critical zone where

attack will occur. The position of this zone in the soil is determined by the presence of susceptible tissue as well as the pathogen (Garrett, 1956). This is elementary. However, elementary points are frequently overlooked.

The majority of plant pathogens, both as to numbers and kinds, are found in the upper 6 inches of the "A" horizon of the soil. This is the "surface soil." Although there is considerable variation in soils, the "A" horizon usually constitutes the upper 12–24 inches. Most of the organic material is usually in the upper 6 inches of this zone. The "A" horizon is the region of maximum salt leaching and most intense microbiological activity. The roots of most annuals and row crops are found in this horizon. Roots of biennials and perennials may extend into the "B" horizon or "sub-soil." This is the nonorganic soil zone, where maximum salt accumulation occurs. It lies below the "A" horizon and may extend to a depth of several feet. Only roots of woody perennials extend into the still deeper "C" horizon of weathered soil parental material ("non-soil") perhaps at depths of 4 ft. and greater.

At least 60% of soil-borne diseases are initiated in the upper 3 in. of the "A" horizon. The dominant diseases are seed and seedling rots caused principally by *Pythium debaryanum*, *Pythium ultimum*, and *Rhizoctonia solani*. Basal stem rots caused by species of *Pythium*, *Phytophthora*, *Fusarium*, *Sclerotinia*, *Helminthosporium*, and *Sclerotium* will also occur. Shallow root rots caused by such fungi as *Aphanomyces* occasionally are found.

Below the 3-inch level in the "A" horizon the stem pathogens give way to root pathogens. Within the 3–12 in. depth we can add another 30% of disease. Here we can find the root rotters *Phytophthora cinnamomi* and *Fusarium solani*, and the vascular invaders *Fusarium oxysporum* and *Verticillium albo-atrum*. Here also are the gall-forming and root-lesion nematodes *Meloidogyne* and *Pratylenchus*.

Below the 12–inch depth and extending on down into the "B" horizon are the strict root pathogens. Embedded in decaying root tissues at these levels lies the desert root rotter *Phymatotrichum omnivorum*. Here also are *Fomes, Verticillium, Meloidogyne, Tylenchulus, Pratylenchus*, and the oak root fungus *Armillaria*. This constitutes the remaining 10% of soil-borne pathogens. Of course, zonal distribution of diseases and organisms is not this definitive. Zones and organisms usually overlap.

Garrett (1956) has rendered a great service in clearly defining the nature and role of soil- and root-invading fungi. The soil inhabitants, being able to survive indefinitely as saprophytes, are found primarily in the 0–6 inch soil zone. The root inhabitants, or those organisms unable to live saprophytically and perforce remaining in a dormant condition in decayed roots, are found principally below the 6–inch zone. This presents an interesting problem. The soil inhabitants, being shallower, are easier to reach with a biocidal treatment. They are harder to control, however, by virtue of their recolonizing ability. The root inhabitants, on the other hand, are more difficult to reach with a biocide, but are easier to control because of their relatively fixed position in the soil.

To summarize, then, in order to control soil-borne disease with a biocide, we must know the general soil zone where the pathogen we wish to control will make contact with the tissue of the host. This will help us to decide what chemical to use and also the method of application.

B. Biocide-Soil Interactions

When a chemical is added to the soil, there are two types of interactions which may occur: (1) the soil acts on the biocide to influence the physical, chemical, and biological properties of the introduced material; and (2) the biocide acts on and affects the components of the soil.

The types of soil-biocide interactions that are encountered depend both upon the properties of the chemical and the soil.

1. Effects of the Soil on the Biocide

A biocide introduced into the soil is acted upon by the components of the soil which results in sorption, reaction with chemicals of the soil, and biological degradation. The degree of dispersion of the biocide in the soil is also affected, and in turn affects interactions. In these interactions the properties of the biocide and the soil are of equal importance. The interrelationships of these effects are shown in Fig. 3.

As shown in Fig. 3, the interactions of sorption, chemical reaction, biological degradation, and dispersion are interrelated and interdependent. Let us consider each of these effects in more detail.

a. Sorption. When a gaseous toxicant which is introduced into soil is retained or held by the soil, we consider that the chemical has been sorbed. Actually, this retention may be due to solution of the chemical in water or organic solvents in the soil, reaction with soil chemicals, or surface-binding attractions. The mechanisms which hold a chemical in the soil are both physical and chemical in nature. Other than solution effects, these binding forces can be reduced to a matter of bonding. A chemical can be held by the components of soil by covalent bonding, ionic bonding, hydrogen bonding, or van der Waal's forces. Sorption in soil broadly may be considered to be the result of any one or combinations of these forces. If covalent bonding occurs between atoms, electrons are shared and there is a true chemical reaction. In ionic bonding salt linkages are formed. Since soil clay micelles are negatively charged, cationic groups are sorbed and held by Coulombic forces. Even anions under certain conditions are sorbed. Pure physical sorption or adsorption is due to van der Waal's forces (Toth, 1955). The types of bonding reactions which occur will depend upon the physicochemical nature of both the soil and the introduced biocide.

Let us consider the influence of the components of the soil on sorption. The principal sorbing agent in the soil is the colloidal alumino-clay micelle, which has a clay mineral core consisting of sheets of silica

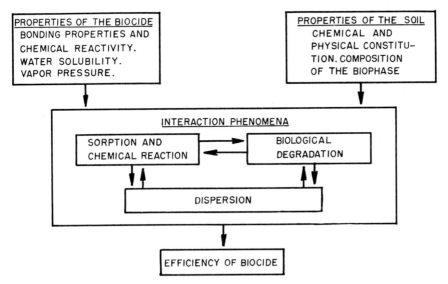

FIG. 3.   Interactions in the effects of the components of soil on the biocide.

and alumina giving it its fundamental properties. Although the mont-morillonite, kaolinite, or illite core forms the principal mass of the clay particle, it may also contain organo-silicate gel complexes (Grim, 1953).

The sorption of chemicals to soil micelles is influenced first by the nature of the mineral forming the core of the clay particle (Jurinak, 1957). Nonpolar chemicals such as ethylene dibromide are less readily sorbed on montmorillonite, than on kaolinite or illite (Jurinak and Vol-man, 1957). Montmorillonite, because of its structure, seems to offer less sorbing surface to nonpolar chemicals than kaolinite or illite do. Water, bound into the porous montmorillonite lattice, seems to block mechani-cally the sorption of nonpolar chemicals such as ethylene dibromide (Call, 1957a).

Soil particle size is important in the sorption of chemicals. The smaller the particle, the more surface exposed, and hence the greater the degree of sorption. The sorption of the soil fungicide chloropicrin increases with decrease of particle size (Stark, 1948). The more clay in a soil, the greater the degree of sorption.

Although cations are predominately sorbed into the outer shell of clay micelles, anions can be sorbed under certain conditions. The degree of anion sorption is influenced by the SiO_2/R_2O_3 ratio or the ratio between Si and Al and/or Fe (Toth, 1955). The lower this ratio, the greater the degree of anion sorption. Soils containing halloysite, illite, or kaolinite clays should then sorb anionic materials more readily than those containing montmorillonite clays, since montmorillonite is highest in SiO_2. Montmorillonite seems to sorb less nonionic and nonpolar chemicals than other clays.

One of the difficulties in interpreting much of the sorption research with clays and introduced organic chemicals is that in most cases the clays used are quite dry. Clays in normal soil are not dry, and we know that the presence of water shells greatly affects sorption. The research is of value, however, in that it does tell us something basic about the influence of the dominant clays on the sorption of organic chemicals.

Sorption is affected by the degree of hydration or water content of clay micelles. Highly polar chemicals such as allyl alcohol or formaldehyde are more readily sorbed with increased micelle hydration and less sorbed as micelle hydration decreases. On the other hand, water insoluble and nonpolar chemicals such as methyl bromide, carbon disulfide, and ethylene dibromide are less readily sorbed as micelle hydration increases (Chisholm and Koblitsky, 1943; Hannesson, 1945; Hanson and Nex, 1953). Ethylene dibromide actually can be desorbed from soil by water vapor (Call, 1957a). This is also true for dibromochloropropane.

In our studies with the nonpolar volatile fungicide chlorobromopropene we found that it was sorbed far more tightly by an air-dried soil, than by soils of moderate or high moisture content. Soil moisture levels appeared to be more important in determining the degree of sorption of this chemical than in varying the clay content of the soil.

One final point should be made on the effect of soil on sorption of introduced biocides. Increased organic matter as a rule increases sorption. This appears to be true for dichloropropene-dichloropropane mixture (Allen and Raski, 1950), methyl bromide (Munnecke and Ferguson, 1953), and ethylene dibromide (Siegel et al., 1951). According to Stark (1948), however, this was not true for chloropicrin.

Increased organic material increases the possibility of both covalent bonding and solution in solvents of an organic nature; therefore, we would not expect all biocides to respond alike. Sorption of ethylene dibromide and dichloropropene-dichloropropane mixture is increased more by the presence of organic matter in soil than by clay (Siegel et al., 1951). The term "chemisorption" has been used occasionally to describe the type of sorption involved in such cases. This word is confusing even to the chemists. It therefore should be expunged from usage and buried under 6 ft. of clay loam.

We are now ready to consider the influence of the biocide on sorption. A chemical capable of forming covalent bonds with a wide variety of materials will be bound readily by soil. This is due to the complexing of the chemical with organo-gels and reaction with free chemicals in solution in the soil. Fuhr et al. (1948) noted that H_2S, HCN, SO_2, and $COCl_2$ were strongly sorbed by soils, whereas CH_3Br, CO, and CS_2 were not. In general, chemicals which readily form covalent bonds with a variety of organic materials are not useful as soil biocides.

Materials that readily ionize or tend to form ionic bonds are usually strongly sorbed by soils. This is especially true of cationic materials. For example, NH_3, which is a fairly good volatile fungicide, will not serve double duty in the soil as a biocide and as a fertilizer. Ammonia is bound into the outer shell of clay micelles because of its positive charge. Cationic detergents are adsorbed in soil more readily than anionic or nonionic detergents (Ivarson and Pramer, 1956). It follows that emulsified aqueous drenches of biocides to be used on soil should contain nonionic or, at most, anionic detergents.

An interesting sidelight on the problem of ionically bound materials is the effect of soil pH on amphoteric substances. Amphoteric materials, such as proteins, are affected by soil pH and can be bound as cations— especially by montmorillonite (Toth, 1955; Ensminger and Gieseking, 1942). Large complex cations in the molecules of streptomycin, tyrothricin, subtilin, and streptothricin are sorbed by soils (Siminoff and Gottlieb, 1951). This is why most basic antibiotics will not work as soil fungicides.

It has already been mentioned that polar and nonpolar compounds may vary considerably in their sorptive properties. A good general rule seems to be that sorption of polar chemicals increases with increase in soil moisture, while the reverse is true in the case of nonpolar materials.

It is recognized that a certain degree of retention or sorption will always occur when biocides are introduced into soils. Under certain conditions sorption may be advantageous, as in the case where ethylene dibromide is sorbed to dry soil and is gradually released as soil moisture increases. In general, however, sorption of the biocide by components of the soil is undesirable. The greater the degree of sorption, the lower the efficiency of the introduced nematocide or fungicide. It follows that materials which are highly sorbed by soils are unsuitable as soil biocides. A biocide sorbed by soil is not going anywhere.

b. *Chemical Reaction.* Little is known regarding the fate of nematocides and fungicides which have been introduced into soil. When biocides are sorbed to the organic-mineral fraction of the soil, they may undergo chemical reactions and/or be attacked by resistant microorganisms which utilize the biocide or a degraded form of the biocide as a source of energy. We know something about the chemical reactivity of the biocides which are introduced into soil. There are, therefore, some predictable reactions.

Nematocides and fungicides introduced into the soil represent a wide range of chemical structures. The types of chemicals used include halogenated aliphatic saturated and unsaturated hydrocarbons, aldehydes, unsaturated alcohols, halogenated nitrobenzenes, halogenated quinones, heterocyclic materials, dithiocarbamates, and organo-metallic compounds.

The halogenated aliphatic saturated hydrocarbons are represented by such chemicals as the general biocide methyl bromide (CH_3Br) and the nematocides ethylene dibromide (CH_2BrCH_2Br) and 1,2-dibromo-3-chloropropane ($CH_2BrCHBrCH_2Cl$). Methyl bromide, which is an extremely volatile biocide having a vapor pressure of 1420 mm. of Hg at 20° C., will escape quickly from soil unless held by a seal. It is the most reactive of this group of relatively nonreactive chemicals. If sealed in the soil, some of the methyl bromide should react with the basic amines in organic material, acting as a methylating agent to produce methyl-ammonium bromide derivatives. The dissociating hydrobromide should then be converted into inorganic bromides:

$$CH_3Br + RNH_2 \rightarrow RNHCH_3 \cdot \overset{(+)}{H} \quad \overset{(-)}{Br} \tag{1}$$
$$RNHCH_3 \cdot HBr + Na_2CO_3 \rightarrow NaBr + H_2CO_3 + RNHCH_3$$

This same type of reaction should occur between methyl bromide and organic material containing —SH groups, as follows:

$$CH_3Br + RSH \rightarrow RSCH_3 + HBr \tag{2}$$

Direct hydrolysis of methyl bromide would be an unlikely reaction, but it could occur in this manner:

$$CH_3Br + HOH \rightarrow CH_3OH + HBr \tag{3}$$

The HBr in all cases should react to form inorganic bromides.

The nematocides ethylene dibromide and 1,2-dibromo-3-chloropropane are considerably less reactive as well as less volatile than methyl bromide; however, their longer carbon chains should increase van der Waal's bonding forces (Albert, 1951). If sorbed or otherwise held in the soil, these chemicals could undergo reactions typical of equations (1), (2), and (3), and also may enter into a fourth reaction known as dehydrohalogenation (DeWolfe and Young, 1956). This can be illustrated using ethylene dibromide:

$$CH_2BrCH_2Br \rightarrow CH_2{=}CHBr + HBr \qquad (4)$$

The vinyl bromine atom remaining can then be removed by hydrolysis, forming the corresponding alcohol.

The olefinic halogenated hydrocarbons are represented by the nematocides 1,3-dichloropropene ($CHCl{=}CHCH_2Cl$) and 1,4-dichloro-2-butene ($CH_2ClCH{=}CHCH_2Cl$); and the fungicides allyl bromide ($CH_2{=}CHCH_2Br$) and 1-chloro-3-bromopropene ($CHCl{=}CHCH_2Br$). Because of the double bond, these materials are far more reactive than corresponding saturated aliphatic halides (DeWolfe and Young, 1956). The halogen, activated by virtue of the double bond, insures reaction with organic constituents such as $-SH$ groups.

If these halogenated olefins are retained in the soil by slow volatilization and/or sorption, they should undergo reactions in the following preferred order: hydrolysis to form corresponding unsaturated alcohols (Hatch and Moore, 1944) and reactions with amine and thiol groups in organic matter similar to those in equations (1) and (2) (Dorier, 1933).

At this point the historically important soil fumigant carbon disulfide is worthy of brief discussion. Dimond and Horsfall (1944) showed that the fungicidal action of carbon disulfide was enhanced by the addition of dimethylamine. There may be a very good explanation of this phenomenon. If held by the soil, carbon disulfide should react with organic amines as follows:

$$CS_2 + 2RNH_2 \rightarrow RNHC(S)SH \cdot H_2NR \qquad (5)$$

The dithiocarbamate resulting from this reaction might then decompose to form $RN{=}C{=}S$ with its potential fungicidal isothiocyanate grouping. In other reactions involving carbon disulfide, metallic sulfides of the $RNC(S)SM$ type could be formed.

Another important group of compounds are the well-known dithiocarbamates. These materials are principally fungicides, the most effective being tetramethyl thiuramdisulfide

$$(CH_3)_2NCSSCN(CH_3)_2$$
$$\underset{S}{\overset{\|}{}} \quad \underset{S}{\overset{\|}{}}$$

disodium ethylene bisdithiocarbamate

$$Na-\underset{\underset{S}{\|}}{S}CNHCH_2CH_2NH\underset{\underset{S}{\|}}{C}S-Na$$

and sodium N-methyl dithiocarbamate,

$$CH_3NH\underset{\underset{S}{\|}}{C}SNa$$

These materials owe their activity to the formation of volatile and highly biocidal isothiocyanates (van der Kerk, 1956):

$$RNH\underset{\underset{S}{\|}}{C}SH \rightleftharpoons H_2S + RN=C=S \tag{6}$$

A new fungicidal and nematocidal soil biocide, 3,5-dimethyltetra-hydro-1,3,5,2H-thiadiazine-2-thione, which is essentially a cyclic dithio-carbamate, breaks down in soil to form methyl isothiocyanate (Torgeson *et al.*, 1957):

$$\begin{array}{c} S \\ \diagup \quad \diagdown \\ H_2C \qquad C=S \\ | \qquad\qquad | \\ CH_3-N \qquad N-CH_3 \\ \diagdown \qquad \diagup \\ C \\ H_2 \end{array} + 2H_2O \rightarrow H_2S + 2CH_2O + CH_3NH_2 + CH_3N=C=S \tag{7}$$

It is also likely that the experimental nematocide 3-p-chlorophenyl-5-methyl rhodanine changes by hydrolytic reaction in the soil to form an isothiocyanate. The expected reaction, according to van der Kerk (1956), would be:

$$\begin{array}{c} R-N-\!\!\!-C=O \\ | \qquad | \\ S=C \qquad CH_2 \\ \diagdown \quad \diagup \\ S \end{array} + H_2O \rightleftharpoons RNS\underset{\underset{S}{\|}}{C}SCH_2COOH \rightleftharpoons RN=C=S + HSCH_2COOH \tag{8}$$

It appears then that wherever the

$$-NH-\underset{\underset{S}{\|}}{C}-S-$$

linkage is involved, a volatile chemical of the $RN=C=S$ type is formed. From a biocidal standpoint, this is a potentiation effect even though it involves an actual degradation of the chemical in the soil. This is a very handy reaction indeed.

One further point should be made before leaving the dithiocarbam-ates. Nabam, or disodium ethylene bisdithiocarbamate, is unstable

(Horsfall, 1956). The heavy metal analogs of nabam, such as zineb or maneb, are better fungicides than the sodium salt. Being insoluble in water, however, the heavy metal salts are difficult to distribute in the soil. Barratt and Horsfall (1947) showed that in the presence of CO_2 the sodium in nabam will exchange for heavy bivalent metals. Such a reaction could occur in this fashion:

$$\begin{array}{c} S \\ \parallel \\ NaSCNHCH_2 \\ | \\ NaSCNHCH_2 \\ \parallel \\ S \end{array} + ZnSO_4 \rightarrow Zn\left\langle \begin{array}{c} S \\ \parallel \\ SCNHCH_2 \\ | \\ SCNHCH_2 \\ \parallel \\ S \end{array} \right. + (Na)_2SO_4 \qquad (9)$$

The formation of such heavy metal salts might improve the performance of nabam in the soil.

In summary, in the case of highly volatile materials chemical reactions may occur only to a limited extent. This is because the chemical may be lost from the soil in a matter of hours. This is not true in the case of nonvolatile materials or compounds with low vapor pressure. These residual chemicals are subject to chemical reactions.

Irrespective of the degree of chemical alteration in soil the biocides which are introduced into the soil will be attacked by various microorganisms, which utilize what is left as a source of energy as the chemical is slowly broken down to simple sulfides, halides, ammonia, carbon dioxide, and water.

c. *Biological Degradation.* Soil chemical reactions and biological degradations probably occur simultaneously and act jointly to break down the organic biocide to form simple inorganic salts, water, and carbon dioxide. Almost any chemical remaining in the soil for any extended period of time will be acted upon by microorganisms and utilized.

In 1946 Zobell stated that "nearly a hundred species of bacteria, yeasts, and molds representing thirty genera have been described which attack one or more kinds of hydrocarbons." The passage of time since Zobell's paper was published has but served to increase both the numbers and kinds of degrading microorganisms as well as the chemicals attacked. In summary, we can only agree with Thornton and Meiklejohn's (1957) statement that "there are few substances which are so insoluble, or so toxic that soil microorganisms cannot dispose of them."

A biocide is never a permanent fixture in the soil. For that matter, nothing is.

d. *Diffusion.* Dispersion in soil can mean the success or failure of a fungicide or a nematocide. If a chemical is not mechanically mixed into a soil, there are only two ways through which it can be distributed: (1) dispersion in water solution or (2) diffusion as a vapor. There are two primary factors which influence diffusion. These are: the chemical and physical nature of the diffusing materials and the nature of the medium in which the material diffuses. In our case, the diffusing material is the biocide, and the medium in which it diffuses is the soil. The biocide and the soil may interact, bringing about sorption and chemical reactions which affect the degree of diffusion.

Let us consider first the influence of the chemical itself on its dispersion through the soil. The three basic properties of a soil biocide involved are: vapor pressure, water solubility, and bonding properties or general reactivity.

First, there are those biocides, which in order to be effective must penetrate soil as water solutions. These would include volatile but highly water soluble chemicals such as allyl alcohol and formaldehyde as well as the nonvolatile sodium ethylene bisdithiocarbamate and sodium N-methyl dithiocarbamate.

Nonvolatile and water insoluble fungicides such as maneb, zineb, and captan must be mechanically mixed with soil for effective results (Kendrick and Zentmyer, 1957).

Most of the information on diffusion comes from the work on biocides, or soil fumigants, which move in the soil in vapor phase. The potential diffusibility of a volatile biocide in soil is enhanced by high vapor pressure, low bonding properties, and low water solubility. The degree of diffusion of a chemical through soil as a gas is reduced with decrease in vapor pressure, increase in bonding properties, and increase in water solubility. This is a good general rule to remember.

Increased quantities of chemical introduced into soil increase the degree of gaseous diffusion. This has been observed for carbon disulfide (Bliss, 1948) and for dichloropropene-dichloropropane mixture (Baines et al., 1956).

The second over-all important factor in the diffusion of a biocidal fumigant is the nature of the medium in which the diffusion occurs—the soil. The important soil factors are porosity, type and composition, structure, compaction, moisture content, and temperature.

As we might expect, the degree of porosity is the most important soil factor in diffusion (Call, 1957b; Hanson and Nex, 1953). In general, the more porous the soil, the greater the degree of gaseous diffusion. Factors such as soil type, soil moisture content, and soil compaction influence the degree of soil porosity. Soil type directly affects porosity. Carbon disulfide (Hannesson, 1945), dichloropropene-dichloropropane mixture (Baines et al., 1956), and chloropicrin (Stark, 1948) all diffuse best in sandy soils, and least in clay soils. This may not be entirely a matter of porosity; it will be recognized that sorption may also be involved.

The texture and structure of a soil may influence the movement of a gaseous material in the soil. The lighter the texture, the better the gaseous flow of a soil fumigant (Hannesson, 1945).

Soil compaction also affects soil porosity. The greater the compaction, the less permeable the soil to the movement of volatile chemicals (Hagan, 1941). A combination of rain and the use of heavy farm machinery brings about maximum compaction of the soil. Judging from some of the agricultural practices in the western United States, one is inclined to believe that an effort is being made to attain this goal.

The plow sole is a compacted layer commonly encountered 8–12 in. below the surface of the soil. It is formed by mechanical compaction and the deposition of mineral salts. This hardened layer is impermeable to carbon disulfide, ethylene dibromide, dichloropropene-dichloropropane mixture, and chlorobromopropene (Hagan, 1941; Throne, 1951; Jensen et al., 1954).

Increased water content of soils decreases their porosity. This in turn interferes with the movement of nonpolar chemicals by mechanical blockage. This is an old observation. Sabaté, one of the pioneers in the use of carbon disulfide, is quoted by French (1893) as stating "never inject a solution into damp soil, because the diffusion of the poisonous gases has no effect beyond the sides of the hole made by the injector." High soil moisture impedes the diffusion of carbon disulfide (Thomas and Lawyer, 1939), dichloropropene and ethylene dibromide (Siegel et al., 1951; Call, 1957b), dichloropropene-dichloropropane mixture (Schmidt, 1947), and chloropicrin (Stark, 1948).

Even moderate soil moisture interferes with the movement of polar chemicals. In our studies we learned that even soil moistures of 50% of the moisture equivalent reduce the diffusion of allyl alcohol and other volatile polar materials in the soil. Contrariwise, the movement of nonpolar materials shows no interference until the soil moisture content equals or exceeds the soil moisture equivalent.

Soil temperature also affects the diffusion of volatile soil biocides. With an increase in soil temperature the diffusion of ethylene dibromide, chloropicrin, and dichloropropene is accelerated (Hanson and Nex, 1953; McClellan et al., 1949). This would be an expected response in accordance with the gas laws.

A discussion of diffusion would not be complete without some consideration of diffusion patterns of soil fumigants. When a volatile chemical is applied in the soil at a single point, it diffuses as a gas outward from this point forming a pattern of definite size and shape. The size and shape of the pattern is usually determined by the limits of biocidal effectiveness. The radius of the pattern has been called the "k value" (Taylor, 1939).

We know something about the general diffusibility of fumigants in soil and the shape which diffusion patterns assume. If a volatile chemical is injected in the soil at a standard depth of 6–7 in. the pattern which forms at first is elongated or prolate in shape. Gradually the chemical extends laterally, and as the pattern becomes larger, it tends to appear flattened or becomes oblate. Siegel et al. (1951) observed this sequence with ethylene dibromide and 1,3-dichloropropene. We have observed this effect also in using chloropicrin and other materials.

Diffusion pattern data—unless related to all of the factors which influence diffusion—are difficult to interpret. Comparisons cannot be made between chemicals unless tests are conducted under identical conditions. Recently we compared the diffusion patterns of allyl alcohol and chloropicrin, following injections in a sandy loam soil in optimum planting condition. Allyl alcohol at a dosage of 1.0 ml. gave a spherical pattern with a maximum radius of only 2 inches. Chloropicrin, using 0.5 ml. of material, gave an oblate pattern with a maximum radius of 10 inches.

The type of pattern formed is influenced also by the presence or absence of a soil "seal." As a general rule, if a fumigant is not sealed into the soil by use of surface watering or a surface cover, a lethal concentration of fumigant fails to build up in the top 2-inch zone. This has been noted following the use of carbon disulfide (Higgins and Pollard, 1937), chloropicrin (Stark, 1948), dichloropropene-dichloropropane mixture (Allen and Raski, 1950), and dibromochloropropane (Ichikawa et al., 1955).

Chemicals differ markedly in the speed with which diffusion patterns form. Methyl bromide and chloropicrin diffuse rapidly; dibromochloropropane appears to move slowly. Ichikawa et al. (1955) found that dibromochloropropane injected at the rate of 0.22 ml. per foot in field tests attained its maximum diffusion radius of 15 inches 9 weeks after application.

One of the most important factors determining the depth of fumigant penetration into soil is the quantity of material used. Baines et al. (1956) using dichloropropene-dichloropropane mixture in sandy loam soil for the control of the citrus nematode *Tylenchulus semipenetrans* found that 45 gallons of chemical per acre were needed to control nematodes to a depth of 3 ft. To obtain control at 6 ft., however, 80 gallons per acre were required. Other studies of this general type giving comparable results have been made using carbon disulfide (Thomas and Lawyer, 1939; Bliss, 1948).

It is evident that more comparative and carefully controlled work on diffusion patterns is needed.

2. Effects of the Biocide on the Soil

Previously we have been considering the influence of the soil on the biocide. We have seen that these soil effects depend upon not only the physical and chemical nature of the biocide, but the nature and condition of the soil as well.

It is now the time to take the reverse position and examine the impact of the biocide on the soil and its components. This is a large order. It involves the action of the introduced chemical on (1) the chemical composition of the soil, (2) the physical constitution of the soil, and (3) the living portion of the soil, or the biophase.

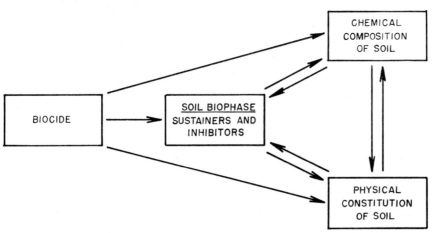

FIG. 4. Effects of the biocide on the soil.

The influence of the introduced biocide on the chemical composition of soil can be separated into effects on soil pH, salt content, toxic residues, minor element content, and major nutrient content. The effect on the physical constitution of soil involves soil permeability and aggregation. The most important action of the biocide on soil, however, is on the sustainers and inhibitors in the biophase. This involves the important end result—that of control of plant pathogens.

The influence of the biocide on the soil and its component parts are shown in Fig. 4.

The biocide acts on the biophase, which in turn influences the chemical and physical constitution of the soil. The chemical and physical constitutions of the soil may be directly affected by the biocide, and in turn affect each other as well as the biophase.

Some of these influences shown are known; some are merely postulated. Some are minor; some are major.

a. *Effects of the Biocide on the Chemical Composition of the Soil.* The principal actions of the biocide on the chemistry of the soil are on the salt content, major and minor element composition, and organic content.

The effect on major and minor elements is actually indirect for the most part, since microorganisms are involved in the formation, binding, or releasing of these plant nutrients. Since the end result is on the chemical composition of the soil, we shall discuss the biocide's influence on major and minor element content here instead of under the "Impact of the Biocide on the Living Portion of the Soil."

Let us consider minor elements first. There are considerable data in the literature showing that rhizosphere flora and organic matter in soils can bind manganese, thus making it unavailable to the crop plant (Gerretsen, 1937; Heintze and Mann, 1949). There is also little doubt that zinc, iron, molybdenum, and copper are bound and released by soil organisms (Thornton, 1956).

Treatment of the soil with volatile biocides temporarily increases the quantity of minor elements in the soil by killing organisms capable of binding these elements. Manganese deficiency has been overcome by treatment of soil with ethylene dibromide and dichloropropene-dichloropropane mixture (Martin *et al.*, 1953). On the other hand, toxic levels of both copper and manganese have been released following soil treatment with chloropicrin (Dalton and Hurwitz, 1948).

There is a good deal of information available on the effect of soil treatment on major nutrients. The greatest volume of data is on the subject of nitrogen. Soil fumigation, especially with biocides such as chloropicrin and dichloropropene, inhibits and kills nitrifying organisms. On the other hand, the wide variety and types of ammonia-forming microorganisms permits an escape of resistant ammonifiers and their consequent rapid build-up following soil fumigation (Tam and Clark, 1943; Newhall, 1955).

The calcium content of a soil also can be affected by soil treatment. Aldrich and Martin (1952) noted a temporary increase in soluble calcium in citrus soils treated with dichloropropene-dichloropropane mixture and chloropicrin.

Soil fumigants also can alter the quantity and quality of salts in soil. Inorganic chlorides and bromides are eventually formed in small amounts in the soil by hydrolysis or dehydrohalogenation following the application of nematocides and fungicides of the halogenated hydrocarbon type. Although the quantities of such materials formed are not great, they can be unfavorable to certain types of halogen-sensitive plants. Phytotoxic residues have been formed, especially by bromine-containing fumigants such as methyl bromide, ethylene dibromide, and chlorobromopropene. Bromine-sensitive plants include *Salvia, Dianthus, Antirrhinum, Allium* and *Citrus* (Williamson, 1953; Martin *et al.*, 1956). No adverse effects, except in the case of tobacco, have been reported for increased chlorides resulting from fumigation with chlorine-containing hydrocarbons (Gaines and Graham, 1953).

Finally, biocides may be sorbed to form complexes with the organo-mineral colloids of the soil. These materials which are formed are therefore of indefinite and complex composition, and undoubtedly have a marked effect on the chemistry of the soil zones in their immediate vicinity.

b. *The Biocide and the Physical Constitution of the Soil.* There is no evidence to show that soil biocides have a significant influence on the physical constitution of soil.

Aggregating substances such as polyuronides temporarily can increase following soil fumigation with chloropicrin, dichloropropene-dichloropropane mixture, and ethylene dibromide. Theoretically, however, aggregation should be decreased by repeated treatments of soil without additions of organic matter (Martin and Aldrich, 1952).

No adverse results on permeability or structure have been observed following treatment of soil with biocides.

We can conclude that the influence of biocides on the physical structure of soil is negligible.

c. *Impact of the Biocide on the Living Portion of the Soil.* When a biocide is added to the soil to control pathogenic nematodes or fungi, the biophase is distorted. The shotgun blast of the chemical into the heterogeneous soil population makes little distinction between friends and foes. Some plant inhibitors and sustainers are killed outright; some are prevented from further growth; while still others may not be greatly affected. The organisms which escape tend to multiply. The biological equilibrium is changed for better or for worse (Martin, 1950).

Not only do fungi differ in their susceptibility to biocides, but they differ in their capacities to recolonize fumigated soils. *Penicillium* has been observed to increase in soils previously treated with chloropicrin (Katznelson and Richardson, 1943) or carbon disulfide (Garrett, 1957) or even tetramethyl thiuramdisulfide (Richardson, 1954). *Trichoderma viride,* the famed antagonist, has been found to be the dominant recolonizer of soils treated with formaldehyde (Mollison, 1953), chloropicrin (Smith, 1939), dichloropropene-dichloropropane mixture (Martin, 1950), allyl alcohol (Overman and Burgis, 1956), and tetramethyl thiuram-disulfide (Richardson, 1954). *Trichoderma viride* develops rapidly in soils fumigated with carbon disulfide, thereby controlling the oak root fungus *Armillaria mellea* by antagonistic action (Bliss, 1948). The reason for the stimulation of *T. viride* may be in a shift in the microbiological equilibrium.

Actinomycetes and bacteria are generally more resistant to the effect of soil biocides than are fungi, and frequently increase in soils which have been fumigated with chloropicrin (Moje *et al.*, 1957; Katznelson and Richardson, 1943). Martin and Aldrich (1952) found that bacteria increased in alkaline soils, and fungi dominated in acid soils treated with chloropicrin, carbon disulfide, and dichloropropene-dichloropropane mixture. This manifestation is not limited to volatile biocides. Bacterial populations of soils increased following soil treatment with tetramethyl thiuramdisulfide (Cram and Vaartaja, 1957).

Some of the changes in the biophase following fumigation are not beneficial. Soil fungicides such as allyl alcohol, formaldehyde, methyl bromide, and sodium *N*-methyl dithiocarbamate apparently have a deleterious effect on mycorrhizal fungi (Wilde and Persidsky, 1956; Hacskaylo and Palmer, 1957).

Other unfavorable results are those of disease accentuation and disease exchange. Collectively, this might be called the boomerang phenomenon. Accentuation of disease can occur as a result of soil treatment for the control of soil inhabitants. We have observed rapid reinvasion of soils treated with chloropicrin and chlorobromopropene by *Rhizoctonia solani* and species of *Pythium*. Disease accentuation from damping-off organisms has resulted following the use of organic mercurials (Gibson, 1956). Such effects are undoubtedly the result of the killing or inhibition of antagonists, permitting the reinvading pathogen to grow speedily through the soil without biological opposition.

An interesting boomerang effect was observed by H. C. Smith, according to Garrett (1956). Smith found that the pathogen antagonist *Trichoderma viride* increased in a fumigated soil. If, however, *Pythium ultimum* was introduced into this treated soil, it gave greater damage than in untreated soils. A likely reason for this effect was not only the direct removal of *Pythium* antagonists by the chemical, but the inhibitory effect of *Trichoderma viride* on surviving antagonists such as *Rhizoctonia*. Butler (1957) has shown that *R. solani* parasitizes species of *Pythium*. In investigating Butler's claim we found that *Rhizoctonia solani* had a definite antagonist effect on *Pythium ultimum* when both fungi were added simultaneously to steamed soil.

There are numerous cases of disease trading following soil treatment. Soil treatments with chlorobromopropene controlled bulb rot of iris, caused by *Sclerotium rolfsii*, but increased infection induced by bulb-borne *Fusarium* (Haasis, 1952). The situation was corrected by formaldehyde treatment of the bulbs. Fumigation of the soil apparently removed the natural antagonists of *Fusarium*.

Disease trading should be more marked when specific and non-volatile fungicides are used. Frequently, we have observed increased severity in attack of sugar beet seedlings by *Pythium ultimum* and *P. aphanidermatum* following soil treatment with pentachloronitrobenzene for the control of *Rhizoctonia*. Fulton *et al.* (1956) observed that although chloronitrobenzene eliminated *Rhizoctonia solani* and *Macrophomina phaseoli* in soils, it increased the incidence of disease in cotton seedlings, caused by *Fusarium moniliforme* and *Colletotrichum gossypii*. Organic mercurials can also produce a disease exchange. Gibson (1953) observed that the use of these fungicides decreased pre-emergence losses in beds of groundnut seedlings, but increased subsequent damage from crown rot, caused by *Aspergillus niger*. In this case *Aspergillus niger* was apparently less susceptible to mercury poisoning than its antagonists.

All of these effects are due to shifts in the microbiological equilibrium. The end result seems to depend for the most part on (a) the relative degree of susceptibility or resistance of plant sustainers and inhibitors to chemical poisoning, and (b) assuming equal susceptibility to this poisoning, their relative ability to recolonize the soil swiftly as saprophytes. We have a lot to learn in this uncharted territory.

This brings us to the practical phases of disease control by chemical treatment, which is still a result of the effect of the biocide on the living components of soil.

III. Practical Aspects

We are now ready to consider the practical phases of disease control by soil treatment. Major emphasis will be placed on chemical treatments: the compounds in use, their properties, and methods of application. A brief discussion on heat treatment is included.

First let us review the beginnings of chemical treatments for the control of soil pathogens. There is a little history that is worth recounting. It represents hard work and thought over a 90-year period.

A. *History of Chemical Treatments*

Soil treatment with nematocides and fungicides had its beginnings in applied entomology in 1869 in the researches of Thenard and Monestier and his co-workers in 1873 (Fleming and Baker, 1935; Newhall, 1955). The destructive *Phylloxera* threatened the vineyards of

Europe. To combat this pest, soil fumigation with carbon disulfide was introduced.

Some fields which were free of *Phylloxera* were treated. Vines growing in these fumigated fields showed a surprising increase in vigor. This "extra kick" reaction was observed by Sabaté, who was so impressed that he wrote "sulfur of carbon . . . becomes a necessity for the strengthening of vegetable growth" (French, 1893).

By 1900, however, following the introduction of *Phylloxera*-resistant rootstocks into European vineyards interest in carbon disulfide soil fumigation had faded away (Newhall, 1955). A huge stride forward had been made in chemical control, however. The idea of soil treatment with chemicals for soil pests was established.

In 1891 Thaxter dusted sulfur into the open furrows in which onion seeds were being planted for the control of *Urocystis*. This was the first application of a soil fungicide (Horsfall, 1956). This was followed by Selby's successful work in 1900 for the control of onion smut, using the formaldehyde drip-in-the-row method, and his formaldehyde waterdrench on soil to control *Rhizoctonia solani* in 1906.

A new avenue for the control of soil pathogens was opened next by Riehm in 1913, who made his great discovery that the treatment of wheat seed with chlorophenol mercury would control bunt. It is doubtful whether Riehm realized the dual nature of organic mercurial seed treatment: that of disinfesting not only the seed coat, but a small zone of soil surrounding the seed as well.

The concept of killing pests in chemical vapor phase had not been forgotten. As a result of World War I, large stocks of the war gas chloropicrin were on hand in 1917 (Newhall, 1955). Within the next 3 years it was discovered that the vapors of chloropicrin were toxic to both insects and fungi (Moore, 1918; Bertrand and Rosenblatt, 1920).

A crisis in the pineapple industry in Hawaii set the stage for the large scale use of soil fumigants (Newhall, 1955). Pineapple yields had deteriorated over the years, and Hawaiian researchers were ready to apply anything to correct the "sick" soils. The first successful soil treatments were made by Johnson and Godfrey (1932), using chloropicrin. Within the next 3 years Godfrey (1934, 1935, 1936) demonstrated that chloropicrin, if used with a paper soil seal, was not only an effective soil nematocide, but a soil fungicide as well.

Investigators began to cast around for other types of potential volatile soil fumigants. Richardson and Johnson in 1935 had demonstrated that the vapors of methyl bromide were highly toxic to insects. Following this lead, Taylor and McBeth (1940) found that if methyl bromide was injected into soil and covered with a paper seal, it would control root knot nematodes.

All the research done thus far was informative, but the cost of application was excessive except for high value crops.

The first practical breakthrough came in Carter's discovery in 1943 of the remarkable nematocidal and "growing promoting" properties of the cheap, crude, dichloropropene-dichloropropane mixture following its use in the pineapple fields of Hawaii. The second break came in Christie's discovery in 1945 that ethylene dibromide, another cheap material, was a highly effective nematocide. The long-suffering nematologists, who had been shouting since the days of Cobb (1914) about the general seriousness of the nematode problem, at last had practical tools to prove their contentions.

The applied mycologists had not been idle during this period. In the early 1930's the chloronitrobenzenes were introduced. Brown, in 1935, found that they were effective as soil treatments against clubroot and damping-off pathogens of crucifers. These relatively nonvolatile chemicals were tested in the following years by various European investigators for the control of *Sclerotinia minor* (Wasewitz, 1937), *Sclerotium tuliparum* (Buddin, 1937), *Streptomyces scabies* (Meyer, 1940), and *Rhizoctonia solani* (Smieton and Brown, 1940). Smieton and Brown first noted that pentachloronitrobenzene was ineffective against *Pythium*. We now know that pentachloronitrobenzene is quite specific in its action (Kendrick and Middleton, 1954).

Selby's row-application concept was revived about this time by Horsfall (1938), who in conducting tests with formalin and copper sulfate for the control of damping-off of seedlings observed that "chemical drips in the row show distinct promise especially in the field." This concept was still good; all that was needed were newer and better materials for the row-application researches of Leach and Snyder (1947), Hildebrand *et al.* (1949), and Watson (1951). The discovery of the thiuram sulfides and metallic methyl dithiocarbamates (Tisdale and Williams, 1934), the metallic ethylene bisdithiocarbamates (Dimond *et al.*, 1943), and the tetrahydrophthalimide fungicides (Kittleson, 1952) accelerated research in the field of row fungicides.

Along other lines the search had continued for eradicant-type volatile fungicides. The successes of the cheap nematocides had fired the imaginations of plant pathologists. Dichloropropene-dichloropropane mixture, and especially ethylene dibromide, were unsatisfactory as soil fungicides. More effective volatile soil fungicides such as allyl bromide (Christie, 1947), chlorobromopropene (Kreutzer and Montagne, 1950), dichlorobutene (Lear, 1950), and dibromobutene (Kreutzer *et al.*, 1951) were found. These chemicals had certain drawbacks, but progress was being made.

Larger scale field applications of chloropicrin were conducted (Wilhelm and Koch, 1956). The old formaldehyde-drench concept was also being utilized in the search for new materials. Allyl alcohol had been found to be an effective water-soluble eradicant for seedbed pests (Clayton *et al.*, 1949; Overman and Burgis, 1956).

New and very effective soil nematocides and fungicides are being discovered. Some are volatile and some are not. Examples are: tetrahydrothiadiazine thione (Anderson and Okimoto, 1953), chlorophenylmethyl rhodanine (Tarjan, 1954), dibromochloropropane (McBeth and Bergeson, 1955), sodium methyl dithiocarbamate dihydrate (Kingsland and Rich, 1955), dichlorophenyl diethyl phosphorothioate (Manzelli, 1955), pyridinethione oxide (Allison and Barnes, 1956), and the tetrahydrothiophene dioxide (Schuldt and Bluestone, 1957). It is apparent that we are getting more tools for the job. Some of them should be useful.

B. *The Chemicals and Their Uses*

We are now ready to discuss the chemicals which are in commercial or experimental use as soil fungicides and nematocides. Knowledge of the physicochemical and biological properties of these compounds is an essential guide for correct use.

The physicochemical properties of biocides involving volatility, water solubility, and general reactivity have been previously considered. The biological properties of the chemical are equally important. We should know, as Kendrick and Zentmyer (1957) have emphasized, whether the chemical is a "killer" or an eradicant, or whether it is a growth inhibitor or a protectant. Volatile chemicals act as eradicants; nonvolatile chemicals most frequently act as protectants. A fast-acting eradicant may work well in the control of root inhabitants, but be unsatisfactory for the control of soil inhabitants. It is also essential to know whether the biotoxicant is generally poisonous to all organisms or specifically toxic to a broad or narrow range of microorganisms. Finally, the cost of the chemical must be balanced against its efficiency in controlling disease.

Soil biocides can be classified according to their chemistry, their biological properties, or their uses. A broad chemical classification of these materials would cover such groups as inorganic and organic heavy metal salts, the sulfur-containing dithiocarbamates and heterocyclics, aldehydes and unsaturated alcohols, halogenated nitrobenzenes, saturated and unsaturated aliphatic halides, organo-phosphorus compounds and antibiotics.

A detailed classification based on chemical structure is more useful to the chemist than the biologist. The biologist needs a breakdown of biocides based on function rather than on structure.

With these points in mind, the following classification of soil nematocides and fungicides is given. Seed-treating materials are excluded.

1. General Biocides

These compounds include both relatively volatile and nonvolatile eradicants. Since they are generally biotoxic, their use is contingent upon a waiting period between treatment and planting.

a. *Volatile Water-Insoluble Compounds.* The chemicals of this group form effective diffusion patterns in soils. They include the commercial soil fumigants methyl bromide (CH_3Br) and chloropicrin (CCl_3NO_2) as well as such experimental materials as chlorobromopropene ($CHCl = CHCH_2Br$) and allyl bromide ($CH_2 = CHCH_2Br$). All of these compounds are toxic to nematodes, fungi, insects, and weed seeds in soil at dosage rates of 100–500 lb. per acre. Chloropicrin and the olefinic bromides are the most potent fungicides. Methyl bromide, although highly effective against weed seeds, is the least fungitoxic (Stark and Lear, 1947).

Of these four materials, chloropicrin gives the most extensive diffusion patterns, but penetrates tissue poorly. Methyl bromide and chlorobromopropene are outstanding in their ability to permeate into such structures as unrotted nematode galls and sclerotial bodies of fungi (Stark and Lear, 1947; Kreutzer, unpublished data).

The most volatile chemical in this group is methyl bromide (boiling point 4° C.), which for effective results must be applied under a gastight cover (Taylor and McBeth, 1940). The olefinic bromides and chloropicrin can be applied without a soil-surface seal, although chloropicrin will give better results with a water seal or gas-tight cover (Kreutzer and Montagne, 1950; Wilhelm, 1957).

Methyl bromide and chloropicrin leave the soil more rapidly and completely than chlorobromopropene or allyl bromide. For normal soil conditions, waiting periods between the end of treatment and planting of 12–24 hours for methyl bromide, 3–6 days for chloropicrin, and 4–10 days for allyl bromide and chlorobromopropene are required.

All of these materials are poisonous to mammals. With the exception of methyl bromide they all possess lachrymatory warning properties.

b. *Unstable Chemicals.* In this series are the nonvolatile compounds which break down in soil to form a volatile biocidal end product. This group includes the water-soluble commercial biocide sodium N-methyl dithiocarbamate ($CH_3NHCSSNa$) and the nonwater soluble experimental biocides 3,5-dimethyltetrahydro-1,3,5,2H-thiadiazine-2-thione

and 3-p-chlorophenyl-5- methyl rhodanine

The dithiocarbamate is believed to be the decomposition product of the thiadiazinethione (Kendrick and Zentmyer, 1957). All three materials are unique in that by hydrolytic action they are believed to form the volatile and biocidal methyl isothiocyanate $CH_3N = C = S$ (van der Kerk, 1956; Torgeson et al., 1957).

Sodium methyl dithiocarbamate has been used successfully as an aqueous soil-surface drench for the control of *Fusarium solani* (Kingsland and Rich, 1955), general damping-off fungi in seed beds (Taylor, 1956), and *Phytophthora cinnamomi* (Zentmyer and Erspamer, 1957). Effective dosages in the field for the control of fungi vary from 25–400 lb. per acre (Fink, 1956; Taylor, 1956; Young and Tolmsoff, 1957).

Thiadiazinethione is also a good all-around biocide (Anderson and Okimoto, 1953; Kendrick and Middleton, 1954). Chlorophenyl methyl rhodanine has given best results as a nematocide at dosages of 0.5 to 4 gm. per square foot (Tarjan, 1954). Both of these water-insoluble materials must be mixed in the soil.

In the cases of all of these chemicals a waiting period of several days between treatment and planting is necessary.

c. *Volatile Water-Soluble Materials.* Representatives of this group are the general biocides formaldehyde (HCHO) and allyl alcohol ($CH_2 = CHCH_2OH$), which will not diffuse well as vapors in normal soils because of their water solubilities.

Formaldehyde is the oldest of the soil biocides, having proved effective in water solution against dominant soil-surface pathogens (Selby, 1906). Allyl alcohol used as a water drench is a better soil biocide than formaldehyde, being outstanding in the control of weed seeds and such fungi as *Pythium* and *Rhizoctonia* in the upper 2-inch soil zone (Overman and Burgis, 1956).

2. Specific Biocides

These are the volatile and nonvolatile chemicals which are useful primarily against either nematodes or fungi, but not both. These compounds may be toxic to numerous organisms (broad spectrum) or to only a few organisms (narrow spectrum). The phytotoxicity of these chemicals is variable.

a. *Volatile Eradicants.* There are two types of water-insoluble volatile eradicants in this category: the strict nematocides, and the nematocides with narrow-spectrum fungicidal properties. The restricted nematocides are the least phytotoxic of volatile soil biocides. These compounds are effective against such genera as *Meloidogyne, Pratylenchus,* and *Tylenchulus;* but relatively ineffective against cyst-forming nematodes (*Heterodera*). There are two commercially available nematocides in this group: ethylene dibromide (CH_2BrCH_2Br) and dibromochloropropane ($CH_2-BrCHBrCH_2Cl$). Both chemicals are efficient nematode killers; ethylene dibromide being effective at 2–8 gallons per acre and dibromochloropropane giving control at 0.5–4 gallons per acre (Newhall, 1955; McBeth and Bergeson, 1955). Except to bromine-sensitive plants, dibromochloropropane is perhaps the least phytotoxic. Both chemicals have been used successfully to side-dress growing plants (Newhall, 1955; Potter and Morgan, 1956).

In general, these chemicals at nematocidal levels are not toxic to bacteria, actinomycetes, or fungi. Ethylene dibromide, however, has given control of disease complexes involving nematodes and such fungi as *Fusarium oxysporum vasinfectum, Ceratostomella fimbriata,* and *Rhizoctonia solani* (Smith, 1948; Meuli and Swezey, 1949; Reynolds and Hanson, 1957).

The chemicals of the second class are volatile and water-insoluble nematocides with some narrow-spectrum fungicidal properties. These materials include the commercially available dichloropropene-dichloropropane mixture or technical dichloropropene ($CHCl = CHCH_2Cl$) and the experimental dichlorobutene ($CH_2ClCH = CHCH_2Cl$). Carbon disulfide (CS_2) is placed in this class since it is a nematocide with some fungicidal properties.

Dichloropropene-dichloropropane mixture is highly efficacious in soil at 200–400 lb. per acre in controlling most plant parasitic nematode genera with the exception of *Heterodera* (Peters and Fenwick, 1949; Allen and Raski, 1950). Dosages of dichloropropene mixture, 2 to 3 times greater than usual nematocidal levels, have controlled species of *Phytophthora* (Zentmyer and Klotz, 1949). This fumigant also has been reported to be effective against organisms such as *Rhizoctonia solani*

(Middleton *et al.*, 1949) and *Streptomyces ipomoea* (Martin, 1953). Most of these effects, however, are due in all likelihood, to the control of nematode-fungus complexes (Reynolds and Hanson, 1957).

The experimental dichlorobutene has shown up especially well against the hard to kill species of *Heterodera* (Lear *et al.*, 1952). Unfortunately, it may leave phytotoxic residues in the soil. Dichlorobutene also has some fungicidal properties.

Carbon disulfide is the oldest of the soil fumigants. It is only marginally good as a nematocide, but it has been outstanding in the practical control of *Armillaria mellea* in the United States (Fawcett, 1936).

b. *Nonvolatile Protectants.* This group of nonvolatile and specific biocides includes two expermiental nematocides and a miscellaneous lot of old and new fungicides.

The nematocides are two materials, O-2,4-dichlorophenyl-O,O-diethyl phosphorothioate (Manzelli, 1955) or

$$(C_2H_5O)_2-\overset{\overset{\text{S}}{\|}}{P}-O-\underset{}{\bigcirc}-Cl$$

and 3,4-dichlorotetrahydrothiophene 1,1-dioxide (Schuldt and Bluestone, 1957) or

$$\underset{\overset{\text{S}}{O_2}}{\overset{Cl\quad Cl}{\bigwedge}}$$

Both chemicals are nonvolatile and water-insoluble solids, being relatively nonfungicidal and low in phytotoxic effects.

Broad and narrow-spectrum fungicides of varying water solubility also are placed in this class. Broad-spectrum and water-soluble chemicals are represented by copper sulfate, the soluble mercurials (mercuric chloride and cyano methylmercuri guanidine), and disodium ethylene bisdithiocarbamate (nabam). Water-soluble mercurials have been effective in controlling turf diseases (Monteith, 1927), clubroot of cabbage (Snyder *et al.*, 1955), and damping-off (Ark and Sibray, 1954). The ancient copper sulfate, when used in water solutions, also has been useful as a row treatment in the control of damping-off pathogens and soil-borne *Phytophthora* (Horsfall, 1938; Kreutzer and Bryant, 1946).

Nabam has proved efficacious as an aqueous drench to soil for the control of species of *Phytophthora* (Stoddard, 1951; Zentmyer, 1952). It is also promising as a row-treating material for the control of root rot fungus complexes of beans and cotton (Leach and Snyder, 1947).

Water-insoluble and broad-spectrum fungicides include the commercially available tetramethylthiuram disulfide (thiram), zinc ethylene bisdithiocarbamate (zineb), and N-trichloromethylthio 1,2,3,4-tetrahydrophthalimide (captan). Thiram, zineb, and captan have been tested and used as row fungicides for the control of seed and seedling root and stem fungus diseases (Hildebrand *et al.*, 1949; Cooper, 1954; Young and Brandes, 1955).

Other representatives of this class of materials are the experimental pyridinethiones, represented by 2-pyridinethione 1-oxide disulfide, which has the structure:

The pyridinethiones have shown promise as soil fungicides in preliminary testing (Allison and Barnes, 1956).

The only narrow-spectrum protectant fungicides available at present are the chloronitrobenzenes. The most important of these chemicals is pentachloronitrobenzene, which is effective in soil against such genera as *Sclerotinia, Sclerotium, Rhizoctonia, Streptomyces,* and *Plasmodiophora,* but innocuous to *Pythium, Fusarium, Phytophthora, Verticillium, Thielaviopsis,* and *Colletotrichum* (Smieton and Brown, 1940; Kendrick and Middleton, 1954). This chemical is low in phytotoxicity and is relatively nonhazardous. It is finding its principal use in row treatments, alone and in combination with captan or the dithiocarbamates, for the control of seedling-rot complexes (Cooper, 1954; Brinkerhoff *et al.*, 1954). The most important effect of pentachloronitrobenzene, however, has been on the thinking of plant pathologists. Specificity is a fascinating subject.

Other materials which should be mentioned as soil fungicides are the antibiotics cycloheximide (Vaughn, 1951) and griseofulvin (Brian, 1949). The antibiotic approach is a good one. A lot of exploring could be done here in the search for new soil fungicides.

So much for the chemicals. We are now ready to discuss the principles of their application.

3. General Application Principles

In the application of soil nematocides and fungicides the important considerations are: (1) the soil condition, (2) the formulation of the biocide, and (3) the methods of application of the biocide in "space and time."

a. *Soil Condition.* There are certain rules that have been laid down to guide us in the preparation of the soil prior to treatment (Leavitt, 1948). Soils to be treated should be worked to plow depth into good seedbed condition. All clods should be thoroughly broken up.

The water content of the soil for fumigant-type chemicals should be optimum for planting (60–80% of the moisture equivalent); very wet or dry soils should be avoided. For residual nonvolatile chemicals where mixing is required, a drier soil is preferred, since it lends itself more readily to treatment. For all types of biocides the soil should be relatively free of plant "trash" (undecayed roots, stems, and leaves).

Excessively high (above 80°) or low (below 50°) soil temperatures should be avoided. High temperatures accelerate chemical decomposition and loss from the soil, while low temperatures retard dispersion of a biocide in soil.

b. *The Chemical and Its Formulation.* The volatility or water solubility of a chemical aids in determining the method of formulation as well as the method of applying the biocide to the soil.

Water-soluble chemicals such as the mercuric guanidines, copper sulfate, formaldehyde, allyl alcohol, and sodium N-methyl dithiocarbamate are applied best to the soil as aqueous drenches. Moderately volatile and water-insoluble chemicals such as ethylene dibromide and dichloropropene-dichloropropane mixture can be used as water emulsions. Moderately volatile materials such as the halogenated hydrocarbons and the lachrymator chloropicrin, however, are applied best unformulated or in suitable organic or hydrocarbon solvents. An extremely volatile material, exemplified by methyl bromide, is applied in undiluted form or in mixtures with chemicals such as chloropicrin.

Relatively nonvolatile and water-insoluble materials such as thiadiazine thione, zineb, and captan can be formulated as powders for dusting and spraying.

c. *Applications in Space and Time.* The application of chemicals to soil must be considered from the viewpoint of four dimensions. The volume of soil takes care of three dimensions. The time of application in relation to the time of planting is the fourth. The things that determine the "space and time" aspects of application are the cost of chemical, its relative phytotoxicity, and its control efficiency. High performance helps offset high cost of chemical. If the chemical is relatively low in phytotoxic effects, it can be applied more efficiently (row application instead of an entire area treatment). In the last analysis the best criterion is performance on a cost-per-acre basis. Only an expensive crop can stand an expensive treatment.

A biocide can be added to soil surfaces as a vapor (under a seal) or in liquid or dry form. It can also be mechanically mixed as a liquid or solid into the top few inches of soil or injected as a liquid under the soil surface. From the standpoint of soil area to be treated there are four basic ways in which we can apply a biocide to the soil:

(1) *The general and continuous application of volatile and nonvolatile chemicals.* This method is the treatment of all of the exposed soil of the entire soil area. Examples are: dispersing a nonvolatile biocide such as pentachloronitrobenzene throughout the upper surface area of the soil by mechanical mixing, or applying a highly volatile chemical such as methyl bromide to the surface of the soil under a gas-tight seal.

(2) *The general and discrete application of volatile chemicals.* Here the entire soil area is treated in a discontinuous fashion. Complete coverage is obtained by the overlap of gaseous diffusion patterns. It is the common field method used in the subsurface injections of volatile fumigants such as dichloropropene-dichloropropane mixture, ethylene dibromide, and chloropicrin.

(3) *The local and continuous application of volatile and nonvolatile chemicals.* The soil in only the general planting site is continuously treated. Good examples would be the continuous mixing of tetrahydrothiadiazine thione throughout the planting area of raised beds; and "spot" or bed treatments with water solutions of sodium *N*-methyl dithiocarbamate. The soil between the beds would not be treated.

(4) *The local and discrete application of volatile and nonvolatile chemicals.* The exact planting site (row) is treated in a restricted or discrete fashion. No attempt is made to treat soil outside of this site. This is the method used in row treatment at the time of seeding. An example would be the application of captan-pentachloronitrobenzene mixture by row spraying.

We have now taken care of our three-dimensional or space phase, and are ready to consider the fourth-dimensional aspect or time. Treatments can be made prior to planting, at the time of planting, and during the growth of the plants. The principal considerations here are phytotoxicity of the biocide and the method which lends itself best to practical procedures. Phytotoxicity is the most important factor. A severely phytotoxic chemical can be applied only prior to planting—with a suitable waiting period to allow dissipation of the compound. A marginally phytotoxic material, with sufficient care, can be applied at the time of planting. Only a relatively nonphytotoxic chemical can be applied to soil in which plants are growing.

With the advent of large-scale soil treatment slick, modern, machine-powered injectors have replaced the simple hand guns of the carbon-disulfide era. There are all types and varieties of forced-feed multiple-rowed plow and chisel and blade applicators (Jacks, 1952; Lear *et al.*, 1952; Jensen and Page, 1954). These machines are used to inject ever-growing acreages with dichloropropene-dichloropropane mixture, ethylene dibromide, and chloropicrin.

Equipment is keeping pace with expanding uses. New types of applicators are constantly being developed. Operators can handle noxious and poisonous materials with greater safety, and chemicals can be applied more rapidly and accurately. Cheap plastic sheeting and convenient metered containers improve the ease and speed of methyl bromide applications. Modern planting-row applications have replaced Selby's early crude dribble method. Fan and cone type nozzles apply controlled amounts of fungicides and nematocides in row applications just back of the planting shoe. There are one- and two-nozzle combinations to give better chemical distributions.

Studies are being conducted on the relation of nozzle number and placement to chemical pattern in the soil. Dyes and even radio-tagged chemicals are being used to determine chemical distribution at varying depths (Garber and Leach, 1957). Water-soluble chemicals are being introduced into pipe lines and automatically sprinkled on the soil as dilute water solutions (Zentmyer and Erspamer, 1957).

We haven't seen anything yet, however. Most of our chemical tools are still crude killers today. Tomorrow will be different. There will be specific biocides and therapeutants to do an even better job.

C. Soil Treatment with Heat

The cooking of soil to kill soil pathogens is probably the oldest known method of soil treatment. It was discovered first in all likelihood by neolithic man, who may well have observed salutary responses of plants growing in old fire sites. Sixty years ago (and perhaps even earlier) the practice suggested by this observation was put into effect. Newhall (1955) mentions that the roasting of tobacco seedbed soil by surface burning was a common practice when seedbeds were scattered about in wooded areas. This worked very well until the tobacco growers ran out of wood.

The use of heat sterilization of soil by steam was first used on a practical scale by Rudd in 1893, following Kühn's experimental studies in 1880 and Frank's research in 1888 (Johnson, 1946; Baker and Roistacher, 1957).

There are three ways of disinfesting soil with heat: these are, by use of (1) dry heat, (2) steam, and (3) hot water. Baker and Roistacher

(1957) have evaluated the merits of each method. They conclude that the use of steam is the most effective as well as the most efficient method of heat disinfestation. Dry heat does not conduct well, and hot water not only tends to puddle soil, but it penetrates soil poorly.

Where steam is available (as in greenhouses) its use is preferable to that of chemicals for soil disinfestation. Steam is fast, effective, and leaves no toxic residues. There is little advantage in using steam under pressure over free-flowing steam. The principle problem is to confine the steam to prevent excess heat loss and for a long enough period to heat the soil mass sufficiently to kill pathogens.

Most pathogenic fungi and nematodes can be killed by exposures for a few minutes to temperatures above 50° C. Baker and Roistacher (1957) have pointed out that hot water treatments will kill species of *Pythium, Botrytis, Rhizoctonia, Sclerotium, Sclerotinia,* and *Fusarium* in tissues at temperatures of 46–57° C., in time periods of exposure from 5 to 40 minutes. Nematodes such as *Aphelenchoides* and *Meloidogyne* are killed by hot water at temperatures of 48–53° C. at exposure times of 10–11 minutes.

Under ideal conditions, heating a soil mass to 60° C. for 30 minutes should be sufficient to destroy all plant pathogenic fungi and nematodes. Because of uneven distribution of heat in a soil mass, Baker and Roistacher (1957) recommend that a soil temperature of at least 80° C. be maintained for 30 minutes. In practice, however, these workers feel that to be on the safe side the temperature should be raised to 100° C. for 30 minutes.

Steamed soil is even more likely to be reinvaded by soil-inhabiting fungi than is chemically treated soil. This is because steamed soil usually is more completely disinfested. Well-cooked soil is a fine growth medium for most fungal soil inhabitants. It follows that extreme care should be taken with steamed soil to avoid recontamination.

Many ingenious devices have been developed over the years to apply heat to soil. Newhall (1955) and Baker and Roistacher (1957) have described application equipment and its uses in considerable detail. Stationary soil masses are treated by steam in mobile bins, steam boxes, vaults, cabinets, and autoclaves. Steam can be applied also to soil in benches by the use of inverted pans, perforated pipes, and steam rakes.

Steam does a good job of cleaning up soil. To make the use of steam practical beyond the greenhouse, however, we need cheaper fuels and a lot of engineering. Newhall (1955) estimates that it would require forty tons of coal to supply sufficient heat to disinfest an acre of soil 1 ft. deep. This is a lot of fuel, and the equipment and manpower required for such an application would be very costly. This discouraging picture might be changed by clever engineering and the use of atomic power. Soil disinfestation with heat may get out of the greenhouse yet.

IV. SUMMARY—NOW AND THE FUTURE

In this chapter an attempt has been made to set forth the basic principles of soil treatment primarily with nematocides and fungicides. Heat treatment is included only for the sake of completeness.

Between the plant and its environment there are a series of complex interactions. In agricultural soils, under a given set of conditions, the living phase (biophase) is in a state of dynamic equilibrium. This equilibrium state may be upset by chemical treatment, environmental changes, or cultural practices—causing a succession of transitory states which rapidly proceed toward a new equilibrium.

Since the micropopulation at all times is conceived to consist of organisms which either favor or harm the crop plant (sustainers or inhibitors), the new equilibrium formed is either good or bad for the crop plant.

On a prevalence basis the most important of the obvious soil-borne diseases are those that involve seeds and seedlings. On a broader and less obvious level, however, all plants probably suffer from some degree of root pathogenesis.

When a biocide is added to the soil, interactions will occur which result in changes in both the soil and biocide. The biocide may be hydrolyzed or otherwise degraded by the chemicals as well as by the microorganisms in the soil. The phenomenon of sorption of the biocide to soil colloids is broadly viewed as a type of bonding, whether it be of the covalent, hydrogen, ionic, or van der Waal's variety. The degree and type of sorption encountered, as well as the potential dispersibility of a biocide, will depend upon the properties of both the biocide and the soil.

The soil is affected to a lesser extent from contact with the biocide. Small changes in soil chemistry can occur, whereas there is little to no effect on the physical constitution of the soil. Profound local effects on the soil biophase do occur, with resultant favorable or unfavorable effects reflected by the growing crop plant.

Soil treatments with nematocides and fungicides have given control of diseases of known as well as of unknown etiology. Control responses in diseases of obscure etiology are believed to be the result of correction of unfavorable microbiological balances, control of unknown and undescribed facultative or obligate parasites, or control of toxin-forming organisms.

In looking toward future developments in the chemical control of soil pathogens, we may expect the following:

(1) Greater emphasis will be placed on control of minor and universal root pathogens rather than those causing more spectacular and sporadic lethal maladies.

(2) Research on the organisms of the biophase, particularly the microflora of the rhizosphere, will segregate the inhibitors from the sustainers. Conditions favoring or hindering their development will be learned. By appropriate soil amendments and enlightened cultural practices, the microbiological balance will be shifted toward the sustainer side.

(3) There will be a trend toward the use of more specific and highly efficient fungicides and nematocides. Such materials will be relatively nonphytotoxic and have a long residual action. Increased emphasis will be placed on treatment of critical soil zones at the time of planting and during the growth and development of the plants. Less effort will be made to treat large masses of soil.

(4) Systemically acting chemicals eventually will be found which will be applied by seed treatment, foliage sprays, in fertilizers, or irrigation water. They will be active at very low concentrations. Root and stem infections will be warded off by translocated chemicals, which will act by increasing the resistance of the plant or by inhibiting the developing pathogen.

We will eventually control fungus and nematode attack of stems and roots by not one, but by a combination of these future practices. Not now; but some day.

REFERENCES

Albert, A. 1951. "Selective Toxicity," 1st ed. Methuen, London, 228 pp.

Aldrich, D. G., and J. P. Martin. 1952. Effect of fumigation on some chemical properties of soils. *Soil Sci.* **73:** 149–159.

Allen, M. W., and D. J. Raski. 1950. The effect of soil type on the dispersion of soil fumigants. *Phytopathology* **40:** 1043–1053.

Allison, P., and G. L. Barnes. 1956. Plant disease control by a new class of chemicals, 2-pyridinethiol-1-oxide and derivatives. *Phytopathology* **46:** 6 (abstr.).

Anderson, E. J., and M. Okimoto. 1953. Laboratory studies of effectiveness of 3,5-dimethyltetrahydro-1,3,5,2-thiadiazine-2-thione against certain plant parasitic fungi and nematodes. *Phytopathology* **43:** 465 (abstr.).

Ark, P. A., and W. S. Sibray. 1954. Use of panogen drench to control damping-off in nursery flats. *Plant Disease Reptr.* **38:** 204–206.

Baines, R. C., F. J. Foote, and J. P. Martin. 1956. Fumigate soil before replanting to control citrus nematode. *Calif. Citrograph* **41:** 427.

Baker, K. F., and C. N. Roistacher. 1957. Heat treatment of soil. *In* "The U.C. System for Producing Healthy Container-Grown Plants." *Calif. Univ. Agr. Expt. Sta. Manual* **23:** 123–196.

Barratt, R. W., and J. G. Horsfall. 1947. Fungicidal action of metallic alkyl bis-dithiocarbamates. *Conn. Agr. Expt. Sta. Bull., New Haven* **508**: 51 pp.

Bertrand, G., and M. Rosenblatt. 1920. Action de la chloropicrine sur la fleur du vin. *Compt. rend.* **170**: 1350–1352.

Bliss, D. E. 1948. Soil disinfestation in citrus orchards against armillaria root rot. *Phytopathology* **38**: 913 (abstr.).

Bracken, A. 1955. "The Chemistry of Micro-organisms," 1st ed. Pitman, London. 343 pp.

Brian, P. W. 1949. Studies on the biological activity of griseofulvin. *Ann. Botany (London)* **13**: 60–77.

Brinkerhoff, L. A., E. S. Oswalt, and J. F. Tomlinson. 1954. Field tests with chemicals for the control of *Rhizoctonia* and other pathogens of cotton seedlings. *Plant Disease Reptr.* **38**: 467–475.

Brown, H. 1954. "The Challenge of Man's Future," 1st ed. Viking, New York. 290 pp.

Brown, W. 1935. On the Botrytis disease of lettuce with special reference to its control. *J. Pomol. Hort. Sci.* **13**: 247–259.

Buddin, W. 1937. The grey bulb rot of tulips and its control. *J. Ministry Agr. (Engl.)* **44**: 1158–1159; 1938. *Rev. Appl. Mycol.* **17**: 531 (abstr.).

Butler, E. E. 1957. *Rhizoctonia solani* as a parasite of fungi. *Mycologia* **49**: 354–373.

Call, F. 1957a. The mechanism of sorption of ethylene dibromide on moist soils. *J. Sci. Food Agr.* **8**: 630–639.

Call, F. 1957b. Soil fumigation. VI. The distribution of ethylene dibromide round an injection point. *J. Sci. Food Agr.* **8**: 591–596.

Carter, W. 1943. A promising new soil amendment and disinfectant. *Science* **97**: 383–384.

Chisholm, R. D., and L. Koblitsky. 1943. Sorption of methyl bromide by soil in a fumigation chamber. *J. Econ. Entomol.* **36**: 549–551.

Christie, J. R. 1945. Some preliminary tests to determine the efficacy of certain substances when used as soil fumigants to control the root-knot nematode, *Heterodera marioni* (Cornu) Goodey. *Proc. Helminthol. Soc. Wash. D. C.* **12**: 14–19.

Christie, J. R. 1947. Preliminary tests to determine the nematocidal and fungicidal properties of certain chemical compounds when used as soil fumigants. *Proc. Helminthol. Soc. Wash. D. C.* **14**: 23–28.

Clark, F. E., W. J. Zaumeyer, and J. T. Presley. 1957. Soilborne plant diseases. *Yearbook Agr.* (*U. S. Dept. Agr.*) pp. 333–339.

Clayton, E. E., J. G. Gaines, T. W. Graham, and F. A. Todd. 1949. Soil treatments with chemicals for the control of tobacco parasites. *Phytopathology* **39**: 4–5 (abstr.).

Cobb, N. A. 1914. Nematodes and their relationships. *Yearbook Agr.* (*U. S. Dept. Agr.*) pp. 457–490.

Cooper, W. E. 1954. The seed-furrow application of fungicides to control cotton stand failures. *Phytopathology* **44**: 331 (abstr.).

Cornfield, A. H. 1955. The measurement of soil structure and factors affecting it: A review. *J. Sci. Food Agr.* **6**: 356–360.

Cram, W. H., and O. Vaartaja. 1957. Rate and timing of fungicidal soil treatments. *Phytopathology* **47**: 169–173.

Dalton, F. H., and C. Hurwitz. 1948. Effect of volatile disinfectants on survival of microflora in soil. *Soil Sci.* **66**: 233–238.

DeWolfe, R. H., and W. G. Young. 1956. Substitution and rearrangement reactions of allylic compounds. *Chem. Revs.* **56**: 753–901.

Dimond, A. E., and J. G. Horsfall. 1944. Synergism as a tool in the conservation of fungicides. *Phytopathology* **34**: 136–139.

Dimond, A. E., J. W. Heuberger, and J. G. Horsfall. 1943. A water soluble protectant fungicide with tenacity. *Phytopathology* **33**: 1095–1097.

Dorier, C. 1933. Action of beta-chloroallyl chloride on primary aromatic amines. *Compt. rend.* **196**: 1677–1678; *Chem. Abstr.* **27**: 4222.

Duddington, C. L. 1957. The predacious fungi and their place in microbial ecology. *In* "Microbial Ecology, 7th Symposium Society General Microbiology." Cambridge Univ. Press, London and New York. pp. 218–237.

Ensminger, L. E., and J. E. Gieseking. 1942. Resistance of clay-adsorbed proteins to proteolytic hydrolysis. *Soil Sci.* **53**: 205–209.

Fawcett, H. S. 1936. "Citrus Diseases and Their Control," 2nd ed. McGraw-Hill, New York, 656 pp.

Fink, H. C. 1956. Vapam and P.C.N.B. soil treatments for potato scab control. *Plant Disease Reptr.* **40**: 190–192.

Fleming, W. E., and F. E. Baker. 1935. The use of carbon disulfide against the japanese beetle. *U. S. Dept. Agr. Tech. Bull.* **478**: 91 pp.

French, C. A. 1893. "Handbook of the Destructive Insects of Victoria," 1st ed., Pt. II. Robert S. Brain, Gov't. Printer, Melbourne, Australia. 222 pp.

Fuhr, I., A. V. Bransford, and S. D. Silver. 1948. Sorption of fumigant vapors by soil. *Science* **107**: 274–275.

Fulton, N. D., B. A. Waddle, and R. O. Thomas. 1956. Influence of planting dates on fungi isolated from diseased cotton seedlings. *Plant Disease Reptr.* **40**: 556–558.

Gaines, J. G., and T. W. Graham. 1953. Soil fumigation to control root ills. *Yearbook Agr. (U. S. Dept. Agr.)* pp. 561–567.

Garber, R. H., and L. D. Leach. 1957. The use of chemical indicators in the study of distribution of row-treatment fungicides. *Phytopathology* **47**: 521 (abstr.).

Garrett, S. D. 1956. "Biology of Root-Infecting Fungi," 1st ed. Cambridge Univ. Press, London and New York. 292 pp.

Garrett, S. D. 1957. Effect of a soil microflora selected by carbon disulphide fumigation on survival of *Armillaria mellea* in woody host tissues. *Can. J. Microbiol.* **3**: 135–149.

Gerretsen, F. C. 1937. Manganese deficiency of oats and its relation to soil bacteria. *Ann. Botany (London).* **1**: 207–230.

Gibson, I. A. S. 1953. Crown rot, a seedling disease of groundnuts caused by *Aspergillus niger*. II. An anomalous effect of organo-mercurial seed dressings. *Trans. Brit. Mycol. Soc.* **36**: 324–334.

Gibson, I. A. S. 1956. An anomalous effect of soil treatment with ethyl mercury phosphate on the incidence of damping-off in pine seedlings. *Phytopathology* **46**: 181–182.

Godfrey, G. H. 1934. The confinement of chloropicrin and other gases for fumigation purposes. *Phytopathology* **24**: 1366–1373.

Godfrey, G. H. 1935. Experiments on the control of the root-knot nematode in the field with chloropicrin and other chemicals. *Phytopathology* **25**: 67–90.

Godfrey, G. H. 1936. Control of soil fungi by soil fumigation with chloropicrin. *Phytopathology* **26**: 246–256.

Grim, R. E. 1953. "Clay Mineralogy," 1st ed. McGraw-Hill, New York. 384 pp.

Haasis, F. A. 1952. Soil fumigation with chlorobromopropene for control of *Sclerotium rolfsii* in Dutch iris. *Plant Disease Reptr.* **36**: 475–478.

Hacskaylo, E., and J. G. Palmer. 1957. Effects of several biocides on growth of seedling pines and incidence of mycorrhizae in field plots. *Plant Disease Reptr.* **41**: 354–358.

Hagan, R. M. 1941. Movement of carbon disulfide vapor in soils. *Hilgardia* **14**: 83–118.

Hannesson, H. A. 1945. Movement of carbon disulfide vapor in soils as affected by soil type, moisture content, and compaction. *Hilgardia* **16**: 503–510.

Hanson, W. J., and R. W. Nex. 1953. Diffusion of ethylene dibromide in soils. *Soil Sci.* **76**: 209–214.

Hatch, L. F., and A. C. Moore. 1944. Dehydrochlorination of 3-chloro-2-propen-1-ol: preparation of propargyl alcohol. *J. Am. Chem. Soc.* **66**: 285–287.

Heintze, S. G., and P. J. G. Mann. 1949. Studies on soil manganese. *J. Agr. Sci.* **39**: 80–95.

Higgins, J. C., and A. G. Pollard. 1937. Studies in soil fumigation. II. Distribution of carbon disulphide in soil fumigated under various conditions. *Ann. Appl. Biol.* **24**: 895–910.

Hildebrand, A. A., W. E. McKeen, and L. W. Koch. 1949. Row treatment of soil with tetramethylthiuram disulfide for control of black root of sugar beet seedlings. I. Greenhouse tests. *Can. J. Research* **C27**: 23–43.

Horsfall, J. G. 1938. Combating damping-off. *N. Y. State Agr. Expt. Sta. (Geneva, N. Y.) Bull.* **683**: 46 pp.

Horsfall, J. G. 1956. "Principles of Fungicidal Action." Chronica Botanica, Waltham, Massachusetts. 279 pp.

Ichikawa, S. T., J. D. Gilpatrick, and C. W. McBeth. 1955. Soil diffusion pattern of 1,2-dibromo-3-chloropropane. *Phytopathology* **45**: 576–578.

Ivarson, K. C., and D. Pramer. 1956. The persistence and biological effects of surface active agents in soil. *Proc. Am. Soc. Soil Sci.* **20**: 371–374.

Jacks, H. 1952. Soil disinfection. XIII. An injector for field fumigation. *New Zealand J. Sci. Technol.* **B34**: 139–145.

Jensen, H. J., and G. E. Page. 1954. An experimental blade-type soil fumigant applicator. *Plant Disease Reptr.* **38**: 401–402.

Jensen, H. J., F. E. Caveness, and R. H. Mulvey. 1954. A modification of Thorne's technique for examining soil diffusion patterns of nematocides. *Plant Disease Reptr.* **38**: 680–686.

Johnson, J. 1946. Soil-steaming for disease control. *Soil Sci.* **61**: 83–91.

Johnson, M. O., and G. H. Godfrey. 1932. Chloropicrin for nematode control. *Ind. Eng. Chem.* **24**: 311–313.

Jurinak, J. J. 1957. Adsorption of 1,2-dibromo-3-chloropropane vapor by soils. *J. Agr. Food Chem.* **5**: 598–600.

Jurinak, J. J., and D. H. Volman. 1957. Application of the Brunauer, Emmett, and Teller equation to ethylene dibromide adsorption by soils. *Soil Sci.* **83**: 487–496.

Katznelson, H., and L. T. Richardson. 1943. The microflora of the rhizosphere of tomato plants in relation to soil sterilization. *Can. J. Research.* **C21**: 249–255.

Kendrick, J. B., Jr., and G. A. Zentmyer. 1957. Recent advances in control of soil fungi. *Advances in Pest Control Research* **1**: 219–275.

Kendrick, J. B., Jr., and J. T. Middleton. 1954. The efficacy of certain chemicals as fungicides for a variety of fruit, root, and vascular pathogens. *Plant Disease Reptr.* **38**: 350–353.

Kingsland, G. C., and A. E. Rich. 1955. Studies on the cause and control of pea root rot in New Hampshire. *Phytopathology* **45**: 185 (abstr.).

Kittleson, A. R. 1952. A new class of organic fungicides. *Science* **115**: 84–86.

Koch, L. W. 1955. The peach replant problem in Ontario. I. Symptomatology and distribution. *Can. J. Botany* **33**: 450–460.

Kreutzer, W. A., and L. R. Bryant. 1946. Certain aspects of the epiphytology and control of tomato fruit rot caused by *Phytophthora capsici* Leonian. *Phytopathology* **36**: 329–339.

Kreutzer, W. A., and J. T. W. Montagne. 1950. Chlorobromopropene, a potential fungicidal soil fumigant. *Phytopathology* **40**: 16 (abstr.).

Kreutzer, W. A., C. W. McBeth, M. Turner, G. B. Bergeson, and R. R. Whetstone. 1951. The fungicidal and nematocidal properties of dibromobutene. *Science* **113**: 657–658.

Leach, L. D., and W. C. Snyder. 1947. Localized chemical applications to the soil and their effects upon root rots of beans and peas. *Phytopathology* **37**: 363 (abstr.).

Lear, B. 1950. Efficacy of dichlorobutene as a soil fumigant against *Heterodera rostochiensis* Wollenweber, and *Heterodera marioni* (Cornu) Goodey. *Phytopathology* **40**: 17 (abstr.).

Lear, B., W. F. Mai, J. Feldmesser, and F. J. Spruyt. 1952. Soil fumigation experiments on Long Island, New York to control golden nematode of potatoes. *Phytopathology* **42**: 193–196.

Leavitt, F. H. 1948. Observations on the mechanics of soil fumigation. *Proc. Am. Soc. Sugar Beet Technologists, 5th Gen. Meeting* pp. 509–513.

Loew, O. 1909. Soil disinfection in agriculture. *Puerto Rico Univ. Agr. Expt. Sta. Circ.* **11**: 12 pp.

Manzelli, M. A. 1955. A residual organophosphorus nematocide. *Plant Disease Reptr.* **39**: 400–404.

McBeth, C. W., and G. B. Bergeson. 1955. 1,2-Dibromo-3-chloropropane—a new nematocide. *Plant Disease Reptr.* **39**: 223–225.

McClellan, W. D., J. R. Christie, and N. L. Horn. 1949. Efficacy of soil fumigants as affected by soil temperature and moisture. *Phytopathology* **39**: 272–283.

Martin, J. P. 1950. Effects of fumigation and other soil treatments in the greenhouse on the fungus population of old citrus soil. *Soil Sci.* **69**: 107–122.

Martin, J. P., and D. G. Aldrich. 1952. Effect of fumigation on soil aggregation. *Proc. Am. Soc. Soil Sci.* **16**: 201–203.

Martin, J. P., and D. G. Aldrich. 1954. Effect of various exchangeable cation ratios on kinds of fungi developing during decomposition of organic residues in soil. *Proc. Am. Soc. Soil Sci.* **18**: 160–164.

Martin, J. P., D. G. Aldrich, W. S. Murphy, and G. R. Bradford. 1953. Effect of soil fumigation on growth and chemical composition of citrus plants. *Soil Sci.* **75**: 137–151.

Martin, J. P., G. K. Helmkamp, and J. O. Ervin. 1956. Effect of bromide from a soil fumigant and from CaBr$_2$ on growth and chemical composition of citrus plants. *Proc. Am. Soc. Soil Sci.* **20**: 209–212.

Martin, J. P., R. C. Baines, and J. O. Ervin. 1957. Influence of soil fumigation for citrus replants on the fungus population of the soil. *Proc. Am. Soc. Soil Sci.* **21**: 163–166.

Martin, W. J. 1953. Circular spot, a disease of sweet potato roots. *Phytopathology* **43**: 432–433.

Meuli, L. J., and A. W. Swezey. 1949. Soil fumigation for control of sweet potato black rot (*Ceratostomella fimbriata*). *Phytopathology* **39:** 861 (abstr.).

Meyer, C. 1940. Eenige resultaten van proeven en waarnemingen over het optreden van Aardappelschurft. *Tijdschr. Plantenziekten* **46:** 19–29.

Middleton, J. T., M. W. Stone, and J. B. Kendrick, Jr. 1949. Incidence of lima bean root rot in soils treated with fumigants and insecticides for control of wireworms. *Phytopathology* **39:** 813–821.

Millard, W. A., and C. B. Taylor. 1927. Antagonism of micro-organisms as the controlling factor in the inhibition of scab by green-manuring. *Ann. Appl. Biol.* **14:** 202–216.

Moje, W., J. P. Martin, and R. C. Baines. 1957. Structural effect of some organic compounds on soil organisms and citrus seedlings grown in an old citrus soil. *J. Agr. Food Chem.* **5:** 32–36.

Mollison, J. E. 1953. Effect of partial sterilization and acidification of soil on the fungal population. *Trans. Brit. Mycol. Soc.* **36:** 215–228.

Monteith, J., Jr. 1927. Winter injury of turf. *Bull. U. S. Golf Assoc. Green Sect.* **7:** 62–76.

Moore, W. 1918. Fumigation with chloropicrin. *J. Econ. Entomol.* **11:** 357–362.

Morton, D. J., and W. H. Stroube. 1955. Antagonistic and stimulatory effects of soil microorganisms upon *Sclerotium rolfsii*. *Phytopathology* **45:** 417–420.

Munnecke, D. E., and J. Ferguson. 1953. Methyl bromide for nursery soil fumigation. *Phytopathology* **43:** 375–377.

Newhall, A. G. 1955. Disinfestation of soil by heat, flooding, and fumigation. *Botan. Rev.* **21:** 189–250.

Overman, A. J., and D. S. Burgis. 1956. Ally alcohol as a soil fungicide. *Phytopathology* **46:** 532–535.

Park, D. 1955. Experimental studies on the ecology of fungi in soil. *Trans. Brit. Mycol. Soc.* **38:** 130–142.

Peters, B. G., and D. W. Fenwick. 1949. Field trials with D-D mixture against potato-root eelworm. *Ann. Appl. Biol.* **36:** 364–382.

Potter, H. S., and O. D. Morgan. 1956. Nemagon control of root-knot nematode on strawberries. *Plant Disease Reptr.* **40:** 187–189.

Reed, H. S., and T. Frémont. 1935. Factors that influence the formation and development of mycorrhizal associations in citrus roots. *Phytopathology* **25:** 645–647.

Reynolds, H. W., and R. G. Hanson. 1957. Rhizoctonia disease of cotton in the presence or absence of the cotton root-knot nematode in Arizona. *Phytopathology* **47:** 256–261.

Richardson, H. H., and A. C. Johnson. 1935. Studies of methyl bromide in greenhouse and vault fumigation. *U. S. Dept. Agr. Tech. Bull.* **853:** 20 pp.

Richardson, L. T. 1954. The persistence of thiram in soil and its relationship to the microbiological balance and damping-off control. *Can. J. Botany* **32:** 335–346.

Riehm, E. 1913. Prüfung einiger Mittel zur Bekämpfung des Steinbrandes. *Mitt. Kaiserlichen biol. Reichenstalt Land-u. Forstwirtsch.* **14:** 8–9.

Schmidt, C. T. 1947. Dispersion of fumigants through soil. *J. Econ. Entomol.* **40:** 829–837.

Schuldt, P. H., and H. Bluestone. 1957. Nematocidal properties of 3,4-dichlorotetrahydrothiophene-1,1-dioxide (PRD). *Contribs. Boyce Thompson Inst.* **19:** 63–75.

Selby, A. D. 1900. Onion smut—preliminary experiments. *Ohio Agr. Expt. Sta. Bull.* **122:** 71–84.

Selby, A. D. 1906. Soil treatment of tobacco plant beds. *Ohio Agr. Expt. Sta. Circ.* **59:** 3 pp.

Siegel, J. J., A. E. Erickson, and L. M. Turk. 1951. Diffusion characteristics of 1-3 dichloropropene and 1-2 dibromoethane in soils. *Soil Sci.* **72:** 333–340.

Siminoff, P., and D. Gottlieb. 1951. The production and role of antibiotics in the soil. I. The fate of streptomycin. *Phytopathology* **41:** 420–430.

Smieton, M. J., and W. Brown. 1940. Botrytis disease of lettuce, its relation to damping-off and mildew, and its control by pentachloro-nitrobenzene dust. *Ann. Appl. Biol.* **27:** 489–501.

Smith, A. L. 1948. Control of cotton wilt and nematodes with a soil fumigant. *Phytopathology* **38:** 943–947.

Smith, N. R. 1939. The partial sterilization of soil by chloropicrin. *Proc. Am. Soc. Soil Sci.* **3:** 188.

Snyder, W. C., L. D. Leach, and R. H. Sciaroni. 1955. Chemical control of club-root disease of Brussels Sprouts. *Calif. Agr.* **9:** 8, 10.

Stark, F. L., Jr. 1948. Investigation of chloropicrin as a soil fumigant. *Cornell Univ. Expt. Sta. Mem.* **278:** 61 pp.

Stark, F. L., Jr., and B. Lear. 1947. Miscellaneous greenhouse tests with various soil fumigants for the control of fungi and nematodes. *Phytopathology* **37:** 698–711.

Steinberg, R. A. 1956. Production and prevention of frenching of tobacco grown in the greenhouse. *Plant and Soil* **7:** 281–289.

Stoddard, E. M. 1951. Control of strawberry red stele by chemotherapy. *Phytopathology* **41:** 858.

Tam, R. K., and E. E. Clark. 1943. Effect of chloropicrin and other soil disinfectants on the nitrogen nutrition of the pineapple plant. *Soil Sci.* **56:** 245–261.

Tarjan, A. C. 1954. Controlling root-knot infections of greenhouse tomatoes with 3-p-chlorophenyl-5-methyl rhodanine. *Phytopathology* **44:** 112 (abstr.).

Taylor, A. L. 1939. Efficient spacing of soil fumigants for field applications. *Proc. Helminthol. Soc. Wash. D. C.* **6:** 62–66.

Taylor, A. L., and C. W. McBeth. 1940. Preliminary tests of methyl bromide as a nematocide. *Proc. Helminthol. Soc. Wash. D. C.* **7:** 94–96.

Taylor, G. S. 1956. Tobacco seedbed treatments for control of weeds and soil-borne pathogens. *Phytopathology* **46:** 242 (abstr.).

Thaxter, R. 1891. Further experiments on the smut of onions. p. 103–104. Report of the mycologist. *Ann. Rept. Conn. Agr. Expt. Sta., New Haven* **1890:** 113 pp.

Thomas, H. E., and L. O. Lawyer. 1939. The use of carbon bisulfide in the control of armillaria root rot. *Phytopathology* **29:** 827–828 (abstr.).

Thorne, G. 1951. Diffusion patterns of soil fumigants. *Proc. Helminthol. Soc. Wash. D. C.* **18:** 18–24.

Thornton, H. G. 1956. The development and present problems of soil microbiology. *J. Sci. Food Agr.* **7:** 93–101.

Thornton, H. G., and J. Meiklejohn. 1957. Soil microbiology. *Ann. Rev. Microbiol.* **11:** 123–148.

Tisdale, W. H., and I. Williams. 1934. Disinfectant. *U. S. Patent No. 1,972,961.*

Torgeson, D. C., D. M. Yoder, and J. B. Johnson. 1957. Biological activity of Mylone breakdown products. *Phytopathology* **47:** 536 (abstr.).

Toth, S. J. 1955. Colloid chemistry of soils. *In* "Chemistry of the Soil." Reinhold, New York. pp. 85–106.

van der Kerk, G. J. M. 1956. The present state of fungicide research. *Achtste Jaarlijks Symp. over Phytopharm. Ghent, Belgium* pp. 305–339.

Vaughn, J. R. 1951. Cycloheximide, an antibiotic effective against turf diseases. *Phytopathology* **41**: 36 (abstr.).

Waksman, S. A. 1947. "Microbial Antagonisms and Antibiotic Substances," 2nd ed. Commonwealth Fund, New York. 415 pp.

Waksman, S. A. 1952. "Soil Microbiology." Wiley, New York. 356 pp.

Wasewitz, H. 1937. Die Salatfäule und ihre Bekämfung. *Kranke Pflanze* **14**: 71–73; 1937. *Rev. Appl. Mycol.* **16**: 652 (abstr.).

Watson, R. D. 1951. Method for use of soil fumigants to control root rot and seed decay in peas and beans. *Plant Disease Reptr.* **35**: 324–325.

Weindling, R. 1932. *Trichoderma lignorum* as a parasite of other soil fungi. *Phytopathology* **22**: 837–845.

Weindling, R., and H. S. Fawcett. 1936. Experiments in the control of rhizoctonia damping-off of citrus seedlings. *Hilgardia* **10**: 1–16.

Wensley, R. N. 1956. The peach replant problem in Ontario. IV. Fungi associated with replant failure and their importance in fumigated and nonfumigated soils. *Can. J. Botany* **34**: 967–981.

Wilde, S. A., and D. J. Persidsky. 1956. Effect of biocides on the development of ectotrophic mycorrhizae in Monterey pine seedlings. *Proc. Am. Soc. Soil Sci.* **20**: 107–110.

Wilhelm, S. 1957. Chloropicrin gives promising control of verticillium wilt in strawberry. *Phytopathology* **47**: 37 (abstr.).

Wilhelm, S., and E. C. Koch. 1956. Verticillium wilt controlled. *Calif. Agr.* **10**: 3, 14.

Williamson, C. E. 1953. Methyl bromide injury to some ornamental plants. *Phytopathology* **43**: 489. (abstr.).

Young, D. W., and G. A. Brandes. 1955. Effect of zineb (Dithane Z-78) on the survival of cotton seedlings. *Phytopathology* **45**: 350 (abstr.).

Young, P. A. 1940. Soil fumigation with chloropicrin and carbon bisulfide to control tomato root knot and wilt. *Phytopathology* **30**: 860–865.

Young, R. A., and W. J. Tolmsoff. 1957. Cultural and chemical treatments for control of the early maturity disease of potatoes. *Phytopathology* **47**: 38 (abstr.).

Zagallo, A. C., and H. Katznelson. 1957. Metabolic activity of bacterial isolates from wheat rhizosphere and control soil. *J. Bacteriol.* **73**: 760–764.

Zentmyer, G. A. 1952. Evaluation of soil fungicides for the control of *Phytophthora cinnamomi. Phytopathology* **42**: 24 (abstr.).

Zentmyer, G. A., and J. L. Erspamer. 1957. Vapam as a soil fumigant and as a chemotherapeutant. *Phytopathology* **47**: 38–39 (abstr.).

Zentmyer, G. A., and L. J. Klotz. 1949. Soil fumigants for the control of phytophthora root rots. *Phytopathology* **39**: 26–27 (abstr.).

Zobell, C. E. 1946. Action of microorganisms on hydrocarbons. *Bacteriol. Revs.* **10**: 1–49.

CHAPTER 12

Performance of Fungicides on Plants and in Soil — Physical, Chemical, and Biological Considerations

H. P. BURCHFIELD

Boyce Thompson Institute for Plant Research, Inc.,
Yonkers, New York

I. INTRODUCTION

The only criterion by which to judge an agricultural fungicide is its success, but this is composed of many things. To protect plant surfaces, the fungicide must be deposited uniformly and adhere well. It must withstand weathering by sunlight, air, and water, and if used in the soil, it must survive attack by microorganisms and spontaneous reactions with metabolic debris until it has halted the advance of the fungi. Somehow it must do all this inexpensively without injuring the host plants. Therefore it should be no surprise that few out of many candidate compounds succeed. Yet from each failure there is a lesson to be learned if we look closely enough.

Sometimes failure may result from a defect in formulation, or then again it may arise from an intrinsic weakness in the compound that can be remedied only by the synthesis of a new derivative with improved properties. Often the case is hopeless. Whatever the cause, an understanding of the basic scientific principle involved will help clear the way for future successes. Good fungicides may still be discovered by accident, but at least these should be planned accidents based on what plant pathologists and chemists have learned about their interactions with their environments during the past 75 years. This chapter summarizes some of these lessons.

II. Protection of Plant Surfaces

A. *Physical Factors Influencing Deposition and Distribution*

1. *Mechanics of Deposition and Spreading*

Protectant fungicides are applied to fruit and foliage as dusts or sprays. To be able to settle on the plants the particles must have enough momentum to overcome repulsive forces which exist near surfaces. These may be electrostatic in nature or they may arise from convection currents caused by temperature differentials between the surfaces and the surrounding atmosphere. Furthermore, the high velocity air streams used to propel dusts and concentrate sprays tend to glide around plant surfaces. Consequently the particles carried by them must have enough momentum to strike the plant surfaces, instead of being carried away by the deflected air current. Momentum is the product of mass and velocity; hence when the particles are extremely minute, they must be projected at high speeds to pentrate these barriers. However, direct impingement of the particles on the surfaces accounts for only part of the fungicide deposited. Much of it must miss the main targets and eventually settle on the plants by gravity. Consequently particle size cannot be too small, for the limiting velocity a spherical object can attain on falling through still air is given by Stokes' law as

$$v = \frac{2r^2g(d - d_0)}{9\eta} \tag{1}$$

where d is the density of the fungicide, d_0 the density of air, r the particle radius, g the acceleration of gravity, and η the viscosity of air. Calculations made from this equation show that a particle with a radius of 10μ and a density of 2 gm. per cm.^{3} would reach a limiting velocity of 2.3 cm. per second and have a momentum of 1.9×10^{-8} gm. cm. per second. This is about the minimum value that would enable it to penetrate the barriers created by repulsive forces at the plant surfaces. Thus dust particles would have to be about 20μ in diameter or form aggregates of about this size to obtain satisfactory deposit build-up. Unfortunately particles or aggregates of particles in this size range are easily dislodged by wind and rain, so dusting has never been a highly satisfactory method for protecting crops.

Overcoming the repulsive forces at surfaces is not the only problem in the deposition of small particles, for calculations from Stokes' law (equation 1) show that a particle 100μ in diameter with a density of 1 will fall at a rate of 30 cm. per second in still air, while a 1μ particle has a limiting velocity of only 10 cm. per hour. Thus, air currents may tend to carry the dust away from the area of application faster than it settles.

Occasionally it has been suggested that the deposition of dusts may be promoted by the presence of positive electrostatic charges on the individual particles induced by friction in the blowing apparatus, which would cause them to be attracted to negatively charged surfaces of leaves by electrostatic forces. However, the charges induced on dusts during blowing are weak, and they vary in sign, so it is unlikely that they improve deposition significantly (Gill, 1948). Recently, Bowen et al. (1952) have described an electrostatic duster which is said to impart very high charges to particles by application of a 12,000 volt potential difference in the same manner used for the electrification of dusts in industrial precipitators. The authors state that a particle 5μ in radius, bearing a high charge, would be attracted to a surface by an image force about equal to gravity at a distance of 100μ. This calculation is based on the assumption that plant surfaces are perfect conductors, which is probably untrue. Interestingly enough, good deposition was obtained when the particles were negatively charged. This shows that the image charge induced on the surfaces of the plants by the dust cloud was positive in sign even though it is generally assumed that leaves are negatively charged. Deposition was superior to that of uncharged dusts, but the particle size range of the preparation used was not given.

Many of the disadvantages of dusts are eliminated in sprays. Here the small primary particles of fungicide are encapsulated in larger liquid droplets that can be given sufficient momentum to penetrate the barrier immediately surrounding the foliage. The droplets spread on impact, and when the liquid carrier evaporates, the fungicide particles are left on the fruit and leaves. Coverage is never as uniform as that obtained with a dust distributed randomly, but smaller particles can be deposited and the tenacity of the residue is greater.

In conventional high volume sprays applied at rates of 75 to 300 gallons per acre, drop size is likely to be of the order of 0.5 to 3 mm. If properly formulated, these large drops easily acquire enough momentum to drench the leaves thoroughly. However, in concentrate spraying, as little as 1 to 15 gallons of liquid per acre may be used to distribute the same amount of chemical. Drop size must therefore be reduced drastically to achieve adequate coverage of the foliage. For application of concentrate sprays from the ground with air blast equipment, optimum radius is 15 to 40μ, while for aircraft application it is about 35 to 70μ (Potts, 1958). While this size range is considerably above the minimum required to overcome the repulsive forces at the surfaces, it is sufficiently small so that high velocities must be imparted to the particles to carry them to their destinations. Yeomans and Rogers (1953) state that the maximum distance a particle can move in a direction parallel to the ground is directly proportional to its initial velocity and to the square of its radius. Consequently, very small particles will be stopped much more readily than large ones. For example, a droplet with a radius of 50μ and an initial velocity of 112 m.p.h. will travel 150 cm., while a 5μ droplet ejected at the same speed will be stopped after penetrating only 1.5 cm. of air. Therefore small drops must be carried by air currents moving at high velocities to obtain good deposition of concentrate sprays.

However, delivery of droplets to plant surfaces may not always be enough to insure good deposition. Thus, Burchfield and Goenaga (1957b) found that deposit build-up of 10-10-100 Bordeaux mixture on young banana leaves was very slow when the leaves were kept in motion during spraying. Careful inspection revealed that the spray droplets were bouncing off the surface as if they were minute rubber balls. Evidently the contact angles between the leaves and droplets were too high to permit retention of the spray under these conditions.

Contact angle (θ) is defined by

$$\cos \theta = \frac{W_a - \pi_e}{\gamma_L} - 1 \tag{2}$$

where γ_L is the surface tension of the liquid, W_a the work of adhesion, and π_e a quantity that can be determined from the Gibbs adsorption isotherm. The contact angle is critical in determining whether a spray suspension will spread uniformly on the surface of a plant. A contact angle approaching zero indicates that the liquid is attracted to the surface by forces as high as the internal forces of cohesion, so that the spray droplets tend to flatten and form thin films. Conversely, a contact angle approaching 180° indicates that wettability is so poor that the droplets do not adhere to the surfaces. Actually these extreme values are never reached, the contact angle of water on paraffin being only about 100°. Evidently a similar situation occurred when the young banana leaves were sprayed with Bordeaux. When a nonionic surfactant was added to the formulation to reduce interfacial tension, the leaves were wet uniformly and the amount of copper deposited under the same conditions increased fivefold. Deposit build-up with ordinary Bordeaux was faster on older leaves, but in all cases it was improved by the surfactant. However, caution must be used in generalizing on the effects of spreaders, since Somers (1957) found that some anionic surfactants decreased deposit build-up severely on easily wettable leaves although he also found that nonionic adjuvants were beneficial.

Somers (1957) states that the advancing contact angles of waterdrops on the upper surfaces of leaves of potato, bean, and laurel were 35°, 49°, and 81°, respectively, and that their wettability decreased in that order. Generally, deposit build-up is poorest on plants with smooth waxy surfaces and best on rough or moderately hirsute leaves. Thus, peppers, crucifers, and tropical plants such as banana accumulate less chemical under equivalent conditions of spraying than crops such as beans, potatoes, and eggplant. Usually deposition can be improved by the incorporation of suitable surfactants, but the value of this is governed in each individual case by the crop and the spray volume. This latter factor is particularly important, since the amount of fungicide deposited on leaf surfaces at equal total doses tends to decrease as the volume of carrier liquid is increased. This is because run-off of the spray occurs earlier at high volumes and some of the fungicide is carried away with the water. Adding surfactant to such mixtures decreases the volume of spray required to obtain run-off still further, and consequently decreases deposit. For example, Cupples (1941) found that improved wetting properties led to lower fungicide deposits on apples. Presumably at intermediate and low gallonage applications runoff would not occur, so that only the beneficial effect of the spreader would be retained. Thus, Swales and Williams (1956) report that inclusion of nonionic surfactants in lime-sulfur, sulfur, and ferbam (ferric dimethyldithiocarbamate) concentrate spray mixtures improved their effectiveness for the control of apple scab. While this may have resulted in part from improved distribution of the fungicide, it appears that over-all deposition could not have been reduced seriously by the adjuvants.

Other things being equal, the amount of fungicides deposited on plant surfaces should be directly proportional to its concentration in the spray suspension. Factors which might tend to obscure this simple relationship include changes in the droplet size of the spray and deposition after runoff. Most fungicide formulations contain surfactants. Consequently the surface tensions of sprays should be somewhat less at high concentrations than at low. Low surface tension is known to cause the formation of small drops, which might reduce deposition through greater drift of the spray with wind. However, indirect proportionalities have been reported between concentration and deposit where this could not be a factor. Thus, Rich (1954) found that the amount of Bordeaux deposited on leaves of beans and celery tended to reach a limiting value as the concentration in the spray tank was increased, while zineb (zinc ethylenebis[dithiocarbamate] deposits increased linearly with concentration in the range studied. He pointed out that Bordeaux particles are positively charged—a fact which might cause them to be attracted to negatively charged leaf surfaces by electrokinetic forces. As the unoccupied sites on the foliage surfaces became reduced in number, rate of deposition would tend to decrease. These results seem inconsistent, since zineb particles are negatively charged and thus should be deposited with less rather than greater efficiency than Bordeaux. However, the concentration range studied was not the same for the two fungicides, so more evidence is required. The most reasonable explanation for this phenomenon is that deposit was directly proportional to concentration up to the point of runoff. When this condition was finally exceeded, Bordeaux continued to be deposited at a slower rate, the runoff water being slightly poorer in copper than the impinging spray droplets. Thus, deposition might not cease abruptly when runoff is reached, but continue awhile beyond it until the capacity of the leaves for retaining fungicide is exhausted. This could not occur when runoff is very rapid and insufficient time is allowed for the fungicide to become attached to the leaves. It has not been established whether electrokinetic effects are involved in this process. However, in view of the finding by Somers (1957) that negatively charged surfactants such as sodium dioctyl sulfosuccinate decrease deposit build-up a reinvestigation of this problem would be of great interest.

2. Role of Particle Size and Redistribution in Disease Control

Deposition of a fungicide on a plant surface is not by itself sufficient to insure the utmost utilization of its capacity for controlling disease. It must be distributed so that the maximum number of potential loci of infection is protected. Wilcoxon and McCallan (1931) found that there were significant differences in toxicity between sulfur dusts having different particle sizes when they were compared on an equal weight basis, the more finely divided dusts being able to inhibit spore germination at lower doses. When the dusts were compared on the basis of an equal number of particles per unit area, there was no major difference in toxicity. This illustrates the importance of good coverage in protecting surfaces and stresses that the number of particles used is most critical when they are distributed randomly in the infection court. However, the sizes of the individual particles cannot be neglected entirely, for this would imply that small particles containing minute amounts of fungicide would be as effective as large ones for preventing infection by the parasite. This supposition may be approximately correct within a limited range, but must be invalid when the particles become extremely small. This is shown by the findings of Burchfield and McNew (1950), who measured the capacity of different particle size fractions of dichlone (2,3-dichloro-1,4-naphthoquinone) to control early blight of tomatoes in greenhouse tests. When particle size was reduced from a mean radius of 24.5μ to 0.45μ, only one-fortieth as much dichlone was required to maintain disease control. Fungicidal efficiency was not directly proportional to the number of particles on the surface. Instead, a limiting value was approached at small particle sizes, indicating that capacity for controlling disease was proportional to the logarithm of the number of particles per unit area of surface, or

$$1/G = m \log_e \frac{3G}{4\pi r^3 d} + q \qquad (3)$$

where G is the weight of fungicide per unit area required to control the disease, d its density, r the mean particle radius, and m and q are empirical constants.

This equation suggests that two basic factors are involved in the protection of surfaces by fungicides. These are: first, that the number of particles necessary to insure that each potential locus of infection is given nominal protection is constant and independent of the dose; and second, that on subdivision of a constant weight of material the rate of change of fungicidal effectiveness is inversely proportional to the number of particles present at the time of the change. The first of these assumptions is based on the supposition that the fungicide is randomly distributed in the infection court. If this occurs, a small number of large particles will lead to superabundance of chemical in some localities and little or none in others, while subdividing the material will tend to equalize coverage at various loci of potential infection.

Equation (3), as well as the practical results of many workers, shows that improvement in efficiency of utilization by reducing particle size soon reaches a limiting value beyond which it is uneconomical to go. Thus the effectiveness of dichlone in protecting tomatoes from early blight was increased by only 25% on decreasing mean radius from 0.81 to 0.45μ, while the specific surface of the powder, which is related to the work required for comminution, was almost doubled.

Furthermore, it suggests that weak fungicides which can be used at high doses because of low cost are not likely to be improved as much by extreme subdivision as compounds with high intrinsic toxicity. A material with very low toxicity would have to be applied at such high doses to obtain any disease control at all that the surface would be saturated with respect to coverage at comparatively large particle sizes. Conversely, when intrinsic toxicity is very high, great care must be taken to distribute the smaller amount of material in such a way that all the potential infection loci are protected. For example, compounds which must be used at relative doses of 100, 10, and 1 units because of differences in intrinsic toxicity would give equivalent coverage at mean particle radii of 3.2, 1.6, and 0.7μ, respectively.

Even in greenhouse tests coverage is never so complete as would be predicted from particle size alone, since sprays are deposited unevenly. Often the droplets coalesce and runoff occurs, leaving different amounts of fungicide on the tips and mid-veins of leaves than found on the edges and interiors of the blades. Field applications are even more spotty, and this condition is likely to be aggravated in deposits formed from low gallonage concentrate sprays where as little as 15% of the plant surfaces may be coated with fungicide. In these cases, disease control in unprotected areas may be achieved through redistribution by dew and rain, so that physical factors other than particle size become important (Rich, 1954). Thus, Björling and Sellgren (1957) found that rain treatments improved the protection of potato foliage by Bordeaux mixture against infection by *Phytophthora infestans* when the fungicide was applied as small droplets in small volumes, while deposits formed from large drops applied at high volumes were not affected significantly. They ascribed this improvement to the local redistribution of the fungicide by weathering. However, they found that the effect of rain on zineb deposits was irregular. Improvements in disease control were recorded in a few tests, but more often deterioration of the protective power of the residue occurred. Perhaps this difference arose in part from the fact that Bordeaux mixture is much more tenacious than particulate fungicides and that the effects of redistribution were not overshadowed by a high over-all loss in residue (Burchfield and Goenaga, 1957a). Furthermore, the dosage-response curve of Bordeaux mixture is exceedingly flat, so that disease control would not be seriously reduced in protected areas by the removal of sizable amounts of fungicide. The redistribution of comparatively small amounts of copper in previously unprotected spots might result in more effective disease control in these locations. Thus the over-all result might be favorable despite a net loss of fungicide. However, this behavior would not be expected from compounds having very steep dosage-response curves and poor tenacity, since control in protected areas might be decreased sharply without commensurate improvements in other localities owing to the relatively small amount of toxicant redistributed.

Butt (1955) investigated the movement of captan [N-(trichloromethylthio)-4-cyclohexene-1,2-dicarboximide] deposits on pear leaves and obtained no evidence to show that it was translocated in leaf tissue. He assumed that its fungicidal action was exerted through water layers linking the captan to the spores. Photomicrographs of captan deposits in waterdrops suggested that particles of the fungicide may become detached from the leaves and be redeposited near the periphery of the original residue, thus resulting in an expansion of the protected area. Presumably this process would be carried out more efficiently by gentle dews than by driving rain, since the latter would be expected to result in an over-all loss of the spray deposit with negligible opportunities for redeposition of dislodged particles and aggregates.

Contrary to the finding of Butt, Napier, et al. (1957) present evidence which they interpret to mean that captan exerts systemic action in the protection of broad beans against Botrytis fabae. They found that sprays applied to the dorsal surfaces of leaves resulted in significant reductions in the number of lesions found on the ventral surfaces, although complete disease control was never achieved. Furthermore, treatment of the first leaves of bean resulted in reduction of the infection incidence of the second and third leaves. While diffusion of captan through leaves via dorsal and ventral stomata and the loosely organized structure of the spongy parenchyma is possible, translocation through greater distances in the vascular tissue of the plant is unlikely, owing to the extremely high instability of captan in aqueous media (Burchfield and Schechtman, 1958). It should be noted that the bean plants used in these experiments were incubated in a moist chamber for 18 hours to provide conditions suitable for infection by the pathogen. Thus the fungicide may have been redistributed in small moisture droplets or conveyed to the spores via the vapor phase by convection currents. It must be considered that some metals have high enough vapor pressures to kill spores by fumigant action in enclosed spaces. Examples from the history of plant pathology show that similar cases of "action at a distance" have been misinterpreted. Therefore, experiments which show that protectant fungicides can be redistributed by translocation within the plant must be re-evaluated critically before final acceptance.

B. Interactions of Fungicides with Their Environments

1. Extrinsic Factors in the Persistence of Fungicides

Particles may be bound to surfaces by London-van der Waals' forces, electrostatic attraction, capillarity, or some combination of these effects (Burchfield, 1959). Most physical studies on the adhesion of small particles have been made on smooth homogeneous surfaces, such as those of glass or quartz. Even so, there is disagreement among physicists as to the relative importance of these forces and the distances over which they are effective. Plants are grounded semi-conductors with rough surfaces. Moreover, the leaves of many of them excrete waxy blooms in uneven patterns, so that some particle surfaces may be in contact with wax and others with cell walls. Consequently, areas of close contact between particles and leaves are likely to be small and heterogeneous. Furthermore, changes in the moisture content of the air might shift the balance of forces responsible for adhesion. At high humidities electrostatic potentials between particles and leaves might be discharged because of the high conductivity of the air, while capillary attraction through the formation of films of water connecting the particles to the surface would tend to increase. As a result of the instability of the environment, the heterogeneity of the surfaces, and the multiplicity of forces involved, it is unlikely that the mechanism of adhesion of pesticides to plants will be clarified for some years to come, except in general terms.

The attachment of pesticide particles to plants is weak compared to the strengths of bonds created by adhesives. Thus, Somers and Thomas (1956) found that wind alone reduced cuprous oxide deposits by more than 50% after 27 days' exposure, while Byrdy et al. (1957) report significant reductions in the toxicity of DDT residues after exposing them for 5 minutes to air currents with a velocity of 3.5 meters per second. Rain removes spray deposits considerably faster than wind, but in the field the action of wind is more prolonged. Burchfield and Goenaga (1957a) found that 43% of the cuprous oxide deposited on banana leaves was removed by the first quarter inch of rain. However, the next quarter inch removed only 4%, and succeeding treatments removed only about 1 to 2% per 0.5 inch of rain. Similar results were obtained with cuprous oxide on artificial surfaces (Somers and Thomas, 1956) and with captan and maneb (manganous ethylenebis[dithiocarbamate]) on tomato foliage (Burchfield and Goenaga, 1957a), suggesting that 30 to 80% of most fungicides is deposited in forms that have very poor residual properties. Pond and Chisholm (1958) recently reported that 26 to 63% of the amount of DDT on potatoes was lost during 24 hours weathering in the field, so it appears that as much as one-half of the value of the chemicals used for plant protection is expended with small return. Reduction of this figure should be one of the chief goals of formulation research, since it may represent an annual loss of the order of $100,000,000 in the United States alone.

One reason for this high initial disappearance of fungicide may be unfavorable particle size distribution. Many workers have shown that the tenacities of fungicides increase with decreasing particle size, probably owing to higher specific surface. This allows for a greater total area of contact between the fungicide deposit and the leaves. Since the total force of adhesion is the product of the contact area and the force per unit area, it is evident that increasing the former automatically results in an increase in total force of adhesion. Furthermore, small particles should resist dislodgement better since they are lighter in weight. Thus it is possible that the high initial losses experienced on weathering arise from a rapid and complete loss of large particles, while the tenacious part of the residue consists of small particles. Ground powders contain many more small particles than large ones, but the large ones usually contribute most to the weight. Thus one particle with a radius of 10μ would weigh as much as 1000 particles with radii of 1μ. Therefore, if particle size is a predominating factor in regulating tenacity, a high initial rate of loss should occur as large particles are removed, followed by a slower rate of loss of the remainder of the fungicide as is found in practice. In other words, the spray deposit is heterogeneous with respect to particle size and consequently tenacity, so that plots of the logarithm of the deposit retained against inches of rain are usually curvilinear (Burchfield and Goenaga, 1957b).

Primary particle size of the fungicide alone probably does not account for all of this effect, because aggregates of small particles can be formed which might behave like large particles in weathering tests. Thus Gullstrom and Burchfield (1948) found it necessary to use a 0.25% solution of dispersing agent to deflocculate dichlone to the point where the particles would sediment individually rather than in groups. This is far in excess of the amounts of these agents that would be included in commercial fungicide formulations, so it is likely that most materials are aggregated to a greater or lesser extent in the spray tank and that these agglomerates are carried over onto the leaves. Further evidence for the occurrence of interactions between particles can be adduced from the finding of Somers and Thomas (1956) that the tenacities of copper fungicides increased with decreasing initial deposit. This agrees with the earlier observation of Turner and Woodruff (1948) who suggested that particle-surface adhesion governs the tenacity of sparse spray deposits while particle-particle cohesion becomes important with increasing deposit. This is equivalent to saying that aggregates have lower tenacity than discrete particles. Assuming ideal (random) distribution of the fungicide on the plant surface, lateral associations between particles would be negligible since scale drawings have shown that dichlone can control tomato early blight when most of the surface is unoccupied by particles (Burchfield and McNew, 1950). However, in practice, distribution of primary fungicide particles is probably far from random, owing to the presence of aggregates in the spray tank.

Tenacity can be influenced by the spreading properties of the spray on foliage. Thus Bordeaux mixture applied to the waxy leaves of bananas collects as discrete droplets at the leaf veins (Burchfield and Goenaga, 1957b). On drying, these form small friable pellets of Bordeaux which are easily dislodged mechanically by the first rain. The addition of a nonionic surfactant to the mixture reduces interfacial tension so that the droplets spread. The deposit that is formed is exceedingly tenacious, even in the presence of 3 times the amount of surfactant required for good spreading. Similar results were obtained with copper oxide deposits on banana leaves, so evidently these observations hold for particulate fungicides as well. Presumably, good spreading results in the formation of smaller and fewer aggregates during drying. However, the use of large amounts of surfactants may lead to premature runoff in high gallonage applications, and the foliage may be more easily rewet by rain. Spreaders could probably be used most advantageously in medium and low gallonage applications, providing they do not accentuate phytotoxicity.

It might be possible to minimize some of the undesirable residual properties of spreaders by creating compounds with labile bonds that will hydrolyze within a few hours after they are dissolved in water. Thus a nonionic material such as

$$\langle \bigcirc \rangle - (CH_2)_n - CH_2 - O - M - O - CH_2 - CH_2(CH_2CH_2O)_m - CH_2 - CH_2OH$$

might be synthesized, where M is a substituent which forms easily hydrolyzable bonds. Conceivably, the intact molecule could be a good spreader, while the fragments formed on cleavage at the O—M or C—O bonds would be inert. Thus, advantage could be taken of the beneficial effects of spreaders without encountering residual detergent properties.

Stickers have also been used in attempts to improve performance.

Unfortunately much of the early work was done with proteins such as casein. Evidently such materials are not successful stickers in agricultural applications possibly in part because they tend to decrease the toxicities of copper fungicides, owing to the formation of metal complexes (Heuberger and Horsfall, 1942). Recently, Somers (1956) evaluated forty-seven materials for their abilities to improve the retentiveness of cupric oxide to cellulose acetate surfaces. Encouraging results were obtained with agar, linseed oil, lime-casein, polyvinyl acetate, coumerone resin, rubber latex, and polyvinyl chloride. However, with the exception of polyvinyl acetate and chloride, all of these materials decreased the toxicity of the CuO to *Alternaria tenuis* in *in vitro* tests, and none of them improved control of potato blight in field tests. This is typical of experience with stickers. They sometimes improve tenacity, but usually at the expense of fungitoxicity.

The tenacity of Bordeaux mixture is outstanding, compared to that of most other fungicides (Burchfield and Goenaga, 1957b). When freshly prepared or suitably preserved with adjuvants, it has the properties of a deformable hydrogel, and spreads over the plant surface to form more or less continuous films. The first 0.5 inch of rain removes only 10% of the deposit, and 70% of the initial residue remains after 8 inches of rain. Furthermore, the logarithm of the tenacity is directly proportional to inches of rain. This suggests that all components of the spray deposit adhere equally and that the amount of fungicide removed with each rainfall treatment is a constant percentage of the amount present at its beginning. This shows that the deposit is essentially homogeneous. On aging, 10-10-100 Bordeaux forms spherulites about 5 to 6μ in diameter which have almost no resistance to weathering. However, 10-3.2-100 Bordeaux and similar preparations retain absorbed water and good tenacity indefinitely, even though X-ray diffraction data show that small crystallites are formed very rapidly after mixing (Magdoff *et al.*, 1958). The superior tenacity of Bordeaux hydrogels suggests that tank mix preparations of ziram (zinc dimethyldithiocarbamate) made by adding zinc sulfate to an aqueous solution of the sodium salt might be superior to the wettable powder for similar reasons (Wilson, 1953). The iron, zinc, manganese and copper salts of dithiocarbamic acid and of 8-hydroxyquinoline could also be prepared as hydrated gels which might adhere to surfaces better than the corresponding wettable powders if sprayed before sizable crystallites had a chance to form.

No matter how good the tenacity, spray deposits will be attenuated by plant growth during the early and middle parts of the growing season. Usually the grand period of growth for foliage occurs earlier than for fruit, thus lengthening the period during which frequent sprays must be applied. Frear and Worthley (1937) found that apple leaves on trees grown in southern Pennsylvania attained 28% of their full size at the first cover spray on May 28, while development was 98% complete by June 6. By contrast, the surface area of the top fruit doubled between July 1 and July 26. At the time of the last cover spray there were 10 to 16 times more chemical (lead arsenate) on the fruit than on the foliage. This must have been caused in part by the earlier growth of the former. Thus the limiting factor in the efficiency with which plant protectants can be used is the time and rate of expansion of the surfaces which must be protected.

2. *Intrinsic Properties Influencing Performance*

a. *Physical Considerations.* Intrinsic properties of fungicides, such as water solubility, volatility, and chemical reactivity may often play major roles in their performance in the infection court. Compounds such as copper sulfate and quaternary ammonium salts give good control of diseases in greenhouse tests but are ineffective in the field because they are easily washed from plant surfaces by rain. Consequently, successful foliage fungicides, with the potential exception of systemics, should usually have low water solubility. This property may also govern the rates at which chemical changes take place in the infection court, because reactions such as hydrolysis are probably confined to the dissolved portion of the fungicide in the moisture films at plant surfaces.

The rate at which a solid will dissolve in water under continuous agitation is given by:

$$\frac{dx}{dt} = kA(S - x) \tag{4}$$

where x is the concentration of solute in the aqueous phase at time t, S its solubility, A the surface area of the solid and k a proportionality constant. The rate of solution therefore depends on water solubility as well as specific surface.

Although most fungicides are generally regarded as being insoluble, this is only true in a relative sense. If a compound were truly insoluble it would be unlikely to be fungitoxic because of its inability to reach and permeate the protoplasm of spores and mycelia. From the standpoint of toxic dose, commercial fungicides have appreciable solubility in water, that of Dyrene being about 10 p.p.m. and that of dichlone about 7 p.p.m.[1] Compounds with solubilities greatly exceeding these values would probably have poor residual properties when exposed to rain,

[1] Burchfield, H. P. Unpublished data.

while compounds which are insoluble compared to dichlone might be unable to reach vital sites in the fungi.

Fungicides can also disappear from the infection court by sublimation. The air in direct contact with small spherical particles of volatile compounds is saturated with vapor, and the rate of exchange of molecules between the solid and its surrounding shell of vapor is very rapid, compared to the rate at which the vapor can diffuse away into the air. Consequently, rate of evaporation is determined in part by rate of diffusion through the surrounding air, and is given by

$$ -\frac{dm}{dt} = \frac{4\pi r D M p}{RT} \tag{5} $$

where $-dm/dt$ is the rate of weight loss of a single particle, r the radius of the particle, D the diffusion coefficient of the compound, M its molecular weight, p its vapor pressure, R the gas constant, and T the absolute temperature. Thus the molecular weight of the compound and its diffusion coefficient, as well as vapor pressure, influence rate of dissipation by sublimation. It is also noteworthy that the weight loss of small particles is proportional to their radii and not to their surfaces.

Thatcher and Streeter (1925) have shown that sulfur deposits are attenuated by sublimation. More recently Miller and Stoddard (1957) found that o-chloronitrobenzene had strong fumigant action, pentachloronitrobenzene moderate fumigant action, and captan and chloranil (tetrachloro-p-benzoquinone) weak fumigant action when tested against 4 species of fungi in closed containers. Thiram (tetramethylthiuram disulfide) and other related compounds were ineffective. This suggests that sublimation might be an important factor in the disappearance of some of these compounds from the infection court and be negligible in others. Decker (1957) regards sublimation to be highly important in determining the rate of residue loss of insecticides. He points out that persistence is directly proportional to the logarithm of the time of exposure under conditions where losses caused by wind, rain, and plant growth are negligible. Furthermore persistence of insecticides on foliage decreases in the order: DDT > methoxychlor > toxaphene > dieldrin > chlordan > heptachlor > aldrin > lindane, which is the order of increasing volatility. Since most of these compounds are stable chemically, sublimation appears to be the only reasonable way to account for their disappearance.

As shown earlier, fungicides must be ground to small particle size to obtain adequate coverage of plant surfaces. However, extreme subdivision may lead to poor persistence when the compound is volatile or can react chemically in the infection court. The total surface of fungicide per unit area of plant or fruit is

$$A = 3G/rd \tag{6}$$

where A is the surface, G the weight of fungicide per unit area, d its density, and r the particle radius. Thus the surface of fungicide exposed to weathering is 10 times greater at a particle radius of 0.5μ than at 5μ. Burchfield and McNew (1950) suggest that a compromise between coverage and surface exposed might be reached by selecting a particle radius near where disease control is achieved at minimum total surface of fungicide. Theoretical calculations based on data obtained on dichlone show this to be

$$r = \left[\frac{3}{8mde^{2-q/m}} \right]^{1/3} = 4.9\mu \tag{7}$$

where the constants are the same as those of equation (3). This relation is based on the fact that when particle size is large, specific surface is small. However, so much material is required to give disease control that the total surface of the fungicide per unit area of plant is large, showing that it is not being used efficiently. As particle radius is reduced, coverage improves faster than specific surface increases, so that the total surface of fungicide required for control of the disease decreases. Finally, when the surface nears saturation with particles, the effect of increased specific surface predominates, and the total surface of fungicide per unit plant area required for disease control increases. The radius of 4.9μ given by equation (7) is at the minimum of this curve.

When dichlone preparations having mean particle radii of 1.5 and 3.6μ were evaluated for capacity to control tomato early blight, fungicidal efficiency diminished by only 30% when the plants were held in the greenhouse for one week between spraying and inoculation. At radii less than 1μ, 80% of the protective value of the fungicide was lost, and at radii of 8.4μ and above it disappeared altogether. Presumably the total failure of the larger particle size preparations to control the disease arose from poor tenacity even in the absence of rain. Sulfur has also been shown to have impaired residual properties at very small particle size, but fixed coppers do not, possibly because they are chemically stable and have negligibly low vapor pressures (Horsfall, 1956). Thus the optimum size distribution for good persistence is regulated by the intrinsic chemical and physical properties of the fungicide.

b. *Chemical Reactions.* Plant protectant fungicides are labile chemicals that can react within spores or in the external environment. Typical reactions which can take place at foliage surfaces include oxidation, carbonation, photolysis, and hydrolysis. In some cases metal ions can be chelated by components of guttation fluids or substances excreted by fungus spores.

Many compounds such as dihydric phenols and mercaptans are susceptible to oxidation. Thus aqueous solutions of hydroquinone and 1,4-dihydroxynaphthalene become orange-red on exposure to air, particularly at high pH values. This results from oxidation to quinones which can react further to yield colored polymeric materials called humic acids. In the case of hydroquinone, the following reactions probably take place at pH 8:

When all of the hydrogen atoms adjacent to the carbonyl groups of the quinones are replaced with chlorine atoms, as in chloranil and dichlone, secondary reactions with hydrogen peroxide cannot occur. The reduction products of these toxicants, tetrachlorohydroquinone and 2,3-dichloro-1,4-dihydroxynaphthalene, respectively, are as good plant protectants as the parent quinones. This observation has no practical significance from the standpoint of disease control, since it is more convenient to use these compounds in their oxidized states. However, it serves to point out that many fungicides can exist in oxidized and reduced forms, and that these may be interconvertible on plant surfaces.

The best authenticated example of the oxidative activation of a fungicide in the infection court is represented by nabam (disodium ethylenebis[dithiocarbamate]. Nabam is a water soluble compound that is fungistatic but not fungicidal. Spores immersed in a 10% solution of it are able to germinate after they are removed and washed with water. Even though water soluble, it often gives good persistence and disease control on foliage, suggesting that it is converted *in situ* to water insoluble compounds with high fungitoxicity. Ludwig *et al.* (1954) demonstrated that it can be oxidized to ethylenethiuram monosulfide and polymers and that these materials appear to be toxic to fungus spores. Sijpesteyn and van der Kerk (1954) confirmed these findings but suggested that the toxic principle is ethylene diisothiocyanate, generated either directly from nabam or its oxidation products. This conclusion was later supported by Thorn and Ludwig (1954). Thus satisfactory evidence is available that nabam is oxidized on plant surfaces to a material with good residual properties and that this deposit then generates a nascent toxaphore.

Aside from oxygen, carbon dioxide is the only component of dry air known to react with fungicides. It converts the excess lime of Bordeaux mixture to calcium carbonate within a few hours after spraying. The copper components of Bordeaux mixtures containing more than 2.5 lb. of lime per 10 lb. of cupric sulfate have average compositions of $Cu_4Ca_nSO_4(OH)_{8+2n} \cdot x\ H_2O$ (Magdoff et al., 1958). Carbonic acid may react with some of these highly basic materials to form products with different physicochemical properties. On prolonged washing of Bordeaux deposits with water, calcium and sulfate ions are removed, and the amount of soluble copper increases. Reckendorfer (1936) suggests that the copper in Bordeaux mixture is solubilized by the formation of copper bicarbonate. However, Wilcoxon and McCallan (1938) point out that basic copper carbonate, rather than $CuCO_3$, is obtained by ordinary methods of preparation, and they state that it is unlikely that an acid carbonate could be formed under as low pressures of CO_2 as exist in the atmosphere. Free (1908) found that CO_2 increased the amount of soluble copper in equilibrium with insoluble basic copper carbonate by a factor of 5. The additional copper thus dissolved is insignificant stoichiometrically, but could have a pronounced influence on preventing germination of fungus spores. The exact role of carbon dioxide is regulating the properties of Bordeaux is uncertain. Similarly there is very little information available on its effects on lime-sulfur deposits, where it could play a dominating part in regulating the properties of the residues.

The decomposition of some groups of pesticides can be initiated by light. Thus, p-benzoquinone yields hydroquinone and a product believed to be a dimer when exposed to light of wavelength less than 5770 A. The quantum yield is 0.505. The efficiency of the photochemical process decreases as chlorine atoms are substituted into the molecule, so that the quantum yield for chloranil is only 0.095. Despite this low efficiency, aqueous solutions of it are very unstable unless stored in the dark.

The threshold wavelength region for the photolysis of quinones decreases with decreasing oxidation potential. Thus, chloranil with a potential of 0.73 volt and a threshold region in the neighborhood of 5770 A., should decompose more readily when exposed to light than dichlone, which has an oxidation potential of only 0.42 volt. Measurements of the decomposition rates of the two compounds in dioxane-water solutions exposed to sunlight show that dichlone is the more stable

(Burchfield and McNew, 1950). This agrees with practical experience, for although chloranil is a good seed protectant, it has poor persistence on foliage, while dichlone is an effective fungicide in both areas of application.

Many fungicides containing reactive halogen atoms can hydrolyze in solution. These include captan, Phaltan [N-(trichloromethylthio) phthalimide], Dyrene [2,4-dichloro-6-(o-chloroanilino)-s-triazine], dichlone, and chloranil. Generally the reactions proceed by replacement of a halogen by a hydroxyl ion, so that they take place more rapidly in alkaline than in acid media. Thus, Daines et al. (1957) found that captan decomposes slowly at pH 7 and instantaneously in the presence of sodium hydroxide. Actually, decomposition is rapid even in neutral solution, as shown by the finding that captan has a half-life of only 2.5 hours in aqueous buffer at pH 7 (Burchfield and Schechtman, 1958). However, it persists much longer than this on foliage because of its low solubility in water and the fact that only material in true solution can hydrolyze. Nevertheless it is an unstable compound in this respect, compared to Dyrene, which has a half-life of about 22 days under similar conditions (Burchfield and Storrs, 1956). This shows that hydrolysis might be an important factor in the depletion of captan residues, and inconsequential in the case of Dyrene.

Some fungicides containing copper and perhaps other metals can be chelated by amino acids, hydroxy acids, and other compounds found in the guttation fluids of higher plants and excretions of fungus spores (Horsfall, 1956). Thus glycine, aspartic acid, and sodium malate will sequester copper from Bordeaux mixture, and even sucrose will complex it at high pH values. This has led to a wealth of work and speculation on whether the copper in Bordeaux deposits is mobilized by the action of the host plants or by the spores themselves. McCallan and Wilcoxon (1936) found that water extracts from 100,000,000 fungus spores dissolved from 0.013 to 1.01 mg. of copper from Bordeaux mixture, depending on the species. In the case of Neurospora sitophila, the amount of copper solubilized was about 3500 μg. per gram of spores, exclusive of the amount that might have been taken up by them. Determination of the total solids excreted by the spores showed that the species excreting the most were also most active in dissolving copper from Bordeaux mixture. Furthermore, the five fungi tested differed little in susceptibility to copper poisoning when it was administered as cupric sulfate, but in general the species capable of solubilizing the greatest amount of copper from Bordeaux mixture was most sensitive to it. Malic acid was identified as one of the excretion products of N. sitophila. Its copper complex had about the same toxicity to spores as copper sulfate, suggesting that at least part of the copper dissolved by the action of the spores may be present in a form readily assimilable by them. This is not always true. Glutamine, asparagine, and some proteins are known to reduce the toxicities of copper fungicides (Horsfall, 1956). Probably each copper chelate has its own unique bioactivity depending on its stability constant, diffusion coefficient, and capacity to permeate spores.

The nature of the host leaves and invading fungus also influences the toxicity of Bordeaux mixture. Yarwood (1943) found cupric sulfate to be 100 times more toxic than Bordeaux to rust spores *in vitro*, but only one-tenth as effective for preventing infection of bean plants by the fungus. This seems to have arisen from a synergistic interaction between the Bordeaux deposit and bean leaves rather than from secondary effects such as poor weathering of the cupric sulfate residue, for the protective action of Bordeaux deposits was not potentiated when used for the control of downy mildew of cucumber. Thus, organic copper chelates may have been formed by chemical reactions on the bean foliage that were more toxic than the original spray residue.

3. *Physicochemical Basis of Phytotoxicity*

Injury to the host plant is often a limiting factor in the use of fungicides. This must be expected, since most chemicals used as protectants can react with components of protoplasm, chelate essential metals, or accumulate at vital biological interfaces. They are less specific in their action than antimetabolites such as the sulfanilimides, and are likely to be phytotoxic if they can penetrate the cuticularized tissue protecting the host. Thus compounds such as dichlone, which otherwise can be used safely on many plants, will cause severe burning when mixed with oils. Presumably, the fungicide dissolves in the hydrocarbon, which enables it to permeate the leaf tissues more efficiently.

Sometimes the difference between a safe fungicide and a phytotoxic compound is determined by the length or nature of a side chain. In a study of imidazoline derivatives Wellman and McCallan (1946) found that optimum fungitoxicity was obtained when the alkyl side chain substituted in the 2-position of the heterocyclic ring contained 17 carbon atoms, but when it contained 11 carbons the compound was phytotoxic. Similarly, Schuldt and Wolf (1956) showed that derivatives of 2,4-dichloro-6-anilino-*s*-triazine are good protectant fungicides, while Koopman and Daams (1958) found that similar triazines containing alkyl in place of aryl groups are herbicides.

Some of these differences in specificity of action may arise from changes in solubility relationships:

100 p.p.m.
(I)

60 p.p.m.
(II)

10 p.p.m.
(III)

Thus, Compound (I) is not accumulated rapidly by fungus spores, and is ineffective for the control of early and late blights of tomato. Its solubility in water is about 100 p.p.m., and it injures the test plants. Substitution of a methyl group in the *ortho* position of the benzene ring (II) reduces solubility to 60 p.p.m. and results in improved fungitoxicity, while a chlorine atom in this position (III) enhances its properties still further. The solubility of Dyrene (III) in water is only 10 p.p.m. and it is a far better fungicide than (I). Furthermore, it is not phytotoxic to the test plants under conditions where (I) produces severe injury. Since both compounds react with the same metabolites and compete for the same sites within fungus spores, it is likely that they have the same mode of action (Burchfield and Storrs, 1957a). Therefore the difference in phytotoxicity between these compounds may arise from a difference in solubility, and hence in rate of movement. Compound (I), being 10 times more soluble in water than (III), might dissolve faster in moisture films and move into the host plants through the stomata. Water seems to be implicated in the movement of these compounds, since Dyrene causes necrotic flecking and defoliation of pepper plants when they are incubated in a moist chamber for 24 hours before being placed in a greenhouse. Plants sprayed with Dyrene and transferred directly to the greenhouse bench are unaffected. The leaves are dropped while still turgid by disintegration of the abscission layer, so evidently this compound can be translocated to some extent under extreme conditions of humidity.

However, solubility cannot be the only factor governing phytotoxicity, since captan is at least as soluble as Dyrene in water, and it is considerably safer for use on apples for the control of scab. An explanation might be sought in the fact that the half-life of captan in buffer at pH 7 is only about 2.5 hours, compared to about 22 days for Dyrene, so that their longevities in the aqueous phase differ by a factor of more than 200. While captan might diffuse far enough to reach fungus spores or localized regions within the plant tissues, it would not have the range of penetration of Dyrene because of its shorter life. Thus the intermeshed effects of water solubility, diffusion coefficient, and hydrolysis rate, in combination with intrinsic biological activity, might help to explain why some compounds are phytotoxic and others are not.

It is interesting that the injury caused by both captan and Dyrene can be reduced by formulation with calcium carbonate. Both compounds produce hydrochloric acid on hydrolysis, and in the case of captan the acidity might become high enough to burn the plants (Daines *et al.,* 1957). The presence of the carbonate would tend to minimize this through neutralization of the acid with the formation of $CaCl_2$ and CO_2. Daines *et al.* (1957) showed that kaolinite, which has a low capacity for disposing of acids, aggravates injury. However, Dyrene decomposes so slowly that the concentration of HCl at the plant surface is never likely to be very high. It is possible that calcium carbonate safens it by accelerating its decomposition rate in the aqueous phase so that the range over which it can diffuse is limited.

Evidently the hydrolysis products of Dyrene are harmless, but in some cases the breakdown products of fungicides are more injurious than the original compounds. Thus, aqueous suspensions of dichlone formulated with some attapulgite clays slowly become deep red in color and are phytotoxic to higher plants. Presumably the red compound is 2-hydroxy-3-chloro-1,4-naphthoquinone. Although it is a weak fungicide compared to dichlone, it can probably permeate leaf tissues more rapidly because of the higher water solubility conferred on it by the hydroxyl group.

Examples where fungicides have conjugates with a basically different type of biological activity are not uncommon. Thus, 1-fluoro-2,4-dinitrobenzene is probably toxic to spores because it can participate in substitution reactions with metabolites such as amino acids and proteins, while its hydrolysis product, 2,4-dinitrophenol, uncouples phosphorylation from oxidation. Similarly, pentachloronitrobenzene produces pentachlorophenol on hydrolysis. Both these compounds are good fungicides but have different areas of application, the former being used in soil and the latter for the protection of wood. These observations suggest that the margin of safety which separates a fungitoxic dose of chemical from a phytotoxic dose might be narrowed perilously if interactions in the infection court convert a compound that is predominantly fungicidal to one with herbicidal properties.

III. TREATMENT OF SOILS AND SEED

A. *Chemical and Biological Interactions*

1. *Microbial Conversions*

The large and diversified population of microflora and microfauna inhabiting soils leads to many complications in the control of plant afflictions of subterranean origin that are not encountered above ground. Indiscriminate uptake and dissimilation of pesticides by a variety of parasites, saprophytes, and symbionts is one of these. Thus phenol, which is used as a standard in testing bactericides, can serve as a sole source of carbon for many soil-inhabiting organisms. It is first hydroxylated in the *ortho* position of the benzene ring to yield catechol, which is subsequently oxidized to *o*-benzoquinone. The latter compound then undergoes ring cleavage with the formation of ketonic and aldehydic acids (Evans, 1947).

$$\text{OH} \rightarrow \text{OH, OH} \rightarrow \text{O, O} \rightarrow \text{aliphatic compounds}$$

One of the intermediates is degradation, *o*-benzoquinone, is a highly effective but unstable fungicide (McNew and Burchfield, 1951). Benzoic acid is metabolized similarly, with the probable formation of 3,4-dihydroxybenzoic acid and the corresponding quinone as intermediates. Other aromatic compounds oxidizable by soil microorganisms include *p*-hydroxybenzaldehyde, syringaldehyde, vanillin, and ferulic acid (Henderson and Farmer, 1955). Of 61 fungal isolates from soil that could use these compounds as sole sources of carbon, 2 were *Mucor* species and the remainder, Deuteromycetes.

Even hydrocarbons can be metabolized, as demonstrated by the finding of Murphy and Stone (1955) that naphthalene was destroyed by *Pseudomonas* sp. with the sequential formation of salicylic acid, catechol, and β-adipic acid. *Corynebacterium italicum* degrades hexadecane, tetradecane, and decane completely (Ladd, 1956). This species also oxidizes fatty acids and alcohols containing 1 to 11 carbon atoms as well as several aliphatic aldehydes and higher methyl ketones. Other chemical reactions that can be catalyzed by the enzymes of microorganisms include cleavage of aromatic ethers to yield phenols and decarboxylation of aromatic acids (Henderson, 1957).

Microorganisms isolated from soil can metabolize pesticides containing nitro groups. Thus, Gundersen and Jensen (1956) isolated a strain of *Corynebacterium simplex* that could use 2,4-dinitro-*o*-cresol as a sole source of nitrogen and carbon when cultured in agar or liquid media. Degradation was probably initiated by an attack on the *para* nitro group followed by hydrolysis of the group *ortho* to the hydroxyl, resulting in the elimination of inorganic nitrite and the formation of dihydric and trihydric phenols. One of the nitro groups must be *para* to a hydroxyl group for dissimilation by this particular organism, for *p*-nitrobenzoic acid was not attacked, although it can serve as a sole energy source for the aerobic growth of a strain of *Pseudomonas fluorescens*. Intermediates in the metabolism of this latter compound include *p*-aminobenzoic acid, *p*-hydroxybenzoic acid, and protocatechuic acid (Durham, 1957). This last compound is a naturally occurring fungicide responsible for the resistance of red onions to smudge (Angell *et al.*, 1930). The nitro group of *p*-nitrobenzoic acid is reduced to an amino group, which is then split off by ammonolysis, a reaction that would not occur under physiological conditions unless catalyzed by enzymes.

Other nitro compounds degraded by *Corynebacterium simplex* include *p*-nitrophenol, 2,4-dinitrophenol, and picric acid, all of which have some measure of bioactivity. As might be expected, the bacteria must be adapted to the substrate before they can commence their attack, but this takes place with remarkable rapidity in the case of dinitro-*o*-cresol. Continued treatment of soil with this chemical results in its enrichment in microorganisms active in dissimilation. Thus the toxic effect of dinitro-*o*-cresol to higher plants persists for a long time on the first addition of the compound to soil, but repeated applications result in a gradual shortening of the time required for detoxication. Presumably this treatment kills off highly susceptible organisms and results in the multiplication of species able to use the toxicant for a substrate. Thus continuous use of some pesticides in soils may result in reduced efficiency owing to shifts in the microbial population.

However, changes in microbiological balance might be advantageous when fungicides are selective enough in action to suppress the growth of plant pathogens and at the same time permit multiplication of species naturally antagonistic to them. Thus, Moje *et al.* (1957) found that acetylenedicarboxylic acid treatments stimulated the production of an almost pure culture of *Trichoderma viride* in soil, while crotonic acid resulted in a preponderance of *Fusarium solani*. These authors suggest this might be an indirect method for controlling disease, since *T. viride* is known to be antagonistic towards root rot and damping-off organisms such as *Phytophthora* and *Rhizoctonia* spp. Similarly, Richardson (1954) found that thiram protected pea seedlings for a longer time than it persisted in soil. He suggested that thiram-resistant species such as *T. viride* became dominant, and this suppressed the pathogens through competition or direct antagonism. He pointed out that *T. viride* is known to produce two antibiotics, gliotoxin and viridin, and can protect seedlings of several species of plants from damping-off organisms.

Biologically active compounds might also be generated from inert precursors in soils. Well-attested cases of the *in situ* activation of fungicides in this medium have not been described, but the conversion of 2,4-dichlorophenoxyethyl sulfate to 2,4-D provides a good illustration of this process from the related field of plant growth regulation. The former compound is nontoxic when sprayed on plants, but is a pre-emergence herbicide when mixed in soil. Vlitos (1952) showed that it was hydrolyzed to 2-(2,4-dichlorophenoxy)ethanol by *Bacillus cereus* var. *mycoides* under conditions where acid catalyzed hydrolysis would not be expected to take place. The intermediate alcohol was then oxidized to the active principle 2,4-D. Organisms capable of this latter conversion were not isolated. Thus microbial action, possibly in combination with spontaneous chemical reactions, can create toxicants from biologically inert compounds. This possibility should be kept in mind in designing new organic molecules and in interpreting the results of bioassay. Cases where candidate compounds are highly active in some soil environments and fail miserably in others occur much too frequently to be ascribed entirely to experimental shortcomings.

2. Spontaneous Reactions with Metabolic Debris

Fertile soils are rich in organic matter resulting from the decay of plant and animal debris. Segments of the carbon and nitrogen cycles operate continuously in them and generate a host of metabolites and their degradation products. Many of these contain amino, phenolic, and other nucleophilic groups which can react spontaneously with some fungicides. Thus, Stevenson (1956) isolated 29 ninhydrin-positive compounds from the hydrolyzate of an extract from silt loam soil. The total weight of amino acids averaged 5.7 mg. per gram. Undoubtedly many of these were present originally as components of proteins or polypeptides, since free amino acids are deaminated in 26 to 36 hours when added to soil (Greenwood and Lees, 1956). However, some peptides and proteins are more reactive than their component amino acids with toxicants containing reactive halogen (Burchfield and Storrs, 1956).

Many of the reactions of pesticides with metabolic debris take place

through addition or substitution mechanisms. Fungicides that can undergo addition reactions include some quinones, N-arylmaleimides, and
compounds with double bonds α-β to carbonyl groups. These chemicals
can react with free amino and sulfhydryl groups as follows, using a
maleimide as an example:

Sometimes compounds which appear to undergo substitution reactions
actually combine by addition. Thus bis(β-chloroethyl)sulfone reacts
with amines in a way that ostensibly suggests substitution of a chlorine
atom by nitrogen. Yet it has been shown that dehydrochlorination first
occurs with the formation of vinyl sulfones as intermediates (Price,
1958). The over-all course of the reaction is therefore:

$$(ClCH_2CH_2)_2SO_2 + 4RNH_2 \rightarrow [(CH_2{=}CH)_2SO_2] \rightarrow (RNHCH_2CH_2)SO_2 + 2RNH_3Cl.$$

Fungicides that can participate in true substitution reactions include
dichlone, chloranil, Dyrene, pentachloronitrobenzene, captan, phaltan,
1-fluoro-2,4-dinitrobenzene (FDNB), nitrochlorobenzenes and naphtha-
lenes, and compounds with allylic halogen (Burchfield and Schuldt,
1958). They differ enormously in stability towards hydrolysis and reactivity with various metabolites. Yet their over-all reactions are very
similar, as exemplified by the combination of a *para*-substituted nitro
benzene with an amine:

In this example, NO_2 is the activating group and Y the reactive group.
Usually it is customary to think of Y as a halogen atom as in FDNB,
Dyrene, and similar compounds. This shortsightedness may result in
many missed opportunities in the field of pesticides, for purely chemical
studies have shown that Y can be groups such as $-NO_2$, $-SO_3H$,
$-N(CH_3)_3^+$, $-S(CH_3)_2^+$, $-O\phi NO_2$, and $-SO_2\phi$. Thus the reactive
group in the fungicide pentachloronitrobenzene (PCNB) and some
related compounds is not one of the chlorine atoms as would commonly
be supposed, but the nitro group (Betts *et al.*, 1955).

Most of these compounds probably react with metabolic debris by
one or the other of two basic mechanisms. These are: first order nucleo-

philic substitution (S_{N_1}) and second order nucleophilic substitution (S_{N_2}). In S_{N_1} reactions the rate-controlling step is the ionization of a halogen atom or equivalent group to form a carbonium ion which then reacts with any nucleophile that happens to be handy. The kinetics are therefore first order, so that the rate of disappearance of the toxicant is independent of the concentration of metabolite. Thus a compound reacting by an S_{N_1} mechanism will disappear from soil at constant rate under the same moisture, pH, and temperature conditions regardless of organic matter content. In S_{N_2} reactions a transition complex is formed between the toxicant and metabolite, and the reaction is bimolecular. Therefore the persistence of toxicants which react by this mechanism will be dependent on the concentrations of nucleophilic compounds in soils, assuming of course that losses due to hydrolysis and microbial interactions are not rate-determining. The fungicides Dyrene and FDNB have been shown to react with metabolites by the S_N mechanism (Burchfield and Storrs, 1956, 1957b). Often these reactions take place more rapidly than hydrolysis, so that theoretically at least they could play important roles in the depletion of some fungicides in soils. Thus the half-life of Dyrene in aqueous phosphate buffer at pH 7 is about 22 days, compared to 1 hour when 0.1% of the amino acid hydroxyproline is added. Other metabolites known to react rapidly with Dyrene and related s-triazines include tyrosine, nicotinic acid, p-aminobenzoic acid, and glutathione. Burchfield and Storrs (1956, 1957b) studied the reactions of s-triazine derivatives and FDNB with more than 60 metabolites, and found that apparent velocity coefficients varied by more than one-thousandfold, depending on the functional groups involved and their positions in the molecules.

Only the ionized groups of metabolites (R—NH_2, R—S^-, etc.) are known to participate in these reactions. The R — NH_3^+ and RSH groups are either inert or react extremely slowly. Consequently, apparent reactivity depends on the ionization constants of the functional groups (K) and the hydrogen ion activity of the medium (a_{H^+}). Therefore the second order velocity constant for the reaction of a fungicide at initial molar concentration a with the functional group of a metabolite at concentration b is

$$k = \frac{2.303(K + a_{H^+})}{t(a - b)K} \cdot \log \frac{b(a - x)}{a(b - x)} \tag{8}$$

where x is the amount of fungicide reacted at time t. The reactivities of metabolites with high pK values are therefore dependent on hydrogen ion activity, so that each unit increase in pH represents a tenfold increment in apparent reactivity up to about pH 8 to 10, depending on the substrate. However, the reactivities of molecules with very low pK values, such as p-aminobenzoic acid and pyridine derivatives, are almost completely independent of pH increases above 6. Consequently in alkaline soils S_{N_1} and S_{N_2} toxicants might react preferentially with alpihatic amines and phenols because of the high intrinsic reactivities of the R—NH_2 and ϕ—O^- groups, whereas in soils at pH 5 to 6 they might react preferentially with aromatic amines and compounds related to the pyridine nucleotides because of the greater ionization of these groups under acid conditions. Therefore reaction specificity as well as over-all rate of disappearance of fungicide may be regulated by the pH of the soil.

3. Persistence in Soils

Pesticide residues in soils can be depleted by microbial dissimilation, hydrolysis, and chemical reactions with organic matter as well as by purely physical processes such as evaporation and leaching by water. Therefore, measurements of residual pesticide made by chemical or bioassay methods indicate over-all rate of disappearance only, without providing any information on the fate of the toxicant. Nevertheless, it is possible to gain some insight into the various processes involved by storing treated soils in closed containers at constant temperature and moisture content to minimize some of the physical variables.

Under these conditions the half-life of captan at an initial concentration of 100 μg. of fungicide per gram of composted loam soil was about 3.5 days at 25° C., compared to a stability of only 2 to 3 hours when it was dissolved in aqueous phosphate buffer at pH 7.[2] The greater stability[3] of captan in soil than in water may arise from the fact that it was mixed with soil as solid particles which must dissolve in soil moisture before hydrolysis, uptake by soil microorganisms, or reactions with metabolic debris can take place. The solubility of captan in water is between 8 and 70 p.p.m., so that rates of solution and diffusion might be limiting factors in controlling breakdown rate. This speculation is given some support by the finding that all pesticides containing reactive halogen so far examined are more stable in dry than in moist soil.

In contrast to the behavior of captan, the half-life of Dyrene in moist soil is less than one day, compared to a half-life in aqueous buffer of about 22 days. Since it is about as soluble in water as captan (10 p.p.m. compared to 8–70 p.p.m.), factors other than hydrolysis and solution rate must play important roles in its depletion, for based on the

[2] Burchfield, H. P. Unpublished data.
[3] Hereafter the word "stability" refers to the time required for one half the pesticide to disappear.

soil stability—hydrolysis rate ratio established for captan—it should survive for a minimum of 2 years in soil. FDNB is more soluble in water (about 400 p.p.m.) than captan, and hydrolyzes in aqueous buffer at about the same rate as Dyrene. Yet its stability in moist loam soil is also less than a day. Therefore FDNB and Dyrene must be depleted by soil interactions other than hydrolysis, for they are much more stable than captan with respect to this property, but do not last as long in soil. The higher stability of captan in soil may result from the fact that it does not react rapidly with compounds containing amino groups although it combines with thiols much faster than either Dyrene or FDNB. However, these latter groups are probably not found in soils in appreciable amounts, while amino groups are (Burchfield and Storrs, 1957b). Thus the selectivity of action of toxicants, their reaction mechanisms (S_{N_1} or S_{N_2}), as well as their hydrolysis rates, may influence the length of time residues of fungicides will persist in soil.

The effects of environmental conditions on the stability of PRD (3,4-dichlorotetrahydrothiophene-1,1-dioxide) and related compounds were studied by Schuldt et al. (1957) using a colorimetric method which measures both PRD and its dehydrochlorination product 3-chloro-1,2-dihydrothiophene-1,1-dioxide (Burchfield and Schuldt, 1958). Persistence of residues as measured by total color developed was dependent on the initial concentration of nematocide and temperature. In moist soil in a closed jar at an initial concentration of 100 μg. of PRD per gram of soil the time required for one half the color-forming capacity of the residue to disappear was 20 days at 32° C., 45 days at 22° C. and 115 days at 10° C. This indicates a temperature coefficient (Q_{10}) greater than 2. PRD persisted in dry soil 3 times as long as in moist soil. After 53 days in moist soil at 22° C. the total residue was 2% at pH 8.3, 10% at pH 7.4, and 38% at pH 6.6. Therefore temperature, soil pH, and moisture content were all shown to be influential in governing the longevity of the residue.

Soil type is another important factor. Thus, Sund (1956) found that only 31% of the amount of aminotriazole added to muck soil could be recovered by immediate extraction, while 93% could be recovered from Duke sand. After 21 days the recovery from Duke sand dropped to 54%, while the amount extractable from muck was negligible. Sund pointed out that the base exchange capacity of the muck was 99 milliequivalents per 100 grams of soil, compared to only 3.6 milliequivalents for the sand, and suggested that poorer recovery from muck was caused by stronger sorption of the triazole by soil particles. This may be true in part, but it is also likely that chemical and microbiological degradation occurs more rapidly in soils with high organic matter, as witnessed by the finding that DDT had a residue of 25% after 8 years in muck, compared to 74% in sandy soil (Thomas, 1957). Similar findings are reported by Young and Carroll (1951) who applied PCP (pentachlorophenol) formulated in a petroleum oil to soil at a rate of 15 lbs. active ingredient per acre. The half-life was about 10 to 20 days, with breakdown occurring fastest when the organic matter was high and the water content was close to the moisture equivalent of the soil.

Compounds containing sulfur, as well as those in which the principal substituent is halogen, undergo changes in aqueous solution and in soil. For example Vapam (sodium N-methyldithiocarbamate) is a water soluble fungicide and nematocide that becomes immobile in soils within 24 hours after application, either through sorption or chemical decomposition (Baines et al., 1957). However, it retains its toxicity to nematode larvae for 96 hours after application. In aqueous solution it yields methylisothiocyanate, which is volatile and only slightly soluble. Similarly, Torgeson et al. (1957) found that Mylone (3,5-dimethyltetrahydro-1,3,5,2H-thiadiazine-2-thione) hydrolyzed soon after it was applied to warm moist soil. Among the materials identified were methylisothiocyanate, formaldehyde, hydrogen sulfide, and methylamine. None of these materials when used alone at concentrations that might have evolved from the complete decomposition of Mylone was sufficiently fungicidal to inhibit Pythium sp. in soil. Either uptake of Mylone by fungi prior to hydrolysis or a recombination of its decomposition products into an active fungicide is indicated. Evidently methylisothiocyanate is not by itself sufficiently toxic to control soil-borne organisms.

About 90% of the amount of thiram (tetramethylthiuramdisulfide) added to sandy soil at a rate of 50 p.p.m. disappeared within 5 days as indicated by bioassay with Glomerella cingulata (Richardson, 1954). Only a little over 20% remained after 1 day. Yet it was effective in preventing infection of seedlings in the treated soil for much longer times, probably by encouraging the growth of saphrophytes antagonistic to the damping-off organisms, as mentioned previously. Thus for practical purposes the residual power of a pesticide may not always be directly proportional to the time it remains in soil. A truer measure is the time required for the parasite population to reestablish itself at its former level of inoculum potential. In some instances this may be related to the stability of the chemical in soil, but in others not.

In summary, pesticide residues in soils can be depleted by microbial action, hydrolysis, and chemical reaction, but in certain specific cases activation of biologically inert compounds can occur as well. The time required for toxicants to disappear from soils differs from a few days for captan and thiram to a number of years for chlorinated hydrocarbon insecticides. Breakdown occurs most rapidly at high temperatures and pH values and in wet soils rich in organic matter. It may occur through enzyme action or spontaneous reactions with the environment, including hydrolysis, oxidation, addition reactions, and substitution reactions of the S_{N_1} and S_{N^2} types. In some instances beneficial effects may persist after the toxicant has disappeared, a fact that may be very important in the pre-planting application of phytotoxic chemicals for the control of soil-infesting parasites of higher plants.

B. *Physical Interactions*

1. *Distribution of Solids*

Pesticides with low water solubilities and vapor pressures must be disced or plowed into soil to secure effective results below the surface level. However, compounds with higher water solubility can be broadcast or raked into the top few inches of soil in the expectation that they will be carried to greater depths by the infiltration of irrigation or rain water. The relation of solubility to penetration is shown by the finding that the herbicide monuron is carried to greater depths by an equivalent amount of rain than diuron, while fenuron is more mobile than either (Abel, 1957).

Diuron (40 p.p.m.)   Monuron (230 p.p.m.)

Fenuron (2,400 p.p.m.)

These compounds decrease in water solubility with increasing chlorine substitution in the benzene ring in the order: fenuron > monuron > diuron so that penetration improves with increasing solubility. This is not the only factor involved since diuron is more strongly sorbed by soils than monuron, a fact which would also impede its movement. Thus these two properties reinforce each other, high solubility being coupled with low sorptivity, and low solubility with high sorptivity.

If a compound is soluble enough in water and not too highly sorbed by soil, it can be carried to considerable depths by rain, irrigation, or water used during application. Ofter very large amounts of water are required. Thus Baines *et al.* (1957) found it necessary to apply Vapam in basins of water 6 to 12 inches deep to control nematodes and fungi to a depth of 4 ft. Other procedures such as injection, injection followed by row treatment, or row application of Vapam dissolved in water were ineffectual at this depth.

Schuldt *et al.* (1957) found that the experimental nematocide PRD (3,4-dichlorotetrahydrothiophene-1,1-dioxide) initially moved downward in soil with rain in a zone 3 to 4 inches thick, resembling the distribution of chemical compounds on chromatographic columns. Continued rain drove it still deeper. However, when the soil dried out, the chemical moved upward and was concentrated in the top inch. Presumably, as surface moisture evaporated, water in the lower levels of the soil was drawn to the surface by capillarity, carrying the chemical with it. This is somewhat analogous to the upward movement of chemicals in ascending chromatography. Renewed exposure to rain drove the chemical downward again. Thus, alternating periods of wet and dry weather moved the zone of maximum PRD concentration up and down in the soil. However, the zone gradually widened, so eventually the PRD was distributed more uniformly vertically. In field applications made in the fall, PRD followed this pattern, irrespective of whether it was broadcast or worked into the top 3 to 6 inches. The chemical penetrated to a depth of 15 inches after a total of 6 inches of rain, and about 50% of it was recovered after 178 days in soil at pH 5.

Mobility by means of soil moisture movement is important in the distribution of some compounds, but it seems to occur comparatively rarely. Thus, Newhall (1958) found that only 4 fungicides out of 36 tested were effective against *Fusarium oxysporum cubense* at a depth of 7 inches when they were applied to the surface and attempts made to move them downward by drenching with water. Presumably, this is because most organic fungicides are relatively insoluble in this medium. However, since one-ninth of the materials tested could move through soil to this extent, the search for solid fungicides and nematocides that can be applied by broadcasting should not be abandoned.

2. Diffusion of Fumigants

Nematodes and soil-inhabiting fungi can be killed with compounds having fumigant action, such as EDB (ethylene dibromide) and Nemagon (1,2-dibromo-3-chloropropane). These materials are injected into soils at depths of 6 to 15 in. and spread considerable distances, both vertically and laterally, by diffusion. Some fumigants, such as methyl bromide and carbon disulfide, boil near room temperature, while others are much less volatile. Nemagon, for example, has a vapor pressure of only 0.8 mm. of Hg at 21° C. (Ichikawa *et al.*, 1955). The behavior of such materials must differ somewhat from what would be expected of an ideal gas. Nevertheless their steady-state movement through soils in the vapor phase can be described by Fick's first law, which states that

$$\frac{dm}{dt} = -D_o \frac{dc}{dx} \tag{9}$$

where D_o is the diffusion coefficient of the vapor and dm/dt is the rate at which it diffuses through a plane of unit area against a concentration gradient of dc/dx. The movement of vapors through soils is complicated by many factors not associated with free diffusion, one of the most important of these being sorption by soil. However, by considering only steady-state diffusion this factor can be minimized, since the ratio of the concentration of chemical in the vapor phase to that bound by the soil will be constant. Nevertheless, diffusion takes place much more slowly in soils than in air.

Call (1957b) proposes that the apparent diffusion coefficient of a compound in soil is related to its value in air by

$$D = (S - S') \frac{D_o}{k} \tag{10}$$

where S is the total porosity of the soil, S' is the fraction of pores that are blocked, and k is the average tortuosity of the pores.

The tortuosity factor takes into account the fact that the pores in soils through which vapors diffuse are unlikely to be straight, so that a gas must travel a longer distance to reach any given destination than it would in air.

Call (1957b) studied the steady-state diffusion of EBD in various soils having different porosites, and confirmed that the relation between D/D_o and S was linear. This led directly to values of 0.1 for S' and 1.5 for k. Thus, the distance the vapor had to travel appeared to be about 50% longer than in air, and about 10% of the pores in the soils were blocked off, so that the vapor diffusing into them reached dead-ends. Observed diffusion coefficients in soils varied from 1 to 20% of the value found in air, the higher figure, of course, being for the most porous soil.

These findings support the earlier conclusion of Hanson and Nex (1953) that porosity, or total air space, is the most important single factor governing the movement of EDB in soil. They found that high moisture content increased packing, which in turn decreased diffusion rate. Also, movement of the chemical was slower in compact clay loams than in loose sandy loams. Biological control is also usually poorer in heavy soils than in light soils. This may arise in part from higher sorption of the chemical at soil interfaces, but it appears that failure to diffuse into regions of high inoculum potential may be the predominant reason.

The capacity of fumigants to diffuse rapidly through light sandy soils may be an important factor in achieving biological control, but high mobility may also be detrimental since the loss of chemicals by evaporation at soil surfaces may also be high. Several days after rain the porosities of soils down to 6 or 9 in. are 50 to 100% greater than below this depth, owing to evaporation from the surface and/or drainage to lower levels. Fumigants applied in such soils would move upward rather than downward and would be lost by evaporation into the atmosphere. Concentrations of fumigants near the surface layers of soils are always lower than in the interior for this reason. Consequently, biological control in the top few inches of soil is very poor. This might be improved by using nonvolatile toxicants such as PRD in combination with fumigants, since the former compound is known to move upward in soil and become concentrated in the top few inches during periods of dry weather (Schuldt *et al.*, 1957).

Water seals are used to reduce the escape of volatile compounds such as methyl bromide and chloropicrin from soils. Baines *et al.* (1956) obtained increased kills of citrus nematodes with Nemagon (b.p. 196° C.) in loam soils at depths of 6 to 8 ft. by irrigating 5 to 9 days after treatment with enough water to penetrate to the 8- or 9-foot level. However, no benefit accrued by wetting the top 6 to 8 inches of soil, which should have been sufficient to block the upward movement of vapor. Thus it appears that the large amounts of water used in these experiments may have carried the fumigant down to great depths with it rather than functioning as a seal.

The movement and distribution of fumigants in soil under uniform conditions of moisture and bulk density has most recently been studied by Call (1957c). He treated soils at field capacity with 1 ml. of EDB at a depth of 6 inches, and measured fumigant concentration in the vapor phase at various times and distances from the point of injection. The compound diffused laterally so that a maximum concentration of approximately 20 μg. of EDB per milliliter of air was reached at the end of one day at a point 2 inches away from the site of application. Thereafter the concentration of toxicant at this point diminished. Four inches away from the injection point maximum concentration was reached in 2 days, but it was only 25% as great as was attained at 2 inches. Thus a peak concentration of fumigant traveled through the soil, but it was rapidly damped out by sorption and dispersion over an expanding spherical frontier.

The fumigant diffused vertically in the same manner at a slightly slower rate, but it appeared to travel upward further than downward. This result does not agree with earlier observations that heavy vapors tend to move downward in soil because they are more dense than air. In field experiments the EDB distribution reported by Call (1957c) might be anticipated because of the lower porosity of soil at great depths, but in his experiments the free air space should have been the same throughout unless a porosity gradient developed in his soil through compaction by its own weight. In any event it appears that gravitational effects are negligible, compared with changes in soil porosities at various distances and directions from the site of application.

Thus fumigants can move away from an injection point in all directions by a modified diffusion process. However, horizontal diffusion takes place more rapidly than vertical diffusion. Consequently, the geometrical solid encompassing the maximum lethal range reached by the toxicant approximates an oblate spheroid with its shortest axis in a vertical position, but its bottom is slightly flattened.

3. Sorption of Fumigants

Chemicals can be bound to soils by adsorption at various interfaces, and to a smaller degree through dissolving in free water and organic matter. Hence the purposely vague term "sorption" is used to describe the over-all effect. The quantitative aspects of the binding of monomolecular films to solid surface are predicted adequately by the Langmuir equation. However, multimolecular films are often formed which cannot be treated in this way. In such cases skewed S-shaped isotherms are obtained when the amount of adsorbate bound to the solid is plotted against the equilibrium concentration of the compound in the vapor phase. These data are described mathematically by the Brunauer-Emmett-Teller isotherm, which states that the weight of fumigant adsorbed W at pressure P is

$$W = \frac{W_m C P/P_o}{1 - P/P_o} \cdot \frac{1 - (n + 1)(P/P_o)^n + n(P/P_o)^{n+1}}{1 + (C - 1)P/P_o - C(P/P_o)^{n+1}} \tag{11}$$

where W_m is the weight of a single monolayer, P_o is the saturation pressure, C is a constant related to the heat of adsorption and heat of liquefication of the vapor, and n is the maximum number of layers that can be built up on the surface.

Jurinak (1957) fitted the data obtained during studies on the adsorption of Nemagon by a series of oven-dried montmorillonitic clays to this equation and found that the best straight line for each soil over the greatest P/P_o range was obtained when $n = 4$, indicating that the sorbed film of fumigant can reach a maximum thickness of 4 molecules. On soils containing predominantly kaolin or illite clay minerals the isotherms can be reproduced by the equation up to a P/P_o of 0.6, but n assumes a value of infinity. This indicates adsorption on a free surface so that at the saturation pressure of the gas an infinite number of layers can be built up on the adsorbant. However, the physical significance of these values is questionable since it is now generally agreed that the theoretical basis of the Brunauer-Emmett-Teller equation is unsound, even though it is a convenient empirical method for the evaluation of sorption data (Jacobs and Tompkins, 1955).

When the sorption isotherms for the montmorillonitic series were corrected for the specific surface of each soil, all of the points fell on the same line, showing total surface area to be the principal factor other than those discussed above, such as chemical reaction, diffusion, etc., governing the binding of Nemagon by dry soils. Similar results were obtained with the kaolinitic group, but the corrected isotherms for the two clay types differed appreciably. The sorbtive capacity of a dry soil containing 35% organic matter was relatively low when compared to most mineral soils. Jurinak (1957) pointed out that this is of special interest since more fumigant is usually required to obtain control of soil organisms in organic soils than in mineral soils. However, as will be seen later, this picture changes entirely in soils at field capacity.

The mechanism of binding of fumigants to soils has been studied by Call (1957d), who found that sorption of ethylene dibromide by most soils was highest when the relative humidity of the air in equilibrium with the soils was zero. The isotherms were skewed S-shaped curves, indicating at least qualitative adherence to the Brunauer-Emmett-Teller equation. However, when the relative humidity of the air in equilibrium with the soil was increased to 5 or 10%, sorption of EDB decreased sharply, showing that water molecules were competing with fumigant molecules for sites on the surfaces of soil particles. About 6 to 40 molecules of water were required to displace each fumigant molecule, depending on soil type. However, when the relative humidity of the air was between 10 and 20%, and the soils contained just enough water to form monolayers on all the particles, about 6 water molecules were required to replace each fumigant molecule regardless of soil type.

Evidently, different mechanisms of sorption are possible, depending on moisture relations in soil. In very dry soils multilayers of fumigant are probably formed at the surfaces of clay particles. When water is introduced into the system, fumigant molecules are displaced. However, all of them do not escape into the vapor phase, since calculations made from surface energy values using the Gibbs equation (Call, 1957d) show that 1.6 μg. of EDB per square meter can be accumulated at air-water interfaces at an equilibrium vapor phase concentration of 1 μg. of fumigant per milliliter of air. Moreover, EDB and probably other fumigants can be bound at soil-water interfaces, since soils completely covered by water can still sorb chemicals. True solution of EDB in soil water would not be important until the sorbed moisture films attained sufficient thickness to have the properties of bulk water. This probably occurs to some extent at field capacity. However, measurements made on such soils show that they bind from 2 to 3 times more EDB than can be accounted for by solution of the chemical in water, even assuming that all the moisture in the soil is present as free water. Thus, fumigants can be sorbed in a variety of ways depending on soil composition and moisture content.

The interactions of EDB with montmorillonites are of special interest since, unlike other clays, these minerals sorb more chemical in equilibrium with air at 5 to 20% relative humidity than when dry. This occurs because adjacent sheets of the dry mineral are spaced about 9.5 A. apart, which is sufficient to admit water molecules, but excludes EDB. When the surrounding air contains moisture, water molecules diffuse into the free spaces and expand the crystal lattices—or, in ordinary terminology, the clays swell. Molecules of EDB can then diffuse into the roomier lattices, and compete with water molecules for the newly exposed receptor sites. Thus, water leads the way and the EDB follows. This free ride does not last forever, for when the relative humidity of the air reaches 30%, competition by water molecules for sites in the soil becomes too strenuous and the amount of bound chemical decreases.

However, in all other cases studied, the presence of moisture decreased the amount of fumigant sorbed. Thus, it may seem paradoxical to find that the amount of EDB bound by a series of 20 soils at field capacity increased with increasing moisture content (Call, 1957a). For example, a sandy soil at 10% moisture had a sorption coefficient only one-tenth that of peat soil at 75% moisture. Although water desorbs EDB, the capacity of a soil to hold water is evidently a measure of its capacity for retaining EDB.

Sorptive capacity also increased with increases in specific surface, clay, and organic matter. Variance analysis showed that moisture content alone accounted for 91% of the information, while the 4 parameters taken together accounted for 96%. Correlation of sorption coefficients with clay content was poorest. A soil with a clay content of 46% and an organic content of 4.6% had a sorption coefficient of only 31, compared to a value of 103 obtained on a soil containing 42% clay and 36.5 organic matter. Thus, while clay content and specific surface are the principle factors regulating the sorptive capacities of dry soils (Jurinak, 1957), content of organic matter is critical at field capacity. Presumably soils rich in organic matter contain more extensive networks of water films on which fumigants can be sorbed, for otherwise higher moisture content alone would decrease the amount of fumigant sorbed, as observed for all individual soils and clays with the exception of the montmorillonites.

The proportion of fumigant in the air space of soil is actually very small, varying from 0.28% of the total amount of EDB in peat soil to 3.4% in a sandy soil with a low content of clay and organic matter. Sorption is greater at low than at high temperatures, the ratio of the coefficient at 15° C. to the coefficient at 20° C. being about 1.32 for soils of all types (Call, 1957d).

It is clear that the sorption of fumigants by soils must play an important role in their performance by regulating distance and rate of diffusion, availability to the parasites, and the longevity of residues. More work on determining vapor pressures, diffusion coefficients, and sorptivities of individual chemical compounds, as well as on the physicochemical properties of various soil types, seems a promising goal for future research.

C. Treatment of Seed

1. Seed Protection

The protection of seed and seedlings from soil pathogens with chemicals is not complicated by the host of problems associated with other soil treatments for one overriding reason. The chemical is applied to the seed in massive doses and often stuck to it with stickers. Thus the fungicide occupies a strongly fortified position within a microenvironment of the soil rather than being dissipated throughout it. Furthermore it need not travel anywhere, either by diffusion or the haphazard movement of soil moisture. Consequently compounds such as thiram, captan, and dichlone, which are poor to fair soil fungicides, are among the best seed treatments available commercially. As shown previously, these compounds have very poor residual properties when distributed uniformly in organic soils. It is not known whether their comparatively high success as seed protectants results from their capacity to persist in soils for a longer time when concentrated at seed-soil interfaces or whether they kill most of the pathogens in the microsphere surrounding the seed very soon after application. In either event the use of organic compounds as seed treatments has met with far more rapid acceptance than their use as soil fungicides or as fumigants.

Particle size, which is very important in the protection of foliage surfaces, has only secondary influences on the performance of seed treatments because of the comparatively large doses that are used (Burchfield and McNew, 1950). Thus, pea seed treated with 10 μ (radius) particles of dichlone at a rate of 0.12% by weight would contain 2.5×10^4 fungicide particles per cm.^{2} of surface. By contrast only 600 particles of dichlone per cm.^{2} of leaf area were required to obtain 95% control of tomato early blight when the particle radius was 8.4 μ. Since most, if not all, seed treatments are ground to powders with mean radii much less than 10 μ, it is evident that inadequate coverage of the seed surface should not be an important consideration in failure to control diseases. This surmise was confirmed by some experiments in which pea seed was treated with a series of 4 dichlone formulations having average radii of 2.3 to 9.5 μ (Burchfield and McNew, 1950). No significant differences in per cent emergence of seedlings could be detected 10 days after the seed were planted in infested soil. In a similar series of experiments with chloranil some lack of control was experienced with very large particles (35 μ), but this may have been caused by failure of the dust to adhere to the seed. It is probable that the particle size of seed protectants should be fairly small to secure good adhesion or good suspendibility, if a slurry method of application is used. However, if too small, the fungicide may be vulnerable to attack by deteriorating influences in the soil.

Seed treatment is not without its problems, however, for compounds must be formulated to give optimum performance in application equipment, while injury to seed or seedlings by the chemical may often be a factor limiting usefulness. Chemicals which are highly toxic to seed will usually be eliminated in screening. However, chemicals can perform satisfactorily in some locations and cause damage in others. Thus chloranil is an outstanding treatment for legume seed, particularly peas and beans. In addition to being effective against most soil-inhabiting fungi it is safe on many crop seed, and otherwise has some very desirable properties. It is nonirritating to humans and has a lubricating effect on seed somewhat like graphite. This latter property facilitates the flow of seed through the cups of grain drills, and thus eliminates much of the seed injury caused by other treatments. However, it is unsatisfactory for the treatment of spinach and beet seed when they are planted in alkaline soils of mineral origin, although excellent results were secured on peat soils. Presumably, chloranil hydrolyzes in alkaline media to yield water-soluble phytotoxic compounds such as chloranilic acid (McNew and Burchfield, 1951). Thus, interactions with the environment can lead to serious problems in the protection of seed with chemicals.

2. Seed Disinfection

Cereal seed are enclosed in husks or fruit coats. Some fungi which attack these crops can penetrate the husks and overwinter as mycelia inside them. When the seed are planted, the mycelia become active and attack the young seedlings. Seed protectants, such as thiram and captan, cannot permeate the husks, so volatile fumigants, such as organic mercury compounds, must be used for disinfection. Although they act as fumigants, their vapor pressures are very low, being of the order of 10^{-5} mm. of Hg. They are applied to seed as dusts or liquids. The amounts used are as small as 0.2 ml. per 100 grams of seed, so that uniform distribution is critical. Lindström (1958) recently studied the action of mercurials and concludes that coverage occurs in two steps: distribution on the seed in the treating equipment and redistribution by evaporation and resorption of the compound. In this latter process the chemical tends to leave locations where it is abundant and be resorbed where it is scarce, so that in time uniform coverage is achieved. Lindström (1958) believes that two kinetic processes are involved in the movement of mercurials, namely, evaporation rate and diffusion rate, and of the two he considers diffusion to be the slower or rate-controlling step. He found the distribution of Panogen [cyano(methylmercuri)guanidine] to be satisfactory 2 hours after mixing. There was a further small improvement at increased storage time, but the gain was of no practical importance.

Distribution of a nonvolatile placebo dressing labeled with Th^{204} was surprisingly good when used at a rate of 0.2 ml. per gram of seed, but even so, Lindström concludes that redistribution of mercurial fungicides by evaporation and resorption improves the uniformity of the deposits obtained initially and may compensate in part for poor mixing. Even more important is his finding that the ratio of β to γ radiation emitted from Hg^{203} labeled Panogen decreased from about 90 on a nonpermeable surface to about 30 to 50 on seed. This suggests that much of the weak β radiation emitted by the mercury was not detected because the fungicide was located behind a barrier which absorbed the softer β rays while the hard γ rays were not absorbed. Lindström presents data which suggest that the reduction in β/γ ratio is about what would be expected if the barrier were 100 μ thick. This corresponds roughly to the thickness of the fruit coats of wheat kernels. Additional evidence for this will be required, but it appears that one more of the important physical problems of plant pathology is near solution.

References

Abel, A. L. 1957. The substituted urea herbicides. *Chem. & Ind. (London)* **33**: 1106–1112.

Angell, H. R., J. C. Walker, and K. P. Link. 1930. The relation of protocatechuic acid to disease resistance in the onion. *Phytopathology* **20**: 431–438.

Baines, R. C., F. J. Foote, and J. P. Martin. 1956. Fumigate soil before replanting to control citrus nematode. *Calif. Citrograph* **41**: 427, 448.

Baines, R. C., R. H. Small, T. A. DeWolfe, J. P. Martin, and L. H. Stolzy. 1957. Control of citrus nematode and *Phytophthora* spp. by vapam. *Plant Disease Reptr.* **41**: 405–414.

Betts, J. J., S. P. James, and W. V. Thorpe. 1955. Metabolism of pentachloronitrobenzene and 2:3:4:6-tetrachloronitrobenzene and the formation of mercapturic acids in the rabbit. *Biochem. J.* **61**: 611–617.

Björling, K., and K. A. Sellgren. 1957. Protection and its connection with redistribution of different droplet sizes in sprays against *Phytophthora infestans. Kgl. Lantbruks-Högskol. Ann.* **23**: 291–308.

Bowen, D., P. Hebblethwaite, and W. M. Carleton. 1952. Application of electrostatic charging to the deposition of insecticides and fungicides on plant surfaces. *Agr. Eng.* **33**: 347–350.

Burchfield, H. P. 1959. Physical chemistry of fungicidal action: physical properties and chemical reactivities in relation to the effectiveness of fungicides. *In* "Plant Pathology—Problems and Progress, 1908–1958," (C. S. Holton, G. W. Fischer, R. W. Fulton, Helen Hart, S. E. A. McCallan, eds.), pp. 293–303. Univ. of Wisconsin Press, 588 pp.

Burchfield, H. P., and A. Goenaga. 1957a. Equipment for producing simulated rain for measuring the tenacity of spray deposits to foliage. *Contribs. Boyce Thompson. Inst.* **19**: 133–140.

Burchfield, H. P., and A. Goenaga. 1957b. Some factors governing the deposition and tenacity of copper fungicide sprays. *Contribs. Boyce Thompson Inst.* **19**: 141–156.

Burchfield, H. P., and G. L. McNew. 1950. Mechanism of particle size effects of fungicides on plant protection. *Contribs. Boyce Thompson Inst.* **16**: 131–161.

Burchfield, H. P., and J. Schechtman. 1958. Absorptiometric analysis of *N*-(trichloromethylthio)-4-cyclohexene-1,2-dicarboximide (captan). *Contribs. Boyce Thompson Inst.* **19**: 411–416.

Burchfield, H. P., and P. H. Schuldt. 1958. Pyridine-alkali reactions in the analysis of pesticides containing active halogen atoms. *J. Agr. Food Chem.* **6**: 106–111.

Burchfield, H. P., and E. E. Storrs. 1956. Chemical structures and dissociation constants of amino acids, peptides, and proteins in relation to their reaction rates with 2,4-dichloro-6-(*o*-chloroanilino)-*s*-triazine. *Contribs. Boyce Thompson Inst.* **18**: 395–418.

Burchfield, H. P., and E. E. Storrs, 1957a. Effects of chlorine substitution and isomerism on the interactions of *s*-triazine derivatives with conidia of Neurospora sitophila. *Contribs. Boyce Thompson Inst.* **18**: 429–452.

Burchfield, H. P., and E. E. Storrs. 1957b. Relative reactivities of 1-fluoro-2,4-dinitrobenzene and 2,4-dichloro-6-(*o*-chloroanilino)-*s*-triazine with metabolites containing various functional groups. *Contribs. Boyce Thompson Inst.* **19**: 169–176.

Butt, D. J. 1955. Spray application problems. XXVI. The range of fungicidal action of micro-deposits of captan on artificial surfaces and on leaves. *Ann. Rept. Agr. Hort. Research Sta. Long Ashton Bristol* **1955**: 127–135.

Byrdy, S., K. Gorecki, and A. Kotodziejczyk. 1957. Badanie przyczepności pylistych i ptynnych środków ochrony roślin przez zmywanie i zdmuchiwanie. *Przemysł Chem.* [N. S.] **13**: 351–353.

518   H. P. BURCHFIELD

Call, F. 1957a. Soil fumigation. IV. Sorption of ethylene dibromide on soils at field capacity. *J. Sci. Food Agr.* **8:** 137–142.

Call, F. 1957b. Soil fumigation. V. Diffusion of ethylene dibromide through soils. *J. Sci. Food Agr.* **8:** 143–150.

Call, F. 1957c. Soil fumigation. VI. The distribution of ethylene dibromide round an injection point. *J. Sci. Food Agr.* **8:** 591–596.

Call, F. 1957d. The mechanism of sorption of ethylene dibromide on moist soils. *J. Sci. Food Agr.* **8:** 630–639.

Cupples, H. L. 1941. Relation between wetting power of a spray and its initial retention by a fruit. *J. Agr. Research* **63:** 681–686.

Daines, R. H., R. J. Lukens, E. Brennan, and I. A. Leone. 1957. Phototoxicity of captan as influenced by formulation environment and plant factors. *Phytopathology* **47:** 567–572.

Decker, G. C. 1957. Pesticide residues on plants. *Agr. Chem.* **12**(2): 39–40, 97–98.

Durham, N. N. 1957. Studies on the metabolism of *p*-nitrobenzoic acid. *Can. J. Microbiol.* **4:** 141–148.

Evans, W. C. 1947. Oxidation of phenol and benzoic acid by some soil bacteria. *Biochem. J.* **41:** 373–382.

Frear, D. E. H., and H. N. Worthley. 1937. Deposition and retention of sprays on apples. *Penn. State Univ. Agr. Expt. Sta. Bull.* **344:** 1–32.

Free, E. E. 1908. The solubility of precipitated basic copper carbonate in solutions of carbon dioxide. *J. Am. Chem. Soc.* **30:** 1366–1374.

Gill, E. W. B. 1948. Frictional electrification of sand. *Nature* **162:** 568–569.

Greenwood, D. J., and H. Lees. 1956. Studies on the decomposition of amino acids in soils. I. A preliminary survey of techniques. *Plant and Soil* **7:** 253–256.

Gullstrom, D. K., and H. P. Burchfield. 1948. Agricultural dusts: determination of particle size distribution. *Anal. Chem.* **20:** 1174–1177.

Gundersen, K., and H. L. Jensen. 1956. A soil bacterium decomposing organic nitro compounds. *Acta Agr. Scand.* **6:** 100–114.

Hanson, W. J., and R. W. Nex. 1953. Diffusion of ethylene dibromide in soils. *Soil Sci.* **76:** 209–214.

Henderson, M. E. K. 1957. Metabolism of methoxylated aromatic compounds by soil fungi. *J. Gen. Microbiol.* **16:** 686–695.

Henderson, M. E. K., and V. C. Farmer. 1955. Utilization of soil fungi of *p*-hydroxy-benzaldehyde, ferulic acid, syringaldehyde and vanillin. *J. Gen. Microbiol.* **12:** 37–46.

Heuberger, J. W., and J. G. Horsfall. 1942. Reduction in fungicidal value of copper by organic materials. *Phytopathology* **32:** 370–387.

Horsfall, J. G. 1956. "Principles of Fungicidal Action." Chronica Botanica, Waltham, Massachusetts. 231 pp.

Ichikawa, S. T., J. D. Gilpatrick, and C. W. McBeth. 1955. Soil diffusion pattern of 1,2-dibromo-3-chloropropane. *Phytopathology* **45:** 576–578.

Jacobs, P. W. M., and F. C. Tompkins. 1955. Surfaces of solids. In "Chemistry of the Solid State" (W. E. Garner, ed.), Chapt. 4. Academic Press, New York. pp. 91–122.

Jurinak, J. J. 1957. Adsorption of 1,2-dibromo-3-chloropropane vapor by soils. *J. Agr. Food Chem.* **5:** 598–601.

Koopman, H., and J. Daams. 1958. Investigations on herbicides. I. 2-(Substituted amino)-4,6-dichloro-1,3,5-triazines. *Rec. trav. chim.* **77:** 235–240.

Ladd, J. N. 1956. Oxidation of hydrocarbons by soil bacteria. I. Morphological and biochemical properties of a soil diptheroid utilizing hydrocarbons. *Australian J. Biol. Sci.* **9:** 92–104.

Lindström, O. 1958. Mechanism of liquid seed treatment. *J. Agr. Food Chem.* **6:** 283-298.

Ludwig, R. A., G. D. Thorn, and D. M. Miller. 1954. Studies on the mechanism of fungicidal action of disodium ethylene bisdithiocarbamate (nabam). *Can. J. Botany* **32:** 48–54.

McCallan, S. E. A., and F. Wilcoxon. 1936. The action of fungous spores on Bordeaux mixture. *Contribs. Boyce Thompson Inst.* **8:** 151–165.

McNew, G. L., and H. P. Burchfield. 1951. Fungitoxicity and biological activity of quinones. *Contribs. Boyce Thompson Inst.* **16:** 357–374.

Magdoff, B. S., H. P. Burchfield, and J. Schechtman. 1958. Chemistry and crystallography of some polybasic cupric calcium sulfates (Bordeaux mixtures). *Contribs. Boyce Thompson Inst.* **19:** 267–288.

Miller, P. M., and E. M. Stoddard. 1957. Importance of fungicide volatility in controlling soil fungi. *Phytopathology* **47:** 24.

Moje, W., J. P. Martin, and R. C. Baines. 1957. Structural effect of some organic compounds on soil organisms and citrus seedlings grown in an old citrus soil. *J. Agr. Food Chem.* **5:** 32–36.

Murphy, J. F., and R. W. Stone. 1955. Bacterial dissimilation of naphthalene. *Can. J. Microbiol.* **1:** 579–588.

Napier, E. J., A. Rhodes, D. I. Turner, J. Tootill, and A. Dunn. 1957. Systemic action of captan against *Botrytis fabae* (chocolate spot of broad bean). *J. Sci. Food Agr.* **8:** 467–474.

Newhall, A. G. 1958. An improved method of screening potential soil fungicides against *Fusarium oxysporum* F. *cubense*. *Plant Disease Reptr.* **42:** 677–679.

Pond, D. D., and D. Chisholm. 1958. Influence of weathering on DDT coverage in a potato spray program. *Can. J. Plant Sci.* **38:** 81–83.

Potts, S. F. 1958. "Concentrated Spray Equipment, Mixtures and Application Methods." Dorland Books, Caldwell, New Jersey. 598 pp.

Price, C. C. 1958. Fundamental mechanisms of alkylation. *Ann. N. Y. Acad. Sci.* **68:** 663–668.

Reckendorfer, P. 1936. Über den Zerfall des Kupferkalkbrühe-Komplexes. (Ein analytischer Beitrag zur Kenntnis des "wasser-löslichen" Kupfers). *Z. Pflanzenkrankh. u. Pflanzenschutz* **46:** 418–438.

Rich, S. 1954. Dynamics of deposition and tenacity of fungicides. *Phytopathology* **44:** 203–213.

Richardson, L. T. 1954. The persistence of thiram in soil and its relationship to the microbiological balance and damping-off control. *Can. J. Botany* **32:** 335–346.

Schuldt, P. H., and C. N. Wolf. 1956. Fungitoxicity of substituted *s*-triazines. *Contribs. Boyce Thompson Inst.* **18:** 377–393.

Schuldt, P. H., H. P. Burchfield, and H. Bluestone. 1957. Stability and movement studies on the new experimental nematocide 3,4-dichlorotetrahydrothiophene-1,1-dioxide in soil. *Phytopathology* **47:** 534.

Sijpesteyn, A. K., and J. G. M. van der Kerk. 1954. Investigations on organic fungicides. VII. Action of bisdithiocarbamates and diisothiocyanates. *Biochim. et Biophys. Acta* **13:** 545–552.

Somers, E. 1956. Studies of spray deposits. I. Effect of spray supplements on the tenacity of a copper fungicide. *J. Sci. Food Agr.* **7:** 160–172.

Somers, E. 1957. Studies of spray deposits. III. Factors influencing the level of "run-off" deposits of copper fungicides. *J. Sci. Food Agr.* **8:** 520–526.

Somers, E., and W. D. E. Thomas. 1956. Studies of spray deposits. II. The tenacity of copper fungicides on artificial and leaf surfaces. *J. Sci. Food Agr.* **7:** 655–667.

Stevenson, F. J. 1956. Isolation and identification of some amino compounds in soils. *Soil Science Soc. Am. Proc.* **20:** 201–204.

Sund, K. A. 1956. Adsorption of amino triazole by soil particles. *J. Agr. Food Chem.* **4:** 57–60.

Swales, J. E., and K. Williams. 1956. Non-ionic surfactants in concentrate mixtures for the control of apple scab. *Can. J. Agr. Sci.* **36:** 36–40.

Thatcher, R. W., and L. R. Streeter. 1925. The adherence to foliage of sulfur in fungicidal dusts and sprays. *N. Y. State Agr. Expt. Sta. (Geneva, N. Y.) Tech. Bull.* **116:** 1–18.

Thomas, F. J. D. 1957. The residual effects of crop-protection chemicals in the soil. *In* "Plant Protection Conferences 1956." Butterworths, London, pp. 215–222.

Thorn, G. D., and R. A. Ludwig. 1954. Studies on the mechanism of fungicidal action of the ethylenebisdithiocarbamates. 2. Theoretical considerations. *Phytopathology* **44:** 508.

Torgeson, D. C., D. M. Yoder, and J. B. Johnson. 1957. Biological activity of Mylone breakdown products. *Phytopathology* **47:** 536.

Turner, N., and N. Woodruff. 1948. Toxicity of DDT residues: effect of time of exposure of insects, coverage and tenacity. *Conn. Agr. Expt. Sta. Bull., New Haven* **524:** 1–35.

Vlitos, A. J. 1952. Biological activation of sodium 2-(2,4-dichlorophenoxy)ethyl sulfate by *Bacillus cereus* var. *mycoides*. *Contribs. Boyce Thompson Inst.* **16:** 435–438.

Wellman, R. H., and S. E. A. McCallan. 1946. Glyoxalidine derivatives as foliage fungicides. I. Laboratory studies. *Contribs. Boyce Thompson Inst.* **14:** 151–160.

Wilcoxon, F., and S. E. A. McCallan. 1931. The fungicidal action of sulfur. III. Physical factors affecting the efficiency of dusts. *Contribs. Boyce Thompson Inst.* **3:** 509–528.

Wilcoxon, F., and S. E. A. McCallan. 1938. The weathering of Bordeaux mixture. *Contribs. Boyce Thompson Inst.* **9:** 149–159.

Wilson, J. D. 1953. Wettable powder versus tank-mix dithiocarbamates on potatoes and tomatoes in Ohio. *Ohio Agr. Expt. Sta. Research Circ.* **9:** 22 pp.

Yarwood, C. E. 1943. The function of lime and host leaves in the action of Bordeaux mixture. *Phytopathology* **33:** 1146–1156.

Yeomans, A. H., and E. E. Rogers. 1953. Factors influencing deposit of spray droplets. *J. Econ. Entomol.* **46:** 57–60.

Young, H. C., and J. C. Carroll. 1951. The decomposition of pentachlorophenol when applied as a residual pre-emergence herbicides. *Agron. J.* **43:** 504–507.

CHAPTER 13

Biological Interference with Epidemics

H. DARPOUX

Station Centrale de Pathologie Vegetale, Centre National de Recherches Agronomiques, Versailles, France

I. INTRODUCTION

Various biological factors can influence the living pathogens of cultivated plants and their hosts. The living world is a complex system where
organisms fight for their existence, often to the prejudice of other organisms. Sometimes, however, beneficent associations are realized. In the
natural biological medium, pathogens are submitted to the influence of
neighboring organisms during their parasitic life, saprophytic phases, or
during rest periods. Even the susceptibility of the host plant may be
modified by biological factors.

Sometimes the pathogen may be parasitized by another fungus or

521

bacterium. The latter live at the expense of their hosts by drawing from them the materials necessary to their nutrition. These are hyperparasites or parasites of the second degree, and the phenomenon itself is hyperparasitism. In other cases, antagonism exists between microorganisms living side by side, some inhibiting the growth of others. This phenomenon is frequent, particularly in the soil. Organisms may compete with one another on the host surface. In other cases, organisms associate together and cause complex diseases. Thus, viruses may infect plants simultaneously, or a virus and another pathogen on the same plant may affect one another. Nematodes are known to act similarly with other pathogens.

Certain animals, generally predators, sometimes act as antagonists by feeding on plant pathogens.

In this chapter the different types of interrelations of organisms will be discussed in relation to their role in epidemiology and control.

II. HYPERPARASITISM: PARASITES ON FUNGI

Certain fungi and bacteria are parasitic on plant pathogens. The genus *Ciccinobolus* includes species of fungi which attack fungi of the family Erysiphaceae. Thus, *C. cesatii* de Bary develops as thin mycelial threads inside the hyphae and conidiophores of *Erysiphe graminis*. It fructifies in pycnidia having unicellular spores. Other species, *C. ewonymi japonici* on *Oidium ewonymi japonici* and *C. asteris* on *Oidium astericolum*, act in a similar way (Hino and Kato, 1929). These fungi can hinder the growth of the pathogen so that its mycelium contracts and shrinks, while the formation of oidia is very much impeded. However, *Ciccinobolus* seldom reduces attacks of the powdery mildews in nature because it seldom occurs in large quantities. *Ciccinobolus* can be cultivated on artificial media, however, and some encouraging results have been obtained by artificial inoculation.

Species of the genus *Darluca* live in the sori of Uredinales. The best-known species is *D. filum*, which is found in the uredospores or teleutospores of many rusts. *Darluca* also is cultivatable in artificial media. This hyperparasite also seems to play but a limited role in reducing epidemics of rust on plants.

The genus *Tuberculina* also includes species which attack Uredinales. *T. persicina* establishes itself in the aecidia of *Puccinia poarum*, *Gymnosporangium sabinae*, *G. juniperum*, and in the teleutospore sori of *Endophyllum sempervivi* and *Puccinia vincae*. In these organs it forms violaceous sporodochia. *T. maxima* is known as a parasite of *Cronartium ribicola*. It vigorously attacks pycniospores and thus can reduce or inhibit the formation of aecidiospores. The local and natural establishing of *T. maxima* has been observed in pine plantings attacked by rust, but its extension has always been limited to small areas. In culture it develops slowly and sporulates sparsely. Artificial inoculations are not easy to realize (Hubert, 1935).

Among the hyperparasites of Uredinales let us also mention *Cladosporium aecidiicola,* which grows in aecidia—especially in *Puccinia conspicua* (Keener, 1954)—and *Verticillium hemileiae,* in which the thin mycelium lives in uredospores of *Hemileia vastatrix* (Bourriquet, 1946).

Bacteria can also parasitize fructifications of Uredinales (Levine *et al.,* 1935). According to Borders (1938) *Erwinia urediniolytica* attacks pedicels of spores. Pon *et al.* (1954) studied the parasitism of *Xanthomonas uredovorus* on *Puccinia graminis,* which grows on or in uredospores at a high temperature (30° C.) and in a saturated atmosphere. The bacteria, which inhabit the soil, are spattered by rain up to the rust sori on the low part of the plant. The temperature requirements of the parasite must, however, limit its biological role.

Among fungi the genus *Trichothecium* includes species that attack plants as secondary parasites, are antagonistic to other microorganisms, or grow at the expense of plant pathogens. The fruiting bodies of the grape-downy-mildew fungus *Plasmopara viticola* sometimes exhibit a brick-red coloring, due to the growth of a fungus, *Trichothecium plasmoparae* (Viala, 1932). Its thin mycelium lies beside the conidiophores and conidia of *Plasmopara,* absorbing the protoplasm, and the conidial fluff then becomes matted. This *Trichothecium* is unable to penetrate the host membranes, and so cannot reach the mycelium of *Plasmopara* in the tissues of the leaf. It is favored by hot, wet weather, and fears acidity.

Trichothecium roseum sometimes grows on the stromas of certain pathogens, inhibiting the formation of perithecia and sometimes limiting the growth of the fungus it attacks. Thus, Koch (1934) observed it in summer on the stromas of *Dibotryon morbosum,* the agent of black knot of *Prunus* and succeeded in inoculating *Dibotryon* with it artificially. In autumn *T. roseum* can attack the stromas of *Polystigma rubrum* on plum trees, sterilizing the stromas by killing ascogenous elements of the *Polystigma* (Yossifovitch, 1954). By artificial inoculations an important increase of diseased stromas has been obtained. On artificial inoculation of *Polystigma, Trichothecium* increased the number of stromas formed, and these later became diseased. This fungus has a similar effect on the perithecia of *Gnomonia veneta,* and Viennot-Bourgin (1949) has found it on the stroma of *Nectria cinnabarina.*

That certain fungal plant pathogens are parasitized in the soil by fungi and bacteria has been demonstrated in the laboratory by growing pairs of microorganisms side by side. Weindling (1932) has demonstrated the parasitism of *Trichoderma lignorum* on *Rhizoctonia solani*, *Phytophthora parasitica*, *Pythium* sp., *Rhizopus* sp., and *Sclerotium rolfsii*. The fungus acts to inhibit or kill the host hyphae by direct parasitism or, alternatively, by antagonism, as will be discussed later. Thus the hyphae of the *Trichoderma* may wind around the aerial hyphae of the host fungus, penetrating and growing inside them. Sometimes, however, *Trichoderma* acts at a distance on the hyphae of another fungus nearby.

The use of *T. lignorum* has been considered to fight damping-off of seedlings during their short period of susceptibility. This method has not been too successful in practice because (a) *Trichoderma* is not usually dominant at the soil surface, (b) it has a high moisture requirement, and (c) it autolyzes readily.

A species of *Papulospora*, isolated from the soil, has shown a parasitism on *Rhizoctonia solani* in artificial medium similar to that of *T. lignorum*. Its hypae wind around those of the host or enter and grow inside (Warren, 1948).

Rhizoctonia solani, the well-known pathogen of many higher plants, can also attack other fungi, nearly all belonging to the Phycomycetes. Butler (1957) has studied this parasitism on agar media by sowing the host fungus and *R. solani* on opposite sides of a petri dish. When the two colonies meet, the *Rhizoctonia* is stimulated at first, forming a thick mycelial zone at the juncture of the two colonies. This mycelium first invades the host about 24 hours after the two colonies meet, and after 72 hours invasion becomes general.

The parasite attacks the aerial hyphae and sporophores of its host in two ways. It may penetrate into the hyphae of the host and grow rapidly inside or it may wind around and constrict a part of the host. The protoplasm of the encircled hyphae either becomes coagulated or else it becomes less optically dense and vanishes. When this happens the aerial hyphae of the host fungus sink down.

Not all cultures of the host fungus are destroyed, however. It may resist infection by lysis of parasitized hyphae or by isolation of infected hyphae with a partition. The degree of parasitism varies also with the culture media, temperature, and light.

Because *Rhizoctonia solani* is itself a pathogen, it cannot be used to fight other pathogens. But these observations suggest how competition among fungi can occur in nature.

Certain species of the genus *Pythium* parasitize adjoining species. Drechsler (1943b) showed that *P. oligandrum* could attack *P. ultimum*, *P. debaryanum*, or *P. irregulare* by encircling their hyphae or by penetrating them. Conidia and young oogonia are also parasitized. The destruction is so rapid that the oospores generally do not get formed.

Fungi can parasitize the oospores of root-rotting Oomycetes. For instance, the imperfect fungi *Trinacrium subtile, Dactylella spermatophage,* and *Trichothecium arrhenopum* destroy the oospores of *Pythium, Phytophthora,* or *Aphanomyces.* Infection is accomplished by successive perforations of the cell walls of the oogonium and oospore, followed by growth within the oospore of branches, sometimes lobed, and of big suctorial organs (Drechsler, 1938, 1943a). The chytrid *Phlyctochytrium* can attack and inhibit the germination of the oospores of *Peronospora tabacina* (Person, 1955).

These fungi seem to play an important role in the soil, reducing the germination of oospores and their infectivity of higher plants. Even in soils where quantities of oospores are found, the percentage of diseased plants after the first infection remains slight, owing to the presence of these hyperparasites.

The sclerotia of certain fungi are also frequently attacked and killed in the soil. *Coniothyrium minitans* has been observed on sclerotia of *Sclerotinia trifoliorum.* By artificial inoculation in certain types of soil 85 to 99% of the sclerotia were killed in 11 weeks (Tribe, 1957).

In other cases it is difficult to determine whether hyperparasitism or antagonism is involved. Thus, Clark and Mitchell (1942) showed that the sclerotia of *Phymatotrichum omnivorum* survived in sterilized soils whether they received organic amendments or not, but in unsterilized, amended soils microbial activity has led to destruction of sclerotia. The action is temperature dependent. Thus, the percentage of sclerotia losing their viability was 12, 30, 70, and 90, respectively, for temperatures of 2°, 12°, 28°, and 35° C. Moisture was required.

III. BACTERIOPHAGE

In 1917 d'Herelle presented evidence for a transmissible lytic principle that acted on the Shiga bacillus, showing that the bacteria have their infectious diseases, too. These infectious agents are now known as bacteriophages and are usually considered as ultraviruses. Although pathogens of man and animals have been particularly studied, some work has been done on phages of plant pathogens. Phages have been isolated from fragments of diseased plants, contaminated soils, and from bacterial cultures.

By now phages have been discovered for many phytopathogenic bacteria: *Agrobacterium tumefaciens, Aplanobacter stewarti, Erwinia aroideae, E. carotovora, E. atroseptica, Pseudomonas angulata atrofaciens, P. coronofaciens, P. glycinea, P. lacrymans, P. phaseolicola, P.*

pisi, P. syringae, P. tabaci, P. xanthoclora, Xanthomonas citri, X. malvacearum, X. orizae, X. phaseoli, X. pruni, X. solanacearum, and *X. translucens.* In 1953 Newbond found a phage of *Streptomyces scabies.*

To act, a phage must encounter a bacterium able to fix it. Once fixed, the phage enters the bacterial cell and multiplies within it. Eventually, the bacterium is lysed, and sets the phage particles free. They are then able to infest other bacteria.

Unhappily, this lysis is rarely complete in a culture. The appearance of secondary cultures of the host bacterium is frequently noted in the same plate. The bacteria of these colonies usually have the same morphologic and physiologic characters as their parents and generally acquire their resistance to the phage through mutation.

In other cases the appearance of lysogenic strains can be noted, as Okabe and Goto (1954) showed with *Pseudomonas solanacearum.* Lysogenic bacteria are genetically able to tolerate phages that multiply in them under certain conditions. In these bacteria the virus is in the form of a prophage that is neither infectious nor pathogenic. Lysogenic bacteria are insensitive to the phages they produce, thus showing a real phenomenon of premunition.

Phages differ in their action. Some are polyvalent, while others have high specificity. Sometimes two forms of the same bacterial strain differ in their reactions to the same phage. Thus, form S of *Pseudomonas phaseolicola* is more sensitive to the phage than form R.

In human pathology some success has attended efforts to use bacteriophages in fighting certain infectious diseases. In plant pathology, however, attempts at phagotherapy have been unsuccessful. The first work was done in 1925, when Coons and Kotila (1925) prevented the rotting of carrot slices by *Erwinia carotovora* through adding the homologous bacteriophage. But the results were not clear-cut with *Erwinia atroseptica* on potato slices. Israilsky (1926, 1927) thought he had shown that the previous inoculation of a phage of *Agrobacterium tumefaciens* into a plant impeded the subsequent growth of tumors, but Kaufman (1929) could not confirm his results.

R. C. Thomas (1935, 1940) treated corn seeds with a phage of *Aplanobacter stewarti,* and then inoculated them with the pathogen. He obtained 18% disease in control plants but only 1.4% disease in treated ones. A bacteriophage, isolated from tobacco leaves invaded by the wildfire bacterium, reduced infection to 50% when dusted on test plants (Novikowa, 1940). Also, Kawamura (1940) reduced infection of tomato by *Pseudomonas solanacearum* through applying a bacteriophage to the soil.

Fulton (1950) studied two bacteriophages active against certain strains of *Pseudomonas tabaci* and *P. angulata,* isolating them from diseased tobacco leaves. He compared their lysogenic and other properties, especially their inactivation by cations. As Novikowa (1940) has shown, he obtained a reduction in diseased tobacco seedlings by treating them with a suspension of phage before inoculation. This reduction was greater when he dusted with a mixture of the two phages rather than with one alone.

From infested fields Fulton (1950) obtained more bacteriophages of *Pseudomonas tabaci* and *P. angulata* as the disease levels increased. On this basis Fulton suggests that the phages could limit the amount of disease. This is related to the action of the rhizobiophages, which are in part responsible for the "tiredness" of alfalfa fields, because of their action on *Rhizobium* in the nodules of leguminous plants. Possibly, the persistence of the wildfire bacterium in soils is controlled by bacteriophages. This hypothesis wants a precise experiment.

IV. PREDATORS AND ANTAGONISTIC ANIMALS OF PATHOGENS

A good many insects live at the expense of the higher fungi. They grow in the carpophores, eating either the flesh of the fungus or its spores or both. Many species of Coleoptera, belonging more particularly to families of Scaphidiidae, Liodidae, Staphylinidae, Erotylidae, Cryptophagidae, are mycophagous. A few species specialize on one type of fungus. For instance, *Gyrophaena strictula* limits itself to the Polyporacae.

A succession of several species of Coleoptera feeds upon one fungus, one feeding at one growth stage, another later on, until the rotting fungus is fed upon by the last in the succession. The coleopterous mycetophiles require moisture. When fungi are normally moist, the number of visitors can be very high, but the number decreases with dryness.

Fewer Hymenoptera attack carpophores. Possibly the Lepidoptera in the imago stage suck the droplets secreted by fungi. Some larvae that eat fungi are known.

The fungus is merely a shelter for the majority of the Hemiptera found on Polypores. The Aradides and Dysodiides are considered as mycophagous and are often seen between the lobes of Polypores (Rehfons, 1955).

The inoculum of plant pathogens (smuts, rusts, mildews) can be appreciably reduced by Coleoptera and Diptera that subsist on these fungi, among them being (Phalacridae; Coccinellidae, etc. . . .) (Itoni-didae-(Cecidomyidae) Fungivoridae, etc. . . .).

Among the representative mycophages of the family of Phalacridae is *Phalacrus caricis* Sturm, observed by d'Aguilar (1944) in a *Cintractia-*

smutted head of *Carex riparia*. The larva subsists exclusively on spores of *Cintractia subinclusa*, these spores being evident inside the alimentary canal of the insect. When adults appear at the end of July, they have the same diet of fungus.

Many species of the race *Phalacrus* destroy the smut spores produced on grasses (Friedrichs, 1908). The spores of these insects have lost in the excrements their viability. Hence insects are not dispersal agents of the Ustilaginaceae. When Friedrichs (1908) placed material drawn out of the posterior intestine on nutrient agar, the contained spores did not germinate. The same was true of spores drawn out of the middle intestine. However, the spores from grain that sheltered larva of *Phalacrus* germinated readily.

The larva and adults consume quantities of spores. This regimen and the abundance of *Phalacrus fimetarious* on the ears of cultivated plants parasitized by Ustilaginae give to the genus *Phalacrus* a certain economic importance.

Other examples of insect predators of fungi include *Deuterosminthus bicinctus* var. *repanda*, which browses on conidiophores and conidia of the downy mildew fungus of grape, *Plasmopara viticola* (Grassé, 1922).

Finally, let us report the antagonistic action of certain inferior representatives of the animal kingdom. In artificial media the mycelium of *Verticillium dahliae* does not grow, and its pseudosclerotia do not germinate in presence of infusoria of the race *Culpoda*. Tomato plants grown in nutrient solution containing pseudospores of *V. dahliae* wither rapidly, although no infection occurs when the solution contains active infusoria. In infested soils when *Culpoda* is present, the intensity of the disease is decreased (Brodski, 1941). The mode of action of the protozoan is unknown.

V. Microbial Antagonisms

A. *Phenomena of Antagonism*

The phenomena of antagonism between microorganisms have been particularly studied in recent years with the development of antibiotic substances. When a nutrient medium is sown with two microorganisms, one frequently inhibits the growth of the other (Fig. 1).

Different classic techniques demonstrate this phenomenon. They consist of sowing two or more organisms at different points on the surface of an agar medium and allowing them to grow or in inoculating a plate with fungus spores or bacteria and then placing a fragment of agar bearing another organism on the surface nearby. Inhibition zones are then often observed (Fig. 2). In the periphery of the zone, morpho-

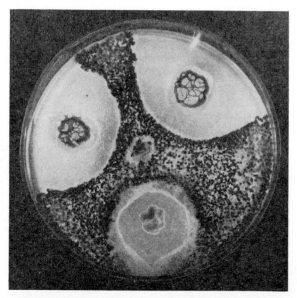

FIG. 1. Antagonistic action of three bacterial stocks on *Sclerotinia minor.*

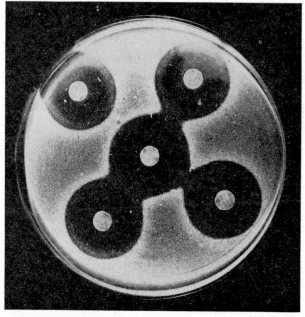

FIG. 2. Action of a filtrate of a liquid nutritive medium of an antagonistic organism on a phytopathogenetic fungus.

genic effects exist. Deformations or the lysis of vegetative elements of the inhibited organism are observed. A short distance beyond stimulation occurs in the form of much-branched hyphae, increased sporulation, etc. Temperature, composition of nutrient media, and other factors affect antagonistic phenomena.

Many microorganisms, bacteria, actinomycetes, fungi isolated from the soil, or various substrata can thus act on phytopathogenic agents (Fig. 3).

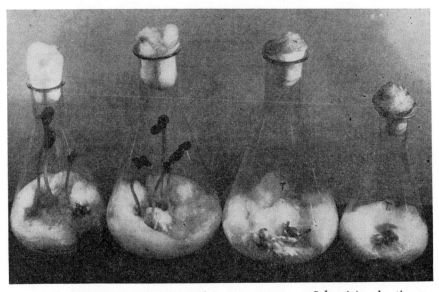

FIG. 3. The antagonistic action of an actinomycete on *Sclerotinia sclerotiorum*. Left: two Erlenmeyer flasks in which the Actinomycete has inhibited the *Sclerotinia*. Right: two check flasks in which the actinomycete has not been introduced.

In a study on several thousand isolates 256 of them, including 60 strains or species of bacteria, 90 strains or species of actinomycetes, and 106 strains or species of fungi, have revealed antagonistic action on phytopathogenic agents. The latter included 10 bacterial species and 43 fungal species belonging to various families: Phythiaceae, Ustilaginaceae, Telephoraceae, Erysiphaceae, Heliotiaceae, Sphaeriaceae, Valsaceae, Phomaceae, Melianonaceae, Moniliaceae, Dematiaceae, and Tuberculariaceae (Darpoux and Faivre-Amiot, 1950). Other studies have increased this list, and it is probable that most or the whole of the phytopathogenic agents are susceptible to antagonistic organisms.

In certain cases no distinct zone is established, but the growth of the pathogen is inhibited by the invasion of the hyphae of the antagonist. That may be accompanied by the winding of the antagonistic hyphae around those of the inhibited fungus and sometimes by active hyperparasitism.

Moreover, the action can be mutual. Thus, *Alternaria solani* inhibits the growth of *Streptomyces griseus,* but its growth is also inhibited and its mycelium deformed by the influence of *Streptomyces.*

The liquid nutrient medium on which an antagonistic organism has grown can also inhibit the growth of a pathogen. This can be demonstrated by the disk or link method (Fig. 2).

Waksman (1957) has discussed how antagonism arises. In the competition for space the vegetative vigor of one organism can impede the growth of another (many Mucoraceae).

Also, physicochemical changes of the medium such as oxidation-reduction potential, osmotic pressure, and pH can inhibit growth. Thus species of *Aspergillus* can acidify the medium or make it unsuitable for the growth of other organisms. Organisms often compete for a valid nutrient source. Sometimes antibiotic substances are produced.

In some cases of antagonism these mechanisms probably occur together or successively. On artificial media the chief causes are competition for nutrients and the production of antibiotic substances.

The inhibitory action of culture filtrates can be explained by physical changes in the medium during growth and the production of antibiotics. This last point has been the subject of much study ever since the discovery of penicillin. By isolation and purification of compounds in filtrates, antibiotic substances have been obtained which are used in fighting infections in man and animals. But the antibiotics are active against plant pathogens as well.

B. *Microbial Antagonisms in Soil*

Phytopathologists have neglected for a long time the role of the microbial population of the soil, considering only the parasite and the disease.

Sanford (1926) and Millard and Taylor (1927) began the study of the relations existing between soil microorganisms and the pathogen-host complex. Sanford proposed that the beneficent action of certain green-manuring crops in reducing the common scab of potato is indirect and results from the effects of bacteria antagonistic to *Streptomyces scabies.* Millard and Taylor (1927) then suggested that under certain conditions attacks by *S. scabies* was reduced by an antagonist, *S. praecox.*

Recent study of biological activity in the soil has resolved paradoxical observations and experimental results, and has suggested the possibility of fighting certain diseases by biological means.

1. Antagonists Isolated from the Soil

The microbial population of the soil is abundant. According to Pochon and deBarjac (1958) the number of actinomycetes varies between 100,000 and 36,000,000 per gram in most soil. Bacteria and fungi are also very abundant.

Alexopoulos (Alexopoulos and Herrick, 1942; Alexopoulos et al., 1938), studying the antagonistic properties of 80 strains of actinomycetes from the soil, used *Colletotrichum gleosporioides* as a test organism and found that 17% of actinomycetes were strongly inhibitory, 39% were slightly inhibitory, and 44% had no action.

In Louisiana, where sugar cane rot occurs, the frequency of actinomycetes antagonistic to the pathogens was studied. From 18% to 31% of the actinomycetes isolated were antagonistic to one of the casual organisms, *Pythium arrhenomanes, Pythium ultimum,* and *Rhizoctonia solani.* Some actinomycetes were antagonistic to all three fungi; others only to one (Cooper and Chilton, 1947, 1949, 1950). About 15% of isolated fungi, chiefly species of *Penicillium, Aspergillus,* and *Spicaria,* were antagonistic to *Pythium arrhenomanes* (Luke, 1952). Only 3% of the isolated bacteria were antagonistic to this fungus (Connell, 1952). In certain soils where the Panama disease caused by *Fusarium oxysporum* f. *cubense* prevails, Meredith (1944) classified the organisms occurring there in three groups: those which apparently increase the pathogen, those having no effect on its growth, and those which are antagonistic to it. Among the 1020 organisms isolated and tested *in vitro,* 66 showed a slight antagonistic action, 39 a middle antagonistic action, and 17 were strongly antagonistic to the pathogen. The distribution of antagonists varied widely according to the different samples of the soil. Among the many antagonistic bacteria was *B. subtilis,* and the most frequently occurring antagonistic fungi were species of *Penicillium, Aspergillus, Trichoderma,* and *Trichothecium.*

Organisms antagonistic to *Ophiobolus graminis* are also common. Thus, Broadfoot (1933) isolated from the soil 66 bacteria and fungi, 15 of which were antagonistic, and Sanford and Broadfoot (1931) noted 36 species antagonistic to *O. graminis.* Some microorganisms, such as *Rhizopus* sp., stimulated this pathogen.

Antagonists in the soil of *Streptomyces scabies* (Lochhead and Landerkin, 1949), *Pythium graminicola* (Meredith and Semeniuk, 1946), *Fusarium lini* (Anwar, 1949), and *Colletotrichum linicola* (Lachance, 1951) have also been reported.

Thus, many fungi, bacteria, and actinomycetes in the soil are antagonistic *in vitro* to pathogens. One wonders what these microorganisms do in the soil and whether they are useful in fighting certain plant diseases.

2. Action of Antagonists in the Soil on Plant Diseases

Experiments *in vitro* demonstrate that microbial antagonists can decrease the virulence of phytopathogenic agents and protect the plant from the infection. Sunflower seedlings in Erlenmeyer flasks have been protected from attacks of *Sclerotinia sclerotiorum* by introducing a strain of an antagonistic actinomycete (Darpoux and Faivre-Amiot, 1950).

Jaarsveld (1942) cultivated Chinese cabbage seedlings in test tubes on sterile media. They were then inoculated with *Rhizoctonia solani,* plus one or several antagonists. Clear antagonistic actions have been obtained with two strains of *Trichoderma lignorum,* followed by *Pyronoma confluens, Cylindrocarpon didymum, Penicillium expansum, Cladosporium herbarum,* and *Absidia spinosa.* The effect of several antagonists seems additive. However, *C. didymum* decreased the antagonism of the others. Disease levels were reduced when experiments were conducted in a previously sterilized soil, but in natural soils results have often been disappointing.

Let us examine some experiments on several types of pathogens and the diseases that they cause.

a. *Phytophthora and Pythium.* Hartley (1921) several years ago investigated damping-off in the seed bed, caused by *Pythium debaryanum.* The seeds were sown in pots in a previously sterilized soil and then inoculated with the pathogen and various organisms, including *Trichoderma koningi, Phoma* spp., *Chaetomium* sp., *Rhizopus nigricans, Trichothecium roseum, Aspergillus* spp., *Penicillium* spp., *Bacterium* sp., and unidentified fungi. In all cases the emergence of seedlings was increased over the check samples. However, these saprophytes were ineffective in nonsterilized soil.

In the case of the damping-off of tomato seedlings, caused by *Phytophthora parasitica* and *P. cryptogea,* disease levels were reduced in sterile soils when *Aspergillus clavatus* or *Penicillium clavatum* in organic suitable medium were introduced before the pathogen. Glucose improved their effect (Grossbard, 1948, 1952).

In greenhouse or hotbeds *Trichoderma koningi* decreased the attacks of *P. parasitica* on tomato (Katzer, 1939), and in previously sterilized soils *Pythium* on cucumber seedlings were reduced by a species of *Trichoderma* (Allen and Haenseler, 1935); of a *Pythium* on sugar cane seedlings, by actinomycetes isolated from the soil (Tims, 1932); of a

Pythium on alfalfa, by *Pullularia pullulans* or by *Penicillium expansum* (Van Luijk, 1938); and of *Pythium arrhenomanes* on wheat roots, by several actinomycetes and fungi belonging to the genera *Spicaria, Penicillium,* and *Aspergillus* (Johnson, 1952).

Many results have been negative, however. Certain organisms, having strongly antagonistic properties *in vitro,* were without action in the soil.

Physical and chemical properties of the soil play an important role. Thus, Wright (1956b) prevented the attacks of a *Pythium* on white mustard seedlings by adding *Trichoderma viride, Penicillium nigricans, P. frequentans,* and *P. godlewski* in a lime fertilized soil, while results were negative in acidified soil.

In natural, unsterilized soils, positive results are still more uncommon. Thus in a sterile soil to which 1% glucose had been added *Trichoderma lignorum* or *Streptomyces* sp. considerably reduced the damping-off of alfalfa by *Pythium debaryanum* and *P. ultimum.* But in natural soil the results were generally negative, except when a large, antagonistic inoculum was used.

b. *Rhizoctonia solani.* The reduction of attacks of *Rhizoctonia solani* by *Trichoderma viride* has often been noted. Although *Trichoderma* can parasitize hyphae of *Rhizoctonia,* it also is antagonistic. Some strains of *Trichoderma* produce gliotoxin or viridin.

In sterile soils the addition of *Trichoderma viride* decreases the attacks of Rhizoctonia on cucumber seedlings (Allen and Haensler, 1935), on peas (Cordon and Haenseler, 1939), and on lettuce plants (Wood, 1951). In natural soils, Cordon and Haenseler (1939) have obtained good results on peas and cucumbers. On lettuce plants Wood (1951) demonstrated inhibition of the pathogen at first, but the effect rapidly disappears. *Bacillus simplex, Bacillus subtilis,* and *Papulospora stoveri* showed themselves antagonistic to the *Rhizoctonia solani* in soil.

c. *Phymatotrichum omnivorum.* It has been possible to modify the flora in contact with roots by direct inoculation. *Aspergillus luchiensis, Penicillium luteum,* and *Trichoderma lignorum* are all antagonistic to *Phymatotrichum omnivorum* in the laboratory. They can be established and apparently increase in the rhizosphere of the cotton roots in experimental plots. All of these organisms were recovered in greater quantity than in check soils at a distance from the point of introduction (Morrow *et al.,* 1938). Inconclusive results have been obtained with other antagonistic organisms.

d. *Streptomyces scabies.* Fungi such as *Trichoderma* are antagonistic to *S. scabies in vitro.* The intensity of potato scab has been decreased by applying this fungus in the furrow around the growing tubers. But even in sterile soils other antagonistic microorganisms (*Penicillium*, bacteria, actinomycetes) had no effect (Daines, 1937).

e. *Ophiobolus graminis*. *O. graminis* decreased in virulence in a sterile soil that then was recolonized by a saprophytic flora. Here the disappearance of the pathogen was sometimes more rapid than in a natural soil, probably because of the growth of strongly antagonistic organisms.

f. *Fusarium culmorum and Helminthosporium sativum*. In greenhouse soils *Trichoderma lignorum* and *Pyronema confluens* reduced the pathogenicity of *F. culmorum* (Johnston and Greaney, 1942). When a soil is inoculated with *H. sativum* or *F. culmorum*, the virulence of these fungi is decreased by degrees, but much more quickly in a natural than in a sterilized soil, thus suggesting the role of the soil microflora. Further, *H. sativum* cannot colonize unsterilized corn stubbles, whereas it easily establishes itself on this substratum after sterilization.

g. *On Different Pathogenic Agents*. In experiments in sterile soils species of the genera *Rhizopus, Penicillium,* and *Fusarium* reduced attacks by *Cephalothecium roseum* (Greaney and Machacek, 1935). In sterilized greenhouse soil different fungi and bacteria have reduced pink root rot (*F. culmorum*) and the bacterial fading of carnation (*P. caryophylli*) (Thomas, 1948). *Fusarium udum*, which causes the fading of the gray pea (*Cajanus cajan*) was more virulent in sterile than in natural soil. Several antagonistic organisms were isolated from the natural soil (Vasudeva and Roy, 1950). A species of *Chaetomium*, added to a sterilized soil, then infested by *Fusarium lini*, reduced the intensity of the flax wilt (Tervet, 1938). In pots in a sterile soil inoculated with antagonistic bacteria the infection of corn seedlings by *F. graminearum* (*Gibberella saubinetii*) was prevented. Similarly the inoculation of unsterilized soil on which diseased flax had previously grown reduced the infection by *F. lini* of a second crop of flax seedlings from 26.6% for the tests to 9.5% (Novogrudski, 1937).

3. Factors That Modify the Biological Equilibrium and Act on the Disease

Many factors favor an antagonistic role for microorganisms. We have long known that certain cultural practices alter the attacks of various pathogens, sometimes favorably and sometimes not. Fallow land aids the development of soil saprophytes (Henry, 1931). But to know whether a cultural practice acts on the virulence of the pathogen or on the resistance of the host directly or whether the effect is indirect by changing the soil-biological equilibrium is not easy. Various studies bear on this point.

The number of actinomycetes in a soil and their relative abundance in relation to the microflora as a whole can be considerably influenced by the crop plants present, as Lockhead (1940) has shown. Indeed, the roots secrete soluble compound or tissue losses: losses from the root cap and from epidermal and cortical cells. Also, the plants secrete toxic substances into the soil that inhibit certain microorganisms. It is small wonder, then, that the microflora of the rhizosphere varies considerably with the species of plant—even with varieties—and also with their development period.

The action of green manuring on the disease development in relation to potato common scab, caused by *Streptomyces scabies*, and the role of certain microbial antagonists, especially to S. *praecox*, has already been discussed. Green manuring with soybean in pots of naturally infested soil has reduced disease, while rye and clover had no effect. Soybean residues considerably increased the population of all soil organisms, especially soil fungi, whereas rye acted only on the bacterial population (Atkinson and Rouatt, 1949).

If a soil is poor in organic matter, green manuring makes available quickly the elements favoring development of antagonists. Green manuring can also modify the pH, and some failures have occurred when the soil pH was unfavorable to antagonists.

The influence of green manuring and of amendments and fertilizers on development of the root rot of cereals, caused by *Ophiobolus graminis*, has been extensively studied. This organism grows in two phases: a parasite phase on the growing plants and a saprophytic phase on the roots and stubble. In unsterilized soils its disappearance varies with soil type and with temperature, moisture, and soil fertility.

During the parasitic phase it is possible to reduce the disease by increasing the amounts of assimilable P, nitrate N, organic amendments, oligo-elements, etc. All of these treatments increase the soil microflora, as shown by increased CO_2 production by soils after their addition. In the saprophytic phase the microflora is primarily responsible for the disappearance of the pathogen.

O. graminis is not continuously a saprophyte in the soil. It disappears rapidly as the crop residue is decomposed. It is ill-suited for competing with the soil microflora. It is a poor thing, a guest in an inhospitable society. Its disappearance depends on the soil type and medium conditions. Stubble and material rich in carbohydrates and poor in nitrogen (starch, raygrass flour) hasten its disappearance. A clover crop grown on stubble has the same effect. In this case the action is double. The growth of antagonists is increased, and competition between the crop and the pathogen for the assimilable nitrogen is assured (Garrett, 1936, 1937, 1938, 1944).

In the case of the cotton root rot, caused by *Phymatotrichum omnivorum*, many authors have shown that the addition of organic manures reduces the intensity of the disease in infested soils. The microbiological activity is much more intensive (high release of CO_2) in soils to which such manures have been applied for a long time. The incorporation of green manures in the soil (sorghum, chickpea) also has a good effect. Bacteria and actinomycetes increase considerably, the fungi only a little (Mitchell *et al.*, 1941). Farm yard manure and chopped sorghum also inhibit the growth of *P. omnivorum* (Mitchell *et al.*, 1941) in the soil.

Nitrate nitrogen and maize flour reduce the disease levels of *Rhizoctonia solani* and also its persistence in the soil, while sugars, lime, magnesium sulfate, and sulfur favor the disease (Sanford, 1947). Maize flour is especially effective when new antagonists are added to soil (Wood, 1951). Other amendments give good results in natural soils, but do not act in sterilized soils, thus demonstrating their influence on the soil microflora. Damping-off of alfalfa, caused by *Pythium ultimum* and *P. debaryanum*, is reduced by applying 1% of oat straw and antagonists to a natural infested soil (Gregory *et al.*, 1952).

Soil temperature influences both the soil microflora and pathogens. Thus damping-off of alfalfa, reduced by applications of oat straw at low temperatures, was hardly affected at high temperatures (Gregory *et al.*, 1952). The action of *Trichoderma* sp. and *Penicillium vermiculatum* against *Rhizoctonia solani* is much more noticeable at 28° C. than at 18° C. (Boosalis, 1956).

The pH of the soil affects not only the pathogen but also the action of antagonists. The common scab of potato, caused by *Streptomyces scabies*, and the root rot of wheat, caused by *Ophiobolus graminis*, are frequent in certain limed soils of recently reclaimed heath. A biological lack of balance, unfavorable to the antagonists, resulted from the liming. Furthermore, pH influences the action of *Trichoderma viride*.

The addition of a suspension of *Trichoderma* spores in a boggy soil was effective in reducing the attacks of *Rhizoctonia solani* on *Citrus*. The amount of disease reduction was correlated with pH, being excellent for the low pH of 4.5, moderate for a medium pH of 5.7 to 6.1, and inactive at pH 7.0 (Weindling and Fawcett, 1936). Soil acidification with aluminum sulfate or sulfuric acid has also been recommended by Wiant (1929) for the control of *Rhizoctonia solani* on forest tree seedlings.

Trichoderma viride is also a natural antagonist of *Fomes annosus* and prevents the establishment of this pathogen on stumps of trees in acid soils. *F. annosus* does not appear in a natural acid soil. However, in the same soil after sterilization *Fomes* becomes established unless it is stopped by introducing *Trichoderma* (Treschow, 1941). The importance of the disease in alkaline soils has been attributed to the lack of *Trichoderma* (Rishbeth, 1950).

Chemical treatments can also favor antagonistic microorganisms. Carbon disulfide is especially active in reducing the attacks of *Armillaria mellea* on *Citrus*. The pathogen, established on the roots or the trunk of a host plant, is protected by a stratum of pseudosclerotia that permit it to survive in the soil for several years and to resist the attack of soil organisms, especially *Trichoderma viride*. After fumigation *T. viride* is almost always found in the roots of *Citrus* in which the pathogen has been destroyed.

At first, it was thought that *T. viride* resists fumigation and is the first in colonizing the dead mycelium of the pathogen. However, the pathogen does not grow in mixed culture with the antagonist. Added to soils, *T. viride* destroys the pathogen by itself. Moreover, the carbon disulfide is inactive against the pathogen in soil unless the antagonist is present.

Thus, in natural soils *T. viride* is not dominant enough to destroy the *Armillaria*. But after partial sterilization of the soil, *Trichoderma* becomes dominant and colonizes the pathogen (Bliss, 1951).

On occasion 2,4-D may have similar effects. Thus, Warren *et al.* (1951) have reported the prevalence in the soil of an actinomycete after treatment of tomato plants with 2,4-D. This microorganism on agar medium is antagonistic to many fungi, such as *Rhizoctonia solani, Sclerotinia cinerea, Sclerotium rolfsii,* etc.

4. Mechanisms of Action of Antagonists

Different mechanisms of action for antagonism have been noted above. Some postulated mechanisms of antagonism involve the large increase in microflora, following the adoption of a cultural practice, such as the application of a green manure. Large amounts of CO_2, which may affect the pathogen, are produced in this process.

Blair (1942, 1943) has suggested such a mechanism for the disappearance of *Rhizoctonia solani*. Alternatively, an increase in the microfloral activity can lead to the loss of certain elements, particularly of nitrogen.

Sanford (1926) showed that certain bacteria, when cultured in solution, make the solution too acid for the germination of *S. scabies*. Thus the growth of these bacteria in the soil can lead to a modification of the pH, unfavorable to the pathogen.

But very many antagonistic organisms can produce antibiotic substances in culture on artificial media. This raises the problem of the production and role of antibiotics in the soil.

5. Production and Role of Antibiotics in the Soil

Most of the known antibiotics are produced by soil microorganisms. We may ask if the soil is a medium suitable for antibiotic production and whether such substances are sufficiently stable in the soil to have a biological role there.

The relations of soil microorganisms in respect to antibiotic production have been studied by Jefferys *et al.* (1953) in a sandy and acid podsol. They isolated 65 species, half of which produced antibiotics. The most widely distributed species included the most important percentage of producers. Some common and nonproducing species are comparatively resistant to the antibiotic substances coming from other species. These facts suggest that the production of antibiotics by soil microorganisms may have ecologic significance.

The first experimental work on the production of antibiotic substances in the soil was reported by Grossbard (1948). The author showed that in a sterilized soil enriched with glucose, wheat straw, or beet pulp, *Penicillium patulum* produces an antibacterial substance, patulin. Later studies showed that patulin is produced by other species of *Penicillium* and by 2 species of *Aspergillus* as well when they grow in sterilized soil, enriched with carbohydrates or other assimilable organic substances.

The production of patulin is strongly decreased when other microorganisms are present. Under these conditions the soil must be heavily inoculated with *P. patulum* if antibiotic activity is to appear during the following days. There the production is improved by such organic materials as flour, glucose, and corn steep liquor.

Chloromycetin is produced by *Streptomyces venezuelae* and actidione by *S. griseus* is sterilized soil amended with various organic elements (Gottlieb and Siminoff, 1952).

Wright (1954, 1955, 1956a, c; Wright and Grove, 1957) has especially studied antibiotic production by common fungi in the soil. She obtained gliotoxin from a strain of *Trichoderma viride* in two types of sterilized soils (podsol at pH 3.9 and garden soil at pH 6.3), receiving an organic amendment. When no organic matter was added, gliotoxin production was appreciable only in the podsol. Acidification of garden soil favored antibiotic production. In unsterile soils no antibiotic was produced in the garden soil amended with corn flour, but in a podsol enriched with corn flour production was appreciably increased.

For the production of griseofulvin by *P. nigricans* the main factors were sterilization and addition of organic nutrients. But here fungus growth and antibiotic production were better in the garden soil than the podsol. Griseofulvin production was decreased by inoculation of the soil with various microorganisms.

The production of antibiotics in the soil can be influenced by many factors, especially the soil type, its pH, the sterilization, and the addition of organic elements. The beneficial effect of sterilization may eliminate competing organisms and may also increase the availability of nitrogenous organic compounds.

One wonders if the production of antibiotic substances is homogeneous in a soil or if its importance is only locally important near the roots. To answer this question, Wright (1956a) studied the production of gliotoxin by *T. viride* in and around straws sunk into the soil. The production was more important in the straw than in the soil around it. The pH of the soil, and especially the pH of the nutrient substratum, had a large effect. The sterilizing of the soil or the straw also played a role.

These studies demonstrate that antibiotics can be produced in the soil at least under some conditions. Presumably antibiotic production can be increased when the influencing factors are better known.

The composition of the nutrient medium has a profound effect on the yield of antibiotic. Thus boron stimulates the production of penicillin; manganese, that of streptomycin; iron and zinc, that of patulin.

Some carbohydrates produce a larger yield than others. *Penicillium notatum* prefers lactose in order to produce penicillin. *Streptomyces griseus* prefers starch and glucose for streptomycin and mannose for actidione.

Meat extracts, soybean hydrolyzates, and corn steep liquor provide the amino acids necessary for antibiotic production by the organism. Some compounds serve as precursors, containing groupings found in the molecule of the antibiotic and thus stimulate its production. Examples are phenylacetic acid, β-crotonic acid, glycocoll, and folic acid for penicillin; inositol for streptomycin; tyrosine, phenylalanine, and tryptophan for chloromycetin.

Antibiotics vary in stability in the soil. Gottlieb and Siminoff (1951) noted that streptomycin is so strongly adsorbed by clay in the soil that it loses its activity. Pramer and Starkey (1951) reported that it disappears more rapidly in unsterile than in sterile soil. Thus in addition to adsorption, degradation by soil microorganisms takes place. This was confirmed by Jefferys (1952), who showed the influence of the soil type and its pH. In some cases, when the adsorptive capacity of the soil is saturated, activity can persist when high concentrations are employed, but one has difficulty in seeing how streptomycin can increase in a natural soil and play an appreciable biological role.

Chloromycetin is produced in the soil by S. *venezuelae*. Gottlieb and Siminoff (1952) showed that this neutral antibiotic is not adsorbed by clay, and activity persists in sterile soil. However, it is less toxic than in a nutrient medium, the soil having a protecting effect on the sensitive germs. In pure culture various bacteria detoxify chloromycetin by hydrolyzing the molecule or reducing the nitro group. Presumably, microorganisms can have the same effect in soils. In fact, chloromycetin disappears in unsterile soils.

Clavacin is another antibiotic that is not readily adsorbed by the clays of the soil. It is stable for a long time in a sterile soil, but the microflora in a normal soil degrade it. The microbial population increases in a soil containing clavacin. Gottlieb *et al.* (1952) reported the development of fungus strains resistant to this antibiotic. Differences depending on the soil type have been observed (Jefferys, 1952).

Penicillin is detoxified by many microorganisms that secrete penicillinase. In some neutral soils, however, it can maintain its activity sufficiently long to be biologically effective (Brian, 1949; Jefferys, 1952).

Jefferys (1952) studied the stability of ten antibiotics in podsolic soils and in neutral garden soil. Eight of them were produced by fungi isolated from podsols. Some were more stable than others, the stability varying from one soil to another. Four types of inhibition were determined: (1) The natural pH of certain soils is responsible for the instability of albidine, frequentin, gliotoxin, penicillin, and viridin. (2) The soil microorganisms detoxify griseofulvin, mycophenolic acid, and patulin. (3) The soil especially absorbs streptomycin. (4) Inhibition of toxicity occurs in a poorly understood manner, probably of chemical nature. Examples are gladiolic acid, penicillin, and streptomycin. These antibiotics were more stable in acid podsolic soils than in the neutral garden soils. In some soils the stability was sufficient to permit a biological effect when they are produced.

Gottlieb and Siminoff (1952) divide the antibiotics into three groups: the basic antibiotics which are widely inactivated, e.g., streptomycin and streptothrycin; the neutral antibiotics which are slightly inhibited but which maintain a relatively high activity in the soil, e.g., chloromycetin and actidione; and the acid antibiotics, the activity of which is intermediate between the basic and neutral substances, e.g., clavacin.

6. Antibiotic Action

In the soil the stable antibiotics that are produced can act directly on pathogenic microorganisms to inhibit their growth. Action of antibiotics *in vitro* includes preventing growth and the deformation—and sometimes the lysis—of vegetative organs. Some antibiotics can also be absorbed by the plant root and translocated to different plant organs without losing their activity. Such substances are called "systemic." A classic example is streptomycin. Plants differ in this respect, however. For example, penicillin is absorbed by bean seedlings, but not by cucumber or maize.

On the other hand, high activity can be found in aerial plant organs only if the antibiotic concentration in contact with the roots is high. Because streptomycin is rapidly inactivated in the soil, it cannot have a systemic role in nature. Chloromycetin, on the contrary, is more stable in the soil, and can be absorbed by the plant if present in sufficient quantity. However, chloromycetin is probably not produced in sufficient quantities in the soil to play a significant biological role in the plant.

The substances produced in the soil by microorganisms do not always play a favorable role. According to Agnihothrudu (1954), *Fusarium oxysporum* f. *vasinfectum* secretes fusaric acid into the soil, and this can be absorbed by roots and damage the plant as it moves through the tissues. The "tiredness" of soils seems to be due in part to the secretion of toxins by fungi such as *Mucor, Alternaria,* or *Cladosporium herbarum,* which live on fragments of diseased plants. Thus, the toxins aid the action of the pathogen.

7. Discussion: the Biological Struggle among Soil Organisms

Two aspects of the biological struggle among soil microorganisms can be considered: (1) the specific contribution of antagonistic microorganisms in the soil; and (2) the ways in which the antagonistic functions can be favored.

The first of these can be illustrated simply after sterilization of the soil by heat. Such a soil can be recolonized quickly by antagonistic saprophytes which impede establishment of pathogens. For successful antagonism, favorable conditions must be provided.

Antagonistic organisms often fail to become established in natural soils. In competition with the natural flora, the new organism is often eliminated. However, certain cultural methods or chemical treatments sometimes are successful, e.g., fumigations with carbon disulfide, which favors growth of *Trichoderma.*

Gregory *et al.* (1952) have shown that the use of antagonists in order to fight the damping-off of leguminous plants may be possible. However, these antagonistic organisms must be inactive against nodule bacteria (*Rhizobium*), which makes the problem complex but not insoluble. Thus an actinomycete was found which was very active on *Pythium* without affecting the establishment of *Rhizobium* on alfalfa seedlings.

We have seen that antibiotics can be produced in the soil. However, when an organism that produces antibiotics is introduced in a soil, it runs the risk of being quickly inhibited. Even if antibiotic production occurs for a short time only, this can suffice to control a disease such as damping-off, to which only the seedling plant is susceptible. In this case the antagonist permits the plant to grow through the decisive period of susceptibility, after which it is resistant. Possibly the period of susceptibility can be shortened by increasing the rate of growth of the plant by high temperatures, for example.

Favoring the growth of naturally established antagonists in the soil is more likely to be successful than introducing new ones. The judicious utilization of certain green manures, amendments, and various fertilizing elements will often give positive results. More studies must be made (1) on the growth conditions of antagonists and the production conditions for antibiotic substances, (2) on the stability of these antibiotics and their action mechanism, (3) on the virulence of the pathogen, and (4) on the host susceptibility. These studies, along with some good luck, should bring more precision and success in the biological control of soil-borne pathogens.

C. Antagonism and Competition at the Time of Sowing the Seeds

The normal saprophytic flora of the surface of seeds limits the attack of certain pathogens. Simmonds (1947) reported that the percentage of corn seedlings attacked by *Helminthosporium sativum* was decreased by incubating the seeds for 24 hours in a humid room before inoculation. Probably the moisture favored the growth of antagonistic saprophytes on the integuments of the seed.

Ledingham *et al.* (1949) and Sallans *et al.* (1949) demonstrated that when chemical treatment removed the surface flora from seeds, there was an increase in attack by *H. sativum*. Formaldehyde or lactic acid acted in this way. Thus the seedlings of treated seed which was then inoculated were more frequently diseased than were untreated seed, especially in sterile soil.

This raises a problem about seed disinfection. When the superficial saprophytes are eliminated, pathogens in the integument can grow without hindrance.

In pure culture many organisms which are antagonistic to pathogens have been isolated from the surface of the seed integuments. Attempts have been made to utilize these or other organisms in fighting pathogens that attack seeds.

Novogrudski (1937) recommended bacterial inoculation of seeds to combat *Fusarium lini* and *Colletotrichum linicola* on flax. With various bacteria he was able to decrease the percentage of diseased plants. Beresova and Nauomova (1939) obtained similar results. The attack of *Fusarium graminearum* was reduced by treating corn seed with cultures of *Pseudomonas* or *Achromobacter*. Similarly, Krasilnikov and Raznitzyna (1946), by using similar microorganisms, controlled *Fusarium* on seeds of *Pinus sylvestris*.

By using such species of *Chaetomium* as *C. cochlioides*, Tveit and Wood (1955) obtained as good control of the blight of barley seedlings, caused by *Fusarium nivale*, as when organo-mercurials were used. Apparently the antagonist was able to establish itself and to persist for some time in the soil.

The inoculation of seeds with antagonists may eliminate not only the seed-borne pathogens but soil microorganisms that parasitize the seedlings. Soil saprophytes sometimes decrease the virulence of seed-borne pathogens, as shown by the differences obtained after sowing in natural soil and in sterilized soil. The antagonism phenomena on seeds are doubtless the same as those described in the case of the soil.

Production of antibiotic substances in the integument of seeds was studied by Wright (1956c), who noted that pea seedlings arising from seeds inoculated with spores of *Trichoderma viride* had chlorotic cotyledons, similar to those observed on seedlings growing in gliotoxin solutions. Thus *T. viride* probably produces gliotoxin on the seed in concentrations sufficient to damage the seedlings. This hypothesis was verified: the concentration of gliotoxin in the integuments of pea seeds inoculated with spores of *T. viride* was appreciable 3 days after germination and reached a maximum about the fifth day. The quantity of gliotoxin was much higher in the integument than in the soil around the seed. Moreover, Wright demonstrated that *Penicillium frequentans* could produce frequentin and *Streptomyces venezuelae*, an unidentified antibacterial substance that seems to differ from chloromycetin.

D. *Antagonism on Fruit During the Storage*

Cases of antagonism have been noted on organisms attacking fruit in storage. Thus two strains of *Bacillus subtilis* are antagonistic *in vitro* to several pathogens of citrus fruit and to *Penicillium digitatum* especially (Gutter and Littauer, 1953).

E. *Antagonisms on a Level with Aerial Organs*

The mixing of an antagonist with the inoculum of a pathogen can reduce the infection. Thus Bamberg (1931) isolated bacteria which *in vitro* were antagonistic to *Ustilago zeae*. The culture filtrate of these bacteria had no effect on the pathogen. But when the bacteria were mixed with smut inoculum, they reduced the infection rate of corn, and inhibited the germination of chlamydospores. They also seemed to cause disintegration of the galls.

In nature the antagonistic saprophytes seem to play a biological role in relation to wound pathogens or pathogens that establish themselves by first colonizing the dead tissues. By invading these tissues before the pathogen does so, antagonists can prevent infection or at least limit it. Thus *Stereum purpureum* establishes itself easily on freshly cut tissues, but does so with difficulty on 3-month-old lesions that are already colonized by saprophytic microorganisms (Brooks and Moore, 1926).

The studies of Wood (1951) demonstrate the importance of microflora on leaf tissue. After attacks of *Botrytis* on lettuce in the field more young plants survived in the hollows than where the ground was flat. In the hollows, Wood reasoned, the dried leaves at the base of the plant were sometimes covered by water which had run from the surrounding soil. This permitted the growth of saprophytes antagonistic to the *Botrytis* on the dead tissues. Wood (1951) analyzed this phenomenon experimentally, and concluded that: many microorganisms are antagonistic to *Botrytis cinerea* at 25° C. but are less so at lower temperatures and that certain of them prevent the rotting of loose lettuce leaves when the antagonist is inoculated prior to or simultaneously with *B. cinerea*.

In a similar way Newhook (1951, 1957) isolated organisms antagonistic to *B. cinerea* from lettuce and tomato. Cultures of *Bacillus*, *Pseudomonas*, and *Chromobacterium* from lettuce leaves were more strongly antagonistic to *B. cinerea* at one temperature than at another. On nutrient agar these bacteria raised the pH so high that the growth of *B. cinerea* and its pectolytic activity were inhibited. However, the antagonism was largely due to antibiotic production. In association with many bacteria *B. cinerea* increased or decreased its sporulation, or its hyphae were distorted. In the field, organisms isolated from the soil prevented the establishment of *B. cinerea* on dead tissues of different plants. The antagonism of saprophytes must play an important part in the growth of *B. cinerea*. As dampness occurs, it favors the establishment and growth of the pathogen and the development of antagonistic microorganisms simultaneously.

Can antagonistic saprophytes be used to combat pathogens of aerial organs of plants? The growth of saprophytes is possible either when dead tissue is present for colonization or when a suitable nutrient medium is provided for them on the plant. The protection of the living tissues from pathogens by applying nutrients is a theoretical possibility that has not been crowned with success.

However, attempts to establish an antagonistic saprophyte on dead tissues of the host has given some results. *B. cinerea* attacks the fruit only after becoming established on dead petals. In greenhouse experiments Newhook (1957) applied spores of antagonistic saprophytes of *Botrytis cinerea*, especially *Cladosporium herbarum* and one *Penicillium*, to tomato petals directly after the fruit was set. This was completely successful when recently dried petals were treated and only 30% successful when applied to petals that had dried for several days. Thus it is possible to guide the colonization of drying organs. On the other hand, natural colonization occurs on organs that have been dead for some time. If these saprophytes are active antagonists of the pathogen, no inoculation need be done because there is a natural protection. If they are not, it seems very difficult to substitute them with others.

Sometimes other treatments have an indirect effect on the colonization by saprophytes of host organs. Newhook (1957) reports that if growth substances are applied to avoid the fall of tomato fruit, natural colonization by *Cladosporium herbarum* or *Penicillium* is favored. Then, the infection of *Botrytis* is reduced from about 50% on untreated plants to about 2% on treated plants.

How do these antagonistic saprophytes prevent the attack by *Botrytis cinerea* of lettuce and tomato? Newhook (1957) reported that nearly all the saprophytic fungi isolated from the dry petals of tomato are antagonistic to *Botrytis cinerea*. Apparently these fungi have a common method of inhibition that is less specific than antibiotic production. The inhibition of growth of *B. cinerea* is not a nutrient competition because its spores do not even begin to germinate when they come in contact with petals invaded by saprophytes. In culture the antagonists also prevent spore germination of *Botrytis*. The possibility of an unfavorable pH in the tissues, created by the antagonist, must also be eliminated.

Among the naturally occurring saprophytes of dry petals of tomato *Cladosporium herbarum* is a most effective antagonist. Some of these saprophytes are very active against *B. cinerea* on sterile tomato petals. Although *Cladosporium herbarum* is not among the most active, it plays an important role in greenhouse culture as an antagonist to *Botrytis* on tomato. *Cladosporium* is able to grow under drier conditions on dying petals than the other microorganisms are. Therefore it more easily colonizes the dead tissues, and thus more completely protects them against *Botrytis* infection.

What are the effects of fungicide treatments on these antagonists? The fungicide, in destroying antagonistic saprophytes, may weaken the natural protection of the dead tissues. But resistant saprophytes, such as *Penicillium*, presumably still protect the dried petals even after treatment. On the other hand, the antagonistic saprophytes that are fungicide sensitive can also protect the dead tissues that were poorly covered with fungicide.

VI. INTERACTIONS IN THE FUNGAL AND BACTERIAL DISEASES

When several pathogens are simultaneously or successively establishing on a plant, several cases can exist:

(a) A competition occurs on the living tissues of the host. An example is given by *Tilletia foetida* and *T. caries*, both of which infect wheat. While plants in the field are attacked by either pathogen singly, the simultaneous presence of the two *Tilletia* on a same plant is rarely reported. One eliminates the other. The fact has been experimentally demonstrated by Bamberg *et al.* (1947). Seeds were artificially inoculated with *T. foetida* and sown in a soil infested with *T. caries*. The presence of *Tilletia foetida* on the seeds and then on the seedlings very clearly reduced the infection by *T. caries*. Another example is *Penicillium digitatum* versus *Penicillium italicum* on citrus fruits. When citrus fruits are treated with borate of soda, the first fungus is destroyed and the second then grows freely. In this case, *P. digitatum* prevails because of the density of its mycelium.

(b) The damage to the plant, caused by one pathogen, can impede the growth of another. When *Botrytis fabae* attacks the leaflets of field beans and causes them to dry out, attack by *Uromyces fabae* is impeded.

(c) The actions of pathogens complement each other in certain simultaneous infections. One pathogen may aid another in entering the host. In other cases one pathogen may provide growth substances needed by another. In still others one may take part in the destruction of living tissues, thus aiding the attack by another. When a wheat plant is attacked by *Ophiobolus graminis*, bacteria can provide thiamine or biotin, substances which increase the virulence of the pathogen.

Sometimes there is a synergism between bacteria and fungi. For instance, Sabet (1954) has demonstrated synergism between *Bacillus polymyxa* and *Rhizopus nigricans* on potato slices. *Erwinia carotovora* and *B. polymyxa* are synergistic at 35° C. and nearly indifferent at lower temperatures.

O. graminis is more damaging when wheat seedlings have been submitted for several weeks to various organisms, especially *Cladosporium herbarum*. Probably the toxins of *Cladosporium* increase the susceptibility of the plant. This effect is more marked in light soils having a slight absorbent power, because in these soils the toxins move more readily and reach the roots much more easily (Brömmelhues, 1935).

Another pair of pathogens that act synergistically are *Diplodia natalentis* and *Colletotrichum gloeosporioides* on the citrus fruits (Fawcett, 1931).

(d) Fungi attacking one host in serial order may become dominant over the initial invader. The fungi establish themselves only on dead tissue, often follow and sometimes supplant the primary pathogen. The physiologic condition of the host plant or host organ influence this. Thus, the potato tuber which becomes depleted of its reserves in the spring is less and less suitable for the growth of *Phytophthora infestans* and more so for the invasion by pathogens of old tissues.

Successive infections on fruits have been the most thoroughly studied. Scab attack on apples and pears, caused by *Venturia inaequalis* and *Venturia pirina*, favors the establishment of other pathogens: at first, *Monilia fructigena*, the cause of brown rot, and later, during storage, *Trichothecium roseum* and also *Gloeosporium fructigenum* on apples. The invasion by these fungi into the pulp is made easier by the existence of corky callus tissue in the scab spots. Where these join with the skin of the fruit, imperfections occur that offer an easy entry. *Gloeosporium fructigenum* often attacks apples having rust lesions, caused by *Gymnosporangium clavariaeformae* (Jørstad, 1938). *Nectria galligena* invades on the branches of apple trees following their injury by *Venturia inaequalis*, the scab pathogen. *Armillaria mellea* very often attacks walnut tree roots following *Phytophthora cinnamomi*.

Complex diseases result from antagonism of pathogens or their competition or their synergism on the plant.

Moreau (1957) shows the different stages of the decline of carnations as follows: (1) weakening of the plant by *Uromyces, Heterosporium*, attack by nematodes or poor nutrient conditions; (2) attack by primary pathogens of declining tissue such as *Verticillium cinerescens* or *Fusarium oxysporum* f. *bulbigenum;* (3) invasion by secondary pathogens such as *Fusarium dianthi, Fusarium roseum, Alternaria dianthi,* and *Rhizoctonia solani;* (4) invasion by cellulolytic fungi such as *Rhizoctonia bataticola, Melanospora* sp., *Chaetomium* sp. and of pectolytic fungi such as *Cladosporium herbarum;* and (5) the interaction of the plant microflora with the soil microflora.

Chevaugeon (1954) has also studied complex diseases of manioc. The chief causes are *Glomerella cingulata, Cercospora henningsii,* and *Cercospora caribae*, which favor the establishment of wound and weakness pathogens, which in turn are followed by saprophytes.

VII. Complexes Associated with Nematodes

Independently of their specific pathogenic action, the phytoparasitic nematodes frequently are involved in the epidemiology of diseases caused by other organisms. The nematodes have many enemies, which influence their numbers in the soil. The apparent effect of edaphic factors on nematode populations is in reality often a result of their effect on the development of natural enemies of nematodes. These effects have been known for a long time. Much of the older work on this subject dealt with the classic species of tylenchids. Biological complexes have much to do with the economic importance of the tylenchids and dorylaimids that are migratory and ectoparasitic.

A. *Hyperparasitism in the Nematodes*

The parasites of the free nematodes are better known than those of the phytoparasitic species. However, hyperparasitism is more diverse among the plant parasitic nematodes.

1. *Bacteria*

Although they have been noted many times in nematodes, the bacteria are but infrequently pathogenic. However, Schuurmans *et al.* (1938) reported an undetermined bacterium to be frequent in *Anguina filiformis*, which frequently showed a partial castration in consequence. In other cases the bacteria can gradually destroy the nematodes. More often they act as symbionts and play a useful role in the digestion.

2. *Microsporidies*

In 1940 Thorne described a microsporidian, *Dubosquia penetrans*, on a member of the Nosematidae family. In the southern United States this organism parasitized 66 and 23% of two types of their host nematode, *Pratylenchus pratensis*. This parasite was found later on in other anguiluls.

3. *Fungi*

Many cases are known of parasitism of phytopathogenic nematodes by fungi belonging to very different groups. In 1934 Rozsypal and Schmidt reported a *Protomycopsis chytridiale* attacking *Heterodera schachtii*. The large and round chlamydospores completely filled the encysted females and the larval content had been destroyed.

In 1877 and 1881 J. Kuhn described a phycomycete, *Tarichum auxiliare*, parasitic on nematodes. A thin mycelium enters the cyst by the anal opening and destroys the embryos; from this mycelium persistent spores are formed, which fill the interior of integuments. This genus is related to *Entomophthora*, several species of which attack nematodes. H. Goffart (1933) recognized that the eggs and embryos of *Heterodera avenae* could be parasitized by an ascomycete, *Cylindro-*

carpon radicicola Wollenweber, known to attack underground parts of various cultivated plants.

Some ascomycetes are able to kill nematodes without a direct contact, perhaps by antibiotic action (Metcalf, 1903). Metcalf noted the impossibility of growing *Rhabditis bievispina* in the presence of an *Aspergillus*.

B. *Predators of Phytophagous Nematodes*

Apart from parasitism, nematodes can be attacked by more or less specialized predators.

1. *Protozoa*

In 1952 Weber and associates noted the existence of an "amoebial" organism acting as a predator of the larvae of *Heterodera rostochiensis* in Holland. Called *Theratomyxa weberi* Zwillenberg, it belongs to the family Vampyrellidae in the order of Proteomyxa. This very elastic rhizopod can attack many small-sized species of nematodes, free or parasitic. Many nematodes can be caught by this organism. Thus, 128 larva of *H. rostochiensis* were once observed in one cyst of digestion. Development of this amoeba occurs under such restricted conditions that it cannot be used to control nematodes. It will not tolerate drying.

This species or another very similar was also found in England attacking the golden nematode and in Canada attacking the beet anguillul *H. schachtii* (Winslow and Williams, 1957).

2. *Hyphomycetes*

The Hyphomycetes as nematode predators are numerous and frequently met in nature. They have been much studied because of the unique character of their method of capturing the nematodes.

Forty species of these fungi have been found; some have been known for a long time, but most of them were described and studied by Drechsler (1937). These belong to the genera *Dactylaria, Acrostalagmus, Dactylella,* and *Arthrobotrys* (10 species in each of the last two). Some have buckles or adhesive nets that emit mycelium filaments to perforate the cuticle of the immobilized nematode; others have adhesive buds, peduncles, conidia, or adhesive hyphae. The most curious traps are formed by constrictor rings, the cells of which suddenly become turgid, thus contracting, when a nematode penetrates into them, e.g., *Dactylella bembicodes*.

Different attempts at practical utilization of these natural enemies have been made, first against the Meloidogynes which attack pineapple in Hawaii (Linford and Yap, 1939), then in France by Roubaud and Deschiens (1939) especially against nematodes parasitic on animals, and recently in England by Duddington in relation to the golden nematode of the potato. Some results have been encouraging, but we are far from using these fungi to control nematodes in agriculture.

3. Other Nematodes

Many nematodes, especially those of the Monochidae, are carnivorous and eat other nematodes. They have an enormous chitineous buccal cavity provided with teeth.

In 1927 Thorne showed that huge populations of these nematodes occur, especially of *Mononchus papillatus*. The numbers vary widely from one year to another because this species is often parasitized by sporozoans, which destroy them, thus limiting their role as biological control agents.

Other nematodes are also nematophagous. Thus, dorylaimids are frequently found inside *Heterodera* cysts; the eggs are empty.

4. Other Nematophages

Although we often lack precise experiments, it seems that many enchytreides, various Acari, and other soil arthropods attack nematodes that they meet.

C. Action of Root Secretions on Nematodes

The action of the flora on the development of the eelworm population can be important because this population is frequently limited by the amount of food in the environment. Obviously the growth of specialized nematodes that can live only on some hosts depends on the frequency with which the host occurs, either as a crop or in the self-sown flora. But to many nematodes, especially Heterodera, the action of plants is more complex. Here the plant host serves not merely as a host, but also induces the larvae to hatch from cysts in the soil, and attracts the larvae.

Sometimes plants exert this action on nematodes which cannot grow in their tissues. Thus in Holland, Hijner (1951) tried to use the wild beet *Beta patellaris* in a practical way because it induces hatching of cysts of *H. schachtii* without permitting the larvae to grow on its roots. The larvae then die for want of a host.

The chemical nature of these hatching factors is generally difficult to determine and not yet known. However, the work of Calam *et al.* (1949) and of Marrian *et al.* (1949) in Great Britain has resulted in the isolation of eclepic acid which is secreted by the potato and stimulates the hatching of the golden nematode *H. rostochiensis*. These authors showed that anhydrotetronic acid has the same property.

In contrast, some plants inhibit the hatching of larvae from eggs even when they are later exposed to hatching factors. The researches of Triffet (1934), Goffart (1934), and Franklin (1937) have described the action of root secretions of many plants on *H. rostochiensis*. Thus, most leguminous plants, white mustard (*Sinapis alba*), maize, various fodder grasses, and other grasses strongly reduce the viability of cysts. Franklin (1937) reports a reduction of 73% by exposure of cysts to *Poa trivialis* and *Poa pratensis*.

Other plants have a direct toxic action on many nematodes such as *Tagetes*, which practically eliminates certain soil species. Their nemato-cidal effect has recently been demonstrated (Slootweg and Oostenbrik, 1956; Uhlenbroek and Bijloo, 1957). The toxic substance is terthienyl, which is active on certain tylenchids—especially larvae of *Heterodera*—at doses as low as 0.1 p.p.m. The dosage required is low for other nema-todes as well, e.g., *Ditylenchus dipsaci*, *Anguina tritici*, and *Pratylenchus* sp. However, the substance has low activity for the neighboring genera *Meloidogyne* and *Hoplolaimus*.

D. *Interation between Nematodes and Other Pathogenic Agents in Complex Diseases*

1. *Cryptogamic Diseases*

As early as 1892 Atkinson noted the simultaneous presence in cotton of the root knot nematode and fusarial wilt. The combined action caused much more severe damage than was caused by either pathogen alone. The use of wilt-resistant varieties has permitted evaluation of the damage done by different nematodes belonging to the genera *Meloidogyne* (causing root knot), *Pratylenchus* (the meadow nematode), and *Bele-nolamus* (sting nematode). Holdeman and Graham (1953) have demon-strated experimentally the role of the latter in increasing the aggressive-ness of wilt for resistant varieties.

The different nematodes affect their host in characteristic ways. Some destroy the root endings, thus providing an entry for fungi. Others inject toxic salivary secretions that cause histologic anomalies in the host that in turn play a similar role in relation to fungi.

More complex interactions can be involved. A nematode may weaken the host generally or cause a specific nutrient imbalance, so that the host becomes more susceptible to fungal attack. An example in cotton is the high potassium required for growth of *Meloidogyne*, which leads to potassium deficiency of the host and greater susceptibility to cotton wilt.

Nematodes and soil fungi are frequently associated in disease. Ex-amples are the association between *Meloidogyne* sp. and black shank of tobacco, caused by *Phytophthora parasitica* var. *nicotiana* (Tisdale, 1931), and that between root knot and tomato wilt (Young, 1939).

Nematodes may act as vectors for fungi, as shown by Barat (1952) for the decline of pepper plants in Indochina. Thus larvae of *Meloidogyne* were reared aseptically on plants attacked by *Fusarium* or *Pythium*. When these nematodes were allowed to attack healthy plants, these fungi rapidly invaded the roots. When similarly reared larvae were treated with bichloride of mercury before being transferred to healthy plants, however, the nematodes grew normally and the roots were not invaded by fungi.

2. Bacterial Diseases

Bacteria and nematodes are sometimes associated in complex diseases. Thus, Crosse and Pitcher (1952) showed that the leafy gall of strawberry is due to the simultaneous presence in the foliage of the bacterium *Corynebacterium fascians* and an *Aphelenchoides*. Alone, neither one produces conspicuous symptoms, but together they produce a disease that leads to monstrous plants. Similar effects have been reported for a disease of wheat, caused by *Corynebacterium tritici*, in association with the nematode *Anguina tritici* (Vasudeva and Hingonia, 1952). The work of Stewart and Schindler (1956) showed that 4 species of *Meloidogyne* as well as *Helicotylenchus nannus* all accelerate the rate of wilting of carnations attacked by the bacterium *Pseudomonas caryophylli*. Except for *M. incognita*, these nematodes alone produced no such effect. When other nematodes attack bacterially wilted carnations, they do not accelerate wilting.

Lucas and Krusberg (1956) observed the same phenomenon on the bacterial wilt of tobacco, caused by *Xanthomonas solanacearum*, and explained it by the nature of the attack of the nematode. *Tylenchorhynchus claytoni*, which has no action on wilt, remains very superficially in the cortex, whereas *Meloidogyne*, which increases the damage from wilt, changes the vascular bundles.

3. Conclusion

The nematodes together with soil-borne microbial pathogens play an important role in complex diseases. Also they frequently accentuate damage caused by other pathogens. Because the nematodes sometimes increase the damage and sometimes reduce it, we must be cautious in interpreting the observed facts. For example, some years ago Lambert and associates (1949) showed that the *"Cephalothecium disease"* of cultivated mushrooms was really due to a *Ditylenchus* that is always associated with a fungus, *Arthrobotrys superba*. Formerly the constant association of the *Arthrobotrys* with this condition misled investigators to think of it as the cause. The fungus does not cause the disease. In fact it reduces the disease by being a predator of the nematode.

The multitude of soil microorganisms leads to many biological equilibria. Linford and Oliveira (1938) counted no less than 52 predators and parasites of the *Meloidogyne* that attack pineapples in Hawaii. There were 18 fungi, 1 protozoan, 24 nematodes, 6 acaridae, and 3 tardigrads. Many of them also attack one another. These interactions, the role of which can be important, have often been neglected in our thinking and have been destroyed before the onslaught of the classic nematocidal treatments.

VIII. INTERFERENCES IN THE VIRUS DISEASE

Interactions between plant viruses and other organisms are little known. For example, potatoes infested by the leaf roll virus are more actively colonized by Doryphors and are quickly eaten. Probably the starch accumulation resulting from virus infection offers a choice food for the Doryphor, which increases its voracity and its proliferation capacity tenfold.

More thorough observations have been made on the relations between cryptogamic and viral diseases. The presence of the viruses X and Y in the potato increases its resistance to late blight, caused by *Phytophthora infestans* (Muller and Munroe, 1956). The leaf roll virus has the same effect on the potato plant, yet this virus is considered to increase the severity of late blight. This effect probably results from the rolling of leaves which retain rain water, thus creating a microclimate favorable to the pathogen (Richardson and Rolling, 1957).

The case where a microorganism creates an environment favoring a virus disease is also known. For example, beans infected by the rust *Uromyces phaseoli* have a content of viruses 50 times superior to the plants free from rust (Yarwood, 1951).

A. *Interaction between Viruses in the Host*

Two different viruses may infect the same plant, thus producing a complex disease. For example, the tomato filiform disease is caused by virus 1 of cucumber and tobacco mosaic virus. The double streak of tomato and tobacco is caused by virus X of potato and tobacco mosaic virus. In both these cases the complex aggravates the symptoms caused by each virus separately. Together they lead to a necrotic disease, the severity of which depends on the virulence of the virus X strain involved. Therefore, virus X is the determinant, and its concentration probably is modified by the presence of tobacco mosaic virus. A similar effect of one virus on the multiplication rate of another in the same host occurs with virus X and Y of potato when they attack potato, tobacco, or *Nicotiana glutinosa*. The titer of virus X is increased up to 10 times the normal concentration if virus Y is inoculated at the same time or afterwards. If virus Y is inoculated first, the titer is less (Ross, 1950).

Two unrelated viruses can antagonize one another. One of the most curious cases is that of the severe etch virus, which not only prevents the multiplication of the virus Y of the potato and virus 3 of henbane, but even eliminates them from an infected plant (Bawden and Kassanis, 1945).

Interaction between viruses, leading to a synergy or inhibition, is not difficult to explain. If each of two unrelated viruses affects the troubles of metabolism of the host in a specific way, an effect on their multiplication could be expected, Bawden and Kassanis (1945) have supposed that antagonism probably resulted from a decrease in the host of either the metabolites or enzymatic system that are necessary to the multiplication of virus Y and virus 3 of the henbane.

In complex diseases the appearance of symptoms can be explained by assuming that symptoms arise from physiological aberrancies in the plant. Thus, if one virus instigates modifications too slight to be translated into symptoms, then two viruses acting together can sometimes produce a visible effect. For example, the necrotic lesions in the case of the double streak caused by a combination of virus X and tobacco mosaic virus.

B. *Interactions between Strains of the Same Virus*

A plant completely infected cannot be reinfected by this same virus or, to be more precise, by the same strain of this same virus. Protection of a plant against reinfection with the same virus is most evident in the case of diseases having a chronic phase. Tobacco ring spot (Wingard, 1928) is manifested by a shock phase immediately after inoculation, followed by a chronic phase during which the content of viruses declines and symptoms disappear. Eventually certain organs are free of virus. When the host is inoculated during the chronic phase, no symptoms are obtained; if it is inoculated on a cured organ, shock symptoms appear.

A plant is not only protected against the strain of virus with which it is infected, but also against all other strains of this virus. This type of interference constitutes premunity and is observed only between closely related viruses. It can be seen only when inoculation is done mechanically. Inoculation by insect vectors and by grafting rarely permit this phenomenon to be observed. A host plant must have been inoculated for a few days in order to be protected against reinoculation. When two strains are inoculated into the host simultaneously, they multiply in competition.

Thung (1931) showed evidence that tobacco infected by the common strain of tobacco mosaic virus is protected against inoculation by the white strains. Salaman (1933) protected potatoes infected by a strain of low virulence against the more virulent strains of the virus X. Recently, Kunkel (1952, 1955) has shown that the usual strain of aster yellows protects the plant not only against the California strain of the same virus, but also protects the insect vector *Macrosteles fascifrons* against the California strain, and vice versa. The virus of the aster yellows multiplies in the insect vector as well as in the plant. This similarity of protection of both plant and animal hosts permits an explanation of premunition that can be accepted.

1. *Antibody Theory*

According to the antibody theory, the plant as well as the animal is able to produce immunizing diffusible substances neutralizing a virus. This theory, which is open to questions in some areas, has, however, the advantage of explaining the strict specificity of premunity. Indeed, interference is produced only between strains of the same virus. This is the best evidence in favor of the presence of antibodies, provided by the curly top virus on tobacco (Wallace, 1944).

The curly top virus of sugar beet illustrates the degrees of interference possible. Protection between different strains is nonexistent in beets. Inoculated into tobacco the virus produces an acute disease followed by a chronic phase. When a tobacco scion in the chronic phase is grafted onto a tomato, a less serious disease results. If, instead of grafting, the insect vector is used to transmit the virus from tobacco to tomato, an acute disease is obtained. Supposedly, antibodies have moved with the virus in grafting.

2. *Theory of Exhaustion of the Precursor of Virus*

The metabolites necessary for the virus synthesis are completely utilized by the first strain, so that a new infection cannot succeed. When the virus is inoculated into a cell, it multiplies rapidly after a latent period, until a certain concentration is attained, when all precursors are converted to viruses. Thereafter the rate of increase is drastically reduced.

The contrary situation was found to exist by Bawden and Kassanis (1945). A strain of the etch virus of low virulence which, with but slight concentration in the plant at best, protects against a virulent strain, the concentration of which is usually much higher. This type of protection obviously cannot be due to exhaustion of the precursor.

3. Theory of the Occupied Receivers

To explain the phenomenon described above, Hutton and Bawden (1950) suggest that unrelated viruses increase on receivers or on specific increasing surfaces. When a virus finds these receivers occupied by the first strain inoculated, they are incapable of duplication.

All the theories recognize that interference between strains of a virus is due to competition. Either the first strain launches the attack on host organs, which will not permit a new inoculation, it exhausts the nutrient reserve of the cell, or it quickly occupies a space. In all these suppositions no direct interaction exists from one virus strain to another strain.

IX. GENERAL CONSIDERATIONS

This chapter has reviewed the many aspects of biological interference as it pertains to plant disease and its epidemiology. The many soil organisms grow, compete with one another, act and interact in a highly complex system. Pathogens tend to be restricted in their development through these interactions. The resulting biological equilibria result sometimes in complex diseases and sometimes in the suppression of pathogens. The use of biological control measures to curb plant diseases has some promise, and exploitation of this idea may some day be more effectively used in curbing plant pathogens.

REFERENCES

Agnihothrudu, V. 1954. Soil conditions and wilt diseases in plants: Rhizosphère microflora in relation to fungi wilts. Thèse Doct. Philos., Univ. Madras, Madras, India.

Alexopoulos, C. J., and J. A. Herrick. 1942. Studies in antibiosis between bacteria and fungi. III. Inhibitory action of some actinomycetes on various species of fungi in culture. Bull. Torrey Botan. Club. 69: 257–261.

Alexopoulos, C. J., R. Arnett, and A. V. McIntosh. 1938. Studies in antibiosis between bacteria and fungi. Ohio J. Sci. 38: 221–234.

Allen, M. C., and C. M. Haenseler. 1935. Antagonistic action of Trichoderma on Rhizoctonia and other soil fungi. Phytopathology 25: 244–252.

Anwar, A. A. 1949. Factors affecting the survival of Helminthosporium sativum and Fusarium lini in soil. Phytopathology 39: 1005–1019.

Atkinson, R. G., and J. W. Rouatt. 1949. The effect of the incorporation of certain cover crops on the microflora of potato-scab infested soil. Proc. Can. Phytopathol. Soc. 16: 15.

Bamberg, R. H. 1931. Bacteria antibiotic to Ustilago zeae. Phytopathology 21: 881–890.

Bamberg, R. H., C. S. Holton, H. A. Rodenhiser, and R. W. Woodward. 1947. Wheat dwarf bunt depressed by common bunt. *Phytopathology* **37**: 556–560.

Barat, H. 1952. Etude sur le dépérissement des Poivriers en Indochine. *Arch. recherches agron. Cambodge, Laos, et Vietnam* **13**: 92.

Bawden, F. C., and B. Kassanis. 1945. The suppression of one plant virus by another. *Ann. Appl. Biol.* **32**: 52–57.

Beresova, J. F., and A. N. Nauomova. 1939. A bacterial method for the control of fungus diseases of agricultural plants. *Chem. Zentr.* **112**: 100–101.

Blair, I. D. 1942. Studies on the growth in soil and the parasitic action of certain *Rhizoctonia solani* isolates from wheat. *Can. J. Research* **C20**: 174–185.

Blair, I. D. 1943. Behaviour of *Rhizoctonia solani* Kuhn. *Ann. Appl. Biol.* **30**: 118–127.

Bliss, D. E. 1951. The destruction of *Armillaria mellea* in citrus soils. *Phytopathology* **41**: 665–683.

Boosalis, M. G. 1956. Effect of soil temperature and green manure amendment of unsterilized soil on parasitism of *Rhizoctonia solani* by *Penicillium vermiculatum* and *Trichoderma* sp. *Phytopathology* **46**: 473–478.

Borders, H. I. 1938. Unpublished M.S. thesis. University of Minnesota.

Bourriquet, G. 1946. Les maladies des plantes cultivées à Madagascar. *Encyclopédie mycol.* **12**: 137–166.

Brian, P. W. 1949. The production of antibiotics by microorganisms in relation to biological equilibria in soil. *Symposia Soc. Exptl. Biol.* **3**: 357–372.

Broadfoot, W. C. 1933. Studies on foot and root rot of wheat. II. Cultural relationships on solid media of certain microorganisms in association with *Ophiobolus graminis* Sacc. *Can. J. Research* **8C**: 545–552.

Brodski, A. L. 1941. Antagonism between soil infusoria and plant pathogenic fungi. *Compt. rend. Acad. Sci. U.R.S.S.* [N. S.] **33**: 81–83; 1943. *Brit. Chem. Abstr.* **A3**: 275; *Rev. Appl. Mycol.* **22**: 267 (abstr.).

Brömmelhues, M. 1935. Die wechselseitige Beeinflussung von Pilzen und die Bedeutung der Pilzkonkurrenz für das Ausmass der Schädigung an Weizen durch *Ophiobolus graminis* Sacc. *Zent. Bakteriol. Parasitenk. Abt. II* **92**: 81–116; 1935. *Rev. Appl. Mycol.* **14**: 688 (abstr.).

Brooks, F. T., and W. C. Moore. 1926. Silver leaf disease. *J. Pomol. Hort. Sci.* **5**: 61–97.

Butler, E. E. 1957. *Rhizoctonia solani* as a parasite of fungi. *Mycologia* **49**: 354–373.

Calam, C. T., H. Raistrick, and A. R. Todd. 1949. The potato eelworm hatching factors. *Biochem. J.* **45**: 513–519.

Chevaugeon, J. 1954. Phytopathologie—A. O. F. *Courier des chercheurs* (O.R.S.T.O.M.) **7**: 161–164.

Clark, F. E., and R. B. Mitchell. 1942. Antibiosis in the elimination of *Phymatotrichum omnivorum* sclerotia from soil. *J. Bacteriol.* **44**: 141 (abstr.).

Connell, T. D. 1952. A survey of bacteria antagonistic to *Pythium arrhenomanes* in Louisiana sugar cane soils. *Phytopathology* **42**: 464 (abstr.).

Coons, G. H., and J. E. Kotila. 1925. The transmissible lytic principle bacteriophage in relation to plant pathogens. *Phytopathology* **15**: 357–370.

Cooper, V. E., and S. J. P. Chilton. 1947. Occurrence of *Actinomyces* antibiotic to *Pythium* in some sugar cane of Louisiana. *Phytopathology* **37**: 5–6.

Cooper, W. E., and S. J. P. Chilton. 1949. Antibiosis of Actinomycetes strains to *Pythium arrhenomanes, P. ultimum, and Rhizoctonia solani. Phytopathology* **39**: 5 (abstr.).

Cooper, W. E., and S. J. P. Chilton. 1950. Studies on antibiotic soil organisms. I. Actinomycetes antibiotic to *Pythium arrhenomanes* in sugar cane soils of Louisiana. *Phytopathology* **40**: 544–552.

Cordon, T. C., and C. M. Haenseler. 1939. A bacterium antagonistic to *Rhizoctonia solani. Soil. Sci.* **47**: 207–215.

Crosse, J. E., and R. S. Pitcher. 1952. Studies in the relationship of eelworms and bacteria to certain plant diseases. I. The etiology of strawberry cauliflower disease. *Ann. Appl. Biol.* **39**: 475–486.

d'Aguilar, J. 1944. Contribution à l'Etude des *Phalacridae, Ann. épiphyt.* **10**: 85.

d'Herelle, F. 1917. Sur un microbe invisible antagoniste des bacilles dysentériques. *Compt. rend.* **165**: 373–375.

Daines, R. H. 1937. Antagonistic action of *Trichoderma* on *Actinomyces scabies* and *Rhizoctonia solani. Am. Potato J.* **14**: 85–93.

Darpoux, H. and A. Faivre-Amiot. 1950. Recherches sur les antagonismes microbiens et sur les substances antibiotiques. *Rev. Pathol. végétale et entomol. agr. France* **29**: 103–113.

Drechsler, C. 1937. Some Hyphomycetes that prey on free-living terricolous nematodes. *Mycologia* **29**: 447–552.

Drechsler, C. 1938. Two hyphomycetes parasitic on oospores of root-rotting oomycete. *Phytopathology* **28**: 81–103.

Drechsler, C. 1943a. Another hyphomycetous fungus parasitic on *Pythium* oospores. *Phytopathology* **33**: 227–233.

Drechsler, C. 1943b. Antagonism and parasitism among some Oomycetes associated with root rot. *J. Wash. Acad. Sci.* **33**: 21–28.

Fawcett, H. S. 1931. The importance of investigations on the effects of known mixtures of microorganisms. *Phytopathology* **21**: 545–550.

Franklin, M. T. 1937. The effect on the cyst contents of *Heterodera schachtii* of the cultivation of maize on potato sick land. *J. Helminthol.* **15**: 61–68.

Friedrichs, K. 1908. Uber *Phalacrus corruscus* als Feind der Brandpilze des Getreides und seine Entwicklung in brandigen Aehren. *Arb. Biol. Anst. f. Land-u. Forstw.* **7**: 38.

Fulton, R. W. 1950. Bacteriophages attacking *Pseudomonas tabaci* and *P. angulatum. Phytopathology* **40**: 936–949.

Garrett, S. D. 1936. Soil conditions and the take-all diseases of wheat. *Ann. Appl. Biol.* **23**: 667–699.

Garrett, S. D. 1937. Soil conditions and the take-all disease of wheat. II. The relation between soil reaction and soil aeration. *Ann. Appl. Biol.* **24**: 747–751.

Garrett, S. D. 1938. Soil conditions and the take-all disease of wheat. II. Decomposition of the resting mycelium of *Ophiobolus graminis* in infected wheat stubble buried in the soil. *Ann. Appl. Biol.* **25**: 742–766.

Garrett, S. D. 1944. Soil conditions and the take-all disease of wheat. VIII. Further experiments on the survival of *Ophiobolus graminis* in infected wheat stubble. *Ann. Appl. Biol.* **31**: 186–191.

Goffart, H. 1933. Untersuchungen am Hafernematoden *Heterodera schachtii* Schm. *Arb. biol. Reich.* **20**: 1–26.

Goffart, H. 1934. Uber die Biologie und Bekämpfung des Kartoffelnematoden (*Heterodera schachtii* S.). *Arb. biol. Reich.* **22**: 73–108.

Gottlieb, D., and P. Siminoff. 1951. The production and role of antibiotics in the soil. I. The fate of streptomycin. *Phytopathology* **41**: 420.

Gottlieb, D., and P. Siminoff. 1952. The production and role of antibiotics in the soil. II. Chloromycetin. *Phytopathology* **42**: 91–97.

Gottlieb, D., P. Siminoff, and M. M. Martin. 1952. The production and role of antibiotics in soil. IV. Actidione and clavacin. *Phytopathology* **42**: 493–496.

Grassé, P. P. 1922. Notes sur la biologie d'un Collembole *Hypogastrura armata Ann. soc. entomol. France* **91**: 190–192.

Greaney, F. J., and J. E. Machacek. 1935. Studies on the control of root-rot diseases of cereals caused by *Fusarium culmorum* (W.G.S.) and *Helminthosporium sativum* P. K. and B. pathogenecity of *Helminthosporium sativum* as influenced by *Cephalothecium roseum* C. in greenhouse pot tests. *Sci. Agr.* **15**: 377–386.

Gregory, K. F., O. N. Allen, A. J. Riker, and W. H. Patterson. 1952. Antibiotics and antagonistic microorganisms as control agents against damping-off of alfalfa. *Phytopathology* **42**: 613–622.

Grossbard, E. 1948. Plant diseases. IV. The control of plant diseases by microbial antagonisms. *Rept. Exptl. Research Sta. Cheshunt* pp. 29–39.

Grossbard, E. 1952. Antibiotic production by fungi on organic manures, and in soil. *J. Gen. Microbiol.* **6**: 295–310.

Gutter, Y., and F. Littauer. 1953. Antagonistic action of *Bacillus subtilis* against citrus fruit pathogens. *Bull. Research Council Israel* **3**: 192–196.

Hartley, C. 1921. Damping-off in forest nurseries. *U. S. Dept. Agr. Bull.* **934**: 1–99.

Henry, A. W. 1931. The natural microflora of the soil in relation to the root-rot problem of wheat. *Can. J. Research* **4C**: 69–77.

Hijner, J. A. 1951. De gevoeligheit van wilde bieten voor het bieten cystenaaltje *Heterodera schachtii. Mededel. Inst. Rationele Suikerprod.* **21**: 1.

Hino, I., and H. Kato. 1929. *Ciccinaboli* parasitic on mildew fungi. *Bull. Miyazaki Coll. Agr. and Forestry* **1**: 91–100.

Holdeman, Q. L., and T. W. Graham. 1953. The sting nematode breaks resistance to cotton wilt. *Phytopathology* **43**: 475 (abstr.).

Hubert, E. E. 1935. Observations on *Tuberculina maxima,* a parasite of *Cronartium ribicola. Phytopathology* **25**: 253–261.

Hutton, E. M., and F. C. Bawden. 1950. Some factors affecting localised and systemic necrotic reactions to virus Y in potato. *Australian J. Sci. Research* **4**: 439.

Israilsky, W. P. 1926–1927. Bakteriophagie und Pflanzenkrebs. *Zentr. Bakteriol. Parasitenk Abt. II.* **67**: 236–242; **71**: 302–311.

Jaarsveld, A. 1942. Der Einfluss verschiedener Bodenpilze auf die Virulenz von *Rhizoctonia solani* K. *Phytopathol. Z.* **14**: 1–75.

Jefferys, E. G. 1952. The stability of antibiotics in soils. *J. Gen. Microbiol.* **7**: 295–312.

Jefferys, E. G., P. W. Brian, H. G. Hemming, and D. Lowe. 1953. Antibiotic production by the microfungi of acid in heath soils. *J. Gen. Microbiol.* **9**: 314–341.

Johnson, L. F. 1952. Control of root rot of corn under greenhouse conditions by microorganisms antagonistic to *Pythium arrhenomanes. Phytopathology* **42**: 468 (abstr.).

Johnston, C. L., and F. J. Greaney. 1942. Studies on the pathogenecity of *Fusarium* species associated with root rot of wheat. *Phytopathology* **32**: 670–684.

Jørstad, I. 1938. Gymnosporangium on pomaceous fruits in Norway. *Nyt. Mag. Naturvidensk.* **18**: 121–126.

Katzer, A. 1939. Weitere Studien zur Anwendung des Antagonismus als praktische

Bekämpfungsmethode des Keimlingssterbens der Tomaten. *Boll. staz. patol. vegetale* [N. S.] **18:** 367–382.

Kauffmann, F. 1929. Zur Biologie der Tumefaciensstämme. *Zent. Krebsforch.* **30:** 290–294.

Kawamura, E. 1940. Bacteriophage of *Bacterium solanacearum*. *Sci. Bull. Fac. Agr. Kyushu Univ.* **9:** 148–156.

Keener, P. D. 1954. *Cladosporium aecidiicola* Thuem and *Tuberculina perscina* (D) Sacc. associated with *Puccinia conspicua* (Arth.), Mains on *Helenium hoopesii* A Gray in Arizona. *Plant Disease Reptr.* **38:** 690–694.

Koch, L. W. 1934. Investigations on Black Knot of plums and cherries II. The occurrence and significance of certain fungi found in association with *Dibotryon morbosum*. *Sci. Agr.* **12:** 80–95.

Krasilnikov, N. A., and E. A. Raznitzyna. 1946. A bacterial method of controlling damping-off of Scot pine seedlings caused by *Fusarium*. *Agrobiologiya* **5:** 109–121.

Kunkel, L. O. 1952. Transmission of alfalfa witch's broom to non-leguminous plants by dodder, and cure in periwinkle by heat. *Pytopathology* **42:** 27–31.

Kunkel, L. O. 1955. Cross protection between strains of yellow type viruses. *Advances in Virus Research* **3:** 251.

Lachance, R. C. 1951. Antagonisme des microorganissmes du sol envers le *Colletotrichum linicola*, agent de l'Anthracnose du Lin. *Can. J. Botany* **29:** 439–449.

Lambert, E. B., G. Steiner, and C. Drechsler. 1949. The *Cephalothecium* disease of cultivated mushrooms caused by a nematode (*Ditylenchus* sp.) evidenced by surface development of predaceous fungi. *Plant Disease Reptr.* **33:** 252–253.

Ledingham, R. J., B. J. Sallans, and P. M. Simmonds. 1949. The significance of the normal flora on wheat seed in inoculation studies with *Helminthosporium sativum*. *Proc. Can. Phytopathol.* **16:** 10–11.

Levine, M. N., H. C. Murphy, and R. H. Bamberg. 1936. Microorganisms antibiotic or pathogenic to cereal rusts. *Pytopathology* **26:** 99–100.

Linford, M. B., and J. M. Oliveira. 1938. Potential agents of biological control of plant-parasitic nematodes. *Phytopathology* **28:** 14 (abstr.).

Linford, M. B., and F. Yap. 1939. Root-knot nematode injury restricted by a fungus. *Phytopathology* **29:** 596–609.

Lochhead, A. G. 1940. Qualitative studies of soil microorganisms. III. Influence of plant growth on the character of the bacterial flora. *Can. J. Research* **18:** 42–53.

Lochhead, A. G., and G. B. Landerkin. 1949. Aspects of antagonism between microorganisms in soil. *Plant and Soil* **1:** 271–276.

Lucas, G. B., and L. R. Krusberg. 1956. The relationship of the stunt nematode to Granville wilt resistance in tobacco. *Plant Disease Reptr.* **40:** 150–152.

Luke, H. H. 1952. Fungi isolated from sugarcane soils of Louisiana and their antagonistic effect of *Pythium arrhenomanes*. *Phytopathology* **42:** 469 (abstr.).

Marrian, D. H., P. B. Russel, A. R. Todd, and W. S. Waring. 1949. The potato Eelworm hatching factor. 3. Concentration of the factor by chromatography. Observations on the nature of eclepic acid. *Biochem. J.* **45:** 524–528.

Meredith, C. H. 1944. The antagonism of soil organisms to *Fusarium oxysporum cubense*. *Phytopathology* **34:** 426–429.

Meredith, C. H., and G. Semeniuk. 1946. The antagonism of some species of Actinomycetes in relation to soil-inhabiting plant pathogens. *Rept. Iowa State Coll. Agr. Expt. Sta.* **1946:** 199–202.

Metcalf, H. 1903. Cultural studies of a nematode associated with plant decay. *Trans. Am. Microscop. Soc.* **29**: 89–102.

Millard, W. A., and C. B. Taylor. 1927. Antagonism of microorganisms as the controlling factor in the inhibition of scab by green manuring. *Ann. Appl. Biol.* **14**: 202–216.

Mitchell, R. B., J. E. Adams, and C. Thom. 1941. Microbial responses to organic amendments in Houston black clay. *J. Agr. Research* **63**: 527–534.

Moreau, M. 1957. "Le dépérissement des Oeillets." *Encyclopedie Mycol.* **30**: 244–248. Lechevalier, Paris. p. 244–248.

Morrow, M. B., J. L. Roberts, J. E. Adams, H. V. Jordan, and P. Guest. 1938. Establishment and spread of molds and bacteria on cotton roots by seed and seedling inoculation. *J. Agr. Research* **66**: 197–207.

Muller, K. O., and J. Monroe. 1956. The affinity of potato virus Y infected potato tissues for dilute vital strains. *Phytopathol Z.* **28**: 70–82.

Newbond, F. H. S. 1953. An actinophage for Streptomyces scabies. *Rev. can. biol.* **11**: 514.

Newhook, F. J. 1951. Microbiological control of *Botrytis cinerea* P. *Ann. Appl. Biol.* **38**: 169–202.

Newhook, F. J. 1957. The relationship of saprophytic antagonism to control of *Botrytis cinerea*. *New Zealand J. Sci. Technol.* **A38**: 479–481.

Novikowa, N. C. 1940. Bactériophage against bacterial wild fire in Makhorka tobacco. *Mikrobiol. Zhur. (Kiev)* **7**: 127–140.

Novogrudski, D. 1937. The use of microorganisms in the control of fungal diseases of cultivated plants. *Bull. Acad. Sci. Biol. U.R.S.S. Ser.* **1**: 273–293.

Okabe, N., and M. Goto. 1954. Studies on *Pseud. solanacearum*. IV. Several lysogenic strains. *Rept. Fac. Agr. Shiznoka Univ. Iwata Japan* **4**: 28–36.

Person, L. H. 1955. A chytrid attacking oospores of *Peronospora tabacina*. *Plant Disease Reptr.* **39**: 887–888.

Pochon, J., and H. de Barjac. 1958. "Traîté de microbiologie des sols." Dunod et Cie, Paris. p. 46.

Pon, D. S., C. E. Townsend, G. E. Wessman, C. G. Schmidt, and C. H. Kingsolver. 1954. A *Xanthomonas* parasitic on uredia of cereal rusts. *Phytopathology* **44**: 707–710.

Pramer, D., and R. L. Starkey. 1951. Decomposition of streptomycin. *Science* **113**: 127.

Rehfons, M. 1955. Contribution à l'étude des insectes des champignons. *Mitt. schweiz. entomol. Ges.* **28**: 1–106.

Richardson, D. E., and D. A. Rolling. 1957. Potato blight and leaf roll virus. *Nature* **180**: 866–867.

Rishbeth, J. 1950. Observations on the biology of *Fomes annosus*, with particular reference to East Anglian pine plantations. I. The outbreaks of disease and ecological status of the fungus. *Ann. Botany (London)* [N. S.] **14**: 365–383.

Ross, A. F. 1950. Local lesion formation and virus production following simultaneous inoculation with potato viruses X and Y. *Phytopathology* **40**: 24.

Roubaud, E., and R. Deschiens. 1939. Capture de larves infectieuses de nématodes pathogènes par des champignons prédateurs du sol. *Compt. rend.* **208**: 245–247.

Rozsypal, J., and Schmidt. 1934. Pilze in Cysten von *Heterodera schachtii* S aus mährischen Rübenböden Vestnik Cesko. *Akad. Zeměděl.* **10**: 413–422.

Sabet, K. A. 1954. Combined infection with rot-causing bacteria and fungi. *Congr. intern. botan. 8th Congr. Paris*, p. 136.

Salaman, R. W. 1933. Protective inoculation against a plant virus. *Nature* **131**: 468.

Sallans, B. J., R. J. Ledingham, and P. M. Simmonds. 1949. Testing wheat seedlings for resistance to *Helminthosporium sativum*, with reference to antibiosis. *Proc. Can. Phytopathol. Soc.* **16**: 11.

Sanford, G. B. 1926. Some factors affecting the pathogenicity of *Actinomyces scabies*. *Phytopathology* **16**: 525–547.

Sanford, G. B. 1947. Effect of various soil supplements on the virulence and persistence of *Rhizoctonia solani*. *Sci. Agr.* **27**: 533–544.

Sanford, G. B., and W. C. Broadfoot. 1931. Studies of the effects of other soil inhabiting microorganisms on the virulence of *Ophiobolus graminis* Sacc. *Sci. Agr.* **11**: 512–528.

Schuurmans Stekhoven, J. H., and R. Teunissen. 1938. Nematodes libres terrestres. *Exploration Parc Natl. Albert Mission* **22**: 1–220.

Siminoff, P., and D. Gottlieb. 1951. The production and role of antibiotics in the soil. *Phytopathology* **41**: 420–430.

Simmonds, P. M. 1947. The influence of antibiosis in the pathogenicity of *Helminthosporium sativum*. *Sci. Agr.* **27**: 625–632.

Slootweg, A. F. G., and M. Oostenbrik. 1956. Root rot of bulbs caused by *Pratylenchus* and *Hoplolaimus* sp. *Nematologica* **1**: 192–201.

Stewart, R. N., and A. F. Schindler. 1956. The effect of some ectoparasitic and endoparasitic nematodes on the expression of bacterial wilt in carnations. *Phytopathology* **46**: 219–222.

Tervet, I. W. 1938. Effect of mixed inocula on the production of seedling blight in flax. *Phytopathology* **28**: 21 (abstr.).

Thomas, R. C. 1935. A bacteriophage in relation to Stewart's disease of corn. *Phytopathology* **25**: 371–372.

Thomas, R. C. 1940. Additional facts regarding bacteriophage lytic to *Aplanobacter stewarti*. *Phytopathology* **30**: 602–611.

Thomas, W. D. 1948. The control of Fusarium root rot and bacterial wilt of Carnations by antibiotic fungi. *J. Colo.-Wyo. Acad. Sci.* **3**: 39 (abstr.).

Thorne, G. 1927. The life-history, habits, and economic importance of some Mononchs. *J. Agr. Research* **34**: 265–286.

Thorne, G. 1940. *Dubosquia penetrans* sp. (*Sporozoa, Microsporidiae Nosematidae*) a parasite of the nematode (*Pratylenchus pratensis*) D. M. *Proc. Helminthol. Soc. Wash.* **7**: 51–53.

Thung, T. H. 1931. Smet stof en plantencel bij enkele virusziekten van de tabaksplant. *Ned.-Indisch Natuurw. Congr. Handelin-gen* **6**: 450.

Tims, E. C. 1932. An actinomycete antagonistic to a *Pythium* root parasite of sugar cane. *Phytopathology* **22**: 27 (abstr.).

Tisdale, W. B. 1931. Development of strains of cigar wrapper tobacco resistant to blackshank. (*Phytophthora nicotianae* B D H). *Florida Agr. Expt. Sta. Bull.* **226**: 1–45.

Treschow, C. 1941. Zur Kultur von Trametes auf sterilisiertem Waldhumus. *Zentr. Bakteriol. Parasitenk. Abt. II* **104**: 186–188.

Tribe, H. T. 1957. On the parasitism of *Sclerotinia trifoliorum* by *Coniothygrium minitans*. *Trans. Brit. Mycol. Soc.* **40**: 489–499.

Triffit, M. J. 1934. Experiments with the root excretion of grasses as possible means of eliminating *Heterodera schachtii* from infected soil. *J. Helminthol.* **12**: 11–12.

Tveit, M., and R. K. S. Wood. 1955. The control of *Fusarium* blight in oat seedlings with antagonistic species of *Chaetomium*. *Ann. Appl. Biol.* **43**: 538–552.

Uhlenbroek, J. H., and J. D. Bijloo. 1958. Isolation and structure of a nematicidal principle occurring in *Tagetes*. *Rec. trav. chim.* **77**: 804–1009.

Van Luijk, A. 1938. Antagonism between various microorganisms and different species of the genus *Pythium* parasitic on grasses and lucerne. *Mededeel. Phytopathol. Lab. Willie Commelin Scholten* **14**: 43–82.

Vasudeva, R. A., and M. K. Hingonia. 1952. Bacterial disease of wheat caused by *Corynebacterium tritici* (H. B.). *Phytopathology* **42**: 291–293.

Vasudeva, R. A., and T. C. Roy. 1950. The effect of associated soil microflora on *Fusarium udum* B., the fungus causing wilt on pigeon-pea (Cajanus cajan). *Ann. Appl. Biol.* **37**: 169–178.

Viala, P. 1932. Un parasite du mildiou de la vigne. *Compt. rend. acad. agr. (France)* **18**: 654–656.

Viennot-Bourgin, G. 1949. "Les champignons parasites des plantes cultivées," Vol. 2, pp. 1444–1448. Masson, Paris.

Waksman, S. A. 1957. Le rôle des antibiotiques dans les processus naturels. *Nature (Paris)* **No. 3266**: 201–207.

Wallace, J. M. 1944. Acquired immunity from curly top in tobacco and tomato. *J. Agr. Research* **69**: 187–214.

Warren, J. R. 1948. An undescribed species of *Papulospora* parasitic on *Rhizoctonia solani* Kuhn. *Mycologia* **40**: 391–401.

Warren, J. R., F. Graham, and G. Gale. 1951. Dominance of an actinomycete in a soil microflora after 2,4-D treatment of plants. *Phytopathology* **41**: 1037–1039.

Weber, A. P., L. O. Zwillenberg, and P. A. Van der Laan. 1952. A predacious amoeboid organism destroying larvae of the potato root eelworm and other nematodes. *Nature* **169**: 834–835.

Weindling, R. 1932. *Trichoderma lignorum* as a parasite on other soil fungi. *Phytopathology* **22**: 837–845.

Weindling, R., and H. S. Fawcett. 1936. Experiments in the control of *Rhizoctonia* damping-off of citrus seedlings. *Hilgardia* **10**: 1–16.

Wiant, J. S. 1929. The *Rhizoctonia* damping-off of conifers and its control by chemical treatment of the soil. *Cornell Univ. Agr. Expt. Sta. Mem.* **124**: 1–64.

Wingard, S. A. 1928. Hosts and symptoms of ring spot, a virus disease of plants. *J. Agr. Research* **37**: 127–153.

Winslow, R. D., and T. I. D. Williams. 1957. Amoeboid organisms attacking larvae of the potato root eelworm (*Heterodera rostochiensis* W) in England and the beet eelworm (*H. schachtii* S) in Canada. *Tijdschr. Plantenziekten* **63**: 242–243.

Wood, R. K. S. 1951. The control of diseases of lettuce by the use of antagonistic organisms. I. The control of *Botrytis cinerea* Pers. *Ann. Appl. Biol.* **38**: 203–230.

Wright, J. M. 1954. The production of antibiotics in soil. I. Production of gliotoxin by *Trichoderma viride*. *Ann. Appl. Biol.* **41**: 280–289.

Wright, J. M. 1955. The production of antibiotics in soil. II. Production of griseofulvin by *Penicillium nigricans*. *Ann. Appl. Biol.* **43**: 288–296.

Wright, J. M. 1956a. The production of antibiotics in soil. III. Production of gliotoxin in wheatstraw buried in soil. *Ann. Appl. Biol.* **44**: 461–466.

Wright, J. M. 1956b. Biological control of a soil-borne *Pythium* infection by seed inoculation. *Plant and Soil* **7**: 132–139.

Wright, J. M. 1956c. The production of antibiotics in soil. IV. Production of antibiotics in coats of seed sown in soil. *Ann. Appl. Biol.* **44**: 561–566.

Wright, J. M., and J. F. Grove. 1957. The production of antibiotics in soil. V. Breakdown of griseofulvin in soil. *Ann. Appl. Biol.* **45:** 36–43.

Yarwood, C. E. 1951. Rust infection increases invasiveness of tobacco mosaic virus in bean. *Phytopathology* **41:** 39 (abstr.).

Yossifovitch, M. 1954. Un hyperparasite du *Polystigma rubrum* (Pers). *Congr. intern botan. 8th Congr. Paris* **2:** 136–137.

Young, P. A. 1939. Tomato wilt resistance and its decrease by *Heterodera marioni*. *Phytopathology* **29:** 871–879.

CHAPTER 14

The Problem of Breeding Resistant Varieties[1, 2]

E. C. STAKMAN AND J. J. CHRISTENSEN

University of Minnesota, St. Paul, Minnesota

1. THE IMPORTANCE OF DISEASE-RESISTANT VARIETIES

The development of disease-resistant varieties of crop plants is of paramount importance in the improvement of agriculture, and the improvement of agriculture is essential to meet the needs of the rapidly increasing human population of the world. We dare not be complacent about the fact that three fourths of the people in the world are now hungry. Nor dare we ignore the fact that the population threatens to double within the next 40 years. How can we feed 5 billion people in

[1] Paper No. 986, Miscellaneous Series, Minnesota Agr. Expt. Station.

[2] The writers are indebted to Bill J. Roberts and Donald P. Taylor for help in preparing certain sections of this paper. They are indebted to Laura M. Hamilton for help in the preparation of the bibliography and for various other kinds of assistance in the preparation of the manuscript.

1998 when we cannot or do not adequately feed half that number in 1958? It appears, in the present state of affairs, that the only hope is to increase greatly the efficiency of agricultural production. The situation could be alleviated but not cured by better distribution of actual and potential production. But better distribution depends more on politics than on science. The total production of basic food and feed crops must be increased and must be insured against violent fluctuations if we are to face the future with confidence.

It is a sound basic assumption that the area of cultivated lands cannot be increased proportionately to the increase of population. It follows, then, that the efficiency of production must be increased. And it is also a sound assumption that plant diseases, in the broadest sense, constitute one of the most formidable obstacles to efficient and assured production. Wheat, rice, maize, sorghums, millets, potatoes, and other basic food crops are subject to debilitating or devastating diseases caused by pathogens. And many of them are grown in large land areas where bad weather and bad pathogens can quickly destroy vast acreages of promising crops. The basic question, however, is how the crops can best be protected against the destructive factors of their physical and biotic environment.

Although there may not be general agreement that drought, heat, and cold cause diseases, there are good reasons for considering that they do. There is no logical or traditional reason for excluding inanimate causes of diseases from the realm of plant pathology. The general improvement of many basic food and feed crops requires the incorporation of genes for drought resistance, heat resistance, and winter hardiness. Even in areas where total annual rainfall usually is sufficient, drought or other unseasonable weather is likely to occur at critical times during the crop season. The problem is world-wide, and world-wide effort is needed to find and combine plant genes to alleviate it. And in that effort plant pathology must render its full measure of service.

Plant pathologists could not, even if they would, shed their share of the responsibility for breeding plants that better resist the violent elements in their physical environment. For there often is a dangerous alliance between debilitating pathogens and destructive weather. Pathogens may predispose plants to injury by bad weather, and bad weather may predispose them to injury by pathogens—even many of the milder ones. Winter injury annually takes a heavy toll of bread grains in the temperate zones, where most of them are grown. And it has long been known that pathogens may aggravate the injury due to winter weather and that winter weather may aggravate the injury caused by pathogens. The average loss of 10 to 15% of the seeded acreage of winter wheat in the United States is too high a tax to pay. The recourse is to develop varieties with combinations of genes that can defy the weather and the pathogens associated with it. The short life of alfalfa and other perennial or biennial legumes in many areas is due to the combined and mutual effects of pathogens and winter weather. Indeed, the complexities of these and numerous other similar weakening and destructive combinations are so great as to defy precise assessment of the guilt of the numerous interacting factors of the physical and biotic environment. For this reason it sometimes is known what the breeding is for, but not exactly what it is against. There is need to develop plants that are well adjusted to their total environment, with ability to profit from the good and to protect against the bad. It is generally assumed that unseasonable and unfavorable weather will reduce crop yields, in the very nature of things natural. But need it always be so; can man not prevail over his environment? If man is to master his environment, he must develop plants that can withstand the destructive elements within it; and, of course, the more he knows about these elements and their interactions among each other, the greater his chances of success. The way may be long and hard, but the need is great.

To preserve himself and his civilization, man must continually fight against the vast and variable world of microscopic organisms and ultramicroscopic viruses which continually menace his crop plants, his domestic animals, and himself. He has learned much about controlling the manifold diseases caused by myriads of pathogens. He has learned how to treat individual animals in order to prevent or cure many diseases, and has devised public health measures to reduce the need for individual treatment. He has been equally successful in devising ways for controlling diseases of many plants by means of protective chemicals.

But the populations of some of the most basic food plants, such as wheat, rice, millets, and sorghums are relatively so vast that individual medication is difficult or virtually impossible. There are about 170 million people and 185 million larger farm animals in the United States, but there are about 40 or 50 trillion wheat plants alone. To apply fungicidal chemicals several times a season to the enormous populations of grain and forage plants, even with the best modern machines, would be a prodigious and a prodigiously expensive operation, even if it were completely effective.

It is not only the enormous populations of many kinds of crop plants but also the enormous amount of wind-borne inoculum of some pathogens that have thus far limited the feasibility of controlling some destructive diseases by spraying or dusting. The cereal rusts, head blights of wheat, rice, and other cereals, the *Helminthosporium* leaf and head blights of cereal grains, and numerous leaf spots of forages certainly could not be controlled economically on large acreages by methods and materials now available. This is not an assertion that feasible methods will never be devised, but merely that they have not yet been devised. There are inherent difficulties, because of the nature of the crop plants and of the pathogens, in controlling many diseases which can quickly become epidemic over vast areas where there is heavy concentration of susceptible hosts. There are other groups of diseases which, by their nature, also are very difficult to control by methods available to individual growers.

It would be extremely difficult or impracticable for individual farmers to control many diseases caused by pathogens that multiply or persist in the soil. Conspicuous among them are flax wilt, cabbage yellows, tomato wilt, the wilt or Panama disease of bananas, all caused by soil-inhabiting species or varieties of *Fusarium*. Although the host range of such pathogens is relatively restricted, crop rotation and other cultural methods have not been sufficiently effective, and chemical treatment of soil on large acreages has been either impracticable or impossible. This is true also of certain bacterial diseases, such as bacterial wilts of alfalfa. The problem is inherently even more difficult with soil-inhabiting pathogens that have a wide host range, such as *Rhizoctonia solani*, *Phymatotrichum omnivorum*, and *Pythium* spp. These fungi are so universally and abundantly present in the soils of many extensive agricultural areas and they can cause debilitating or destructive root rots or basal stem rots on so many kinds of plants as to defy conventional control measures. Some soil-infesting nematodes, such as root knot nematodes, cyst nematodes, meadow nematodes, and stem and bulb nematodes, are long persistent in the soil, and many of them attack several kinds of crops that are grown on extensive acreages. Accordingly, crop rotation is not effective and soil treatment with chemicals is not economically feasible.

Many viruses, such as those causing western wheat mosaic in the United States and Canada, corn streak and stunt, sugarcane mosaic, curly top of sugar beets, oja blanca of rice, and numerous others are not easily amenable to control by artificial means. Virus diseases are among the most insidious and destructive of all diseases and, along with nematodes, were relatively neglected until rather recently. The over-all importance of these two groups of pathogens is just beginning to be appreciated, and each year new ones are being incriminated as agents of disorders that were previously unobserved or attributed to unthriftiness due to unknown causes.

It would be interesting, and possibly profitable, to catalogue diseases on the basis of amenability to control by artificial methods. There would, of course, be a number of groups with intergradations between them. Some can be controlled in most areas by a single, relatively simple and inexpensive operation; others require many repetitive and relatively expensive operations of a single kind; still others can be controlled only by combining several operations of different kinds; and, unfortunately, too many still defy any combined attack that has yet been made upon them. Bunt of wheat—except in areas where it persists in the soil—and certain similar smuts are in the first category. Late blight of potato, the sigatoka disease of banana, and many fruit diseases are in the second. In certain Andean countries potatoes must be sprayed at least 8 times to control late blight. In some of the principal banana-growing areas of tropical America bananas must be sprayed 10 to 13 times, and complete control of sigatoka is not always assured even then, although the application of oil from helicopters is an improvement over methods previously used. The control of many viruses that are carried inside of propagative parts of plants, such as tubers and bulbs, requires a multiple-method control program. Finally, many of the most destructive diseases cannot be controlled at all by any feasible combination of methods.

It is unfortunate but true that many of the most destructive diseases of basic food crops are not now controlled, that the control of many others is very expensive, and that all artificial control measures add something to the cost of production. Plant disease control has become a highly technical art, based on intensive research and extensive experimentation. The improvement of fungicides during the past four decades is an epic scientific achievement, and researches would be worth continuing on a greatly expanded scale for the sake of their scientific interest alone, even if there were not such urgent practical need for them. From the scientific standpoint it would be unfortunate if there were no plant diseases to control. From the standpoint of human progress, on the other hand, it would be an inestimable blessing if there were no need to control them. And, of course, that is exactly what breeding for disease resistance aims to do; it aims to produce varieties of plants that resist diseases so well that growers may be relieved of the work of controlling them.

There can scarcely be any question that the ideal way of controlling all plant diseases would be by means of permanently and universally resistant varieties. The real question, however, is one of feasibility, not of desirability. It has not been possible to control many diseases, at least thus far, by resistant varieties. Nor has it been possible to control some of the most destructive ones by any other method or combination of methods. In the long run several alternative methods may be developed for controlling some diseases that have heretofore been refractory, and it may be expected that the cheapest and most effective will be chosen. The need is to develop them. Partisanship and dogmatism will not satisfy the need; experimentation and research may.

Breeding for resistance is important because plant diseases still are one of the greatest menaces to man's food supplies; and the more the crop plants themselves can ward off the menace, the less work and worry man will have in doing it. Every increment of disease resistance that man can incorporate into plants of economic importance is a contribution to increasing and assuring his food supplies. How resistant can the most important crops become? Future prospects can be based partly on past experience.

II. History of Attempts to Produce Resistant Varieties

A. *Prior to 1900*

Records of conscious and systematic attempts to obtain disease-resistant varieties of crop plants prior to 1900 are meager. That differences in varietal resistance were observed in ancient Greece and Rome is clear from the records of Theophrastus and of various Roman writers on agriculture. It is not clear, however, how much use was made of the information. Varro, in his "Rerum Rusticarum," published shortly before the birth of Christ, recommended that wheat should not be grown on land subject to fogs, very probably because of the danger of rust. But he merely recommended that other kinds of crops, such as rape, turnips, millet, and panic grass be grown on such lands; there is no substantial evidence that conscious effort was made to utilize resistant varieties within one kind of crop. That different varieties were recommended for different areas and for different purposes is clear, but evidence regarding disease-resistant varieties is somewhat fragmentary.

It is unfortunate that systematic and adequate records of the selection of resistant varieties are not available, because it is certain that many diseases were destructive through the centuries and it is probable that the most susceptible varieties were discarded when more resistant ones became available. Knowledge regarding the past could improve perspective regarding the present and future. As perspective cannot well be based on ignorance of the remote past, however, it must be derived from knowledge of the recent past, including only a short half century.

B. *Since 1900*

The history of attempts to produce resistant varieties since about 1900 is fairly clear. As the principal value of past history is in its lessons for the present and future, a limited number of diseases have been selected for discussion because of what they teach. Many others could have been selected, and to omit them for lack of space is not to disparage either the diseases or those who studied them.

It was perhaps natural that early reliance should have been placed on introduction and selection as a means of obtaining resistant varieties. When the early work was started, "Mendelism" was just being rediscovered, and the Darwinian principles of variation and natural selection and—in some cases—the inheritance of acquired characters still tended to dominate the thinking of the pioneer breeders of resistant varieties.

Carleton was among the pioneers who introduced varieties for the definite purpose of finding those best-adapted to the total environment (Clark, 1936). Immigrant farmers had, of course, already brought varieties of wheat and other crops from their various homelands, and some of the varieties had proved their value. But this type of introduction was incidental rather than specifically purposeful. Having repeatedly seen the tragic effects of heat, drought, winter injury, and stem rust on the plains of Kansas, Carleton reasoned that natural selection, aided perhaps by man, must have produced resistant varieties in older wheat-growing areas where the agroclimate was similar to that in Kansas and similar areas. He therefore introduced Crimean winter wheats and durums from Russia, and arranged to have them tested widely in the United States. And finally the hard-red winter Crimean or Turkish types largely supplanted the softer Mediterranean types and reduced the danger of damage by severe weather and by rust. The durums, too, finally found their place and reduced the hazards of weather and rust at certain times and in certain places. Neither group of wheats solved the problems completely but they did alleviate them, and they furnished many genes for further improvement of varieties.

Plant introduction is, of course, one of the oldest methods of crop improvement, but man took a long time in learning that benefits had to be weighed against dangers. For all too often he discovered that he had imported unseen or unknown pests and pathogens with his introductions. As breeding for resistance was undertaken by increasing numbers of scientists in many different countries, the exchange of varieties has increased until it is now a common international practice. Eventually it may be possible to assemble in each country genes for resistance from all countries. But it is necessary to take precautions against importing genes for susceptibility to certain diseases along with those for resistance to others. And, above all, it is essential to avoid importing entirely new pests and pathogens or new races of old pathogens.

Introduction, as a method of plant breeding in the broader sense, may alone result in controlling diseases in similar ecologic zones. Thus the stem-rust-resistant Thatcher wheat was introduced into western Canada from the United States in 1935 and proved so suitable in the prairie provinces that it was grown on upwards of 10 million acres until replaced recently to a considerable extent by the Canadian-bred Selkirk. In 1953 Selkirk was imported in quantity into the United States from Canada, and by 1958 it had become the predominant hard-red spring variety in both countries. This reciprocity is possible, of course, because of the similarity of ecologic conditions in the northern and western prairies and plains in the two countries and of similarity in standards of quality. There has been similar exchange of wheat varieties resistant to yellow rust in certain countries of western Europe. But the direct utilization of introduced materials has not always been possible.

In many of the major breeding programs introduction has been followed by selection or hybridization, because many varieties with desired genes for resistance did not have the required genes for ecological adaptation or for special market quality.

Selection of resistant lines within commercial varieties or within populations of certain species has been highly successful in some cases and not in others. It is, of course, obvious that at least four conditions must be fulfilled if selection alone is to produce a desirable variety: (1) There must be resistant lines or biotypes within the plant populations; (2) There must be reliable methods for identifying the resistant individuals; (3) There must be suitable methods for propagating resistant lines; and (4) The lines selected must have the other characters of a good variety. It follows, therefore, that a prerequisite in selection is abundant development of the diseases in question in order to make it possible to distinguish between resistance and disease escape. These conditions were fulfilled in connection with some of the early successes in selecting resistant varieties, notably against cotton wilt, flax wilt, tomato wilt, and cabbage yellows, all of which are caused by species of *Fusarium*.

The cotton wilt caused by *Fusarium oxysporum* f. *vasinfectum* became so destructive in some of the cotton-growing areas of the southeastern United States shortly before 1900 as to threaten the future of the crop. Orton (1900) observed that some plants survived on very heavily infested soil, selected them, and planted the seed on heavily infested soil the next year. By continued selection and planting on infested soil, he succeeded in obtaining lines of Sea Island and Upland types that yielded well on the most heavily infested soils, where nonselected varieties were very severely injured. This was pioneer work, and some of the pioneers naturally but prematurely concluded that it would be easy to solve other pathological problems by similar methods.

Experience with flax wilt, however, soon indicated that it might be easier to obtain resistant lines than to maintain them.

Flax long had the reputation of being "hard on the soil" because yields tended to decrease sharply with successive cropping. It therefore became a migratory crop in the United States, moving continually westward to new lands. In 1901 Bolley proved that the trouble was due to a *Fusarium*, which he named *F. lini* but which now has the more impressive name *F. oxysporum* f. *lini*, and not to a deleterious effect of flax itself on the soil. Unknown to Bolley, Hiratsuka (1896, 1903) in Japan had come to a similar conclusion in 1896.

By selecting plants that survived in flax-sick soil and following essentially the same methods as Orton had used with cotton, Bolley succeeded in developing highly wilt-resistant varieties of flax in North Dakota, but they did not always remain resistant; they succumbed to wilt at certain times and in certain places. Naturally, this provoked two questions: why was the behavior variable, and what could be done about it? At that time there still was some belief in the inheritance of acquired characters; hence it was postulated that the resistant varieties had acquired resistance by association with the pathogens in the wilt-infested breeding plots and had lost it when grown in noninfested soil. But this did not seem completely plausible to some investigators who had made careful studies while using Bolley's methods in producing resistant varieties. Three important facts had to be discovered to explain the situation: (1) Tisdale (1917) showed that the amount of wilt that developed in resistant and susceptible lines varied with temperatures; (2) Barker (1923) proved that resistance and susceptibility were due to genetic factors which permitted considerable phenotypic variability but that resistance was neither acquired nor lost and that genes for wilt resistance could be combined with genes for other desirable characters; and (3) Broadfoot (1926) demonstrated that the wilt pathogen comprised physiologic races, thus explaining the apparent loss of resistance in some varieties and furnishing a basis for future procedures.

Flax wilt has been controlled in the United States for almost a half century by means of resistant varieties, but it has required continuous effort. Because of the existence of many physiologic races of the pathogen and because of variability in severity of wilt at different temperatures, it became necessary to devise ways of testing varietal populations against an adequate sample of races of the pathogen under conditions of maximum disease development. The first requisite has been met in the United States, principally by screening varieties and breeding materials in permanent wilt plots at the North Dakota and the Minnesota Agricultural Experiment stations. The Minnesota plot was established in

1912 and, from the beginning was inoculated in various ways with infective materials from different sources—with the purpose of providing an adequate sample of the pathogen, whatever that might prove to be. Subsequent to the discovery of physiologic races, attempt has been made to inoculate the plot with all known races. Although temperature cannot be controlled, seed is planted late in the spring to insure as nearly as possible a sufficiently high soil temperature for a good test. Fortunately for the purpose, the wilt organism is very persistent in the soil; it maintains itself during winter, survives other unfavorable conditions, and is little affected by antibiotic organisms, as shown by Anwar (1949). It is not necessary, therefore, to reinoculate the soil every year, which is necessary with certain other pathogens.

Tomatoes resistant to *Fusarium oxysporum* f. *lycopersici* were produced by selection more or less contemporaneously with the pioneer efforts already described. Edgerton and Moreland (1920) found that progress was most rapid and assured when selections were made in disinfested soil inoculated with the wilt organism only. This appeared to be the surest way of eliminating from the population all except the most resistant individuals. Physiologic races of the pathogen were subsequently demonstrated by Wellman and Blaisdell (1940, 1941), thus introducing another complication in the development and maintenance of resistant varieties.

Another conspicuous success story is the use of selection in the development of cabbage resistant to yellows, caused by *Fusarium oxysporum* f. *conglutinans*. Scientifically, two facts are especially noteworthy: (1) There are two types of resistance, one thermolabile and the other thermostable; (2) Physiologic races of the pathogen have not yet been found. The methods in obtaining resistant individuals were similar to those for cotton wilt and flax wilt, with one variation: to obtain adequate seed it was necessary to cross resistant individuals. The first resistant variety, Wisconsin Hollander, was released by Jones and associates in 1916, followed several years later by other varieties (Jones *et al.*, 1920). These varieties were less resistant at high temperature than at low; the resistance was governed by multiple quantitative genetic factors (type B). But plants were found with a thermostable (type A) kind of resistance that is governed by a single dominant gene and is effective at all temperatures. By growing populations at soil temperature of about 24° C., plants of type B are eliminated, thus leaving those with the more desirable type A kind of resistance (Walker and Smith, 1930). This genetic analysis not only clarified understanding and pointed the way to a better control of yellows but also helped to establish an important principle with respect to variability in disease development.

Although selection for resistance to those fusarial wilt diseases discussed is important because important facts and principles were derived during attempts to control them, selection has been very valuable with many other kinds of economic plants, both wild and cultivated. Many wild plants, such as grasses and legumes, comprise biotypes with different degrees of resistance to various diseases, and resistant lines have been selected from many of them. Moreover, some very useful materials have been selected from well-known varieties of crop plants. In some cases the varieties obviously comprised different morphologic types, but in other cases they did not. Selection has been successful with a wide range of plants against many kinds of diseases. There are wide differences in degree of resistance of *Poa pratensis* to stripe smut, *Ustilago striiformis* of *Dactylis glomerata* to *Puccinia glumarum*, and of timothy to *Puccinia graminis*. Many years ago Bain and Essary (1906) selected lines of red clover that were highly resistant to *Colletotrichum trifolii*, and in ordinary fields of this crop there are individuals that differ decidedly in resistance to powdery mildew, caused by *Erysiphe polygoni*. Several wheats with some resistance to stem rust have been selected; among them, Kanred, Kota, and Webster, all of which are important in the history of attempts to control stem rust by means of resistant varieties. According to Coons (1953), the sugar beet industry in irrigated regions of the western United States was saved by selecting for resistance to the virus curly top. Generally speaking, plant populations, although often relatively homogeneous for most visually observable characters, are quite heterogeneous with respect to disease resistance.

The early successes with selection led many plant scientists to believe that the method might be universally applicable. But this proved not to be true; consequently it was necessary to resort to hybridization. It would be neither desirable nor feasible to give a complete record of the accomplishments and disappointments in breeding for resistance. It is important, however, not only to know certain principles but also to know something about their derivation. Much still remains to be learned about breeding for disease resistance, and past experience should furnish some guides for the future. Farrer, in Australia (Campbell, 1912), was among the early pioneers in breeding for disease resistance; he succeeded in developing bunt-resistant varieties of wheat. Among the most instructive early attempts to develop resistant varieties by hybridization were those of Orton (1900, 1909), and of Biffen (1907, 1912, 1931).

In an attempt to obtain watermelons resistant to wilt, caused by *Fusarium oxysporum* f. *niveum*, Orton crossed the susceptible watermelon with the resistant stockmelon or citron. The hybrid had the resistance of the citron but also its undesirable taste. It was therefore crossed back to the watermelon, and lines were obtained that combined edibility with resistance. This was in reality an early use of the backcross method, which has become extremely useful when it is desired to retain many characters in a variety while incorporating disease resistance or some other desired character.

Biffen in England made two very important contributions: he produced good wheat varieties with resistance to *Puccinia glumarum,* and he demonstrated the mode of inheritance of factors for resistance. He showed that resistance in crosses between American club wheat (resistant) and Michigan bronze (susceptible) was inherited as a simple Mendelian recessive, independently of factors for other characters.

The results obtained by Orton and Biffen generated great optimism with respect to controlling diseases by breeding. Selection had proved effective in many cases, and desired characters from several varieties could be combined easily into a single variety by hybridization. Some scientists were skeptical about the universal applicability of the principles derived from these pioneer investigations. After all, there are hundreds of kinds of crop plants, some of them comprising thousands of varieties, and there are thousands of different kinds of pathogens. Two questions arose quite naturally: (1) Was selection universally useful? (2) Was inheritance of factors for disease resistance always simple and independent of other characters? Orton, Biffen, and others soon encountered some more complex situations, and it soon appeared that situations could be much more complex than had been anticipated by the most skeptical.

Stem rust of wheat, *Puccinia graminis* var. *tritici,* long has been a scourge in most of the extensive wheat-growing areas of the world. Some attempts to control it by resistant varieties antedate 1900, but they were mostly incidental to programs of general wheat improvement. The history of breeding for stem-rust resistance in North America is especially illuminating because of the extent of the wheat-growing area, the scale on which the work was done, the large number of pathologists and breeders involved, and the fact that the work has continued and continually expanded during half a century of time. The North American program probably is the longest extensive program of its kind, and for this reason it merits evaluation.

The United States Department of Agriculture initiated the program in 1905 after a destructive stem-rust epidemic in 1904. The need for resistant bread wheat was especially urgent in the spring wheat region of the Dakotas and Minnesota, where stem rust usually was most destructive, and in the winter wheat region centered in Kansas. The present discussion is restricted largely to spring wheat, as most of the important principles can be derived from it, although much history was made elsewhere also. In this program, as in any such program, the first need was to locate sources of resistance. As none were found for some time in the bread wheat group, *Triticum vulgare*, it was apparently necessary to make crosses with resistant varieties of other species, such as *T. monococcum*, einkorn; *T. dicoccum*, emmer; *T. turgidum*, poulard wheats; and *T. durum*, the durums or macaroni wheats. An extensive series of crosses were therefore made.

It became apparent by 1910 that the development of good, stem-rust bread wheats from the interspecific crosses might not be easy, and the supposition was amply confirmed as the complexities of the problem were revealed during the following decades. Some obstacles proved to be less formidable than they appeared at given times; others proved more formidable. Viewpoints therefore changed with experience, and principles had to be modified as additional experience was obtained.

The barriers to progress in developing good wheat varieties universally resistant to stem rust are of the same kind as those encountered with certain other cereal rusts and with some other diseases. In the United States and Canada quality is a prime requisite in the hard-red spring wheats, since milling and baking standards are very exacting. This obviously has been a basic barrier to control of stem rust. In addition the following facts are important:

(1) Resistant lines of desirable *vulgare* wheats were not found during the first decade of the program; hence, crosses were made between susceptible *vulgare* varieties and resistant varieties from certain other species groups.

(2) There was a high degree of sterility in many of the interspecies crosses, but a number of *vulgare* $\times$ durum crosses were obtained.

(3) Undesirable linkages were encountered in some cases.

a. There appeared to be complete linkage between factors for rust resistance and for durum type in the early bread wheat $\times$ durum crosses. The linkage, however, was finally broken when large populations were grown.

b. There is linkage between factors for rust resistance and for susceptibility to certain other diseases in some crosses, such as resistance to stem rust and susceptibility to bacterial black chaff in crosses involving Hope.

c. There is linkage in some cases between factors for rust resistance and undesirable morphologic characters, such as weak peduncles.

(4) Physiologic races of *Puccinia graminis* var. *tritici* were found in 1916 (Stakman and Piemeisel, 1917), and it has subsequently been shown that this variety comprises an indefinite number of phenotypically

variable biotypes, with extensive genetic variation within the variety. In most areas wheat is therefore exposed to large and shifting populations of rust races.

(5) Resistance may be either stable or unstable. For a number of years there was no evidence that varietal resistance could be "broken down" by environmental factors. It was found later, however, that certain wheat varieties may be highly resistant to certain physiologic races at moderate temperatures and completely susceptible at high temperatures.

(6) No combinations of characters have been found that protect wheat completely against all known races of rust under all environmental conditions.

Despite difficulties, many desirable bread wheat varieties resistant to stem rust and to some other diseases have been produced. Unfortunately, however, these varieties have been resistant only at certain times and in certain places. Thus far new rust races have ruined one variety after another. Nevertheless progress has most certainly been made, even though the problem has not been solved.

Several varieties of *Triticum* spp. played so important a part up to 1950 that they require a brief statement in the varietal "Who's Who" in the breeding programs.

Marquis. Produced in Canada, and rapidly assumed first rank among spring bread wheats shortly after 1910. It represented the acme of quality, was relatively early in maturity, relatively resistant to smuts and orange leaf rust, but very susceptible to fusarial head blight and to stem rust.

Iumillo. A durum variety with high resistance to stem rust, appeared to have "generalized," "mature," or "adult-plant" resistance.

Kanred. A hard-red winter wheat selected at the Kansas Experiment Station from Turkey Red and distributed about 1917 when it appeared to be immune to stem rust. It soon became apparent, however, that although immune from some rust races, it was completely susceptible to others.

Kota. A bread wheat, originally imported by Bolley from Russia; became mixed with seed lots of durum, and was selected by Clark and Waldron because it produced plump seeds in the epidemic of 1916.

Webster. A poor bread wheat, but it appeared to have "mature plant resistance" to stem rust; selected by McFadden in South Dakota.

Hope and H-44. Produced by McFadden (1930) as the result of a wide cross, Marquis × Yaroslav emmer. Although not satisfactory bread wheats, Hope and H-44 appeared to be almost immune from stem rust, with a high degree of adult-plant resistance. They were susceptible to the bacterial black chaff, caused by *Xanthomonas translucens*, and to melanosis, but these appeared to be minor defects, and for several years Hope seemed to justify its name so fully that it and its sister line H-44 were widely used as parents in crosses.

Marquis was very popular for a number of years because of its quality, early maturity, and apparent resistance to rusts. It proved to be far more subject to fusarial head blight, however, than the varieties which it supplanted. Moreover, it was so severely injured in the terrific stem rust epidemic of 1916 that it and other bread wheats were supplanted by durums in large areas of the Dakotas and Minnesota. But in 1923 race 11 and certain others attacked the previously resistant durums heavily. As resistant bread wheats were then made or in the making, however, it appeared that the defection of the durums was not too serious.

Kota resisted stem rust so well in the field that the acreage increased rapidly—and seed was in such demand that it was sold for as much as $8.00 a bushel, 3 or 4 times the price of ordinary wheat. But weak straw, orange leaf rust, the smuts, and finally stem rust soon put an end to its career. Marquillo (Marquis × Iumillo) then had its trial, but it could not meet the standard of quality. In 1926, however, Ceres (Marquis × Kota), produced at the North Dakota station, was ready to fill the breach. This it did with real distinction until 1935, when race 56, first found in 1928, devastated millions of acres so thoroughly as to presage the end of Ceres. It seemed incredible but it was true; Ceres was no longer rust-proof. But almost equally incredible was the performance of Thatcher, a new variety that remained uninjured in the midst of general destruction in 1935.

Thatcher, produced cooperatively by the Minnesota Station[3] and the United States Department of Agriculture (Hayes et al., 1936), was first distributed in 1934, a non-rust, drought year. So strong had been the faith in Ceres that there had been reluctance to change to a new variety, and there were only occasional fields of Thatcher in 1935; but these remained unscathed in one of the worst epidemics on record. Thatcher actually did have more resistance than any of its predecessors. It resulted from a double cross: [(Marquis × Iumillo) × (Marquis × Kanred)]. Each parental variety had contributed genes for resistance to certain physiologic races, and Iumillo had, in addition, contributed some genes for adult-plant resistance. But Thatcher was extremely sus-

[3] Breeding for disease resistance in field crops has long been an interdepartmental cooperative program at Minnesota. The major cooperation has been between the Department of Agronomy and Plant Genetics and the Department of Plant Pathology and Botany, but the Department of Agricultural Biochemistry has cooperated closely when studies of quality were needed.

ceptible to orange leaf rust and to fusarial head blight or scab. Nevertheless it withstood the epidemic of 1937 so well (while Ceres and other varieties were again ravaged) that a Thatcher era began. But it soon had competition, for breeders in Canada (Peterson, 1958) and the United States were utilizing Hope and H-44 in many crosses in the hope of producing varieties without Thatcher's defects.

The Hope era began about 1940. Thatcher itself was crossed with Hope (Marquis × Yaroslav emmer), and several backcrosses, with Thatcher as the recurrent parent, were bulked to make the variety Newthatch, which therefore had genes from Marquis, Kanred, Iumillo durum, and Yaroslav emmer (Ausemus et al., 1944). Many varieties with the Hope-type resistance were produced: Rival, Regent, Renown, Pilot, Mida, and Newthatch. Again the stem rust problem in spring wheat seemed to have been solved. And it was—until 1950.

From 1938 to 1950 stem rust was a negligible factor in spring wheat production in the United States and Canada. It appeared, superficially at least, that combinations of genes for resistance to individual rust races and for adult-plant resistance were sufficient protection. Moreover, a combination of barberry eradication and resistant varieties had reduced the number of prevalent races to only four, 17, 19, 38, and 56, which consistently constituted 90% or more of the inoculum each year during this period.

New durums, too, had been produced in North Dakota by crossing Mindum with Vernal emmer and backcrossing to Mindum (Smith, 1943). These varieties, Stewart and Carleton, resisted rust from 1943 until 1950. It looked as if the long war of attrition against stem rust had been successful, for the breeding program had increased the resistance potential of wheats, which in their turn—with aid from barberry eradication— had reduced the virulence potential of rust. In addition, the development of resistant varieties in Mexico (Borlaug et al., 1949) had reduced the danger of inoculum from that country. But in nature's history a dozen years can be too short a span of time. It was in this case.

Race 15B exploded in 1950 and blew up the status quo. It had, of course, been recognized since 1939 that this might some day happen, but there had been no indications that even so virulent a race as 15B would spread over most of North America in a single year. Following its first known appearance in the United States on barberry in central Iowa in 1939, race 15B was found only occasionally and in small quantity in barberry areas of eastern states. Attempts were made to develop resistant varieties for use in case of need, but the need came before the varieties were ready. In 1950 it became evident that the hitherto resistant durums had no protection against this race and that the bread wheats, too, could be destroyed. The terrific epidemics of 1953 and 1954 confirmed the evidence.

Certain Kenya wheats of unknown pedigree and unsatisfactory quality seemed to be most promising as sources of resistance. Crosses, therefore, were made with good bread wheats. It soon became apparent, however, that some of them were resistant at moderate temperature and susceptible at higher temperature. Some also proved to be susceptible to race 139, long known as interesting but unimportant because of apparent lack of aggressiveness and virulence. Moreover, certain winter wheats, such as Bowie and Travis, produced by McFadden for resistance to 15B, soon were attacked by race 29, which has increased sharply in prevalence in Mexico and northward within the past few years. To complicate the situation still more, race 15B itself comprises many biotypes, and exactly what they are, where they are, and what they can do is not yet completely known. The future is again uncertain.

And so the fight against stem rust goes on. Selkirk (Peterson, 1958), produced in Canada, has helped keep the disease in check in the great spring wheat region of that country and the United States for the past three years. It is susceptible to some races under some conditions, however, and has been severely damaged in experimental plots where weather was warm and humid, the conditions under which protection is most needed. How long it will last, nobody knows. In Mexico, where quality is not so important, progress has been made in thwarting 15B, but other races still threaten.

The hopes (which periodically soared very high) of controlling wheat stem rust have not been completely realized. Results have not matched expectations. And yet, much progress has been made. Spring wheat was protected in 20 years of 50 since the breeding program got under way and in 20 of 40 since it began to take effect. Some pessimists branded the program as a failure when rust destroyed 75% of the durum and close to 30% of the bread wheat in the Dakotas and Minnesota, with large losses in Canada also, in the epidemics of 1953 and 1954. But when the present situation is measured against the standard of 1904—and not against the standard of perfection—there is some reason for tempering disappointment with some degree of satisfaction. The following quotation tells why: "Race 15B almost annihilated the durum crops in 1953 and 1954, and what durum there was in 1954 was very light and shrunken. The bread wheats of 1904 would have suffered the same fate as the durums of 1954. The bread wheats of today can also be destroyed, but not so easily as those of 50 years ago. It takes more rust, more time, and more favourable rust weather to destroy them. There has been a net gain even though it is not enough to insure against destruction when weather and other factors favour early and intense epidemics" (Stakman, 1955).

The problems in breeding for resistance to other cereal rusts have been of the same general nature as those in connection with wheat stem rust. An outstanding example is the history of attempts to control the rusts of oats and other major diseases of this crop in the United States and Canada. The time span is almost the same as that for wheat and the same general reasons could be given for selecting the United States and Canadian breeding programs as illustrative of the kinds of lessons that they taught.

The major diseases of oats in the United States and Canada during the decade 1910 to 1920 were stem rust, *Puccinia graminis* var. *avenae;* crown rust, *P. coronata* var. *avenae;* loose smut, *Ustilago avenae;* and covered smut, *U. kolleri.* Although other diseases were known, they seemed to be of minor importance, and effort was therefore concentrated primarily on rust resistance and secondarily on smut resistance, for the obvious reasons that there were no practicable methods for controlling the former and the latter could be controlled by seed treatment. It is not necessary to give all of the historical data, interesting and significant as they are, in order to illustrate principles and procedures. Nevertheless it is important to know the major phases in the progress of the breeding programs as a basis for perspective.

In the earlier phases of breeding oats for disease resistance, the sources of resistance seemed adequate and the problem of combining them did not seem especially difficult. Reliance was placed particularly on the following varieties:

For resistance to stem rust: White Russian (= White Tartar) and Richland.

For resistance to crown rust: Bond and Victoria.

For resistance to smuts: Bond and Black Mesdag.

At Minnesota progress was made by the following series of crosses. The disease reactions are, of course, at the time the varieties were released.

1. Victory × White Russian = Anthony, resistant to stem rust but susceptible to crown rust and smuts.

2. Bond × Anthony = Bonda, resistant to stem rust, crown rust, and some races of smuts.

3. (Minota × White Russian) × (Bond × Black Mesdag) = Mindo, highly resistant to the rusts and the smuts.

In cooperation between the Iowa Agricultural Experiment Station and the United States Department of Agriculture remarkable progress was made by crossing Victoria and Richland. The resulting varieties

(Boone, Tama, and others) seemed to have solved the major disease problems in oats, and were satisfactory in so many other respects also that they soon became tremendously popular. But trouble was ahead, not only for the Victoria × Richland derivative but also for those derived from Bond × White Russian.

Prior to 1943 the only races of oats stem rust that were sufficiently prevalent in the United States and Canada to be important were races 2 and 5, neither of which could attack varieties with the White Russian or the Richland type of resistance. It was known, however, that both of these varieties were susceptible to certain races which were found only occasionally and in small quantities, especially races 6, 7, 8, and closely related ones. It was merely a question as to whether one or more of these races might become prevalent enough to endanger the resistant varieties.

The first indication that one of the nonprevalent races might become dangerous was in 1939 when race 8 and the closely related race 10 together comprised 1.5% of 251 isolates identified in the United States, while races 2 and 5 together still comprised about 97%. During the next 4 years the percentages for 8 and 10 combined were 6.2, 4.9, 2.1, and 20.2, respectively; for 2 and 5 combined they were 93, 94.1, 97.9, and 79.1, respectively. In 1943, then, races 8 and 10 comprised slightly more than 20% of 421 isolates identified, and were found in 14 states of the United States (Stakman and Loegering, 1944). From that year on the Richland type of resistance did not protect varieties adequately against stem rust. The White Russian genes, however, were still effective. Thus, history tended to repeat itself; as in the case of race 56 of wheat stem rust, the race 8–10 complex of oats stem rust increased and finally became widely enough established so that it could persist in the uredial stage independently of barberry, on which it had been dependent. But there was another reason why the career of the Richland × Victoria hybrids was terminated.

The immediate and perhaps more potent cause of the demise of the varieties derived from Richland × Victoria crosses was *Helminthosporium victoriae*, unknown or undetected before these varieties were widely grown. This "new" disease caused such heavy losses that it alone would have ended the usefulness of the varieties with the Victoria genes for resistance to crown rust, for it soon was found that there was linkage between these genes and those for susceptibility to *H. victoriae*. This is a conspicuous example of a minor disease becoming a major disease on new varieties.

The principle that new varieties should be thoroughly tested against all important pathogens and against all potentially important ones has long been recognized. The difficulty is in detecting the potentially important ones when they are as obscure as was *H. victoriae.* It was natural that the danger of new rust races should have been recognized because the rusts had long been known as major diseases of oats and there was precedent for assuming that there might be important changes in the prevalence of races. Major effort was therefore made in studying the potential importance of races. But there was no such precedent for *Helminthosporium* diseases of oats, and there was no major effort in studying them. A new precedent should be established; there should be major effort in studying minor diseases. Heretofore facilities and funds have not been adequate to study adequately everything that should be studied in connection with complex problems of breeding for resistance to complexes of diseases.

When it became apparent that the Victoria × Richland derivatives had fatal weaknesses, more effort was put on crosses between Bond, White Russian, and varieties with smut resistance. But it was known that races 6 and 7 of stem rust, and certain others, could attack White Russian and that certain races of crown rust could attack Bond. Although none of these races were abundant and widely prevalent, there was good reason for supposing that they might sometime become prevalent. Accordingly, attempts were made to broaden the bases for resistance both to stem rust and to crown rust.

As concerns resistance to stem rust, race 7 upset the status quo in 1950, as it suddenly "exploded" along with race 15B of wheat stem rust. Race 7, which can attack varieties with the White Russian type of resistance, was originally found by Waterhouse in Australia (Waterhouse, 1929). It was first found in North America in 1928, when it appeared in small quantities in Canada (Newton and Johnson, 1944). The first isolate in the United States was obtained from barberry at Presque Isle, Maine, in 1933 (Stakman and Loegering, 1951). Race 12 is not always clearly distinguishable from race 7 on the standard differential varieties, and the two were therefore sometimes considered together. From 1934 to 1937, inclusive, neither race was found in the United States. From 1938 through 1949, however, one or both were isolated each year except in 1942, but almost always on or near barberry in eastern United States. For 7 successive years, from 1943 to 1949, inclusive, race 7 (race 12 in 1943) was found near barberry in New York, and in 1947 and 1948 only in New York. In 1949 there was a slight indication that it might extend its geographic range, as it was found once in New York, twice in Michigan, and was isolated from a collection made in the fall in Kansas. But this was only an indication of what might sometime happen; it was not a clear warning of what did happen in 1950, when race 7 was isolated from 54% of the 628 collections of oats stem rust identified in the United States and comprised 44% of the 788 isolates from the 628 collections. As race 8 comprised 23% of the isolates, neither the Richland nor the White Russian genes were sufficient to protect the varieties then grown. Moreover, race 6 and the closely related race 13, found occasionally near barberry, can attack varieties with genes from both Richland and White Russian. Obviously, then, additional genes for resistance were needed.

Welsh and Johnson (1954) reported a "Canadian" type of resistance in segregates from certain crosses with Hajira as one of the parents, which appeared to be effective against all races of stem rust. Apparently, however, the Canadian type of resistance is not effective against certain races, including races 7 and 8, at high temperatures (See Table I).

TABLE I

REACTION OF PARENTS AND HYBRIDS TO RACES 7 AND 8 OF *Puccinia graminis* VAR. *avenae* UNDER CONTROLLED TEMPERATURE CONDITIONS[a]

	Race 7		Race 8	
Parents and hybrids	Temperature			
	Low	High	Low	High
Canadian parents	R[b]	S	R	S
White Russian	S	S	R	R
Rainbow	R	R	S	S
(Canadian + White Russian factors) C + WR	R	S	R	R
(Canadian + Rainbow factors) C + R	R	R	R	S

[a] Based on cooperative studies by plant breeders and plant pathologists at Minnesota.
[b] S = Susceptible, R = Resistant.

As pointed out by Hayes *et al.* (1955), the White Russian gene is epistatic to the Canadian gene for reaction to race 8 at high temperatures and the Rainbow gene is epistatic to the Canadian gene for reaction to race 7 at high temperatures. Welsh and Johnson (1954) found isolates designated as 7A which can attack varieties with the Canadian type of resistance at moderate as well as at high temperatures.

Progress had been made in developing varieties of oats resistant to stem rust, but most of the varieties, valuable as they were, succumbed eventually to races 8 and 7 of stem rust or were at least jeopardized by them, and there was always the menace of race 6 and the closely related 13, which combined the virulence of races 7, 8, and certain other races. Very recently a race of oats stem rust, provisionally designated as 13A, has been identified (Stewart and Cotter, 1958). This race exceeds in virulence all races hitherto found in North America; it attacks varieties with the Richland, White Russian, and Canadian types of resistance at moderate as well as at high temperatures.

Race 13A was evidently produced on barberry, since it was collected in a barberry-infested area in New York where race 7 was found for 7 successive years before it suddenly became widely established in 1950. Races 6 and 13, 7 and 12, and 8 and 10 all were apparently produced repeatedly on barberry in the United States and persisted only in barberry areas for a number of years. Races 8 and 7 became independent of barberry in 1943 and 1950, respectively. Whether races 6, 13, and 13A, the most dangerous of all, will also become widely established remains to be seen. In the meanwhile plant breeders and plant pathologists obviously must assume that the worst may happen and must therefore try to find and combine still more genes for stem rust resistance in oats.

The history of the relation between varieties of oats and races of crown rust parallels that of stem rust. Reliance originally was placed on the resistance of Bond and Victoria, and for almost two decades it seemed adequate, but races to which they are susceptible eventually increased in prevalence. According to Simons (1956), race 202 of crown rust, which attacks Bond heavily, was the most prevalent race in North America in 1955, comprising 47% of all isolates; and race 258, which attacks Victoria, was third in prevalence. The Victoria-attacking races comprised 18% of all isolates and about two thirds of those in the southeastern states of the United States. Bond and Victoria are no longer resistant. Other varieties, however, such as Landhafer and Santa Fe appeared to be generally resistant and were therefore used in breeding programs. But races of crown rust have appeared that attack these varieties also (Simons, 1954). The situation is again uncertain.

The role of the aecial stage on barberry in the production and perpetuation of races of the *tritici* and *avenae* varieties of *P. graminis* is perfectly clear. Although mutation and heterocaryosis or parasexuality may also result in the production of new and dangerous races in nature, those races of stem rust which caused the major changes in the status of resistant varieties in North America, both of wheat and of oats, either originated on barberry or persisted by means of it. Although the long-continued campaign for eradicating barberry from the principal grain-growing areas of northern United States has reduced the danger of new races, the remaining bushes still are a menace. It is pertinent to ask how successful breeding for resistance to crown rust can be, as long as the millions of buckthorn bushes, *Rhamnus* spp., remain in many of the extensive oats-growing areas of northern United States.

The past role of physiologic races in limiting the careers of resistant varieties is not restricted with respect to crop, pathogen, or geographic area of the world. The same kinds of difficulties have been encountered in breeding wheats for resistance to orange leaf rust, *Puccinia rubigovera* var. *tritici,* and to yellow rust, *P. glumarum,* rusts in which the aecial host is rare or unknown, respectively. The origin of important new races of these rusts is not as clear as in the case of stem rust; recombinations of genes for virulence may commonly occur elsewhere than in an aecial stage, as some fungi are unorthodox in their sexual behavior, and these and other rusts may be among them. More needs to be known about the possible role of mutation also. Whatever the origin of races in these and similar rusts, however, their past and potential importance has long been evident.

The smuts of small grains, corn, sorghums, and millets, comprise physiologic races, as the term is used for the smuts, which may differ decidedly in their pathogenicity for varieties within each kind of crop plant (Fischer and Holton, 1957). Shifting populations of races have forced continual effort in obtaining and combining additional genes for resistance in the host plants. More than 30 years ago, as one example, it appeared as if the bunt problem in the principal wheat-growing areas of the Pacific northwest of the United States had been virtually solved by resistant varieties. But new races of the bunt fungi decreed otherwise. Only a person who experienced the optimism generated by the first successes with bunt-resistant varieties can appreciate the frontispiece in "Biology and Control of the Smut Fungi" by Fischer and Holton (1957).

Potatoes resistant to late blight, *Phytophthora infestans,* and to scab, *Streptomyces scabies,* have been developed repeatedly, only to succumb to new races of the pathogens. Indeed, the examples are so numerous that to cite more of them would be to transcend the space limits for this chapter. Considering the complexities of many of the breeding problems, it is surprising that so much progress has been made in the short space of 50 years. Progress should be more rapid in the future, if full use is made of the lessons learned in the past.

III. Lessons from the Past

It is evident from past experience that more must be learned about the total genic potential for virulence in specific pathogens; more must be learned about the total genic potential for resistance in crop plants; and more must be learned about the nature and variability of resistance in specific host-pathogen combinations. For it is clearly evident that too little was known about the vast and shifting populations of biotypes within species of some pathogens and about the methods of identifying and classifying them as a basis for determining their pathogenicity. Prediction must be based on knowledge, not ignorance; there was too little knowledge in the past. Consequently there was too much reliance on too narrow a base of resistance in many cases; and in relatively few cases was there enough knowledge to enable definite predictions regarding what would happen. Even after enough information had been obtained to justify prediction regarding what could happen, there often was reluctance to believe that it would happen. The nature of many problems had to be learned while attempts were being made to solve them. Facts were accumulated, techniques were devised, and concepts were evolved largely from the breeding work itself, not from a pre-existing compendium of facts and procedures.

Because of limited knowledge, the concept of what constituted an adequate sample was often too restricted. The principles of adequate sampling and of replication were, of course, recognized; but too often they were recognized in principle only, not in application to specific problems. It is certainly clear from many of the past experiences that there were not adequate samples of resistant breeding materials, nor of races of pathogens, nor of the effects of different environments, both biotic and physical, on the disease process and its variability.

There was a continual succession of discoveries, including many surprises: new genes for resistance in crop plants; new physiologic races of pathogens among viruses, bacteria, and fungi; and new reactions between varieties and races under certain environmental conditions. That nature was dynamic, not static, had long been known; but wide experience in time and space was prerequisite to an understanding of how dynamic many disease situations can be.

Concepts regarding the variability of resistance changed several times during the half century in which systematic attempts have been made to breed resistant varieties. At the beginning of the epoch the doctrine of predisposition, as portrayed by Sorauer and others, was widely accepted. It was found, however, that it was not always easy to distinguish between the effects of presumed predisposing factors on the resistance of the host and their effects on the pathogen. Many attempts were made to increase the resistance of susceptible varieties and to increase the susceptibility of resistant ones. When it became evident that resistance was due to genetic factors, there was a tendency to assume that resistance and susceptibility could fluctuate within certain limits within each category but could not be shifted from one category to another. And in many cases experimental evidence supported this view; indeed this still is true of some race-variety combinations. But it is now known that varieties of some crop plants may be almost immune from some physiologic races of pathogens at certain temperatures, but completely susceptible at others. Generalizations at times rested on too narrow a base of experience, just as the resistance of certain varieties rested on too narrow a base of genes.

It was found by experience also that more adequate testing was needed against pathogens that were either inconspicuous or harmless when breeding programs were started. The complexities were created not only by races within species of pathogens but also by different species of pathogens. It was known, naturally enough, that a variety might be resistant to some diseases and susceptible to others; but it had to be learned that varieties which were produced primarily for resistance to certain diseases might prove unprecedentedly susceptible to previously minor diseases. Thus, smooth-awn barley varieties were produced by the United States Department of Agriculture and the Minnesota Agricultural Experiment Station by crossing desirable rough-awn Manchuria types with smooth-awn Lion barley, but, after having been distributed, they proved so susceptible to the complex of effects produced by *Helminthosporium sativum* that their distribution was discontinued. Smooth-awn varieties with resistance were then developed cooperatively by plant breeders and plant pathologists at the Minnesota station and distributed under the appropriate names Glabron and Velvet. The resistance of certain rough-awn Manchuria selections that survived in a *Helminthosporium*-infested plot had been combined with the smooth-awn character of Lion. But after these excellent varieties had been grown for several years they were found to be very susceptible to loose smut, *Ustilago nuda*, and to fusarial head blight, commonly known as scab. There were good reasons why it was not easy to predetermine the susceptibility to loose smut and to scab. At the time even less was known than now about methods for creating epidemics of loose smut, and weather seldom was favorable for the development of scab at the Minnesota station.

But this and other similar experiences did stimulate the establishment of "plant disease gardens," where an attempt was made to inoculate parental breeding materials and hybrids with an adequate sample of presently and potentially important pathogens under favorable conditions for abundant disease development. Effort was made to devise methods for "making weather to order" in the field: (1) by providing supplemental soil water in the plots during dry weather; (2) by providing large tents in which temperature and humidity could be controlled to some extent; and (3) by covering the tent-like enclosures with movable slats which made it possible to control light to some extent. Such plant disease gardens are indispensable in many breeding programs; they are in reality elimination plots designed to make sure that only the fittest materials survive and that the unfit, for whatever good reason, may be eliminated. The success of such plots, of course, depends on having an adequate sample of the eliminating pathogens and on providing environmental conditions that enable them to display their eliminating ability.

The value of disease gardens can be illustrated by one conspicuous example. About 25 years ago several hundred advanced generation lines of "rust resistant" wheat, produced at several experimental stations, where they had been exposed to natural infection only, were grown at the Minnesota station in a root rot plot and in the rust nursery where an artificial epidemic of stem rust had been created by inoculating with what was considered an adequate sample of races. At least 95% of the lines were susceptible to stem rust and 98% were killed or almost completely killed in the root rot plot. Most of the lines were at least in the F_5 generation; hence considerable time and effort had been spent on them, but they obviously had not been exposed to an adequate sample of pathogens and of weather in the area for which they were intended. Subsequent events indicated clearly that they probably would have been injured severely in some seasons and in some localities if they had been distributed for commercial production. Although there was natural disappointment in the defection of these lines, the disappointment would have been far greater if it had occurred on several million acres of commercial fields instead of on a fraction of an acre in experimental plots. Moreover, such experiences as this strengthened the growing conviction that adequate testing was essential, and they stimulated efforts to obtain information and devise practical methods to assure that tests be adequate.

Much of positive value was also learned in the past. It was learned that barriers to wide crosses could sometimes be overcome, that undesirable linkages were sometimes broken when large populations were grown, that backcrossing could be very useful, and that a number of factors—some of them nonspecific in their effects—might confer a certain degree of generalized resistance to varieties, notably in wheat and potatoes. Better methods were devised for identifying races of many pathogens, and much has been learned about methods for finding, classifying, and testing physiologic races.

During the past 50 years there have been many successes and many disappointments in breeding for disease resistance. Disappointment often would have been less if expectations had not been so high. When measured against the standard of perfection, some programs can be considered as failures, but only because they did not attain perfection; when measured against the reality of the prior situations, on the other hand, they must be considered successful even though they fell short of perfection. Too often, however, they have been adjudged complete failures because they were not complete successes. Psychology became mixed with pathology in some cases. There was sometimes a tendency to underestimate the complexities and uncertainties and therefore to overestimate the possibility of completely and permanently controlling diseases by means of resistant varieties. Plant diseases cannot be controlled by partisan pronouncements, but only by objective scientific effort. Presuppositions, preconceptions, and prejudices, wherever they may occur, can be barriers to progress.

Intellectual horizons must continually be broadened, scientific skepticism must be maintained, and competent scientists must be given more adequate facilities than have ever been provided in the past. Plant diseases are indeed very "shifty enemies," and it would be fatal for scientists to repeat many of the mistakes, procedural and conceptual, of the past. Future progress should be much more rapid and substantial if full use is made of the lessons of the past.

IV. THE PRESENT STATUS

Two of the most formidable obstacles to the production and maintenance of resistant varieties, now as in the past, are the multiplicity of requirements for a satisfactory variety and the multiplicity of physiologic races in various pathogens.

It is not always easy to satisfy all of the field and market requirements in a single variety. Varieties of certain basic food and feed crops must be productive under a wide range of edaphic and climatic conditions, even when diseases are not a major factor in production. In areas with a continental climate the range of adaptibility must be wide because of the wide seasonal and interseasonal fluctuations in rainfall and temperature. Even when varieties satisfy all of the producer's demands, they must meet those of wholesale marketers, processors, and ultimate consumers. The market standards are sometimes very exacting and purely traditional, based on superficial rather than intrinsic values: the color of beans, macaroni, and potatoes, the shape of rice grains, and dozens of other characters sometimes are barriers to the acceptance of otherwise valuable varieties.

A. *The Pathogen*

The greatest single handicap to the development of permanently resistant varieties has been the numerous physiologic races within species of most pathogens. The past mistakes of omission and of commission in connection with races must not be repeated in the future if more nearly permanently resistant varieties are to be produced. All races of certain pathogens probably can never be cataloged at any given time for two principal reasons: the practical difficulty of obtaining an adequate world-wide sample from the thousands of cultivated and wild biotypes of the host plants and the difficulty of being sure that the methods of identification are adequate at any given time.

Even if there could be assurance that all races and their effects were known at one time, the information might soon be inadequate because of changes in populations of host varieties and of pathogens. There is a continuous and changing stream of varieties of crop plants and of races of pathogens; hence, there must be continuous effort in studying them. It may be possible to obtain adequate, although not necessarily complete, knowledge of the composition of these streams over a relatively short span of time, but the concept of what constitutes an adequate span of time must be expanded. Likewise, the concept of the numbers of biotypes within species of crop plants and within species of pathogens must be expanded.

There are at least 15,000 recognizably different varieties of wheat, and there are in many breeding nurseries thousands of new lines under test. Naturally, there must be a large number of different genes and combinations of genes to produce so many different characters and combinations of characters. There may be—and sometimes are—a number of known genes for resistance to a single pathogen, but it often is desirable to combine genes for resistance to many pathogens and to numerous physiologic races of each. In some cases this may be relatively easy, but in other cases it is not. For the interactions between genes, linked or otherwise, increases the complications still more. Complications should not be overemphasized in any problem, but neither should they be underemphasized or ignored. The complexities may or may not be important practically, but it is not safe to assume that they are not.

It seems highly probable that there are physiologic races within virtually all species of the various groups of pathogens, including viruses, bacteria, fungi, and nematodes. For fairly obvious reasons it is easier to demonstrate them in the fungi than in the other groups, although some of the general principles are applicable to all groups. Although several investigators had observed that isolates within species of fungi might differ in physiologic characters, Eriksson (1894) published the first comprehensive account of parasitic specialization within a species. He showed that *Puccinia graminis,* as an example, comprised "formae speciales," each of which could attack one kind of crop plant but not certain others. Thus, *P. graminis* became *P. graminis* f.s. *tritici, avenae,* etc. Subsequently other rusts and *Erysiphe graminis,* powdery mildew of cereal grains, were similarly subdivided into "formae speciales," "biologic forms," "physiologic forms," or "physiologic races." These and other terms were used more or less synonymously. For some time it was thought that the rusts and powdery mildews were unique in comprising physiologic races. Moreover, there was a generally prevalent belief that the parasitism of races could be changed readily by host influences, as suggested by the term "Gewohnheitsrassen," which was sometimes applied to them. The experiments of Ward (1903), Salmon (1904), Freeman and Johnson (1911), and others supported this view, and it was therefore fairly prevalent for two decades or longer after races were first clearly recognized.

By 1918, however, Stakman et al. (1918a, b) adduced evidence that biologic forms or physiologic races did not change rapidly as a result of host influences. The apparent changes observed by early investigators could easily be explained because their presumably pure races probably comprised many races. Thus it was found that *Puccinia graminis tritici* comprised a number of races that could be distinguished by their effects on different varieties of wheat (Stakman and Piemeisel, 1917). There were in effect, then, races within races. It was soon shown that *P. graminis avenae* and *P. graminis secalis* likewise comprised races that could be distinguished on different varieties of oats and rye, respectively. The "forms," *tritici*, *avenae*, and others, were therefore elevated to the rank of varieties, as it was found that there were sufficient differences in size of spores to justify the elevation. The races within the varieties were then designated by numbers. But it soon became evident that races were not the ultimate subdivision of the species, as different isolates of what appeared to be the same race might differ somewhat in pathogenicity.

Evidently the concept of races needed clarification, and this required study. Studies finally revealed the fact that the number of races that can be recognized by their parasitic effects depends on the number of differential hosts that can be found. As concerns stem rust, the original differential hosts were wheat, oats, rye, and certain wild grasses—kinds of crop plants; the use of varieties within each kind of crop plant revealed further differences, and the use of still more varieties is revealing still more differences. This has been true both of certain cereal rusts and of *Erysiphe graminis*. Studies of these pathogens, supplemented by studies of certain cereal smuts and some Fungi Imperfecti which can be grown on artificial media, have finally furnished a basis for present concepts about physiologic races.

The basis for concepts about physiologic races is the biotype, a population of individuals having the same genotype. Many species of pathogenic fungi comprise an indefinite number of biotypes, and new ones

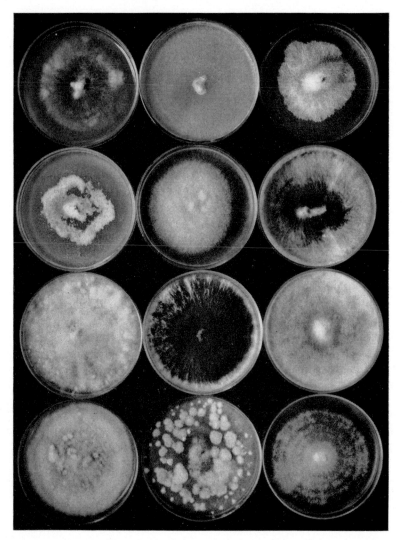

Fig. 1.   Cultural races of *Helminthosporium gramineum*, the cause of barley stripe. Differences in pathogenicity may or may not be associated with cultural differences such as those shown. When a single variety of barley is inoculated with a considerable number of such cultures, decrease of pathogenicity such as that shown in Fig. 3 can be demonstrated—(*Minn. Univ. Agr. Expt. Sta. Tech. Bull.* **95**).

are continually being produced by mutation, hybridization, and other mechanisms of genetic change. It is easier to determine the numbers in fungi that can be grown on artificial media since cultural characters, such as rate of growth, color, size, and topography of colonies, can be observed

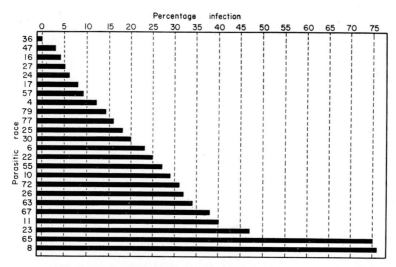

FIG. 2. The relative virulence of 27 physiologic races of *Helminthosporium gramineum* on Peatland barley grown in the greenhouse. The range of infection varied from almost 0 to 77%, depending on the race (Univ. of Minnesota).

FIG. 3. The effect of different physiologic races, mostly derived by mutation, of *Helminthosporium sativum* on a single variety of wheat. On the extreme right, noninoculated. The pot marked "Par" is the parental line, flanked on both sides by mutants, two of which are less pathogenic and two, more pathogenic than the parental line. By inoculating with enough races of the pathogen it is possible to establish a long intergrading series in which the killing of plants ranges from 0 to 100%. (Univ. of Minnesota).

directly and easily on various kinds of standardized media. It is relatively easy also to ascertain the effects of temperature and light and to determine differences in nutrient requirements and in biochemical effects. On the basis of differences in culture at least 1000 biotypes of *Helminthosporium sativum* have been recognized. At least 20,000 haploid biotypes

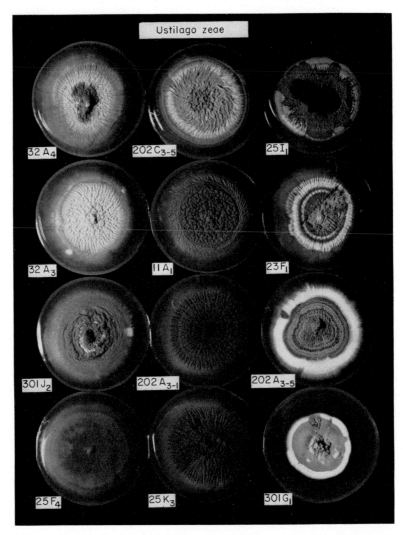

Fɪɢ. 4. Twelve monosporidial lines of *Ustilago maydis* derived from 2 individual sporidia as a result of segregation in a series of crosses originating with the lines from the 2 original sporidia and as a result of mutation. It is apparent that some of the lines shown are producing sector mutants, while others appear constant. Approximately 20,000 different lines, of which these 12 are a small sample, were derived from the two original sporidia. Differences in pathogenicity can be detected by inoculating very young corn seedlings, even though the pathogenicity of the individual lines is restricted (Univ. of Minnesota).

of *Ustilago maydis* were derived from two single sporidia of opposite sex as a result of hybridization and mutation. Similarly, an indefinite number of culturally distinct biotypes of *Fusarium oxysporum* f. *lini* have been studied (Borlaug, 1945). *Rhizoctonia solani* is another conspicuous example of a species that comprises at least hundreds of biotypes that differ in many characters (Kernkamp *et al.*, 1952). All of the hundreds or thousands of biotypes within these species may not differ in pathogenicity, although many of them do. For purposes of breeding resistant varieties the critical question is how many biotypes differ in pathogenicity, how they can be detected, and how they can be classified into races.

FIG. 5. Four degrees of pathogenicity on a single variety of corn inoculated with 4 monosporidial and sexually compatible lines of *Ustilago maydis* (Univ. of Minnesota).

The generalization that there are indefinite numbers of biotypes within some species of pathogenic fungi can be amplified by adding that indefinite numbers of them may differ in pathogenicity as well as in other physiologic characters. If the pathogenicity of a large enough sample of isolates is studied and seriated, one can often demonstrate a variation in pathogenicity, ranging from near 0 to 100, with small intervals between the different isolates. Thus, Borlaug (1945) showed that 15 isolates of the flax wilt fungus killed various percentages of the plants of Redwing flax. The range for all isolates was from 3% to 99%, and the differences between different isolates ranged from 3 to 25%. As

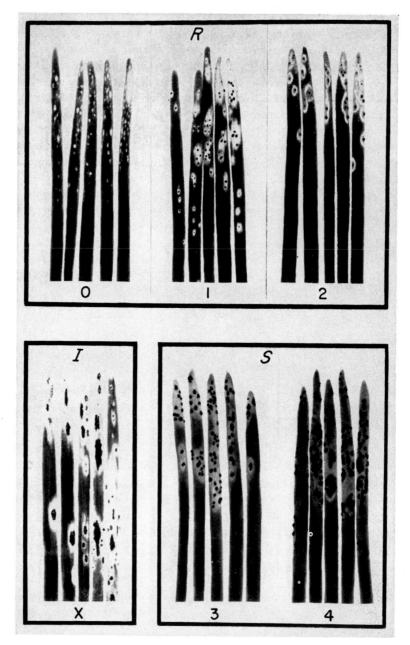

FIG. 6.   The infection types produced by *Puccinia graminis* var. *tritici* on wheat.
These results can be obtained by inoculating a single variety with 6 races or by
inoculating 6 varieties with a single race. The type marked 0 is usually designated

is evident from Figs. 1 and 2, there are many cultural types among isolates of *Helminthosporium gramineum*, the cause of barley stripe, with many degrees of pathogenicity for barley (Christensen and Graham, 1934). The same trend is evident with *H. sativum*, which causes root rot, foot rot, spot blotch, and other effects on barley, wheat, and many wild grasses. As can be seen in Fig. 3, isolates can be arranged in order of virulence for a single variety, and, in many cases, the length of the series and the proximity of the items in the series is merely a function of the numbers of isolates tested. That different dicaryophytes of *Ustilago maydis* have different degrees of pathogenicity for corn has long been known (see Figs. 4 and 5). But it has been shown also that haploid lines of *U. maydis*, which have limited pathogenicity, cause different degrees of curling or distortion on very young seedlings of corn. Similarly, preliminary indications of degrees of pathogenicity of different paired haploid lines of *Sphacelotheca sorghi* for sorghum can be obtained by the degree of chlorosis which they cause (Vaheeduddin, 1942). If enough combinations are tested, it is possible to arrange the inoculated plants in an ascending series—from no chlorosis to very pronounced chlorosis, with slight but perceptible differences between the effects caused by the different pairs in the series.

For many obvious reasons it is harder to detect biotypes and to distinguish fine differences between them in obligate parasites such as the rusts and powdery mildews. It is certain, however, that there are very large numbers of biotypes that can be distinguished from each other on a single variety of host plant. Thus, in Fig. 6 there are six distinct infection types caused by six physiologic races of stem rust on a single variety of wheat, and it would easily be possible to multiply the number until the differences between the contiguous types were almost imperceptible.

Phenotypic variability can easily obscure the genetic differences between closely related biotypes. It would be completely impracticable, for example, to construct a usable key for the determination of the thousands of haploid biotypes of *Ustilago maydis* or of many of the other pathogens discussed. Nor would such a key be particularly useful for practical purposes. Classification of individual biotypes is simply not feasible in many cases; accordingly the keys that have been devised

---

"zero semicolon" (0;) when there are necrotic flecks such as those shown. There is also a type 0 in which no flecks are produced. For the purpose of determining races, only the reaction types shown are used; 0, 1, and 2 indicate resistance; I indicates intermediate or mesothetic reaction; 3 and 4 indicate susceptibility. It will be noted that there are several degrees both of resistance and of susceptibility (U. S. Dept. of Agr. and Univ. of Minnesota).

point the way to the classification of groups of biotypes, or races, rather than to individual biotypes.

In breeding disease-resistant varieties it would be very desirable to have a perfect and changeless system for classifying all biotypes of important pathogens, with a numerical formula indicating the past, present, and future importance of each one. Unfortunately, omniscience is still theoretical rather than real in this and many other fields of biology. For practical purposes physiologic races, not individual biotypes, are classified.

As the term is generally used, physiologic race connotes a biotype or a group of biotypes that can be distinguished with relative facility and consistency from other biotypes or groups of biotypes within the same species by physiologic characters. Like the classification of physiologic races, the definition may not be perfect, but it can be useful—at least for purposes of thinking.

1. *Keys for the Determination of Races*

In constructing keys for the determination of races the first requisite is to select appropriate differential varieties; the second is to establish classes indicating degrees of infection; the third is to determine the degree of phenotypic variability within each class, including overlap between classes; and the fourth is to provide physical facilities for standardizing environmental conditions and for varying them if necessary. The investigator has no control over the numbers of biotypes within species; nature made the biotypes and the best that man can do is to group them as best he can. The establishment of classes and recognized races that may have meaning to different investigators must depend on feasibility. The results of race determinations must be reproducible at different times and places insofar as possible. The difficulties are greatest, of course, when there are hundreds of biotypes, differing in small degrees without wide intervals between them. Differences may be quantitive only or they may be qualitative or the two may be combined.

Difficulties of classification are obviously very great when there are only quantitative differences. Thus, the 15 isolates of the flax wilt fungus previously mentioned killed 3, 6, 9, 12, 22, 25, 29, 35, 42, 67, 70, 75, 88, 90, and 99% of the plants of Redwing flax. Each of the first four differ by only 3%, each; then there is a difference of 10%, followed by differences of 3 to 6% between the next group up to 42, followed by a 25% difference between 42 and 67, with small differences between the remaining isolates. The most obvious gaps are between 12 and 22 and between 42 and 67. With enough data it might be possible to establish crude percentage classes, but they obviously would have to be large classes or there would be considerable overlap between them. The same difficulty would be encountered with *Helminthosporium gramineum* (Fig. 2), *Rhizoctonia solani,* and many other pathogens in which the criterion is the percentage of plants killed. A similar difficulty is encountered with those smuts within which races are distinguished principally by the percentages of smutted heads in the differential varieties. For practical purposes, then, biotypes whose effects fall within certain ranges are grouped into races.

Classification is somewhat easier when different biotypes produce different types of effects which can be considered at least partly qualitative rather than purely quantitative. Thus, certain biotypes of *Phytoph-*

TABLE II

DIFFERENTIAL VARIETIES OF *Triticum* SPP. USED IN IDENTIFYING PHYSIOLOGIC
RACES OF *Puccinia graminis* VAR. *tritici*

Triticum compactum	*Triticum durum*
Little Club, C. I.[a] No. 4066[b]	Arnautka, C. I. No. 1493
	Mindum, C. I. No. 5296
Triticum vulgare	Spelmar, C. I. No. 6236
Marquis, C. I. No. 3641	Kubanka, C. I. No. 2094
Reliance, C. I. 7370[b]	Acme, C. I. No. 5284
Kota, C. I. No. 5878	
	Triticum dicoccum
Triticum monococcum	Vernal, C. I. No. 3686
Einkorn, C. I. 2433	Khapli, C. I. No. 4013

[a] C. I. = Cereal Investigations accession number, United States Department of Agriculture.

[b] Certain lines of Jenkin, C. I. 5177, notably Hood, C. I. 11456, may be substituted for Little Club; and, generally, Kanred, C. I. 5146, for Reliance.

thora infestans may produce only necrotic flecks on certain varieties of potatoes and large lesions on other varieties. The size and character of the lesions may therefore be an indication of differences, provided the tests are made under conditions that permit the differences to show clearly. A conspicuous example of what might be termed qualitative differences is furnished by some of the cereal rusts where the degree of necrosis, chlorosis, or combinations of the two, are often associated with size of pustules and amount of sporulation. The principles of classification can be illustrated by *Puccinia graminis* var. *tritici.*

About 40 years ago a standard set of differential varieties was selected from among several hundred varieties of different species groups of wheat that were tested for the purpose. The varieties selected seemed to be adequate for indicating the differences between the races then known. The list is given in Table II.

The infection types produced by different races on these varieties, either by a single race on different varieties within this group or by six races on a single variety are shown in Fig. 6. One additional type might be added, namely, complete immunity. This, plus types marked 0, 1,

TABLE III

KEY FOR IDENTIFYING PHYSIOLOGIC RACES OF *Puccinia graminis* VAR. *tritici* ON THE BASIS OF THEIR PATHOGENICITY ON 12 DIFFERENTIAL VARIETIES OF *Triticum* SPP.

Reaction of differential varieties	Physiologic race (key number)	Races similar to those designated in key
Little Club resistant		
Marquis resistant		
Arnautka resistant	138	
Arnautka susceptible	130	
Marquis mesothetic	99	
Marquis susceptible		
Khapli resistant	131	
Khapli susceptible	41	
Little Club mesothetic		
Marquis resistant		
Kubanka resistant		
Einkorn resistant	103	111
Einkorn susceptible	160	102
Kubanka mesothetic	68	69
Kubanka susceptible	72	
Marquis mesothetic	58	121
Marquis susceptible		
Reliance resistant	161	21
Reliance susceptible	144	40
Little Club susceptible		
Marquis resistant		
Reliance resistant		
Kota resistant		
Arnautka resistant		
Kubanka resistant		
Acme resistant		
Einkorn resistant	111	47, 50, 70, 71, 103
Einkorn susceptible	102	104, 112, 160, 167, 180
Acme susceptible	2	48, 59, 73, 162
Kubanka mesothetic		

and 2, are considered indications of a high degree of resistance. The type X is considered intermediate or mesothetic; types 3 and 4 indicate susceptibility. Plus and minus signs are used to indicate plus and minus deviations from the norm of the type. By using the double signs it is possible to indicate five degrees of infection for each type except 0.

A semicolon after 0 indicates the presence of necrotic flecks. A superscript c indicates chlorosis. It is clear that there are different degrees of resistance and susceptibility within the major groups. For purposes of determining races, however, it seemed expedient to recognize only the three groups marked R, I, and S in Fig. 6.

A trichotomous key is then used to group biotypes into races. A part of the key is reproduced in Table III.

TABLE IV

MEAN INFECTION TYPES PRODUCED BY PHYSIOLOGIC RACES OF *Puccinia graminis* VAR. *tritici* ON DIFFERENTIAL VARIETIES OF *Triticum* SPP.

Physiologic race	Mean reaction of differential varieties											
	Little Club	Marquis	Reliance	Kota	Armautka	Mindum	Spelmar	Kubanka	Acme	Einkorn	Vernal	Khapli
1	4	4−	0	3+	1=	1	1=	3+	3++	3	0;	1=
....												
11	4−	4=	3++	3+	4=	4=	4=	3++	3++	3	1=	1=
....												
15[a]	4	4−	4=	3++	4=	4=	4=	3++	3++	3++	4±	1=
16	4−	2=	0	1	3++	3+	3++	3+	4=	1=	1=	1
17	4	4−	0;	3+	4=	4=	4=	3++	3++	3	1=	1=
18	4	4−	4=	3++	1	1=	1−	3++	3++	3+	1−	1±
19	4	2−	0;	3−	4=	4=	4=	3++	3++	3	0;	1=
20	4	4=	4=	4=	1++	1−	1++	3++	1++	3+	1=	1−
21	4	4	0	3++	4−	4−	4−	4=	3++	1=	0;	1=
....												
29	4	4−	0	3	X++	X±	X+	X	X+	3	1−	1−
....												
56	4	3+	3+	3+	1=	1=	1=	3+	3+	1=	1=	1−
....												
189	4	4	4	3+	4	4	4	4	4	4	4	4c

[a] Infection types given in Table IV are produced by biotypes most frequently encountered up to the present. There may be some deviation from the recorded types when other closely related biotypes are encountered. The following are the most important examples: Race 15A has a tendency to produce weaker infection than is represented by infection types recorded in the table; biotype B has a tendency to produce heavier infection than those recorded.

The mean infection types produced by different races have been recorded in a table, a sample of which is given in Table IV.

When isolates cannot be identified by means of the key or if the mean infection types deviate too much from those given in Table IV, it is assumed that the isolate may represent a new race. This is especially true because occasional isolates may appear to be a certain race on the basis of the infection types which they produce on the limited number of varieties that are used for identifying certain races in the key. As an example, only three varieties are used as indicators for the identity of races 138 and 130. The first four varieties in the set of differentials are resistant to race 130; the next six are susceptible; and Vernal and Khapli are resistant. If an isolate produces type 3 infection on Vernal rather than the type 0 which appears in the table, the isolate obviously would be a mixture of races or a new race. More critical studies are then required to determine its identity.

This system seemed fairly satisfactory for about two decades. It was then found that some important differences between races were not revealed by the key. Different isolates of race 15, for example, produced

TABLE V

THE INFECTION TYPES PRODUCED BY THREE ISOLATES OF RACE 15B OF WHEAT STEM RUST ON KHAPLI EMMER AND KENTANA 52 WHEAT[a]

	Variety and infection type	
Isolate	Khapli	Kentana 52
Iowa	0; (almost immune)	1 (highly resistant)
Virginia	2 (very resistant)	3 (moderately susceptible)[b]
Oklahoma	1 to 3 (moderately resistant)	4 (very susceptible)

[a] Experiments made by Oscar Neri Sosa of Guatemala while a student at the University of Minnesota.

[b] The reaction is intermediate and could be considered either as moderately susceptible or moderately resistant.

somewhat heavier infection than others on some of the standard differentials, but the differences were only in degree of susceptibility, not between susceptibility and resistance. After considerable study it was found that the addition of the new variety, Lee, distinguished clearly between some of the isolates on the basis of resistance or susceptibility; those to which Lee was resistant were designated as race 15, and those to which it was susceptible, as 15B. There were also differences among isolates designated as 15B. The first indications of these differences were on Khapli emmer. These differences are shown in Table V, in which a new variety, Kentana 52, was tested as an additional differential. From Table V it is evident that what appeared to be relatively minor but perceptible differences on Khapli are important on Kentana 52, as it is very highly resistant to the Iowa isolate and very susceptible to the one from Oklahoma.

Experiences such as those with 15 and 15B have necessitated the addition of supplemental differentials to the original set and also the issuance of a supplemental key based on the so-called standard differentials. It is obvious that extensive testing often is necessary before satisfactory additional differentials can be found. As an example, 22 varieties were extensively tested as potential differentials in 1955 at the Cooperative Rust Laboratory, St. Paul, Minnesota. Many of them proved unsatisfactory. In 1956, 19 representative varieties were tested, and in 1957, 7, including Lee, were inoculated with all collections identified. It would obviously be very difficult to construct a completely satisfactory key that included all of the information desirable for breeding resistant varieties. As the breeding itself progresses and new combinations of genes are made, certain new wheat varieties may serve as additional differentials. The situation with respect to wheat varieties and with respect to rust races is dynamic. Continuous effort therefore is required to find out even the most important facts in connection with rust race-wheat variety relationships (see Fig. 7a, b).

2. The Classification of Races

Any system of classifying biotypes into races must necessarily be somewhat flexible, but it should not be so flexible that continuity with the past is completely broken. For this reason it seems desirable to retain differential varieties that have long been in use and to add to them periodically as it becomes necessary. The original 12 differentials for the determination of races of wheat stem rust have now been used for about 40 years; and it has been possible by their use to predict some of the changes that have occurred in prevalence and distribution of races. It has been possible also to develop historical perspective on population trends of certain groups of races. There are more reasons for studying physiologic races than merely to try to find out the direction which breeding programs must take. It should be emphasized, however, that the ability to distinguish clearly between races may always be limited by the number of existing host varieties that can be found to distinguish clearly between them.

A second difficulty in identifying races is the fact that the infection type produced by some of them on some varieties may fluctuate with temperature, light, and certain other environmental factors. Quantitative differences within infection types have long been recognized. As an example, the distinction between type 3 and type 4 of wheat stem rust is not rigidly fixed (see Fig. 6). Under the same environmental conditions races that produce type 3 infection can be distinguished from those that cause type 4 infection on the same variety, but under exceptionally favorable conditions type 3 may be elevated to type 4, and under exceptionally unfavorable conditions type 4 may be depressed to type 3. It was known also for many years that the type X produced by certain races on certain varieties might fluctuate considerably; hence, races 7 and 12 of stem rust of oats are sometimes grouped together for practical purposes, and 17 and 29 of wheat stem rust are sometimes similarly combined. Normal phenotypic variability within infection types has long been known. But it is now known that the reaction of

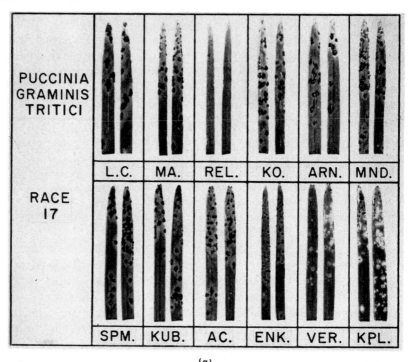

(a)

Fig. 7a. Race 17 of wheat stem rust on 12 standard differentials. Reliance is immune, while Vernal and Khapli are highly resistant, as indicated by the necrotic flecks with a few minute pustules. The other varieties are susceptible. Compare with Fig. 7b.

some varieties to some races can be shifted from near immunity to complete susceptibility by raising the temperature and increasing the amount of light (Gordon, 1933; Hart, 1949). The effect of certain races on certain varieties varies greatly with environmental conditions. As one example, races 49 and 139 of wheat stem rust are beautifully distinct at temperatures up to about 75°F. As the temperature approaches 80°, however, it is more difficult to distinguish between them; and at 85° the two races are virtually indistinguishable. The two races produce essentially the same effects on 10 of the standard differential varieties of wheat, but they differ on Kanred and Kota. At moderate temperature these two varieties are susceptible to race 49 and highly resistant to 139. At 85° both races produce heavy infection. The critical change is in the decidedly different effect of race 139 on Marquis and Kota at high temperatures. Distinguishing among these and similar races is important because their effects may differ in a critical manner on certain of the

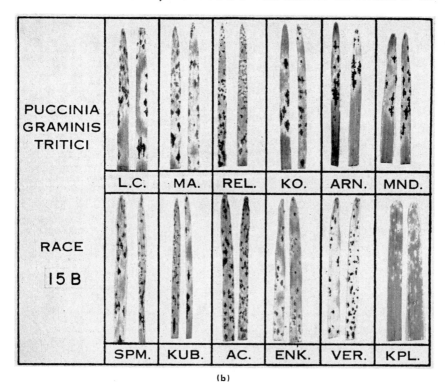

(b)

Fig. 7b.   Race 15B of wheat stem rust on standard differentials. All varieties except Khapli are susceptible (U. S. Dept. of Agr. and Univ. of Minnesota).

newer wheat varieties. Clearly, then, race determinations must be made under conditions that reveal the important differences and the possible variability; hence, physical facilities must be available for providing at least two—and preferably more—temperatures (see Fig. 8).

Temperature control is necessary not only for the identification of certain races but also to determine the resistance of varieties and breeding lines at different temperatures. Since resistance at high temperatures is most important with stem rust, we must know the reaction of varieties at high temperature and relatively high humidity, the conditions under which epidemics usually develop. The same general principle applies to certain other rusts. There is evidence, however, that some races of yellow rust, caused by *Puccinia glumarum*, are more virulent at temperatures lower than the normal for most races and varieties. The most valid conclusion is that it is important to determine the complete range of interaction between races of pathogens and varieties of host plants.

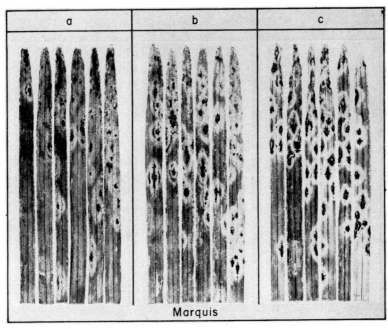

Fig. 8.   The effect of light on the infection type produced by a single race of wheat stem rust on Marquis wheat: a, plants grown in shade; b, in partial shade; c, in full light. There is increasing necrosis around the pustules with increasing light (U. S. Dept. of Agr. and Univ. of Minnesota).

Although the mode of origin of new races of fungus pathogens is primarily a problem in the genetics of fungi and their dissemination and distribution is primarily a problem in ecology, both problems are important in breeding for disease resistance. It is necessary to know not only which races are prevalent in given areas at given times but also what may happen in the future. This requires extensive physiologic race surveys to determine population trends and trends in the geographic distribution of races. There is enough evidence in North America to indicate that races that occur in any part of the area may sooner or later become established in all parts of the principal wheat-growing area. The question naturally arises as to whether new or rare races are disseminated quickly or slowly. There is no single answer to this question. Much depends upon the nature of the pathogen, the mode of its dissemination, the distribution of susceptible host varieties, and upon various combinations of weather conditions. Certain races of wheat stem rust and of oat stem rust were known for a decade or longer before they became widely distributed. Some races, such as race 56 of wheat stem rust and race 8 of oat stem rust, increased gradually in prevalence and extended their geographical range fairly slowly. Race 15B of wheat stem rust and race 7 of oat stem rust, on the other hand, were disseminated and became established over much of North America from small beginnings within a single year (Stakman and Rodenhiser, 1958).

3. The Detection of Races

The practical question arises as to how potentially important races can most easily and certainly be detected. Those which exist in only small quantity are not necessarily detected in systematic race surveys. An indispensable adjunct to these systematic surveys is the maintenance of appropriate nurseries at strategically located places in certain areas. As an example, since 1919 from 8 to 59 nurseries containing susceptible and resistant wheat varieties have been grown at various places in the United States. More recently it has been possible to grow uniform international wheat rust nurseries in many countries of the world. The object is to use these nurseries partly to obtain preliminary indications of the existence of races that attack presumably resistant varieties. Similar nurseries to determine the existence and distribution of dangerous races of P. glumarum are now being grown at strategic places in western Europe.[4] These nurseries of course have the double value of helping to detect dangerous races and of yielding information on the suitability of varieties for commercial production in the test areas or as parental varieties in breeding programs.

4. Physiologic Races of Viruses, Bacteria, and Nematodes

An attempt has been made in the preceding pages to emphasize the importance of physiologic races in the breeding of resistant varieties, and several fungus pathogens have been selected as examples because they have been studied long and extensively. Similar examples could have been selected from viruses, bacteria, and nematodes. There are obvious differences in detail, but the basic principles are similar to those in connection with fungi. The essential facts regarding the existence of

---

[4] III. The situation regarding yellow rust attack in wheat in Europe. International Contact No. 1, 1957, pp. 13–26. (Newsletter of the Netherlands Grain Centre, edited by S. Broekhuizen, 31 Emmapark, Wageningen, Holland.)

races, or strains, the appearance of new ones, and their disruptive effects in breeding are essentially similar—possibly with differences in degree—for all major groups of pathogens.

The development of sugar beets resistant to the virus curly top has been mentioned previously as an illustration of a successful program. It is known, however, that there are strains of the virus which differ in virulence for different varieties of beets and other plants and which conform in general to the principles of physiologic specialization. There are strains, such as the very virulent strain 11—apparently present in small quantities and restricted localities—which can attack at least some, possibly all, of the resistant varieties (Giddings, 1954; Murphy *et al.*, 1959). These virus strains may not be disseminated as far and fast as wind-borne fungi, but their existence constitutes a threat which must be taken into consideration in attempts to preserve past gains and to make future progress in sugar beet improvement.

The role of physiologic races of bacteria in breeding for resistance can be illustrated with *Streptomyces scabies,* which causes common scab of potatoes. At one time it was thought that the production of scab-resistant varieties was an easy and uncomplicated undertaking. But Leach and associates (1939) showed that there were "pathogenic races" within the species. Schaal (1944) made an extensive study of the pathogen and found essentially that the scab organism comprised a numerous and changing population of many biotypes that differed in many characters, including pathogenicity for different varieties of potatoes.

There are physiologic races of some species of nematodes also. Du-Charme and Birchfield (1956) demonstrated three races of the burrowing nematode *Radopholus similis.* One parasitizes citrus only; one parasitizes banana only; and another can parasitize both. Selection and breeding for resistance to various nematodes have been in progress for some time, and the same kinds of difficulties are being encountered as in the breeding for resistance to many fungus pathogens. Thus the production of potatoes resistant to the golden nematode or potato root eelworm *Heterodera rostochiensis* is complicated by the existence of races (Jones, 1957). Jones tested cysts from twenty different localities in Britain against resistant tuber lines, and found that nematodes from at least one source reproduced successfully on all lines tested. He suggests that "resistance-breaking biotypes" have "a fairly wide occurrence" in the United Kingdom. Success has been attained in some programs of breeding for resistance to nematodes. The alfalfa varieties Nemastan and Lahontan, developed in the United States, are widely grown in the Rocky Mountains area because of their resistance to the prevalent and destructive stem nematode *Ditylenchus dipsaci.* The breeding for nematode resistance in Sweden is described by Bingefors (1957). Since physiologic races have already complicated some breeding programs, their possible importance in others needs thorough study.

B. *The Host*

1. *Sources of Resistance to Pathogens*

There have been satisfactory sources of resistance to certain diseases within varieties of some kinds of crop plants. This has been conspicuously true for wilt resistance of flax, yellows resistance in cabbage, and the other cases in which selection already has been successful. There apparently are not enough genes for resistance, however, in ordinary varieties of some of the cereal grains, sugar beets, potatoes, and others. This necessitates extensive search for the desired genes in cultivated crops or in their wild relatives. What is urgently needed is world collections of varieties of many of the principal food and feed crops, with facilities for testing their reaction to diseases at appropriate places in all areas of the world where the crops are grown. In this way the varieties presumably are exposed to infection, sooner or later, by an adequate sample of pathogens. This extensive testing should be supplemented when necessary by bringing an adequate sample of pathogens to the most resistant varieties and using them to create heavy epidemics in isolated islands or other areas where conditions are always favorable for the development of the diseases in question and where there would be no danger of contaminating agricultural areas. This would be especially desirable for such diseases as cereal rusts, late blight of potato, and many virus diseases.

The possibility of finding resistance in wild relatives of crop plants has been explored to some extent, but much more intensive search is needed. It is known that there are important genes for resistance in wild potatoes, wild tomatoes, beets, sugarcane, and several other groups. The problem sometimes is to combine these genes with those for other desired characters in commercial varieties. According to Coons (1953), for example, there are genes for immunity to *Cercospora* leaf spot and the virus curly top in some species of wild beets, such as *Beta patellaris, B. procumbens,* and *B. webbiana.* Attempts are being made to incorporate these genes for immunity into cultivated sugar beets, since the resistant varieties that have been developed fall considerably short of immunity. The difficulty so far, however, has been to obtain hybrids with survival ability. The search for genes in wild plants, where this is necessary, must be continued. But it is only the first step; ways must be found for overcoming obstacles to incorporating them into cultivated varieties.

If satisfactory genes or combinations of genes for resistance cannot be found, can they be created by radiations or other physicochemical methods? Some results (Konzak, 1954) suggest that it may be possible. Radiation or other tools may be useful in breaking undesirable linkages or possibly in deleting inhibitors. Present studies in "radiation genetics," and similar fields should be continued and amplified to determine the possibilities, but, in the present state of knowledge, reliance must still be placed on the principles of conventional genetics as a guide to breeding procedures.

2. Can Varieties Be Produced with Generalized Resistance against Physiologic Races?

It is beyond the scope of this chapter to discuss what is known about the nature of resistance, except as it affects the production and maintenance of resistant varieties. Whether it will ever be possible to produce varieties with specific genes for resistance to all physiologic races of some pathogens, such as the cereal rusts, late blight of potato, powdery mildews, and others, is a question which cannot be answered categorically. An increasing number of experienced investigators are becoming agnostic. There is an increasing tendency, therefore, to find or produce varieties with generalized resistance and tolerance to certain diseases. Adult plant resistance, often called mature-plant resistance, undoubtedly has been of some value in helping to protect certain wheat varieties against stem rust, and there appears to be what is commonly designated as field resistance in some varieties of potatoes. In both cases the resistance is more or less effective against many races. Some studies have been made to determine the characters associated with generalized resistance in wheat and potatoes, but the subject deserves much more thorough study.

It has already been pointed out that many varieties of wheat produced during the past 50 years, although far from immune, are much more resistant in the field than the varieties commonly grown before the resistant ones became available. When varieties with generalized resistance and those without it are grown side by side in the field and inoculated uniformly with races to which both are susceptible in the seedling stage, it becomes clearly apparent that the susceptibility to infection differs greatly. The ratio in number of pustules on the resistant and susceptible varieties may be 1:5 or 1:10 or even 1:20 relatively early in the season. The final amount of rust sometimes is the same, however, if the varieties are inoculated repeatedly over a long period of time. This indicates that there is considerable resistance to entrance of the pathogen; accordingly, it takes more inoculum and more time to produce the same amount of rust on the resistant variety than on a susceptible one. In other cases the percentage of infection never is as high on a resistant variety as on the susceptible one, although the infection type may be essentially the same.

There are known morphological characters in some wheat varieties that affect the length of incubation period, the size of pustule, and possibly the amount of damage caused by a given amount of rust. The relative number and size of collenchyma bundles in relation to the amount and distribution of woody sclerenchyma is known to affect the number, size, and speed of development of pustules. At least a few varieties have lignified epidermis, which tends to lengthen the incubation period and reduce the size of pustules, as the epidermis is ruptured less easily than in those varieties which have nonlignified epidermis.

Clearly, some varieties have combinations of characters that protect them reasonably well against stem rust under a wide range of conditions. Varieties that have only specific resistance against individual rust races are of course at the mercy of those races to which they are susceptible. Thus, Kanred wheat, which is immune from a considerable number of races, is likely to be either rust-free in the field or completely susceptible, depending on the races present. Certain other varieties, such as Newthatch, not only have specific resistance to a number of physiologic races but also a generalized resistance that protects them to some degree against all races, although the combination of specific and generalized resistance is not sufficient to protect against all races under all environmental conditions. A thorough study is needed of all of the physiologic and morphologic characters that may be combined to confer as high a degree of generalized resistance as possible against all physiologic races.

Some varieties apparently have tolerance to certain diseases. Thus, varieties may have the same percentage and apparent severity of infection but may differ in the amount of damage which they suffer. The nature of this tolerance is not well understood in most cases, but it is known to exist. Breeding for resistance against individual races of pathogens will continue for some time, but certainly every effort should be made also to combine all possible characters in a single variety that may confer at least some degree of generalized resistance against all races of the pathogen.

3. Testing and Breeding Procedures

The principles and procedures in breeding for disease resistance are essentially the same as those used in breeding for other characters, with one important exception. In breeding for disease resistance, knowledge is required about the host plant, about the pathogen, and about the disease process. The genetics, the ecology, and the behavioristic physiology of both the host and the pathogen should be known. Moreover, it is of the utmost importance to know the interactions between the two. The disease process must be studied not only under one set of environmental conditions but under many.

As a number of diseases often must be taken into consideration in breeding for resistance, and as many of the pathogens comprise numerous physiologic races, the testing of parental varieties and breeding lines against an adequate sample of the pathogens under an adequate sample of environmental conditions is a prerequisite to success in many cases. One of the simplest ways of trying to assure adequate testing is to maintain so-called disease gardens in which parental materials and hybrid lines are tested against all important races of all important pathogens. There have been many disappointments because parental materials and hybrid lines were exposed only to natural infection in one or a few places. It is of course difficult to be sure that samples of pathogens and environmental conditions are adequate, but it is possible to try to collect infective materials of pathogens, including as many races as possible, from different sources for use in creating artificial epidemics under conditions that favor maximum disease development. It sometimes is necessary to make duplicate plantings in disease gardens, because certain diseases may interfere with the development of others. Thus, if many of the heads of a wheat variety are destroyed by smut, it is difficult to determine the resistance to fusarial head blight. Similarly, if the varieties are inoculated simultaneously with the bacterial black chaff organism and with the *Fusaria* causing head blight, the results may be confusing.

As it is not possible to control environmental factors completely in the field, it is desirable to test critical materials in plant houses where temperature, light, and humidity can be controlled. As it sometimes is necessary to wait several seasons before conditions in the field permit maximum development of certain diseases, the probable seasonal effect must be predicted by testing materials under various combinations of conditions in plant houses.

It is common practice to test parental varieties and hybrid lines in several places in the hope of providing adequate samples of races, of pathogens, of weather, and of soil conditions. For special purposes it is highly desirable to make tests in areas where the weather is always favorable for the development of the diseases in question. To give one example, the United States Department of Agriculture has for several years tested presumably rust-resistant varieties of wheat in Puerto Rico, where the weather is favorable virtually every season for maximum stem rust development. These tests have been extremely useful because epidemics of stem rust usually develop when there is "Puerto Rico weather" in wheat-growing areas, but this type of weather may prevail only in occasional years. The tests in Puerto Rico, therefore, are really a preview

Fig. 9. Testing seedling clones of potatoes for resistance to late blight at Santa Elena Experiment Station, Toluca, Mexico. Many races of the late blight fungus are present in this disease garden or elimination plot. Most of the plants have been killed outright, and only the most resistant have survived. Plots such as these in which heavy epidemics occur are essential in making sure that there have been adequate tests against an adequate sample of physiologic races under conditions that permit maximum disease development. (Oficina de Estudios Especiales. Cooperation between the Mexican Ministry of Agriculture and the Rockefeller Foundation. Photograph furnished by the Rockefeller Foundation).

of what may happen to varieties when they have the greatest need of resistance. This same principle can be applied, with modifications of detail, to many other pathogens (Fig. 9). The testing of varieties should not be restricted by national boundaries; international cooperation is of paramount importance in the development of resistant varieties.

4. The Synthesis of Resistant Varieties

The synthesis of varieties in which disease resistance is an important consideration is accomplished by means of relatively standardized procedures. Where desirable varieties cannot be selected from existing populations of varieties, it often is necessary to cross varieties whose principal virtue is disease resistance with varieties that have other out-standing virtues. In many cases it is necessary to utilize genes for resist-ance from a number of varieties. The backcross method has been used with considerable success when it is desired to incorporate additional genes for resistance in an otherwise desirable variety. Thus, Briggs (1938) successfully added genes for resistance to bunt and stem rust to Baart wheat which had so many desirable characters that it was desired to retain them. By a system of backcrossing, they were able to retain the principal characters of Baart while incorporating genes for bunt resistance from the variety Martin and for stem rust resistance from the variety Hope. The same system has been used with considerable success in other cases also.

Borlaug (1957, 1958) has suggested the use of multilineal wheat varieties to counteract the effects of changing populations of physiologic races of stem rust. Several varieties, each with resistance to certain physiologic races, are used in a backcrossing program with a common variety of desired type. Thus several lines are produced which are similar in agronomic characters but which differ in resistance to individual physiologic races or groups of races. These are then mixed to form a composite or multilineal commercial variety. The individual components of this multilineal variety are also grown separately, so that the per-centage composition of the variety can be changed from time to time as the populations of prevalent races change. This method seems prom-ising (1) because the relative percentage of each line in the variety can be shifted quickly to meet shifts in physiologic races; and (2) because the diverse population is likely to reduce the total rust potential in commercial fields, just as a mixed stand of susceptible and non-susceptible species is less vulnerable to attack than a pure stand of susceptible species.

Resistance is sometimes attained by budding or grafting. A con-spicuous example is the development of Hevea rubber resistant to the destructive leaf spot disease caused by *Dothidella ulei*. Most of the very productive clones developed in Indonesia are extremely susceptible to the disease; but some individuals in native populations of *Hevea* in South America are resistant. As the high-yielding clones are propagated by budding on seedling root stocks, the latex-bearing trunk of the tree has the high-yielding ability of the clone. The leaves, however, are very susceptible to leaf spot; therefore the young trees are cut back and budded with buds from resistant native trees. Thus, the roots came from seedlings, the latex-bearing trunk from high-yielding clones, and the canopy from disease-resistant native trees. Resistance to the virus tristeza of oranges has also been attained by budding on sour-orange stocks instead of sweet-orange stocks. Trees budded to the sweet-orange stocks are highly susceptible to the tristeza, but those on sour orange and certain other stocks are much more resistant, even though they may contain the virus.

5. *The Mode of Inheritance of Factors for Resistance*

It is difficult to generalize about the mode of inheritance of factors for resistance except to say that determinations must be made in each specific case. In his pioneer studies, Biffen (1907) demonstrated that resistance to yellow rust of wheat was inherited as a simple recessive. It was at first thought that this mode of inheritance might be universal, but it is not. The immunity of Kanred wheat from a considerable number of races of wheat stem rust is due to a single dominant gene. In other cases of resistance to stem rust two or more factor pairs are involved; in still others there are multiple factors, some major, some minor. The mode of inheritance, then, within one kind of crop plant to one kind of pathogen may differ greatly in different crosses.

Almost every type of genic relationship has been reported in connection with the genetics of bunt resistance in wheat (Fischer and Holton, 1957). There are many physiologic races of the pathogen and many wheat varieties have been crossed in attempts to checkmate them. In the many crosses between resistant and susceptible varieties, many factors apparently are involved. In some cases a single factor was involved, with or without modifiers; in others there are two, three, or more factors for resistance. Multiple factors have been recorded in many cases. Factors may be strong or weak, linked or independent, effective against a single race or against several. There may be inhibitors of factors for resistance to certain smut races but not to others. In resistant $\times$ resistant crosses, there may, of course be no segregation; in some, there is transgressive segregation.

Generalization regarding mode of inheritance cannot be applied to specific cases. Each must be considered separately. It can only be said, therefore, that the number of genes for resistance varies greatly with the crop plant and with the pathogen, and the way in which they are inherited varies greatly also.

Naturally there are many factors for virulence in species of pathogens that comprise many physiologic races. The final outcome of breeding for disease resistance will be determined by the ability of breeders to find and combine genes for resistance that counteract the genes for virulence in pathogens. As different genes for resistance are often dispersed among many varieties of crop plants and those for virulence often are widely dispersed among many physiologic races of pathogens, it is not an easy task to prognosticate the outcome of many breeding programs. Information is continually being accumulated about the genes for resistance, and some has been accumulated about the genes for virulence, but much more is needed.

Much more needs to be known about the genetics of pathogens. The writers prepared a brief summary in 1953 (Stakman and Christensen, 1953). Flor (1954, 1956) has made an especially comprehensive study of virulence in flax rust, *Melampsora lini*, and of resistance in flax. Flor suggested the presence in flax of a gene for susceptibility or resistance to match each gene for virulence or avirulence in the pathogen. He obtained 30 lines of flax, each apparently homozygous for an individual gene that governs reaction to rust. By using 18 of the lines as differential varieties, it was possible to distinguish 239 races of rust. In crosses between races of rust it appeared that avirulence was dominant over virulence and that from one to three factor pairs were involved. In crosses between resistant and susceptible varieties of flax, resistance was dominant and one to three factor pairs were involved. According to Flor, varieties of flax that carry "LL" genes are resistant to all North American races of rust. More work of this kind is needed.

V. Future Prospects

Progress in the future should be more rapid and more nearly permanent than in the past. Many breeding programs must be international in scope to be successful, simply because different genes for resistance and for virulence may exist in different parts of the world. Varieties with different genes for resistance must be assembled and then tested extensively in different geographical areas and intensively under optimum conditions for disease development. Breadth of experimentation must be combined with intensity of research. Facilities for both types of effort are being improved, but they must be expanded. There must be facilities for more travel in order that all possible information may be obtained from the international disease nurseries that are now growing in number. Large phytotrons are needed at strategic locations so that the most promising plant materials may be tested under necessary combinations of environmental conditions. Appropriate elimination plots are needed where plant materials can be assembled and exposed to infection by a world-wide collection of pathogens. There must be much more intensive research on the genetics, ecology, and physiology of hosts and pathogens and on the nature and variability of disease resistance. These things are prerequisite to most rapid and assured progress. In the meantime progress is being made.

It is possible that attitudes must be changed. It is entirely possible that a succession of varieties may have to be produced to control some diseases, as there can be no assurance that new pathogens or new races of old ones may not appear periodically to disrupt the status quo. The important thing is to anticipate the changes and prepare to meet them. Even if permanent immunity is not attainable, practical field resistance or tolerance may reduce the destructiveness of many diseases. Quality may sometimes have to be sacrificed in order to attain greater resistance and productivity, especially when the standard of quality is not based on real values.

If the efforts to produce resistant varieties are really intelligent, efficiently systematic, and world-wide in scope, there is great promise for the future. Above all, the lessons of the past must not be forgotten and many new ones must be learned in the future. Progress in scientific attitudes and attainments can guarantee progress in the production of resistant varieties.

REFERENCES

Anwar, A. A. 1949. Factors affecting the survival of *Helminthosporium sativum* and *Fusarium lini* in soil. *Phytopathology* **39:** 1005–1019.

Ausemus, E. R., E. C. Stakman, E. W. Hanson, W. F. Geddes, and P. P. Merritt. 1944. Newthatch wheat. *Minn. Univ. Agr. Expt. Sta. Tech. Bull.* **166.**

Bain, S. M., and S. H. Essary. 1906. Selection for disease resistant clover: a preliminary report. *Tenn. Univ. Agr. Expt. Sta. Bull.* **75.**

Barker, H. D. 1923. A study of wilt resistance in flax. *Minn. Univ. Agr. Expt. Sta. Tech. Bull.* **20.**

Biffen, R. H. 1907. Studies in the inheritance of disease resistance. *J. Agr. Sci.* **2:** 109–128.

Biffen, R. H. 1912. Studies in the inheritance of disease resistance II. *J. Agr. Sci.* **4:** 421–429.

Biffen, R. H. 1931. The cereal rusts and their control. *Trans. Brit. Mycol. Soc.* **16:** 19–37.

Bingefors, S. 1957. Studies on breeding red clover for resistance to stem nematodes. *Växtodling* **8:** 1–123.

Bolley, H. L. 1901. Flax wilt and flax-sick soil. *N. Dakota Agr. Expt. Sta. Bull.* **50.**

Borlaug, N. E. 1945. Variation and variability of *Fusarium lini.* *Minn. Univ. Agr. Expt. Sta. Tech. Bull.* **168.**

Borlaug, N. E. 1957. The development and use of composite varieties based upon the mechanical mixing of phenotypically similar lines developed through backcrossing. *Rept. 3rd Wheat Rust Conf. Mexico, D. F., March 18–24, 1956.* pp. 12–18.

Borlaug, N. E. 1958. II. The impact of agricultural research on Mexican wheat production. *Trans. N. Y. Acad. Sci.* [2] **20:** 278–295.

Borlaug, N. E., J. A. Rupert, and J. G. Harrar. 1949. New wheats for Mexico. *(Mex.)* *Ofic. Estud. Esp., Sec. Agr. y Ganaderia, Fol. Divulgación* **5.**

Briggs, F. N. 1938. The use of the backcross in crop improvement. *Am. Naturalist* **72:** 285–292.

Broadfoot, W. C. 1926. Studies on the parasitism of *Fusarium lini* Bolley. *Phyto-*

pathology **16**: 951–978.

Campbell, W. S. 1912. An historical sketch of William Farrer's work in connection with his improvements in wheats for Australian conditions. *Australasian Assoc. Advance. Sci.* **13**: 525–536.

Christensen, J. J., and T. W. Graham. 1934. Physiologic specialization and variation in *Helminthosporium gramineum* Rab. *Minn. Univ. Agr. Expt. Sta. Tech. Bull.* **95**.

Clark, J. A. 1936. Improvement in wheat. *Yearbook Agr. U. S. Dept. Agr.* **1936**: 207–302.

Coons, G. H. 1953. Breeding for resistance to disease. *Yearbook Agr. U. S. Dept. Agr.* **1953**: 174–192.

DuCharme, E. P., and W. Birchfield. 1956. Physiologic races of the burrowing nematode. *Phytopathology* **46**: 615–616.

Edgerton, C. W., and C. C. Moreland. 1920. Tomato wilt. *Louisiana Agr. Expt. Sta. Tech. Bull.* **174**.

Eriksson, J. 1894. Ueber die Specialisierung des Parasitismus bei den Getreiderostpilzen. *Ber. deut. botan. Ges.* **12**: 331.

Fischer, G. W., and C. S. Holton. 1957. "Biology and Control of the Smut Fungi." Ronald Press, New York.

Flor, H. H. 1954. Identification of races of flax rust by lines with single rust-conditioning genes. *U. S. Dept. Agr. Tech. Bull.* **1087**.

Flor, H. H. 1956. The complementary genic systems in flax and flax rust. *Advances in Genet.* **8**: 29–54.

Freeman, E. M., and E. C. Johnson. 1911. The rusts of grains in the United States. *U. S. Dept. Agr. Bur. Plant Ind. Bull.* **216**.

Giddings, N. J. 1954. Two recently isolated strains of curly-top virus. *Phytopathology* **44**: 123–124.

Gordon, W. L. 1933. A study of the relation of environment to the development of the uredial and telial stages of the physiologic forms of *Puccinia graminis avenae* Erikss. and Henn. *Sci. Agr.* **14**: 184–237.

Hart, H. 1949. Nature and variability of disease resistance in plants. *Ann. Rev. Microbiol.* **9**: 289–316.

Hayes, H. K., E. R. Ausemus, E. C. Stakman, C. H. Bailey, H. K. Wilson, R. H. Bamberg, M. C. Markley, R. F. Crim, and M. N. Levine. 1936. Thatcher wheat. *Minn. Univ. Agr. Expt. Sta. Bull.* **325**.

Hayes, H. K., F. R. Immer, and D. C. Smith. 1955. "Methods of Plant Breeding," 2nd ed., Chapt. 9. McGraw-Hill, New York.

Hiratsuka, N. 1896. Report of the investigation on flax wilt-disease. *Hokkai no Shokusan* **48** (in Japanese).

Hiratsuka, N. 1903. On the cause of flax wilt-disease and its prevention. *Bull. Agr. Soc. Hokkaido* **2** (in Japanese).

Jones, F. G. W. 1957. Resistance-breaking biotypes of the potato root eelworm (*Heterodera rostochiensis* Woll.). *Nematologica* **2**: 185–192.

Jones, L. R., J. C. Walker, and W. B. Tisdale. 1920. Fusarium resistant cabbage. *Wisconsin Univ. Agr. Expt. Sta. Research Bull.* **48**.

Kernkamp, M. F., D. J. de Zeeuw, S. M. Chen, B. C. Ortega, C. T. Tsiang, and A. M. Khan. 1952. Investigations on physiologic specialization and parasitism of *Rhizoctonia solani*. *Minn. Univ. Agr. Expt. Sta. Tech. Bull.* **200**.

Konzak, C. F. 1954. Stem rust resistance in oats induced by nuclear radiation. *Agron. J.* **46**: 538–540.

Leach, J. G., P. Decker, and H. Becker. 1939. Pathogenic races of *Actinomyces scabies* in relation to scab resistance. *Phytopathology* **29**: 204–208.

McFadden, E. S. 1930. A successful transfer of emmer characters to vulgare wheat. *Agron. J.* **22**: 1020–1034.

Murphy, A. M., C. W. Bennett, and F. V. Owen. 1959. Varietal reaction of sugar beets to curly top virus strain 11 under field conditions. *J. Am. Soc. Sugar Beet Technologists* **10**: 281–282.

Newton, M., and T. Johnson. 1944. Physiologic specialization of oat stem rust in Canada. *Can. J. Research* **22**: 201–216.

Orton, W. A. 1900. The wilt disease of cotton and its control. *Bull. U. S. Dept. Agr. Div. Vegetable Physiol. and Pathol.* **27**.

Orton, W. A. 1909. The development of farm crops resistant to disease. *Yearbook Agr. U. S. Dept. Agr.* **1908**: 453–464.

Peterson, R. F. 1958. Twenty-five years' progress in breeding new varieties of wheat for Canada. *Empire J. Exptl. Agr.* **26**: 104–122.

Salmon, E. S. 1904. On *Erysiphe graminis* D. C. and its adaptive parasitism within the genus Bromus. *Ann. Mycol. Notitiam Sci. Mycol. Univ.* **2**: 255–267, 307–343.

Schaal, L. A. 1944. Variation and physiologic specialization in the common scab fungus (*Actinomyces scabies*). *J. Agr. Research* **69**: 169–186.

Simons, M. D. 1954. A North American race of crown rust attacking the oat varieties Landhafer and Santa Fe. *Plant Disease Reptr.* **38**: 505–506.

Simons, M. D. 1956. Physiologic races of crown rust of oats identified in 1955. *Plant Disease Reptr.* **40**: 810–813.

Smith, G. S. 1943. Two new durum wheat varieties. *N. Dakota Agr. Expt. Sta. Bimo. Bull.* **5**: 2–3.

Stakman, E. C. 1955. Progress and problems in plant pathology. *Ann. Appl. Biol.* **42**: 22–33.

Stakman, E. C., and J. J. Christensen. 1953. Problems of variability in fungi. *Yearbook Agr. U. S. Dept. Agr.* **1953**: 35–62.

Stakman, E. C., and W. Q. Loegering. 1944. The potential importance of race 8 of *Puccinia graminis avenae* in the United States. *Phytopathology* **34**: 421–425.

Stakman, E. C., and W. Q. Loegering. 1951. Physiologic races of *Puccinia graminis* in the United States in 1950. U. S. Dept. Agr., Agr. Research Admin., and Minnesota Agr. Expt. Sta. Physiologic Races–1950.

Stakman, E. C., and F. J. Piemeisel. 1917. Biologic forms of *Puccinia graminis* on cereals and grasses. *J. Agr. Research* **10**: 429–495.

Stakman, E. C., and H. A. Rodenhiser. 1958. Race 15B of wheat stem rust–what it is and what it means. *Advances in Agron.* **10**: 143–165.

Stakman, E. C., F. J. Piemeisel, and M. N. Levine. 1918a. Plasticity of biologic forms of *Puccinia graminis*. *J. Agr. Research* **15**: 221–249.

Stakman, E. C., J. H. Parker, and F. J. Piemeisel. 1918b. Can biologic forms of stem rust on wheat change rapidly enough to interfere with breeding for rust resistance? *J. Agr. Research* **14**: 111–123.

Stewart, D. M., and R. U. Cotter. 1958. A new and virulent culture of oat stem rust. *Phytopathology* **48**: 389–390.

Tisdale, W. H. 1917. Flax wilt; a study of the nature and inheritance of wilt resistance. *J. Agr. Research* **11**: 573–606.

Vaheeduddin, S. 1942. The pathogenicity and genetics of some sorghum smuts. *Minn. Univ. Agr. Expt. Sta. Tech. Bull.* **154**.

Varro, Marcus Terentius.—On Agriculture I. 1934. "De Re Rustica," English transl. by W. D. Hooper. [Loeb Classical Library.] Harvard Univ. Press, Cambridge, Massachusetts.

Walker, J. C., and R. Smith. 1930. Effect of environmental factors upon the resistance of cabbage to yellows. *J. Agr. Research* **41:** 1015.

Ward, H. M. 1903. Further observations on the brown rust of the bromes, *Puccinia dispersa* (Erikss.) and its adaptive parasitism. *Ann. Mycol.* **1:** 132–151.

Waterhouse, W. L. 1929. Australian rust studies I. *Proc. Linnean Soc. N. S. Wales* **54:** 615–680.

Wellman, F. L., and D. J. Blaisdell. 1940. Differences in growth characters and pathogenicity of Fusarium wilt isolates tested on three tomato varieties. *U. S. Dept. Agr. Tech. Bull.* **705.**

Wellman, F. L., and D. J. Blaisdell. 1941. Pathogenic and cultural variation among single spore isolates from strains of the tomato-wilt Fusarium. *Phytopathology* **31:** 103–120.

Welsh, J. N., and T. Johnson. 1954. Inheritance of reaction to race 7A and other races of oat stem rust, *Puccinia graminis avenae*. *Can. J. Botany* **32:** 347–357.

AUTHOR INDEX

Numbers in italics indicate the pages on which the references are listed at the end of the article.

A

Abel, A. L., 507, *516*
Aberg, E., 393, *424*
Adams, J. E., 534, 537, *562*
Adams, J. F., 72, *91*
Addicott, F. T., 380, *424*
Agnihothrudu, V., 542, *557*
Ainsworth, G. C., 73, *91*
Albert, A., 445, *469*
Aldrich, D. G., 435, 438, 452, 453, 454, *469, 473*
Alexopoulos, C. J., 532, *557*
Allen, M. C., 533, 534, *557*
Allen, M. W., 442, 450, 461, *469*
Allen, O. N., 537, 542, *560*
Allen, P. J., 360, *424*
Allen, T. C., 108, *127*
Allington, W. B., 103, *133*
Allison, P., 458, 463, *469*
Altson, R. A., 49, *53*
Anderson, E. J., 458, 460, *469*
Anderson, L. D., 113, 118, 124, *130*
Anderssen, E. E., 119, *134*, 241, 279, *289*
Angell, H. R., 500, *517*
Anwar, A. A., 532, *557*, 576, *621*
Appel, O., *355*
Aragaki, M., 100, *129*
Ark, P. A., 100, 107, *127, 134*, 462, *469*
Arndt, C. H., 394, 405, *424*
Arnett, R., 532, *557*
Arny, D. C., 410, *424, 427*
Atanasoff, D., 102, *127*
Atkinson, R. G., 536, *557*
Ausemus, E. R., 581, 582, *621, 622*
Avery, G. S., Jr., 394, *424*
Ayers, G. W., 84, *91*
Ayers, T. T., 417, *424*

B

Back, E. A., 336, *355*
Badami, R. S., 107, *127*

Bailey, C. H., 581, *622*
Bain, S. M., 577, *621*
Baines, R. C., 435, 448, 450, 454, *469, 473, 474*, 500, 506, 507, 510, *517, 519*
Baker, F. E., 433, 455, *471*
Baker, G. A., 194, 197, 198, 199, 200, 203, 204, 206, 207, 227, 300, *312*, 381, *429*
Baker, K. F., 399, 411, *424, 425*, 466, 467, *469*
Bald, J. G., 105, 116, 126, *127*
Bamberg, R. H., 523, 544, 547, *557, 558, 561*, 581, *622*
Bant, J. H., 234, *287*
Barat, H., 553, *558*
Bardin, R., 115, *130*
Barker, H. D., 575, *621*
Barnell, E., 41, *53*
Barnell, H. R., 41, *53*
Barnes, G. L., 458, 463, *469*
Barratt, R. W., 4, 22, 447, *470*
Bateman, A. J., 195, 196, *223*
Baunacke, W., 62, *92*
Bawden, F. C., 37, *54*, 74, 89, *92*, 99, 106, 117, 118, *128*, 360, 418, *425*, 555, 556, 557, *558, 560*
Beaumont, A., 234, *287*, 305, *310*
Becker, H., 612, *623*
Beckman, C. H., 299, *310*
Beilin, I. G., 422, *425*
Bennett, C. W., 105, 113, 121, *128*, 612, *623*
Bennett, F. T., 73, *92*
Beresova, J. F., 544, *558*
Bergeron, T., 222, *223*
Bergeson, G. B., 458, 461, *473*
Berkeley, G. H., 262, *288*, 378, 381, 391, 392, 397, 398, 406, 408, 423, *425*
Bertrand, G., 456, *470*
Best, A. C., 214, *223*
Betts, J. J., 502, *517*

625

SUBJECT INDEX

A

Abies concolor, transmission of stain diseases by scolytids, 110

Absidia spinosa, antagonistic action of, 533

Aceratagallia sanguinolenta, vector of potato yellow dwarf virus, 322

Aceria tulipae, transmission of viruses by, 101

Acetylenedicarboxylic acid, effect on occurrence of *Trichoderma viride* in soil, 500

Achromobacter, inhibition of *Fusarium graminearum,* on corn seed, 544

Actidione (cycloheximide), control of *Coccomyces hiemalis,* 417

Actidione, production of, in soil, 539

Actinomycetes
 influence of crop plants on, 536
 inhibitory action of, 532
 resistance to soil biocides, 454

Additives, to fungicides, to improve retentiveness, 489

Adhesion, pesticides, mechanism of, 486

Adjuvants, in sprays, control of apple scab, 481

Aeciospores
 development of, 156
 moisture relations in discharge of, 163

Aecium, structure of, 156

Aerobacter, in soil, 436

Agarics, spore liberation in, 153

Age
 clones, relation to epidemics, 275
 effect on susceptibility of plants to viruses, 118

Aggregation, mycelial, significance of, 43

Agriculture, intensified, relation to disease, 261, 263, 264

Agrobacterium tumefaciens
 hosts of, crop rotation, 408
 phage of, 525, 526

Air
 dispersal of spores through, 14, 169, 299
 laminar layer, role in spore dispersal, 164
 spore content of, vertical distribution, 176

Aircraft
 introduction of pests on, 336
 spore-trapping experiments in, 189

Air movement, horizontal
 in dispersal of spores, 173
 force in spore deposition, 209

Alcohols, oxidation by *Corynebacterium italicum,* 499

Aleuria vesiculosa, spore discharge in, 141

Aliphatic saturated hydrocarbons, halogenated, fungicides and nematocides, 444

Allyl alcohol
 drench, 460
 soil penetration, 448
 Trichoderma viride in soil treated with, 453, 454

Allyl bromide, soil fungicide, 445, 457

Alternaria, reduction of rot by, use of growth substances, 387

Alternaria linicola, occurrence on flax seed, 78, 80

Alternaria solani
 early blight in potatoes, 273
 mutual antagonism with *Streptomyces griseus,* 531

Alternaria tenuis
 toxicity of cuprous oxide, *in vitro,* effect of additives, 489
 viability on oat seed, 76

Altitude, changes in spore concentration, 202

Alumino-clay micelle, sorbing agent in soil, 441

Aluminum, role in root rot of corn and sugar cane, 392

Deflocculation, fungicides, use of dispersing agent, 487

Defoliation, reduction of disease by, 380

Degradation, biological, of toxicants in soil, 447

Delia antiqua, transmission of pathogens of soft rot, 107

Delia sp., symbiotic relation with *Erwinia atroseptica*, on potato, 108

Demeton, aphid control in potatoes, 125

Dendroctonus spp., transmission of brown- and blue-stain diseases, 110

Deposition
  spores, 8, 15, 196, 212, 213
  sprays, 478, 481

Dermatophytes, treatment against, 394

Destruction of inoculum, strategy of, 20

Detergents, adsorption in soil, 443

Detoxification
  antibiotics, in soils, 541
  fungicides, by microorganisms, 499

Deuterosminthus bicinctus var. *repanda*, predator of fungi, 528

Dibotryon morbosum, parasitism by *Trichothecium roseum*, 523

Dibromobutene, soil fungicide, 458

1,2-Dibromo-3-chloropropane, 444, 445, 450, 458, 461, 508

Dichlone, 483, 492, 493, 514

p-Dichlorobenzene, effect on reproduction of inoculum, 17

1,4-Dichloro-2-butene, 445, 462

2,3-Dichloro-1,4-dihydroxynaphthalene, reduction product of dichlone, 493

2,3-Dichloro-1,4-naphthoquinone, dichlone, 483
  reduction product, 493

2,4-Dichlorophenoxyethyl sulfate, conversion to 2,4-D, 501

Dichlorophenyl diethyl phosphorothioate, 458, 462

1,3-Dichloropropene, 445, 449

3,4-Dichlorotetrahydrothiophene 1,1-dioxide, nematocide, 462, 505, 508

Diffusion
  biocides in soil, 447, 449
  fumigants in soil, pattern and speed of, 450
  propagules, derivation of equation for, 193

Diffusion coefficient, fumigant in soil, 509

Dilophospora alopecuri, association with *Anguina tritici*, 102

3,5-Dimethyltetrahydro-1,3,5,2H-thiadiazine-2-thione, mylone, 446, 460, 506

2,4-Dinitro-*o*-cresol, 417, 500

2,4-Dinitrophenol, degradation by *Corynebacterium simplex*, 500

Diobrotica duodecimpunctata, transmission of *Erwinia tracheiphila*, 108

Diobrotica vittata, transmission of *Erwinia tracheiphila*, 108

Diplocarpon rosae, dispersal by affected rose leaves, 85

Diplodia natalensis, control on citrus, 385

Discomycetes, spore discharge of, 141

Disease
  age and susceptibility to, 403
  annual variation in amount of, 309
  control of
    application of growth substances, 394
    biological measures, 557
    feasibility, 571
    in forestry, 274
    measures affecting inoculum, 409
  definition of, 359
  dispersal by insects, geographical distribution, 112
  distribution of, effect of moisture, 399
  effect of pattern of farming on, 261, 269
  estimation of, in small plots, 270
  indigenous crops, endemic nature of, 280
  influence of soil reaction on, 392
  intercontinental dispersal, man as agent of, 223
  introduction of, 314
  losses from, evaluation, 328
  mathematical theory of, prior to epidemic onset, 238
  multiplication rate
    estimation of, 237
    importance in epidemics, 235, 251
  nonpathogenic, postharvest, 386
  outbreaks of, 245, 291, 321

incubation period, effect of temperature, 303
infection gradients of, 255
infection in relation to field area, 266
inoculum potential of, 28
introduction into Europe, 83
nature of epidemics caused by, 232, 233, 244
protection of potato against, by Bordeaux, 484
resistance to, 281, 285, 554, 589
source of inoculum, 85, 257, 294
spread of, from South America, 314
survival of, 63, 293
Phytophthora parasitica, parasitism by *Trichoderma lignorum,* 524
Phytophthora parasitica var. *nicotiana,* disease complex with *Meloidogyne,* 553
Phytophthora ultimum, persistence in soil, 64
Phytoptus ribis, transmission of black currant reversion virus, 101
Phytosanitary certificates, consulate visas with, 354
Phytosanitary services, 332, 348
Phytotoxicity, 461, 465, 496, 498
Phytotrons, use in testing plant material, 620
Picric acid, degradation by *Corynebacterium simplex,* 500
Pierce's disease, 241, 327
Pineapple, leaf tip necrosis of, use of wind break in control of, 422
Pineapple root knot nematode, use of trap crop in control of, 422
Pinus lambertiana, blister rust prevention, 315
Pinus monticola, destruction by blister rust, 315
Pinus strobus, susceptibility to blister rust, 315
Pinus sylvestris, control of *Fusarium* on seed, 544
Plant bugs, transmission of fungi by, 110
Plant consignments, origin of, 351, 352
Plant debris, importance in pathogen dispersal, 84, 86, 90

Plant disease gardens, use in breeding programs, 591
Plant inhibitor, concept of, 437
Plant introduction, method of crop improvement, 573
Plant parts, carriers of pathogens, 83, 84, 337
Plant products
  definition, in trade, 343
  indicating origin of, for transport, 352
  pathogens in, 84, 85, 86, 88
Plant quarantine, for health determination, 86
Plant residues, effect on succeeding crops, 406
Plant sustainer, concept of, 437
Plant vigor, effect of soil fumigation on, 438
Planting stocks, spread of pathogens in, 84, 86, 88
Plants
  cultivated, volunteers as carriers of disease, 52
  density of, relation to disease, 119, 278
  diseased, as source of inoculum, 51
  definition in trade, 343
  importation of, 330, 352
  protection against virus reinfection, 555
  protection agreements, 341, 351
  wild, occurrence of diseases on, 53
Plasmodiophora brassicae, 62, 64, 67, 84, 85, 86, 100, 101, 314
Plasmopara viticola, 523, 528
Pleurage fimiseda, spore discharge in, 141
Poa, root secretions of, effect on viability of nematode cysts, 552
Poa pratensis, resistance to stripe smut, 577
Podosphaera, diurnal cycle, spore liberation, 165
Podosphaera leucotricha, 147, 249
Polyporus anceps, reduction in conifers, pruning methods, 379
Polyporus squamosus, spore liberation by, 152
Polyspora l'ini, seed-borne, 71, 72, 76, 78